# AN INTRODUCTION TO ASTRONOMY

# AN INTRODUCTION

HOLT, RINEHART AND WINSTON, INC.

*New York*

*Chicago*

*San Francisco*

*Toronto*

*London*

© Wes Kemp

# TO ASTRONOMY

CHARLES M. HUFFER
*Professor of Astronomy*
*San Diego State College*

FREDERICK E. TRINKLEIN
*Consultant and Designer for*
*Trippensee Planetarium Co.,*
*Saginaw, Michigan*

MARK BUNGE
*San Jose City College*

# PREFACE

This text has been written to provide the college student in his freshman or sophomore year with a nonmathematical treatment of introductory astronomy. Since the launching of the first man-made satellite, a Russian Sputnik, on October 4, 1957, interest in astronomy has grown very rapidly. The possibility of landing men and instruments on the moon or on a planet caught the fancy of many students, who decided they wanted to know more about the mysteries of astronomy. Classes in elementary descriptive astronomy have grown to previously unheard-of size.

While this text is nonmathematical in its approach, some mathematics is obviously necessary. It is assumed that the student has had the usual high school courses in algebra and plane geometry, can perform the simple operations of arithmetic, and can understand a simple proportion. Material for the advanced student is set off by a colored line rule.

In this text, plane geometry is used for a few simple proofs. In the formula relating the distance and brightness of stars, it is necessary to use a logarithm. Since a logarithm is an exponent, the use of logs is as simple as the operations with exponents learned in high school algebra. The student should learn to use logarithms and be able to do a few easy problems. Many formulas in the text are illustrated with sample problems. Other problems are provided at the end of each chapter. Difficult questions are preceded by an asterisk.

In the field of stellar astronomy and the astronomy of space, the most exciting discoveries have been of the quasi-stellar radio and nonradio sources (quasars), which are discussed in Chapter 22. They include the most distant object ever observed, a new discovery, which will have an important bearing on the theories of the nature and age of the universe. To keep up with new research in astronomy requires constant searching of the newspaper reports, the scientific journals, and personal contacts at professional meetings with the men who are carrying on this research. It is impossible to report all the latest discoveries, but we hope the reader will be interested enough to look for and to understand the articles that appear nearly every day in the papers.

Finally, it is the aim of this book not to give merely the results of the studies of astronomy and all its branches, but to inform the student about the developments that have led up to that knowledge. To give the bare facts about the solar system and its members, the stars and their distribution in space, and the universe and its galaxies, is not enough. The men behind the important discoveries, their thinking and reasoning in stating their theories, and the modern theories of the extent and nature of the universe and its evolution and present state of change, are much more interesting.

The idea of an astronomer as a bearded man wearing a skullcap and peering through a telescope has given way to a more factual view of an astronomer as a scientist who uses complicated mathematics to work out the orbits of comets or a physicist who uses the telescope in addition to the physical apparatus which he needs to investigate the composition, temperature, and motions of stars and collections of stars. It was not until the 1920s that the so-called spiral nebulae were found to lie outside our system of stars and to be in rapid motion away from each other and from an unknown central point in what came to be known as the expanding universe.

Mathematics is still important, but the chemistry and physics of astronomical bodies has become more and more important. When artificial satellites were sent into space, observations from above the earth's atmosphere became possible for the first time. The future of astronomical investigation is very exciting.

We hope we shall interest many in this science and that they will not only continue their interest, but that some will find a place in the future investigations and research in science.

San Diego, California                                                C.M.H.
December  1966                                                         F.E.T.
                                                                       M.B.

# CONTENTS

# AN INTRODUCTION TO ASTRONOMY

# Chapter One

# Introduction to Astronomy

## A BRIEF HISTORY OF ASTRONOMY

### 1.1 Beginnings

Man has watched the sky for thousands of years. He has seen the sun rise and set. He has seen the day fade into night and has wondered about the stars. He has watched the changes in the growth of plants and trees during spring and summer and has seen them change into the dormant stage in autumn and winter. He had need of a calendar for the control of flocks and crops—and so astronomy was born.

Astronomy grew when there arose a need for a method of determining direction and for help in navigating ships across the seas out of sight of land. And it developed into a science which studies the motions, locations, and physical nature of all bodies in the universe. Astronomy is a science in its own right, but it has been the inspiration for the development of other sciences, which it uses for its own purposes.

The Egyptians had carefully watched the sun for hundreds of years. They had counted the number of sunrises and sunsets from one summer to the next and had found that the sun rose and set about 365 times in what we call one year. To anyone who enjoys watching the sun rise or set, it is easy to see that the place of sunrise or sunset moves from day to day. If one begins to count at the time when the sun has reached its most northerly points of sunrise and sunset and continues to count until the sun has reached its most southerly points and returns to the north again, he will find that the number of sunrises and sunsets is about 365. The Egyptians knew this and introduced a calendar containing 365 days, some say in 4236 B.C., others as late as 2560 B.C. While these dates are not accurate, they prove that the study of the motions of the sun dates back more than 4500 years.

The ancient peoples in various parts of the world—Egypt, India, China, and Mesopotamia in particular—had also observed the stars for centuries. It was recognized long ago that it is easier to describe the location of a particular object (a comet, for example) if the stars are divided into recognizable groups. These apparent groupings are called constellations. That the constellations were used many centuries ago can be seen from carvings and paintings in Egypt and Mesopotamia and even in Europe and North America. They were named for mythical heroes, animals, and in modern

1

Fig. 1–1   A long-exposure photograph of the constellation Orion. The central figure consists of three bright stars that form the "Belt" running diagonally and three fainter stars that form the "Sword" running toward the lower edge. The bright star Rigel is the bright star at lower right. Other identifications can be made from the star maps. (Photograph from the Mount Wilson and Palomar Observatories)

times for astronomical instruments. The ancient names of most constellations have been retained even today. (Figure 1–1)

The stars have been called *fixed stars* in contrast with others that apparently change position. Those that appear to move are still called *planets,* meaning wanderers. We of course know that the stars only appear to remain fixed with respect to each other because of their great distances from us. In reality they are all moving through space, some of them at high rates of speed.

The ancient astronomers listed seven planets. Since the sun and the moon can be seen to move among the stars, they also were considered to be planets. The other five were Mercury, Venus, Mars, Jupiter, and Saturn. Venus is the brightest of the five and can at times be seen in the evening sky and sometimes in the morning sky. This led to some confusion. Venus was called Hesperus when visible in the evening and Phosphor, or Phosphorus, when seen in the morning sky. These seven planets were studied by many astronomers, and a planet's position among the fixed stars could be determined in advance with considerable accuracy.

## 1.2   The First Instruments

Positions of stars and planets had been determined before the invention of the telescope by the use of instruments which permitted the astronomer to sight in the direction of the object in order to locate it among the stars. Tycho Brahe was one astronomer who used such crude instruments. (Figure 1–2) Tycho died in 1601, just eight years before Galileo began his studies with the telescope. Tycho's observations were so accurate that his measures of the positions of Mars were used by Johannes Kepler for his discovery that the planets move in elliptical paths around the sun.

The invention of the telescope in Holland in the early part of the seventeenth century and its application to astronomy in Italy in 1609 had a profound influence on the development of astronomy. In the first place, it permitted Galileo, who made the first astronomical telescope, to see objects which were invisible to the unaided eye. (Figure 1–3) He discovered the seas and craters on the moon, the spots on the sun, the moons of Jupiter, and the phases of Venus. In particular, he found that the Milky Way is composed of stars. Any one of these discoveries would have made him famous.

Later, telescopes were mounted on instruments similar to those used by Tycho. This made it possible to locate planets and comets with great precision. Such observations led the mathematical astronomers to their investigations of celestial motions and to the statement of the fundamental laws. The most famous of these men was Sir Isaac Newton, who lived from 1642 to 1727. Because of Newton's laws of motion and his law of universal gravitation, it is possible to calculate the orbits of all the planets, their families of satellites, and all the stray comets which wander in and out of the neighborhood of the earth.

## 1.3 Physical Instruments

It is also possible to attach physical instruments to the telescope for the study of the light they collect. Such instruments include the spectroscope, which breaks the light up into its constituent colors, and the spectrograph, which uses photography to make permanent records of the resulting spectra. The photoelectric cell, developed in the twentieth century, measures the amount of light from a star. These instruments, used with the telescope, have become the most important instruments of astronomy and have led to the branch of astronomy called astrophysics. They are used in studies of the physical nature of stars, planets, comets, and other bodies scattered throughout the universe.

## MODERN ASTRONOMY

### 1.4 Divisions of Astronomy

Modern astronomy is divided into several subclasses, some of which are listed below.

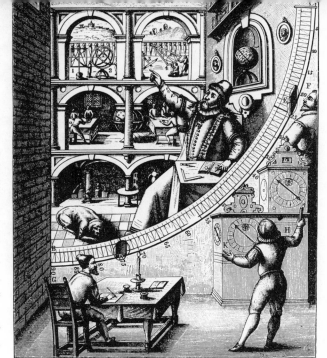

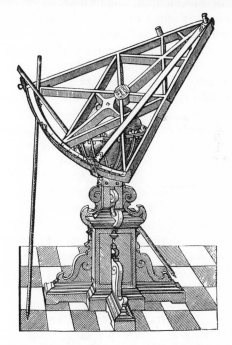

Fig. 1–2 Tycho's wall quadrant (top) and sextant (bottom) were used for accurate measures of star and planet positions before the invention of the telescope. (New York Public Library; The Granger Collection)

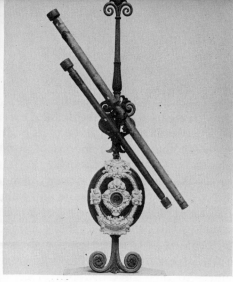

Fig. 1–3 Galileo demonstrated his first telescope in 1609 from the tower of St. Mark's Cathedral in Venice, Italy. At the right are shown two of the telescopes which Galileo used. (Bausch & Lomb; Alinari-Art Reference Bureau)

*Mathematical Astronomy* includes celestial mechanics, which deals with theories of orbits and permits the computation of motions; it predicts the positions of such objects as planets, comets, and asteroids with great accuracy. Most of the great mathematicians of the early part of the nineteenth century worked on the problems of mathematical astronomy. These studies culminated in the *theory of relativity*, developed by Albert Einstein in the early 1900s.

*Astrometrics* is the accurate measurement of positions, and it provides the observations needed as a basis for the calculations of mathematical astronomy.

*Astrophysics* is a branch of astronomy in which the light from all kinds of celestial objects is analyzed and their physical nature is studied. As the name suggests, it depends on the methods and theories of physics. The great reflecting telescopes of the twentieth century were built for these studies. (Figure 1–4)

*Radio Astronomy* detects and analyzes invisible radiation from celestial bodies. In 1931 it was found that there are waves coming from space

that are not classed as visible light, but as radio waves. These waves are part of the electromagnetic spectrum, but are not detectable with ordinary telescopes. They are received by antennas that are similar to the antennas of radios and television sets. (Figure 1–5) The signals are received and recorded on meters where they can be measured and studied at leisure by the radio astronomers. Radio astronomy is the newest branch of the science, but

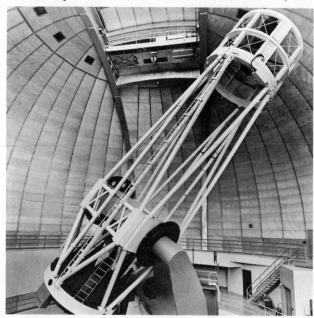

Fig. 1–4 The 120-inch reflecting telescope of the Lick Observatory, University of California, located on Mount Hamilton, near San Jose, California. (Lick Observatory Photograph)

Fig. 1–5   The radio-telescope at Jodrell Bank, near Manchester, England. The dish is 250 ft in diameter. The radio receiver is at the focal point of the parabolic reflector. (British Information Services)

it has already become very important in studies of the sun, planets, and of the most distant types of star clusters and galaxies.

*Cosmology* is a study of the design and extent of the universe. Cosmology includes *cosmogony*, which deals with the origin of the universe and the future destiny of the matter of which it is composed. The problem of cosmogony is to collect all the known data about the universe and its various parts, to put together a self-consistent hypothesis about its structure, and to predict its future.

## 1.5   The Future of Astronomy

A great step forward was taken in the study of astronomy with the launching of the first artificial satellite in 1957. The first satellites described orbits around the earth, but were soon followed by space probes that went into orbit around the sun. At first they contained only electronic equipment, then one had a dog as a passenger and later other animals and birds. It was not until 1961 that a man was sent into orbit around the earth.

Most of the earth satellites were equipped with instruments for particular problems, such as the study of cosmic radiation, cloud formations and storms on the earth, and the study of interplanetary particles. The van Allen radiation belts around the earth were discovered in 1958 by observations made from an American satellite.

It had long been the hope of earth inhabitants to study the moon at close hand or to land human beings on the lunar surface. Many moon probes failed to attain their objectives. The Russians succeeded in photographing the far side of the moon in 1959 and in receiving the photographs by radio. The photos were poor but were followed by another Russian success in August 1965, when improved photographs were received by similar techniques.

American attempts failed until finally in 1964 a rocket was launched that struck the near lunar surface. Everything was successful until the final moments when the television cameras failed. However, the next shot was completely successful and the first close-up photographs ever made of the moon's surface were received on July 31, 1964. This achievement was considered to be the first major advance in lunar studies since the invention of the telescope and its application by Galileo in 1609. Selected moon photographs taken from Rangers VII and IX are shown in Figures 1–6 and 1–7.

Special equipment for observing the sun from above the earth's atmosphere was launched in an orbiting solar observatory (OSO). Several telescopes for special stellar problems were sent up in the orbiting astronomical observatory (OAO). There is a great advantage in making observations beyond the disturbing effect of the air which completely absorbs ultraviolet radiation. Figure 1–8 shows a model of the Orbiting Astronomical Observatory The first OAO went into orbit in 1966; but, because of a battery failure, the instruments failed to operate, and no observations were made.

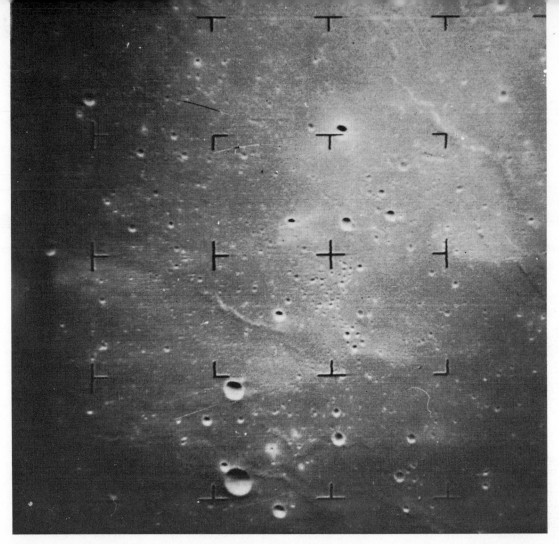

Fig. 1–6  Photograph taken by Ranger VII spacecraft prior to impact on the moon at 6:25 A.M. PDT, July 31, 1964. Altitude above the moon, 85 mi. The photo covers an area 48 mi on a side; it shows craters as small as 500 ft in diameter. (NASA)

### 1.6  The IGY and the IQSY

The International Geophysical Year, or IGY for short, was an organized international program for the study of all branches of science. This "year" lasted 18 months, from July 1, 1957 to December 31, 1958. Astronomical considerations played a major role in the selection of these dates. The sun was predicted to produce an unusual amount of "fireworks" from sunspots and accompanying solar phenomena. Since solar explosions have important effects on the earth and its surroundings, it was desirable to study intensively the sun and its spots, prominences, flares,

and the "solar wind." Sixty-six countries from all over the world took part in this program, which was truly international.

Another reason for starting the IGY during 1957 was the fact that measuring instruments had been developed that were far more accurate than ever before. Electronic meters and computers were available for recording and interpreting data about the universe, which were collected by these instruments. For example, it was possible to equip a rocket with devices that would automatically sample the temperature, pressure, and composition of the air through which it passed. This information could be

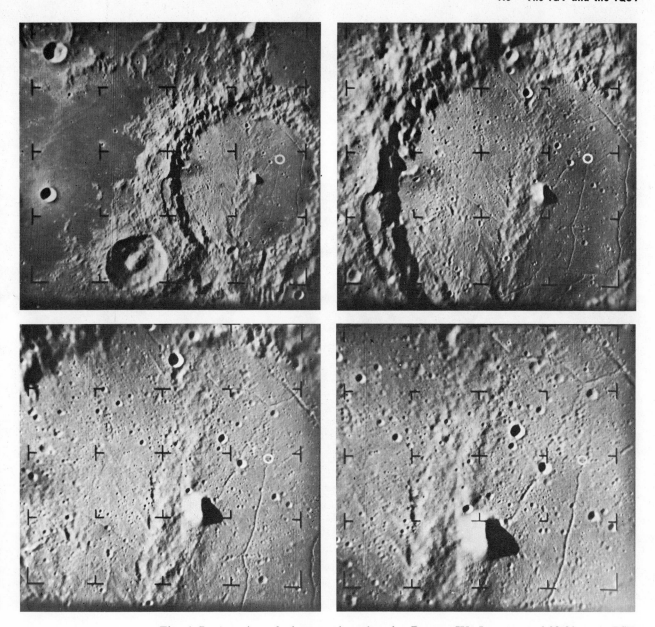

Fig. 1–7   A series of photographs taken by Ranger IX. Impact at 6:08:20 A.M., PST, March 24, 1965. The white circle marks the point of impact in the crater Alphonsus. Top left: Altitude above lunar surface, 266 mi; 3m 02s before impact; area covered, 126 by 133 mi. Top right: Altitude 141 mi; 1m 33s before impact; area covered, 67.5 by 62 mi. Bottom left: Altitude 95.5 mi; 1m 04s before impact; area covered, 46 by 43 mi. Bottom right: Altitude 65.4 mi; 48.9 sec before impact; area covered, 31.6 by 28.5 mi. The floor of Alphonsus shows intricate pattern of ridges, rills, and craters. The central peak is 3000 ft high. (NASA)

Fig. 1–8 The Orbiting Astronomical Observatory (OAO) built by Grumman Aircraft Engineering Corporation for the National Aeronautics and Space Administration. (NASA; Grumman Aircraft Engineering Corporation)

radioed back to the earth, thus making it unnecessary for the rocket and its instruments to be returned undamaged. This was, of course, surpassed by the reception of exceptionally good photographs of the surface of the moon in 1964.

A final reason for the IGY was the need for international cooperation in the study of the universe. Science knows no political boundaries. Almost every great development or discovery is the result of efforts of people in many countries. Television, for example, would not be possible without the work of scientists from Germany, Italy, Scotland, and the United States. Today's vaccines have been developed by men and women in France, Russia, England, Canada, the United States, and a host of other countries. So it was natural that a concentrated study of the universe should be organized on a world-wide scale. Only in that way could the best resources and scientists of each country be put to the best possible use.

An international committee divided the work of the IGY into thirteen major areas: (1) the earth's magnetism (geomagnetism); (2) Northern and Southern Lights (Auroras) and other types of airglow; (3) radiations from space (cosmic rays); (4) glaciers (glaciology); (5) the earth's gravity; (6) the electrically charged layer of the atmosphere (the ionosphere); (7) accurate measurements of the earth's dimensions; (8) weather (meteorology); (9) the oceans (oceanography); (10) earthquakes (seismology); (11) activity of the sun; (12) radioactivity studies (amount of "fallout" on the earth); and (13) rocket and artificial satellite investigations of the upper atmosphere.

The IGY was so successful that it was decided to have another international year at the time when the sun was expected to be quiet. This period of cooperation began January 1, 1964 and ended December 31, 1965. During the IGY the sun was really active, but observations made during 1964 indicated that the sun was far from quiet during the IQSY (the International Year of the Quiet Sun). While the sun was in general fairly free from spots, there were solar areas where a great deal of activity, such as filaments and prominences, could be found.

## 1.7   Astronomy and Other Sciences

For the study of all branches of astronomy (now frequently called space science) it has been the practice of astronomers to borrow the required fields of knowledge from many other sciences. Mathematics is needed for the study of orbits, the motions of all kinds of celestial bodies, and for the system of coordinates used for locations in space. Physics and chemistry are closely related to astronomy, because it is necessary to study the composition of space particles and have a knowledge of atoms and their behavior under all kinds of conditions. Physiology will become increasingly important as astronauts are launched into space and are landed on the moon or on the planets.

Thus it is becoming more and more obvious that all branches of science are to be used in the study of space and the possibility of life existing in other parts of the universe. We should like to know where the material that formed into the solar system came from and how it collected to form the sun and the planets. In spite of the fact that we shall probably never be able to visit the stars nor the systems of stars beyond our own galaxy, the human mind is nevertheless interested in learning as much as possible about the entire universe. The study of space science is inexhaustible. The curiosity of man is insatiable. There is still a great deal to learn about everything in what seems to be an infinite universe.

## 1.8   The Past and the Future

The history of astronomy has filled many books, which take up many feet of space in our libraries. The details of the development and the results of these thousands of years of study, with all the instruments which have been applied to the various branches of astronomy, is presented in many courses in colleges and universities. Research in astronomy requires the lifetimes of thousands of scientists.

In this book we hope to give the student an introduction to astronomy in an elementary form, hoping that he will be inspired to learn more details for himself or to go on to advanced study. Recent developments in astronomy have been very exciting. The future needs research workers and teachers.

Articles on astronomical subjects appear frequently in our serious magazines. Every week the newspapers print stories about recent discoveries or plans for the future. By the time this book is published, there may be one or more observatories orbiting the earth, carrying advanced instruments designed to make investigations that are impossible from the surface of the earth.

We are sure there will be many of you who will want to study further, perhaps to become astronauts, or research astronomers at large observatories, or teachers in schools, colleges, and universities. We hesitate to suggest that some of you will eventually land on the moon, perhaps as tourists, possibly to live there for a time to continue your studies under extreme conditions that cannot be found on the earth.

In astronomy, as in other sciences, the search for knowledge is never finished. Programs like the IGY and IQSY will be carried out again and again (on a greater or lesser scale, depending on international understanding) as man pushes toward an ever better understanding of his universe.

## QUESTIONS AND PROBLEMS

1. List the five divisions of astronomy. What are some of the problems in each division?

2. Compare the photographs from Ranger VII and IX with those taken from the earth. Why are the craters of Figures 1–6 and 1–7 not shown in the photographs of Chapter 11?

3. What is the purpose of (a) OSO? (b) OAO? (c) OGO?

4. What discoveries in astronomy were made during the IGY and IQSY? What problems are being planned for future study?

# Chapter Two

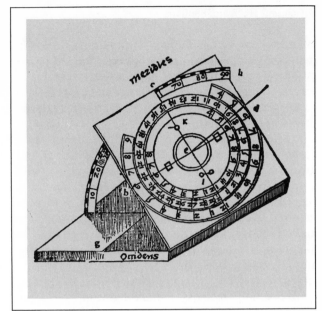

# Atoms and Nuclear Reactions

## THE STRUCTURE OF MATTER

The study of the universe and of the bodies of which it is composed demands a certain knowledge of chemistry and physics. In modern astronomy, a knowledge of the structure of the atom and the properties of the various components of the atom—especially the electron, proton, and neutron—is very important. Chemistry is the branch of science that studies the composition, structure, and properties of substances and of the transformations they undergo during changes of temperature, pressure, and other conditions. One should have some understanding of the elements and their compounds. Physics deals with matter and energy and their interactions. Most of the theories of physics, such as the concepts of mass, weight, velocity, acceleration, and force will be used frequently in the study of astronomy. (The student who has not had courses in high school physics and chemistry or who is encountering for the first time the essential concepts of this chapter and the next should refer to more complete texts in those particular subject areas to supplement his knowledge.)

## 2.1 Matter and Energy

The universe can be divided logically into these two categories: matter and energy. Matter is anything that occupies space and has mass. Energy, on the other hand, does not occupy space and has no mass; but it is, nevertheless, present in space and can be measured. Thus chemistry, which deals with the composition and properties of matter, is closely related to physics, the study of the relation between matter and energy.

Mass refers to the total amount of matter in an object. Mass is frequently confused with weight, since the two are sometimes expressed in the same units. However, weight is the amount of attraction between an astronomical body and an object. For example, the weight of an object varies when it is moved around on the surface of the earth or inside it or above it. But mass remains the same, even in space where it may be weightless. It is usual to speak of a mass of 1 lb to mean the amount of material a weight of 1 lb would have when measured on the earth. To be more exact, in the United States a pound is a specific fraction of a special platinum cylinder kept by the Bureau of Standards in Washington. But a mass of 1 lb would be attracted to the moon by only ⅙ lb or 2.67 oz, if it were weighed by a spring balance on the surface of the moon. And it would be weightless if in a satellite in orbit around the earth or the moon.

Mass is also the measure of the inertia of a body. Inertia is the property of a body which causes it to remain at rest or to move in a straight line with uniform speed unless acted on by a force. This is in accord with Newton's first law of motion. A force is required to overcome the inertia of a body; that is, to make it move, to stop its motion, or to change its direction of motion. Force can be measured as the amount of the mass of the body times the rate at which its velocity changes (acceleration). That is, force is related to mass and acceleration; in mathematical symbols:

$$f = ma. \qquad (2\text{–}1)$$

Mass, force, motion, and distance are related in a complex manner. It is the function of physics to study these relations. This study has been the work of many famous people. The necessary fundamental laws have been completely worked out during the past four or five centuries.

## 2.2 Work and Energy

When a force moves a particle against a resistance it is said to do work. The amount of work ($w$) is proportional to the product of the force ($f$) and the distance ($s$) through which the particle is moved by the force:

$$w = fs. \qquad (2\text{–}2)$$

If the particle is free to move in space, the resistance comes entirely from the inertia of the mass. Of course if there is friction, this also is resistance. So force is required to overcome friction.

Energy is the ability to do work. There are two kinds of energy: *kinetic energy*, the energy of motion, and *potential energy*, the energy of position. If a given amount of work is done on a particle which is free to move, the particle acquires a motion that will give it the ability to do exactly the same amount of work. The kinetic energy (K.E.) of the particle can be computed as one-half the mass of the particle times the square of its velocity ($v$).

Or,
$$\text{K.E.} = \frac{1}{2}mv^2. \qquad (2\text{–}3)$$

Potential energy is the amount of energy a particle has because of its position. For example, if a particle is raised to a position from which it is ready to do work, it has potential energy. The amount of the potential energy is equal to the amount of work done to raise it to its position. A coiled spring has potential energy because it is in position to do work. However, to do work the potential energy must be transformed into kinetic energy. Thus the particle acquires velocity when dropped, and the spring moves the parts of a watch when released.

There are other kinds of energy which are important in astronomy. *Heat* is a form of energy, since heat is capable of setting molecules of water in motion over a fire. *Light* has energy as indicated by a radiometer, or by a photoelectric cell, where electrons from an element are set in motion to produce a current of electricity. Light and heat are part of the electromagnetic spectrum, the frequencies of radiation which include X rays, ultraviolet rays, infrared and radio waves. All these radiations are forms of energy.

## 2.3 The Nature of Matter

Matter exists in three different forms: solid, liquid, and gas. It has been estimated that nearly all the material in the universe is in the gaseous form and that only one part in 1000 is in solid or liquid form. Thus if we are to understand the nature of the material in the universe, we must become familiar with the properties of gases and with the gas laws.

Chemists and philosophers have been trying to divide matter into smaller fundamental particles for more than 2000 years. The Greek philosopher Democritus about 400 B.C. made the first recorded attempt to determine the basic nature of matter. He imagined that all matter is made up of very tiny particles, too small to be seen with the unaided eye. He thought that these particles would be found to be solid and indivisible. He called them *atoms*, meaning indivisible. An atom is now defined to be the smallest particle of an element that has all the properties of the element.

It was originally believed that the universe is composed of four fundamental substances: air, water, fire, and earth. These substances were called *elements*. Later, it was found, for example, that water could be broken down into still more fundamental elements, now called hydrogen and oxygen. The earth is now known to be composed of many other fundamental substances. And so the list of elements grew until today we know that there are more than 100, most of which are found in their natural state, either alone or in compounds. Others can be made in powerful atomic reactors.

Materials that are composed of two or more elements are called *compounds*. Compounds can be decomposed into their basic elements by ordinary chemical means.

Democritus went even further. He taught that the atoms are always in motion and that they come in a variety of shapes and sizes. Some are rough, irregular, and stick tightly together. Metals are made up of these. Others are heavy, smooth, and slide about easily, accounting for the weight and fluidity of liquids. Still others are both light and smooth, thus explaining the behavior of gases.

Robert Boyle, an English scientist, in the seventeenth century, in his study of gases showed that their behavior can best be explained by assuming that they are composed of tiny particles. He also made a list of elements and felt that the large num-

ber of substances proposed by Democritus could be greatly reduced.

In 1789 a French chemist, Antoine Lavoisier, made the first successful list of elements. Using a set of accurate scales he had developed, Lavoisier found that the products formed in burning a piece of wood (ashes, gas, and so on) actually weighed more than the original piece. He rightly concluded that the weight of any product of a chemical combination would always equal the combined weights of the substances entering into the reaction. This principle, known as the *law of conservation of matter*, is usually written: Matter cannot be created or destroyed by ordinary chemical means, but can only be changed from one form to another. This discovery earned for Lavoisier the title Father of Modern Chemistry, for it was the real beginning of analytical methods in this field of learning.

Lavoisier succeeded in listing only 28 of the chemical elements. He had proved, however, that these elements were indestructible, and that they could be traced as they combined with each other to form more complex substances. This laid the groundwork for an intensive study of matter, which would eventually reveal the structure of the atom itself.

John Dalton, an English teacher around 1800, found the relationship between an element and an atom. He studied the *law of definite proportions*, which had been stated by a French chemist, Louis Proust. This law states: The elements of a compound always combine in certain definite proportions. When substances change, the atoms are rearranged. Dalton invented symbols for the elements and combined them to show how new substances are made. (See Figure 2–1.)

Dalton's theory explained perfectly the experiments of Lavoisier. It also started chemists working toward the determination of atomic weights, without which modern chemistry would be impossible.

Dalton's plan was to assign a weight of one unit to the lightest element, hydrogen. Then the other elements usually have weights which are approxi-

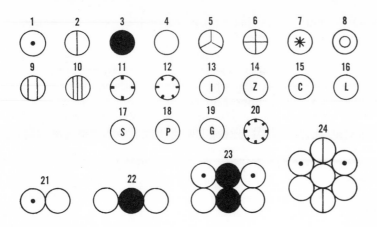

Fig. 2–1  Dalton's symbols for the elements and some common compounds. No. 21 represented water; 22, carbon dioxide; 23, acetic acid; and 24, ammonium nitrate.

mately an integral (whole) number of units greater than hydrogen. Oxygen is about 16 times as heavy, iron nearly 56 times, and so on. The weights compared with hydrogen were called *atomic weights*. We now, however, base the system of atomic weights on that of a form of carbon, taken to be 12. Hydrogen is 1.008 instead of 1.0. With this system, more of the elements have nearly integral weights than with Dalton's plan. The atomic weight, therefore, is not the actual weight of an atom, but is a weight relative to that of carbon.

Amadeo Avogadro, an Italian chemist and physicist, was the first to call a particular combination of atoms a *molecule*. It is the smallest particle of a compound having all the properties of the compound. Today we know that the number of atoms in 1 g (gram) of hydrogen is $6.0238 \times 10^{23}$, which can be written in full as 602,380,000,000,000,000,000,000. (See Appendix.)

## 2.4  Inside the Atom

By the beginning of the twentieth century, it was suspected that the atom might not be indivisible after all. The reason for this was that charges of electricity could be produced by rubbing together different substances. This indicated that atoms might be composed of charged particles.

One solution was suggested by J. J. Thomson, an English scientist. He thought of the atom as a positively charged field with negative particles scattered through it. However, Lord Ernest Rutherford, another English scientist, found that most of the mass of an atom was concentrated in the center and not evenly distributed as in a fluid.

Rutherford succeeded in determining the size of the atomic nucleus and the amount of the positive charge it contained. This was the beginning of the modern atomic theory. To balance the central positive charge, Rutherford believed that there was an equal number of negative charges surrounding the nucleus. The fundamental electrical particle with negative charge was called an *electron*. There was also found a fundamental particle with a positive charge equal in magnitude to the charge on the electron. This particle was called a *proton*. While these two particles had equal charge of opposite sign, the mass of the proton was determined to be 1836 times greater.

A modern interpretation of the structure of atoms was proposed in 1913 by Neils Bohr, a Danish physicist. He suggested that in the hydrogen atom one electron circles one proton, much as a planet circles the sun, except of course for distance apart and number of orbits in a unit of time. He also proposed the theory that the orbits in the hydrogen atom can have only certain sizes in order to explain the positions of certain lines in the spectrum. This theory led to a computation of the orbit sizes and to the periods of revolution of the electron.

In the Bohr theory, the electrons are assumed to stay in a given orbit only as long as there is no exchange of energy with surrounding space. If energy is fed into the atom from outside, the electron jumps a certain distance to another orbit, depending on how much energy is absorbed by the atom. If the atom gives up a small amount of energy, the electron jumps from an outer orbit to an inner one, again depending on how much energy is emitted by the atom. For example, in hydrogen gas the jump from the third to the second orbit produces a red line in the spectrum. These transitions are taking place in the atmosphere of the sun continually and give rise to the red color of the solar prominences. The red line is one of a series of lines in the visible part of the spectrum, called the Balmer series, which is easily produced in the laboratory.

Other transfers of energy in hydrogen produce lines in the ultraviolet, called the Lyman series, which have been photographed in the spectrum of the sun from above the earth's atmosphere. A third series, the Paschen series, has lines in the infrared spectrum of the sun.

The second lightest of the elements is helium. In the Bohr theory, the helium atom was thought to be composed of a nucleus consisting of four protons (since the atomic weight of helium is about four times that of hydrogen) and two electrons to neutralize two of the protons. These were the only subatomic particles known at the time. Circling the nucleus were two electrons, to balance the positive charge of the nucleus due to the other two protons.

However, another subatomic particle was discovered in 1932 that has the mass of a proton but has neither a positive nor a negative charge and is thus neutral electrically. This particle has been named the *neutron*. So the nucleus of the helium atom is now believed to consist of two protons and two neutrons. The electrons, which orbit the nucleus and balance the charge on the two protons, circle the

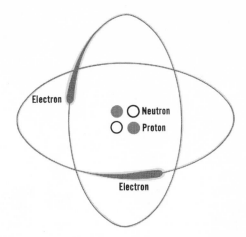

Fig. 2–2   A suggested model of the helium atom, atomic number 2; atomic weight 4. The atom is inert with two electrons in the first shell around the nucleus. Beginning with lithium, additional electrons are located in other shells.

nucleus in orbits, something quite similar to the ones shown in Figure 2–2. The number of protons determines what has been called the *atomic number* of the atom. Thus helium has atomic number 2. It is inert chemically, which means that helium does not easily form compounds with other atoms.

The atom with atomic number 3 is lithium. That is, there are three electrons in orbit around the nucleus. But lithium has an atomic weight of seven. This is interpreted to mean that the nucleus is composed of three protons and four neutrons, the protons being neutralized by the three orbiting electrons. Furthermore, two of the electrons are in a shell close to the nucleus, but the third is in an orbit by itself at a greater distance. Lithium is very active chemically and combines readily with other elements.

In succeeding elements each of the elements is generally heavier than the one preceding and its atomic number increases by one. A list of all known elements arranged in order of atomic number is called the *periodic table of elements*. Table 2–1 lists the elements in alphabetical order. The atomic

TABLE 2–1
The Elements, Their Symbols, Atomic Numbers, and
Approximate Relative Atomic Weights[a]

| Name of Element | Symbol | Atomic Number | Atomic Weight | Name of Element | Symbol | Atomic Number | Atomic Weight |
|---|---|---|---|---|---|---|---|
| Actinium ............ | Ac | 89 | 227 | Iridium .............. | Ir | 77 | 192 |
| *Aluminum* ........... | *Al* | *13* | *27* | *Iron* ................. | *Fe* | *26* | *56* |
| Americium ........... | Am | 95 | 243 | Krypton ............. | Kr | 36 | 84 |
| *Antimony* ........... | *Sb* | *51* | *122* | Lanthanum .......... | La | 57 | 139 |
| Argon ............... | Ar | 18 | 40 | *Lead* ............... | *Pb* | *82* | *207* |
| *Arsenic* ............. | *As* | *33* | *75* | Lithium ............. | Li | 3 | 7 |
| Astatine .......... | At | 85 | 211 | Lutetium ............ | Lu | 71 | 175 |
| *Barium* ............. | *Ba* | *56* | *137* | *Magnesium* .......... | *Mg* | *12* | *24* |
| Berkelium ........... | Bk | 97 | 245 | *Manganese* .......... | *Mn* | *25* | *55* |
| Beryllium ........... | Be | 4 | 9 | Mendelevium ........ | Mv | 101 | 256 |
| *Bismuth* ............ | *Bi* | *83* | *209* | *Mercury* ............ | *Hg* | *80* | *200.6* |
| Boron ............... | B | 5 | 11 | Molybdenum ........ | Mo | 42 | 96 |
| *Bromine* ............ | *Br* | *35* | *80* | Neodymium ......... | Nd | 60 | 144 |
| Cadmium .......... | Cd | 48 | 112 | Neon ............... | Ne | 10 | 20 |
| *Calcium* ............ | *Ca* | *20* | *40* | Neptunium .......... | Np | 93 | 237 |
| Californium ......... | Cf | 98 | 248 | *Nickel* ............. | *Ni* | *28* | *58.7* |
| *Carbon* ............. | *C* | *6* | *12* | Niobium ............ | Nb | 41 | 93 |
| Cerium ............. | Ce | 58 | 140 | *Nitrogen* ........... | *N* | *7* | *14* |
| Cesium ............. | Cs | 55 | 133 | Nobelium ........... | No | 102 | 254 |
| *Chlorine* ............ | *Cl* | *17* | *35.5* | Osmium ............ | Os | 76 | 190 |
| Chromium .......... | Cr | 24 | 52 | *Oxygen* ............. | *O* | *8* | *16* |
| Cobalt ............. | Co | 27 | 59 | Palladium ........... | Pd | 46 | 106.7 |
| *Copper* ............. | *Cu* | *29* | *63.5* | *Phosphorus* ......... | *P* | *15* | *31* |
| Curium ............. | Cm | 96 | 245 | *Platinum* ............ | *Pt* | *78* | *195* |
| Dysprosium ......... | Dy | 66 | 162.5 | Plutonium .......... | Pu | 94 | 242 |
| Einsteinium ......... | E | 99 | 255 | Polonium ........... | Po | 84 | 210 |
| Erbium ............. | Er | 68 | 167 | *Potassium* .......... | *K* | *19* | *39* |
| Europium ........... | Eu | 63 | 152 | Praseodymium ....... | Pr | 59 | 141 |
| Fermium ............ | Fm | 100 | 252 | Promethium ......... | Pm | 61 | 145 |
| *Fluorine* ............ | *F* | *9* | *19* | Protactinium ........ | Pa | 91 | 231 |
| Francium ........... | Fr | 87 | 223 | Radium ............. | Ra | 88 | 226 |
| Gadolinium ......... | Gd | 64 | 157 | Radon .............. | Rn | 86 | 222 |
| Gallium ............ | Ga | 31 | 69.7 | Rhenium ............ | Re | 75 | 186 |
| Germanium ......... | Ge | 32 | 72.6 | Rhodium ............ | Rh | 45 | 103 |
| *Gold* ............... | *Au* | *79* | *197* | Rubidium ........... | Rb | 37 | 85.5 |
| Hafnium ............ | Hf | 72 | 178.6 | Ruthenium .......... | Ru | 44 | 101 |
| Helium ............. | He | 2 | 4 | Samarium ........... | Sm | 62 | 150 |
| Holmium ........... | Ho | 67 | 165 | Scandium ........... | Sc | 21 | 45 |
| *Hydrogen* ........... | *H* | *1* | *1* | Selenium ............ | Se | 34 | 79 |
| Indium ............. | In | 49 | 115 | *Silicon* ............. | *Si* | *14* | *28* |
| *Iodine* ............. | *I* | *53* | *127* | Silver ............... | *Ag* | *47* | *108* |

| Name of Element | Sym-bol | Atomic Number | Atomic Weight | Name of Element | Sym-bol | Atomic Number | Atomic Weight |
|---|---|---|---|---|---|---|---|
| *Sodium* ............. | *Na* | *11* | *23* | *Tin* ................. | *Sn* | *50* | *118.7* |
| *Strontium* ........... | *Sr* | *38* | *87.6* | *Titanium* ............ | *Ti* | *22* | *48* |
| *Sulfur* ............... | *S* | *16* | *32* | *Tungsten* ........... | *W* | *74* | *184* |
| Tantalum ............ | Ta | 73 | 181 | Uranium ............. | U | 92 | 238 |
| Technetium ......... | Tc | 43 | 99 | Vanadium ........... | V | 23 | 51 |
| Tellurium ........... | Te | 52 | 127.6 | Xenon ............... | Xe | 54 | 131 |
| Terbium ............. | Tb | 65 | 159 | Ytterbium ........... | Yb | 70 | 173 |
| Thallium ........... | Tl | 81 | 204 | Yttrium ............. | Y | 39 | 89 |
| Thorium ........... | Th | 90 | 232 | *Zinc* ................. | *Zn* | *30* | *65* |
| Thulium ............. | Tm | 69 | 169 | Zirconium ........... | Zr | 40 | 91 |

[a]The more important elements are printed in *italic* type.

number and atomic weight of each element is given:

When an atom gains or loses electrons without a change in the nucleus, it becomes electrically unbalanced. This is called *ionization*; and the electrically charged atom, which may be either positively or negatively charged, is called an *ion*. The ion has properties different from those of the original neutral atom and gives a different spectrum.

Since the parts of the atom are much too small to be seen, even under the powerful electron microscope, they must be identified by indirect means. That is, these particles have forced themselves onto the attention of the scientists by circumstantial evidence.

One of the most important tools of the nuclear scientist is the cloud chamber. It was invented by C. T. R. Wilson, a British physicist. It is simply a small box with windows and a movable piston at the bottom. When the box is saturated with water vapor and the piston is pulled down, the sudden decrease in pressure causes the water vapor to cool and condense into a fog. This fog forms most easily around particles of dust or electrically charged particles. If an electron passes through the cloud chamber, it leaves a visible vapor trail, like those of high-flying planes.

By studying the direction of the tracks of electrons, protons, and other particles, the weight and charge on the particles can be determined. The *positron*, a particle with the mass of an electron but with a unit positive charge, was discovered in 1932 by the use of a cloud chamber.

In 1929 the Geiger-Müller counter was invented. This instrument has become one of the most important tools of the scientist for the study of radiation.

On August 7, 1912, three men, a navigator, a meteorologist, and a physicist, Victor F. Hess, made a balloon ascension over Austria and Germany with some instruments for measuring radiation. Hess summarized his observations with the statement that "radiation of very great penetrating power enters our atmosphere from above." This was the beginning of many years of research on what are now called *cosmic rays*.

Since that date, cosmic ray research has led to the discovery of other subatomic particles. Among them are mu-mesons and pi-mesons (the word *meson* means in-between particles) that are very short lived. Other results have confirmed a prediction that there must be antiparticles, which, when they collide with their counterparts, produce mutual annihilation. Among these are antiprotons and antineutrons. Such particles make up what has been called *antimatter*. There is evidence that there may be stars which consist entirely of antimatter, which may explain such phenomena as the quasi-stellar sources discovered in 1960.

## THE KINETIC THEORY

### 2.5  Gas Laws

Late in the seventeenth century a very important law was stated by Robert Boyle. *Boyle's law* states: When a gas is compressed and kept at a constant temperature, its pressure times its volume remains constant. ($PV = C$) That is, the volume is inversely proportional to the pressure. This is true for a considerable range of pressure.

A century or more later, Boyle's law was followed by *Charles' law*, which states: The volume of a given gas increases with temperature (provided the pressure is kept constant) by a definite fraction of its volume. At 0°C the volume changes by $\frac{1}{273}$ of the volume for each degree Celsius change of temperature.

Still later a third law, *Joule's law*, stated: There is no change of temperature when a gas expands without doing external work and without receiving or losing heat. Another statement of Joule's law is: A given amount of mechanical energy is always equivalent to a definite quantity of heat energy, and vice versa.

These laws led to the modern kinetic theory. Minute particles of a substance are in vigorous motion. In particular for gases, particles of a gas move in straight lines with high velocities, colliding with each other and therefore changing their directions; pressure is due to the impact of the particles on the container walls.

A cubic centimeter of a gas consists of a multitude of atoms ($2.7 \times 10^{19}$ of them) all moving around at random and colliding frequently with each other. It is estimated that each atom has $6 \times 10^9$ (6 billion) collisions each second. A typical atom at room temperature travels at an average speed of nearly 0.5 km (kilometer) per second (0.3 mi per second). It is about one hundred-millionth of an inch in diameter and its average path (mean free path) between collisions is about 1 three-millionth of an inch long. The atoms are very small compared to their distances apart and occupy less than one thousandth of the space through which they move.

When a piston compresses a gas, the molecules of the gas strike the piston with greater energy. If external work is done on the gas, the temperature rises and the kinetic energy of the gas molecules increases. Hence the molecules move faster and the pressure increases. Since kinetic energy = $\frac{1}{2}mv^2$, it is evident that a heavy gas molecule does not have to move as fast as a light one at the same temperature to have the same kinetic energy.

Not all the heat energy results in more rapid motion of the gas molecules. Some of it may produce internal vibrations in the molecules or may even cause them to spin. The amount of energy absorbed in these ways differs with the structure of the molecules. Because only the forward motion of molecules affects the temperature of the gas, a given amount of heat does not raise the temperature of all gases equally.

If heat is added to a liquid from outside, all the molecules will move faster. Eventually, all of them will have enough energy to break the attractive forces between them and escape rapidly into the air. The temperature at which this happens is called the *boiling point* of the liquid. Since the attraction between molecules differs with the weight and structure of the molecules, boiling points differ for different liquids. For example, water boils at 100°C (212°F), ether at 35°C, and mercury at 357°C.

Melting is explained in a similar fashion. At a critical temperature, the *melting point*, the particles of a solid overcome the forces which keep them rigid and they start moving around at random. Again the melting point of a solid depends on its structure. Water (ice) melts at 0°C (32°F), mercury at −39°C, and iron at 1535°C.

Boiling and melting are examples of changes of state of a substance. Water, for example, exists in three different states: solid (ice), liquid (water), and gas (steam).

Since temperature is the result of the kinetic energy of molecules, the lowest possible temperature is one at which the molecules stop moving. This temperature is called *absolute zero* and is theoretically equal to $-273.16°C$ ($-459.69°F$). Scientists have been able to reduce gases to liquids and even solids with very low temperatures, but have not quite been able to produce a temperature of absolute zero.

We have so far considered only the average velocity of molecules in a gas and have found that the lighter gases have molecules that move faster than those of a heavier gas at the same temperature. Many of the molecules in a gas at a given temperature reach velocities that are much higher than the average. When molecules of the earth's atmosphere reach a critical velocity, called the *velocity of escape*, it is possible for them to leave the earth's gravitational field and jump off into space. The velocity of escape from the earth's surface is just under 7 mi per second (about 25,000 mi per hour). This velocity is determined by the size and mass of the earth, and is the same for all bodies no matter how massive the bodies may be. Only hydrogen and helium at atmospheric temperatures have molecules that reach this critical velocity. The earth is therefore losing some of its hydrogen and helium.

It is interesting to note that an artificial satellite put into orbit just above the surface of the earth, at about 100 mi so it is above most of the atmosphere, must have a velocity of about 5 mi per second (18,000 mi per hour) to keep from falling back onto the earth's surface. If it is launched in an arc approximately parallel to the earth's surface with a velocity between 5 and 7 mi per second, it will go into an elliptical orbit with its greatest distance at increasing distances, depending on the speed. If the speed reaches 7 mi per second, the orbit will be a parabola and the rocket will leave the earth to go into orbit around the sun. The speed which a body at the earth's distance from the sun must reach to leave the sun's gravitational attraction is about 26 mi per second. This is about 7.5 mi per second greater than the speed of the earth in its orbit around the sun.

The velocity of escape from the sun's surface is 384 mi per second and from the moon's surface about 1.5 mi per second. From Mars the velocity of escape is about 3.2 mi per second.

## RADIOACTIVITY

### 2.6 Radioactive Materials

In the nineteenth century, experimenters with electricity used tubes from which some of the air had been pumped. When a current of electricity was passed through such a tube, called a Crookes tube, a purplish glow appeared around the negative end of the tube. When more air was pumped out, the glow became a band of light throughout the length of the tube. This is the same principle as is used today in fluorescent light and television picture tubes.

In 1895 the German scientist, Wilhelm Roentgen, noticed that some radiation from a Crookes tube was causing a fluorescent screen to glow. Roentgen was not sure whether the radiation was from particles or from some wave type of radiation. It turned out that the latter was the correct interpretation. Roentgen called the mysterious beams *X rays*, which as everybody knows have played a great role in medicine.

A year later, a French scientist, Henri Becquerel, found that certain fluorescent materials after exposure to sunlight glow in the dark as the fluorescent screen glows under X-radiation. This discovery showed that some atoms also emit radiation, which is known as radioactivity. The materials are said to be radioactive.

Later, Pierre and Marie Curie in Paris found that uranium was strongly radioactive, but that there were other atoms associated with uranium which were even stronger emitters of radioactivity. They isolated the element polonium and, later, radium, which was the strongest of all.

Experiments with the Crookes tubes showed that stream particles in the tube were negatively charged and were in fact electrons. In the radio-active elements it was found that some of the parti-cles behaved as electrons do in Crookes tubes and are also electrons. They were called *beta particles* and are now designated by the Greek letter *beta* (*β*). Others were shown to be positively, instead of negatively charged and were called *alpha particles*, designated by the Greek letter *alpha* (α). A third class of particles had no charge at all. They were called *gamma rays*, designated by the Greek letter *gamma* (γ). It later developed that the gamma rays are X rays of short wavelength.

Radium is one substance which emits alpha particles. Its atomic weight before the alpha ray is emitted is 226. Afterwards its atomic weight is only 222. It is then called radon. The difference between the two atomic weights is equal to the atomic weight of helium. Hence an alpha particle is a helium nucleus.

A gamma ray is also called a photon. It has zero mass and zero charge. Gamma rays are much more penetrating than either alpha or beta particles. Just how an atom could emit X rays, however, was still a mystery. It turns out that gamma rays are not particles (unless a photon, which is a unit of light intensity, can be called a particle), but are radiations similar to light. X rays, including gamma rays, have wavelengths which can be measured. Gamma rays have the shortest wavelengths of all the waves in the electromagnetic spectrum.

A *transmutation* is a nuclear reaction in which the number of protons in the nucleus changes and the element is changed from one element to another. This term is an old one, which was used by the alchemists who attempted to change the baser metals to gold. In a transmutation there must be corresponding changes in the orbiting electrons to keep their total number equal to the number of protons in the nucleus.

## 2.7  Isotopes

The atomic theory has stated that an element must be composed of a number of electrons and protons and neutrons. How does it happen that the atomic weight of an element is almost always a whole number plus a decimal? For example, the atomic weight of iron is 55.85. If we add up the number of protons, neutrons, and alpha particles in the atom, its atomic weight should be expected to be a whole number, since the mass of the electrons is too small to count. That it does not was explained by the English chemist Frederick Soddy. He found that the elements are mixtures of atoms with the same chemical properties, but with different atomic weights. For example, lead-206 and lead-207 have the same chemical reactions, but lead-207 has an extra neutron in its nucleus. These forms of the same element are called *isotopes* and are usually found mixed together in the natural state.

The isotopes of lead were the first to be found. Later, it was discovered that all the elements occur in two or more isotopic forms. Oxygen may have a mass of 16, 17, or 18. Iron occurs in four natural isotopes of mass 54, 56, 57, and 58. They are mixed in the proper proportions to have an average atomic weight of 55.85.

One of the best known examples of isotopes is the element uranium, which has isotopes of atomic weight 233, 235, and 238. These isotopes have to be separated from each other by very complicated and expensive processes to provide the components of atomic bombs and nuclear power.

Isotopes are very useful as tracers in several fields of science, such as medicine and even agri-culture. They are being used today in the treatment of cancer and in other fields of medicine.

Even hydrogen has three isotopes, but strangely enough, they have been given different names. H-1 is common hydrogen. H-2 is called deuterium or heavy hydrogen. H-3 is called tritium, since its atomic weight is three. Only one atom out of several million hydrogen atoms is tritium. Heavy water is a compound of oxygen and deuterium.

## QUESTIONS AND PROBLEMS

1. Distinguish between mass and weight. Compute your weight for each planet. (See Table 14–1.)

2. What would be the kinetic energy of a meteoroid of mass 1 kg, if its velocity is 40 km/sec?

3. The thrust of a space vehicle's rockets increases its speed by 100 ft/sec every second. What will the acceleration be if (a) the thrust is doubled, (b) the thrust remains the same but the mass is doubled, and (c) both the thrust and mass are doubled? **Ans:** (a) doubled.

4. Which gas would diffuse through a small opening faster, hydrogen or oxygen? Explain.

5. How much more kinetic energy does a car have when traveling at 60 mi/hr than (a) at 20 mi/hr, and (b) at 15 mi/hr? **Ans:** (a) 9 times.

6. What is the ultimate source of the heat energy in an electric toaster? Explain.

7. A gas exerts a pressure of 100 lb/in$^2$ when confined to a volume of 10 ft$^3$. Provided the temperature remains constant, (a) what pressure would be required to compress the gas to 2 ft$^3$? (b) what pressure would the gas exert if expanded to a volume of 30 ft$^3$? **Ans:** (a) 500 lb/in$^2$.

8. What are the ratios of the masses and charges of alpha and beta particles?

9. What two factors determine the nature of the atmosphere which a planet can retain?

10. Natural chlorine gas is a mixture of two isotopes, one of atomic mass 35, the other of atomic mass 37. What must be the ratio of the amounts present to give the natural mixture an average atomic mass of 35.5?

11. The Barringer Crater (Figure 15–8) was formed by the impact of a meteorite. What happened to its original kinetic energy?

12. How many protons, electrons, and neutrons are there in a neutral atom of (a) carbon, and (b) oxygen?

13. How fast would a hydrogen atom have to travel if it had the same kinetic energy as an oxygen atom traveling at 1 mi/sec?

14. How many atoms are there in (a) 6 g of carbon, and (b) 1 g of oxygen? **Ans:** (a) 3 x 10$^{23}$.

15. The diameter of an atomic nucleus is about 10$^{-13}$ in. (a) What fraction is this of the atom's diameter? (b) What fraction of an atom's volume is empty space (neglecting the space occupied by the electrons)?

16. Compare two modern chemical theories with their counterparts in the nineteenth century.

# Chapter Three

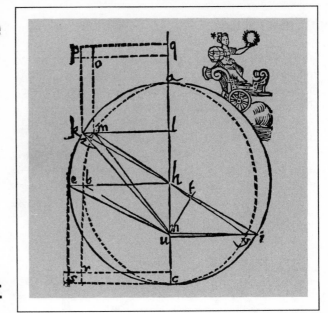

# The Nature of Light

## 3.1  Introduction

In order to understand the principles of optics and of the construction of telescopes, it is necessary to know the fundamental laws of light. To understand how light behaves under all conditions in space, including the interiors of the sun and the stars, it is necessary to know what light is, how it is produced, and how it is related to the atom and the particles of which atoms are composed.

The moon, the planets, the sun, the stars, and all other bodies in space are inaccessible. They cannot be analyzed in the laboratory. The light they give off can be collected and analyzed. Where it came from and what has happened to it on its long journey through space can only be deduced from theories.

It is necessary to investigate the laws of the production of the spectrum and apply these laws to the stars. From them are found such things as the temperature and density of matter in space and the speeds with which objects are moving in all parts of the universe.

## FUNDAMENTAL LAWS

### 3.2  Reflection and Refraction

The simplest law of light is that it travels in a straight line. This can be demonstrated easily. But when this law is investigated carefully and with the most refined instruments, it is found to be not quite true. It is well known that when light strikes a polished surface, all or part of it is reflected. The law of reflection leads to an understanding of the principle of the mirror, and mirrors are used today in all the largest optical telescopes.

Also when light passes from one medium to another, such as from air to water or from a vacuum to air, it is bent. This is called *refraction*. Refraction is used in the spectroscope to produce the spectrum, and in the telescope to form an image. It is, however, troublesome in refracting telescopes, since it interferes with the production of images free from color, as shown in Chapter 4. Also when light passes close to an edge, even the edge of your finger or pencil, it is bent slightly. This is called *diffraction*. Diffraction is also troublesome in the telescope, since it causes the images of stars to appear fuzzy, instead of as sharp as would be desirable. This is because some of the light is diffracted when it passes the edge of the telescope opening.

The *law of reflection* is as follows: The angle of incidence is equal to the angle of reflection.

For an explanation of the law of reflection, refer to Figure 3–1. *MM'* is a reflecting surface—a

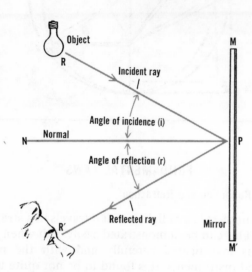

Fig. 3–1   The law of reflection.

mirror. *RP* is a ray of light (incident ray) striking the mirror at some angle *i*, the angle of incidence. *PR'* is the reflected ray of light. *NP* is a line (the normal), which is perpendicular to *MM'* at *P*, the point where the reflection takes place. The angle *r* between *NP* and *PR'* is the angle of reflection. The law states that

$$i = r. \tag{3–1}$$

Alhazen, an Arabian scientist about A.D. 1000, found by experiment that *RP*, *NP*, and *PR'* all lie in the same plane.

This makes it possible to calculate where any ray from an object, such as the electric light shown in the figure, will travel after it strikes the reflecting surface and therefore where to put the eye of the observer. Of course a luminous object will be sending out many rays and more than one ray should be traced. It also shows that a ray of light emitted at *R* can enter the eye at *R'* without traveling in a straight line between two points. This is the principle of the plane mirror.

A ray of light is one of the lines of light that appear to radiate from a luminous object. By *light* is meant the popular understanding of the word— something that makes vision possible.

It will be noted from the figure that if *i* is increased by an angle ($\alpha$), *r* will be increased by the same angle. Thus

$$i + \alpha = r + \alpha. \tag{3–2}$$

Therefore the angle between the incident and reflected rays will be increased by twice the angle ($2\alpha$). Likewise if the angle of the mirror is changed instead of the incident ray, the reflected ray will be changed by twice the angle. This law is very important in the construction of the optical instruments of astronomy, such as the reflecting telescope.

The law of reflection is independent of the intensity (brightness) and color of the light as well as the nature and shape of the reflecting surface. The reflected ray is never as intense as the incident ray, since some of the light is lost at the reflecting surface. If the reflecting surface is a smooth, curved surface, the law will apply; and a beam of parallel light can be brought to a single point (a focus), a principle which is used in designing a mirror for a reflecting telescope. If the surface is rough and uneven, the law will still hold, but the light will be scattered. This scattering is called *diffusion*.

The bending of light as it passes from one transparent substance to another with different density is called *refraction*, from a word meaning a breaking. This results because the velocity of light is different in different materials. The velocity of light in a vacuum is 299,796 km (186,282 mi) per second. In water it is about 140,000 mi per second. Since a beam of light suddenly slows down upon entering water from air, for example, it suddenly changes direction, if it enters the water at an angle which is not 90°. The ratio of the velocity of light in a vacuum to its velocity in a transparent medium is called the *index of refraction.*

## 3.3 Effects of Refraction

The refraction of light as it passes from air to water or from water to air is well known. A stick seems to break when one end is held in the water. Refraction makes a swimming pool seem much shallower than it really is. Perhaps not so well known is the effect of refraction as light passes from the near vacuum of space into the air around the earth. If a parallel beam passes into a different medium at right angles to the surface, there is no bending because all the rays in the beam slow down or speed up at the same time.

However, if the angle is different from 90°, there will be refraction. This holds for the earth's atmosphere as well. A star directly overhead is in exactly the same direction as it appears to be. But a star in any other position looks higher than it really is. The top of the sun appears to be on the horizon at sunrise or sunset, but it is actually below the horizon. This effect makes the days a little longer than they would be if the earth had no atmosphere. At both sunrise and sunset the top of the sun is about 35′ (minutes of arc) below the horizon when it appears to be touching the horizon. This is greater than the apparent diameter of the sun.

Refraction at sunrise and sunset increases the length of daylight by about four minutes. Refraction must be taken into account by the navigator when the sun or another body is observed for the purpose of determining his position on the earth. (See Figure 3–2.)

The atmosphere around the earth is arranged in layers at various heights. It is being stirred constantly by heating and cooling effects which produce

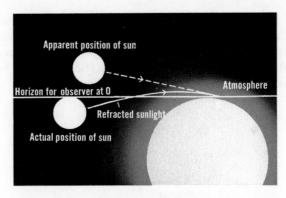

Fig. 3–2 The effect of the earth's atmosphere on the direction of the sun's rays.

the winds. This produces variable refraction, which makes the stars appear to twinkle. Since different colors of light travel through the air with slightly different velocities, the stars seem to change color as they twinkle. This is particularly noticeable with bright stars near the horizon. Variable refraction causes the star images in the telescope to dance around and is very annoying in astronomical observations. Astronomers speak of it as "bad seeing."

## 3.4 The Index of Refraction

The index of refraction can be determined by measurement. This is fortunate, since it may be difficult to determine the velocity of light in all materials with sufficient accuracy. The law of refraction states that a ray of light is bent towards the perpendicular to the surface when entering a denser medium and away from the perpendicular when entering a less dense medium. Figure 3–3 illustrates this law. The angle *i* is the angle of incidence, the angle between the ray and the perpendicular (normal). The angle *r* is the angle of refraction, also measured from the perpendicular. The index of refraction is then defined by the relation:

$$\mu = \sin i / \sin r \qquad (3\text{--}3)$$

or in words, the index of refraction equals the sine of the angle of incidence divided by the sine of the angle of refraction. Both *i* and *r* can be measured with precision in the laboratory. The sines can be looked up in a table of trigonometric functions.

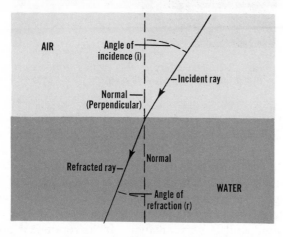

Fig. 3–3   The refraction of light when passing from one medium to another of greater density.

Table 3–1 gives the index of refraction for various transparent substances for ordinary light at room temperatures, except for air, where a temperature of 0°C is used:

TABLE 3–1
**Index of Refraction**

| | |
|---|---|
| Air, dry, 0°C | 1.00029 |
| Alcohol, ethyl | 1.36 |
| Carbon disulfide | 1.63 |
| Carbon tetrachloride | 1.46 |
| Diamond | 2.42 |
| Glass, crown | 1.52 |
| Glass, flint | 1.61 |
| Quartz, fused | 1.46 |
| Water | 1.33 |

## 3.5   Interference of Light

In the early 1800s Thomas Young, an English physicist, and Augustin Fresnel, a French optician and mathematician, performed a series of experiments which showed that light exhibits wave characteristics. The first of these dealt with interference. When water waves are superposed they may fall so that crests are superposed on crests and troughs on troughs. The wave amplitudes are thus reinforced, increasing the height of crests and the depth of troughs. Or a crest may fall in such a manner as to cancel a trough. (See Figure 3–4.)

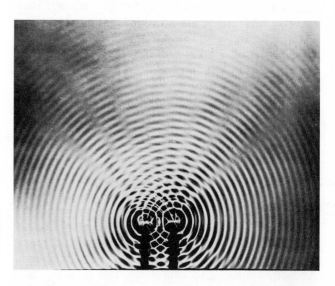

Fig. 3–4   Interference patterns on the surface of water are similar to those produced by the interference of light waves. (D. C. Heath and Company)

Light waves do the same thing. Under certain circumstances some light waves reinforce, while others cancel each other. This is true, for example, when two light waves of nearly the same wavelength meet at the same point. This can be shown very easily by holding two straight edges, such as two pencils, very close together. Between the two will be seen a series of alternating bright and dark bands. They are interference fringes, similar to those resulting from light shining through two narrow slits.

## THE VELOCITY OF LIGHT

### 3.6   Early Methods

Galileo knew that there is a difference between the speed of sound and the speed of light. The sound of thunder is heard several seconds after a flash of lightning is seen; the flash of a gun is seen before it is heard. The speed of sound can be timed rather easily by stationing two men a known distance apart with synchronized clocks which can be used to time the travel of a gunshot report. Galileo thought the same method could be used for the determination of the velocity of light.

He stationed a group of men on a hillside outside the city of Florence in Italy. Another group took a lantern to another hill several miles away. The idea was to uncover one lantern and note the exact time. When the other group saw the light, they immediately uncovered their lantern. The first group then noted the exact time when the returning light beam reached them. However, as we know now, the time it takes for light to travel a few miles and back is much shorter than the reaction time of the men in uncovering the lanterns. So the method failed.

In 1675 Olaus Roemer, a Danish astronomer, used a more satisfactory method and actually determined the velocity of light with considerable accuracy. He used observations based on the times of eclipses and occultations of the four large satellites of Jupiter. His method was as follows:

The four moons could be seen easily with the telescopes of that day. Roemer compiled a table of their periods of revolution around the planet. He could predict the times at which each would be eclipsed as it ran into the planet's shadow or occulted when it passed behind the planet's limb. Roemer found that these phenomena occur sooner than expected during part of the year and later than expected during the other part. He correctly in-

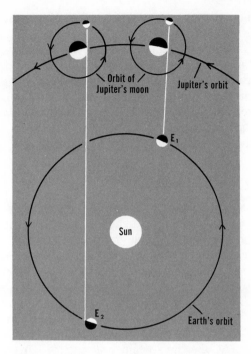

Fig. 3–5   Roemer's method of determining the velocity of light.

ferred that the advance or delay of the occurance was due to the speed of light.

Figure 3–5 explains the method. As the earth makes one complete revolution around the sun, Jupiter advances in its orbit by about 30°. If we assume for simplicity that Jupiter is stationary, it can be seen that when the earth is on the near side of its orbit, the distance between the two planets is smaller than when the earth is on the far side. So if light has a finite velocity, the light from the planet and its moons would reach the earth in a shorter time when the two are closest together than when they are farthest apart.

Roemer's observations of the eclipses and occultations showed that there is a difference of about 16⅔ min at two dates roughly six months apart. In 1675 the diameter of the earth's orbit was calculated to be 192,000,000 mi (about 6,000,000 mi too large). Dividing this distance by the number of seconds in 16⅔ min (1000 sec), the velocity of light came out to be about 192,000 mi per second. Later results differed slightly. Also it was necessary to take account of the elliptical shape of the earth's orbit and the motion of Jupiter in six months. But the modern result, based on the now accepted diameter of the earth's orbit of 186,000,000 mi is only about 3 percent less than that computed by Roemer, which was amazingly accurate for his time.

## 3.7  Michelson's Method

Albert A. Michelson, an American physicist, determined the velocity of light by the use of a rotating mirror. He devoted almost fifty years of his life to perfecting this experiment and was still working on it at the time of his death in 1931. The method is explained in Figure 3–6. Using an octagonal mirror and a distance of 22 mi between two mountains in California, Michelson set his optical system in such a position that when the rotatable mirror was stationary, the light beam was reflected from one face of the octagon to the distant mirror and then back to another face of the octagon. If the first mirror was rotated at just the right speed, the beam was reflected from the distant mirror and onto the next face of the rotating mirror. The time for the

Fig. 3–6   Michelson's method of determining the velocity of light.

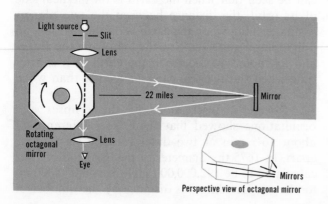

Perspective view of octagonal mirror

mirror to rotate from the first position to the second was equal to the time for the light to travel a distance of 22 mi and back. This time was ¼₂₅₀ sec. Hence the octagonal mirror had to be rotated about 530 times a second. This speed was too great and one of the mirrors exploded before that speed was reached. By using a mirror with 32 faces, a speed of 132 revolutions per second was a little more practical and was finally used.

Michelson continued to refine his apparatus, constantly trying to eliminate any sources of error. He also became convinced that the slight variations in his results were due to changes in the atmosphere. He realized that haziness and air pressure could affect the speed of light in air considerably. In order to eliminate these factors, he finally undertook the difficult task of constructing a mile-long vacuum tunnel in which to carry out his experiment. This part was completed by his associates two years after his death. The velocity of light in a vacuum as found by Michelson's method in 1933 is 299,796 km (186,282 mi) per second. Measurements made since that time have given an average value of 299,793 km per second.

## 3.8  Intensity of Light

The human eye responds very quickly to light and can detect a very small amount of it. The photographic plate has the advantage of building up images by long exposures, which the eye cannot do. However, the eye can see faint images which the photographic plate would fail to see in the same length of time. But the eye is not a good judge of light intensity (the amount of energy emitted by a light source). This inability to differentiate between the brightness of objects is due partly to the eye's sensitivity. The retina is so constructed that its sensitivity increases as the brightness of the light entering the eye decreases.

It is well known that the eye adjusts to light intensity. When a person leaves a brightly illuminated room and goes out into darkness, the pupil expands until the eye is able to see and distinguish faint objects. For example, only the brightest stars can be seen before the pupil adjusts to the proper size. It may take half an hour for the eye to completely adapt itself. Many astronomers claim that the ability to see faint stars can be developed with long practice.

Since the determination of the brightness of celestial objects is very important in astronomy, it is necessary to adopt a standard for comparison of light intensities. For many years a so-called standard candle, made of wax from a sperm whale, was used. The candle was made to a specified size and was burned at a definite rate. This has now been superseded by a more reliable standard, the amount of light emitted by a piece of hot platinum at about 1755°C shining through a hole having an area of ⅟₆₀ square centimeter. This unit is called merely *one candle*, not one candlepower as before. In practice it is more convenient to use a secondary light source which has been compared to the standard candle. We are no longer accustomed to rating electric lamps in candlepower, but use today the number of watts necessary to produce a given amount of light. The efficiency of electric lamps was formerly rated in candlepower per watt.

If a one-candle light source is placed at the center of a hollow sphere with a radius of one foot, the entire surface of the sphere will be illuminated uniformly. If the radius of the sphere is doubled and the light source remains unchanged, the total radiation is still one candle, but it illuminates four $(2^2)$ times as much area, since the area of a sphere is proportional to the square of the radius. Figure 3–7 illustrates the principle with squares placed at

1, 2, and 3 units of distance. This leads to the law of illumination, which states: The amount of light reaching an object decreases as the square of the distance from the light source. This is known as the *inverse square law*.

When the light reaching any surface is reflected, some of it is lost by absorption and some by scattering at the surface. The amount of reflected light is called the brightness of the object. The ratio of the brightness of an object to the amount of light illuminating it is called the *albedo* or *reflectivity* of the object. For example, the albedo of the moon is only about 7 percent, the remainder of the sunlight striking its surface being absorbed and scattered into space in other directions. The planets have different albedos depending on the nature of their atmospheres.

### 3.9  The Spectrum

Earlier in this chapter it was stated that light is refracted when it passes from one medium to another of different density. This is because light travels through different media with different speeds. Newton in 1666 proved that a beam of white light can be broken up into a series of colors, which is called the *spectrum*. To do this, Newton passed white light through a prism of glass. He also let the spectrum pass through another prism and recombined the colors into white light again.

The separation of a beam of light into its component colors is called *dispersion*. It occurs because light of different colors travels through the same medium at different speeds. This produces refraction of different amounts for each color. Thus, since

Fig. 3–7  The inverse square law of light. The amount of energy decreases as the square of the distance from the source.

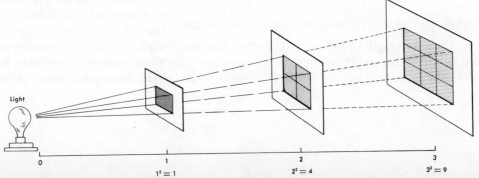

Light

0          1          2          3

$1^2 = 1$          $2^2 = 4$          $3^2 = 9$

white light produces a colored spectrum, it must be composed of light which has traveled through the glass at different speeds. In other words, the index of refraction for glass is different for different colors. This led to the theory that light is a wave phenomenon and that the colors are waves of various lengths.

In order to understand the reason for dispersion and diffraction, it is necessary to assume that the wavelength of light is very small. It can be measured in the physics laboratory by experiments which are based on the theory of wave motion. The necessary definitions used in wave theory are as follows:

1. *Wavelength* is the distance from one point of a wave to the corresponding point on the next wave. (Figure 3–8.)

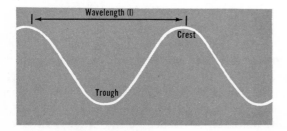

Fig. 3–8   Definition of a wave.

2. *Frequency* is the number of waves passing a given point in a unit of time. For light, the frequency is given in waves per second.
3. The *velocity of light*, the speed with which light travels in a vacuum, is expressed in kilometers or miles per second.
4. The *wave equation* states: The velocity of light is equal to the frequency times the wavelength. Stated in symbols:

$$V = \nu \times \lambda \qquad (3\text{-}4)$$

where $V$ = velocity; $\nu$ = frequency; and $\lambda$ = wavelength.

The wavelength of light is a very small fraction of a centimeter. For visible light, it is between $4 \times 10^{-5}$ and $8 \times 10^{-5}$ cm (centimeter). Since it is so small, it is common practice to use a unit called the *angstrom*, named for a Swedish physicist. The angstrom's length is $10^{-8}$ (1/100,000,000) centimeter. Thus visible light has wavelengths between 4000 A (angstroms) for blue light and 8000 A for red light. Below the blue (or violet) is invisible ultraviolet light, which causes sunburn. Above the red is infrared, which is heat radiation. There are also other radiations which complete the electromagnetic spectrum and which will be discussed later. The eye is thus sensitive to only a very small portion of the total spectrum.

## 3.10   Waves or Particles?

Throughout this discussion, light has been referred to as a ray or beam and as a series of waves. A *ray* may be defined as a stream of particles; a *wave* as a vibration. The question of which best describes light is a very old one. The Greeks said that light consists of particles, to which Newton agreed. Later experimenters, however, disagreed and showed that light behaves as a wave phenomenon.

Newton was convinced that light travels in straight lines. The casting of shadows, even over tremendous distances in the sky as in the case of eclipses, seemed to show this. When Roemer measured the speed of light, there seemed little doubt that light was reaching the earth over the shortest possible path. Newton argued that, if light is a wave motion, it would bend around corners in the same way that water and sound travel around obstacles. To account for the sensation of color, Newton suggested that the particles of light set up vibrations in an imaginary substance called the *ether*, which was believed to permeate all space. These vibrations could vary in frequency and intensity and produce color effects in the eye, just as sound vibrations are responsible for differences in pitch and loudness in the ear. This description of light was generally accepted until the beginning of the nineteenth century, when several discoveries were made showing that light does not always act like a stream of particles.

## 3.11   The Case for Waves

The man who first proposed the wave theory of light was Christian Huygens, a Dutch contemporary of Newton. If light is transmitted from the sun to the earth by a vibratory motion, there must be something in space to vibrate—the ether. It was assumed that the ether is more rigid than steel, but that it allowed the planets to pass through it without friction. The properties of the ether were still being investigated in the early part of the twentieth century. However, Einstein showed in the theory of relativity that light travels through space and that the theoretical ether is unnecessary.

If light is considered as a wave, it differs from sound. Sound waves do require a medium and will not pass through a vacuum. They are propagated in the direction in which the vibration of the medium takes place. They are said to be longitudinal waves. Light waves are thought of as transverse waves with the wave motion at right angles to the direction in which they travel.

The work of Young and others on interference (Section 3.5) was extended by Joseph von Fraunhofer, a German optician. The two holes in a screen used by Young had given only a few faintly colored bands. At first Fraunhofer made gratings by winding fine silver wires closely together and, later, by ruling glass plates with thousands of fine lines. From a knowledge of the distance between the rulings, he was able to measure the wavelength of light. Such gratings are in use today to produce spectra, which are superior to the spectra produced by prisms.

Fraunhofer also made a very important discovery. He examined the spectrum of the sun and found it was crossed by narrow, dark lines. In 1802 William Wollaston, an English chemist, had found that when a beam of sunlight was passed through a narrow slit and then through a prism, the solar spectrum was crossed by seven dark lines. He thought the five strongest lines marked the divisions between the colors in the continuous spectrum. Their true nature was not discovered until 1814 when Fraunhofer began his investigation of the solar spectrum with better optical instruments. The dark lines in the solar spectrum are now called *Fraunhofer lines*. (Figure 3–9.)

## 3.12   The Laws of Spectrum Analysis

There are three laws, called *Kirchhoff's laws* after Gustav Kirchhoff, a German physicist, who in 1859 first explained how the spectrum is produced. They may be stated in modern language as follows:

1. Incandescent (glowing) solids, liquids, or gases under high pressure produce continuous spectra.

In a *continuous spectrum* the colors blend from one into another without interruption. An electric light bulb when viewed through a spectroscope will show a continuous spectrum. Since all solids give continuous spectra when heated to incandescence,

Fig. 3–9   The solar spectrum, showing the Fraunhofer lines. The comparison spectrum on each side of the solar spectrum is that of iron. Since it matches many of the lines in the spectrum of the sun, the sun's atmosphere contains atoms of iron. (Lick Observatory Photograph)

it is not possible in this way to identify the elements which produce them. The reason for a continuous spectrum is that the electrons in the atoms are interfered with by neighboring electrons and are not free to move in their usual orbits, as is possible in gases at low pressure.

2. Incandescent gases at low pressure give discontinuous spectra consisting of bright lines.

These *bright lines* are images of the slit of the spectroscope in various colors and are very narrow when a narrow slit is used. In gaseous form, each element has its own bright-line spectrum, and each line occupies a definite position in the spectrum. For example, hydrogen gas shows a series of lines from the red region into the ultraviolet. Wherever these lines are seen—in the sun, a star, or in space—the element hydrogen can be identified. Salt in the gas flame of a bunsen burner will vaporize and will easily show the two yellow lines of the element sodium. These lines are so close together that they cannot ordinarily be separated by a small spectroscope.

3. If the light from an incandescent solid, liquid, or gas under high pressure is permitted to pass through a cooler gas at low pressure, the spectrum will be continuous (from the hot source) and crossed by darker, narrow lines (from the cooler gas). Each dark line will occupy the exact place of the bright-line spectrum that would have been produced if the cool gas alone were heated to incandescence.

This is called an *absorption spectrum*, because the cool gas absorbs a small amount of energy from the hot source.

Either the bright-line or the absorption spectrum may be used to identify the gas which is producing it. Since the sun shows an absorption spectrum, it is evident that the sun has an interior that is assumed to be a hot incandescent gas under high pressure, surrounded by an atmosphere composed of a cooler gas under low pressure. About 66 different elements known on earth have been identified as present in the atmosphere of the sun. This identification would be impossible without the use of the spectroscope and Kirchhoff's laws. (Figure 3–10)

### 3.13   The Doppler Effect

Another very useful law of the behavior of light is the *Doppler effect*, first stated by Christian Doppler,

Fig. 3–10   Kirchhoff's three laws of spectrum analysis. Continuous, bright line, and dark line (absorption) spectra are shown. *H* with Greek letters are lines of Balmer series; Latin letters are Fraunhofer designations.

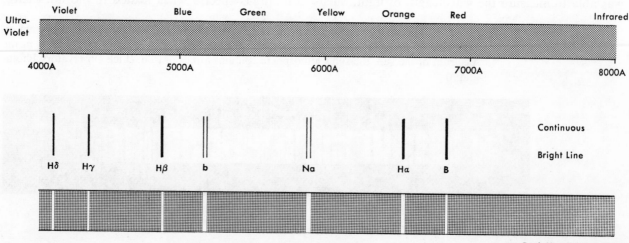

an Austrian physicist, in 1842. Doppler showed that when the source of sound or light is moving toward an observer, more waves will reach him per second than if the source were stationary. This will have the effect of raising the frequency of the sound or light wave. Likewise, the frequency will be lowered for a receding source. It does not matter whether the source or the observer is moving, or both.

In the spectrograph, a light source moving toward the slit will cause the entire spectrum to shift slightly toward the shorter, blue side. In other words, the frequency will be increased. The advantage of having a comparison spectrum alongside that of the source being studied is that the slight shift of the spectrum can be measured easily with respect to the position of the spectrum of a stationary source. (Figure 3–11.)

The Doppler effect is used for the study of the many kinds of motion in the universe. The approach, recession, and rotation of all visible objects in space lend themselves to measurement by this important proportion, as will be shown in later chapters.

If the light is moving away from the slit, the lines will be shifted toward the longer, red end of the spectrum. The amount of the shift in each case is proportional to the velocity of approach or reces-

sion, and the effect will be the same for both bright-line and absorption spectra.

The Doppler effect may be stated as follows:

$$\frac{\text{amount of shift}}{\text{wavelength of spectral line}} =$$

$$\frac{\text{relative velocity of source and observer}}{\text{velocity of light}}$$

or expressed as a mathematical formula:

$$\frac{\Delta\lambda}{\lambda} = \frac{V}{c}. \qquad (3\text{--}5)$$

## QUESTIONS AND PROBLEMS

1. Calculate the velocity of light in flint glass from its index of refraction.

2. (a) Assuming the hills used by Galileo and his assistants in their attempts to measure the velocity of light were 10 mi apart, how long did it take the light to travel this distance? (b) How could they have determined that their reaction times were an insurmountable source of error?

3. Different colors of light travel at different speeds in the same medium. How could Roemer's

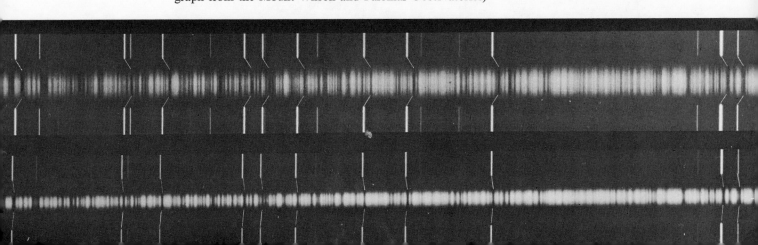

Fig. 3–11   Spectra of two stars, showing Doppler shift toward the red in each. Top: Aldebaran (Alpha Tauri) is receding at 45 mi/sec. Bottom: Arcturus (Alpha Bootis) is receding at 12 mi/sec. The slanting lines connect the stellar lines with the comparison lines, which are placed on each side of the stellar spectra. The stellar lines are absorption lines. (Photograph from the Mount Wilson and Palomar Observatories)

method for measuring the velocity of light be used to determine if different colors also travel at different speeds in space?

4. Calculate the velocity of light from the data given for Michelson's experiment using the rotating mirror with 32 faces.

5. Jupiter is approximately 5 times and Saturn 10 times farther from the sun than the earth is. How much more solar energy does the earth receive per square foot of surface area than (a) Jupiter and (b) Saturn? **Ans:** (a) 25 times.

6. What is the frequency of light of wavelength (a) $6 \times 10^{-5}$ cm, and (b) $4 \times 10^{-5}$ cm? **Ans:** (a) $5 \times 10^{14}$ vib/sec.

*7. Compute the angle of refraction of a beam of light entering water from air, if the angle of incidence is (a) 30°; (b) 45°. (c) Compute the angles for a diamond instead of water.

8. Compute the distance from the earth to the sun, using Roemer's light time of 1000 sec.

9. Compare the brightness of the sun as seen from (a) Venus; (b) Mars; (c) Pluto; and (d) the nearest star, in terms of its brightness as seen from the earth. **Ans:** (c) ¹⁄₁₆₀₀ approximately.

10. Define transverse and longitudinal waves. Why is it that sound does not travel in a vacuum?

11. Why is the sun's spectrum an absorption spectrum?

# Chapter Four

# Optics and the Telescope

## 4.1  Invention of the Telescope

It is not known who first discovered the magnifying power of a lens. This property must have been known before the time of the Arabian scientists, because we know that Alhazen used small glass hemispheres as early as about A.D. 1000. Shortly after that time, lenses were used to correct defective vision.

The manufacture of spectacles became an important industry, especially in Holland, where it appears that a Dutch spectacle maker, Hans Lippershey, discovered the principle of the telescope in the early part of the seventeenth century. Lippershey was famous for his telescopes in 1608, when the discovery came to the attention of Galileo in Italy. The government of Holland awarded Lippershey 900 florins (probably about $360) for his invention, which had been used for military purposes. Galileo immediately constructed a telescope which magnified by only 3 diameters, but soon built an improved model with a magnification of 33 diameters. Turning the telescope toward the sky for the first time, Galileo in 1609 and 1610 made the discoveries for which he is famous. Two of his telescopes are exhibited in the museum in Florence, Italy.

There are four major types of telescope: the refractor, the reflector, the Schmidt camera, and the radio telescope. They all operate on the principle of refraction or reflection, and each is designed for a particular use in astronomy.

## 4.2  The Refracting Telescope

The refracting telescope uses lenses that bring the light from a distant object into focus by refraction. The principal lens, called the *objective*, collects the parallel rays of light from a body and brings them to a point, called the *focus*, where they may be examined by the eye of the observer at a second lens or combination of lenses, called the *eyepiece*. Or, they may be photographed by a light-sensitive film placed in the focus. In the latter case, no eyepiece is used.

The distance from the center of the objective to the focus is called the *focal length, F*. The diameter of the objective, *a*, is called the *aperture*. In the usual visual refractor, the focal length is about 15 times the aperture. The so-called *focal ratio, F/a*, is therefore about 15. This figure varies from telescope to telescope and is sometimes as great as 20.

The function of the eyepiece is to magnify the

image formed by the objective. There are two principal types of eyepieces—positive and negative—with various modifications. The positive eyepiece consists of two plano-convex lenses of the same focal length placed with the curved sides facing each other. The larger of the two is called the field lens; the other is the eye lens. The eyepiece is so placed that the image is in front of the field lens. This eyepiece can also be used as a hand magnifier.

In a negative eyepiece the field lens has a focal length about three times that of the eye lens. They are placed with the flat surfaces facing each other and the image falls between them. The metal tube holding the two components is also provided with a cross of spider web on which the image falls. Since this is to locate the center of the field of view, it is placed on the axis of the telescope. The focal length of the eyepiece, $f$, is the distance from the image to the center of the field lens. A negative eyepiece cannot be used as a hand magnifier.

The *magnifying power* of the telescope, the number of times the telescope enlarges the object compared to its size as seen by the eye alone, depends partly on the focal length of the objective, and partly on the focal length of the eyepiece used. The magnifying power (*M.P.*) can be calculated as the ratio of the two focal lengths; thus,

$$M.P. = \frac{F}{f}. \qquad (4\text{–}1)$$

This can be shown as follows (see Figure 4–1): Tracing the light rays from the two ends of an object in the sky, $MM'$, it is seen from the figure that the angle subtended by the object $MM'$ is equal to that subtended by the image, $mm'$, as seen from the center of the objective. Call this angle $\alpha$. The angle $\beta$ of the image as seen from the eyepiece is larger than $\alpha$, because the eyepiece is closer to the image; that is, the focal length of the objective is always longer than the focal length of the eyepiece. The ratio of the two angles is the magnifying power of the telescope.

By radian measure (see Appendix),

$$\alpha = \frac{MM'}{F} \qquad \text{or} \qquad MM' = \alpha \cdot F \qquad (4\text{–}2)$$

and

$$\beta = \frac{MM'}{f} \qquad \text{or} \qquad MM' = \beta \cdot f \qquad (4\text{–}3)$$

Equating the two,

$$MM' = \alpha \cdot F = \beta \cdot f \qquad (4\text{–}4)$$

and therefore

$$\frac{\beta}{\alpha} = \frac{F}{f}. \qquad (4\text{–}5)$$

It will be noticed that the image is inverted by the objective.

Objectives are expensive because of their large size. Eyepieces are small and inexpensive. It is therefore the custom for observatories to keep on hand a number of eyepieces of different focal

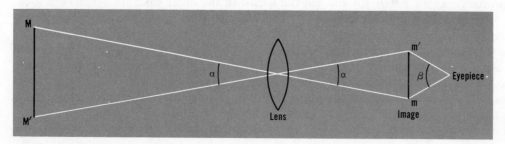

Fig. 4–1 Magnifying power of a telescope.

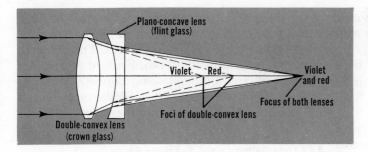

Fig. 4–2 An achromatic objective, showing the paths of violet and red light through a single double-convex lens and after correction by a plano-concave lens.

lengths to be used with a given objective, depending on the magnification desired, the object to be observed, and the steadiness of the air. The function of a telescope is to collect the light, bring it to a focus, and enlarge the image. However, star images are too small to be enlarged in any existing telescope. The use of a photographic plate or film instead of an eyepiece permits making a permanent record. This photograph can be enlarged by well-known photographic enlarging methods, or contact prints can be made. Also the original can be stored for future study.

## 4.3  The Telescope Objective

There are three principal defects in the refracting telescope. First, since light is brought to a focus by refraction, as noted in Chapter 3, the light of different colors is refracted by different amounts. Therefore the component colors of white light are brought to different focal points. This is called *chromatic aberration* and can be very annoying. However, it can be corrected by the use of an achromatic objective.

The *achromatic objective* is composed of two lenses. It would be better to have more than two, but this adds to the cost and also more pieces of glass reduce the available light by absorption. So usually only two lenses are used. In expensive cameras three or four units are used in the lens. (Figure 4–2)

The first lens in an achromatic objective is a double-convex lens, which converges the light toward a focus. This lens is made of crown glass, a type of glass commonly used for window panes. The second lens is a plano-concave lens, which diverts the light and thus prevents it from coming to a focus. However, if the surfaces are ground to the proper curvature, it is possible by a combination of converging and diverging light to bring all the colors to approximately the same focus. To accomplish this, it is also necessary to make the diverging lens out of a different refracting material, usually flint glass, which is harder than crown glass and has a higher index of refraction. (See Chapter 3.) In the refractors of the nineteenth and early twentieth centuries, the achromatic lenses were not quite free from chromatic aberration, but were so built that the visual (yellow and green) light was brought to a common focus. These telescopes were designed to be used visually. The red and blue light, to which the eye is not quite so sensitive, does not come to the same focus as the yellow and green. This produces a yellow-green image of a star surrounded by a purple fringe, which is not troublesome for any objects except the brightest ones. The images of the sun and moon have very noticeable purple fringes caused by chromatic aberration.

For photography with a visual telescope, it is necessary to use a filter that transmits only those rays which are in focus and cuts out all which are not in focus. It is possible to build a lens that will bring the photographic light to a focus. In this case the images seen visually will have blue centers with red fringes.

Photographic refracting telescopes are built today with shorter focal lengths than the visual telescopes. In other words, they have smaller focal ratios and are faster for photographic uses.

A second defect of a telescope is *spherical aberration*. As the name suggests, this defect is most troublesome if the surfaces of the objective are sections of spheres. Aberration means a wandering away, or deviation from a standard. In a lens with spherical aberration, the light rays through the edge of the objective do not come to the same focus as those which pass through the center. This can be corrected by making the surfaces not quite spherical. We shall see later how spherical aberration is corrected in the Schmidt camera. Since an achromatic lens has four surfaces of curvature, two for each component, aberration is difficult to correct. The surfaces must be computed for each size of objective separately. This is a problem in the field of advanced optics, to which the interested student is referred. Such corrections are time consuming and of course add to the cost.

In modern telescopes the two components of the objective are separated; but in small lenses, such as are used in cameras, they are cemented together. In the time of Hevelius, who lived in the seventeenth century, attempts were made to correct for chromatic aberration by making very long telescopes. The long-focus objectives produced less bending of the light and thus less dispersion. It is difficult to see how these telescopes could be handled.

A third defect is called *coma*. This is an aberration which is due to the fact that when light rays strike the lens from an angle, the image is distorted. Technically, this means that objects at an angle with the axis of the telescope are not in focus, but have images that look a little like the short tails of comets, hence the name. This limits the field of

sharp images and is impossible to correct in large telescopes. Spherical aberration and coma are present in both refractors and reflectors. The 200-inch telescope (a reflector) has a usable field of only ten minutes of arc, although some correction is possible by means of a lens of small diameter placed in the beam of light in front of the focus.

### 4.4 Light-Gathering and Resolving Power

The *light-gathering power* of a telescope is a measure of the amount of light which the telescope collects. This measure must be compared to some standard, but is more easily used as a comparison between telescopes of different size. The light-gathering power depends on the area of the objective which collects the light. The area of a circle is proportional to the square of the diameter of the circle. Hence, the light-gathering power of a telescope is proportional to the square of the aperture of the objective. Expressed as a formula,

$$\text{Relative light-gathering power} = \frac{\text{area of lens} \#1}{\text{area of lens} \#2} = \frac{a_1^2}{a_2^2}. \quad (4\text{-}6)$$

As an example, the light-gathering power of a 10-inch telescope is $10^2$, or 100 ($10^2 = 100$), times that of a 1-inch telescope ($1^2 = 1$).

This equation also permits the calculation of the brightness of a star as seen with the unaided eye compared to its apparent brightness through a telescope. In this computation, the size of the pupil of the eye can only be estimated, since it varies with the amount of light entering. A good approximation in the dark is about ¼ in. For example, the ratio of brightness of a star seen through a 10-inch telescope compared to its brightness seen by a ¼-inch pupil is 100 / ¹⁄₁₆ or 1600.

*Resolving power* is the ability of a telescope to form distinguishable images of objects that are separated by very small angles. To the unaided eye, most stars look like single objects. Through a telescope, however, many of these apparently single stars are seen to be two or more stars very close together. The ability of a telescope to "split" such multiple stars is called the resolving power of the telescope. Resolving power is expressed as the angle between two stars which are just barely separated in the telescope under the most favorable atmospheric conditions. The following formula is used:

$$\text{Resolving power} = \frac{4.56''}{a} \qquad (4\text{–}7)$$

where $a$ is the diameter of the objective in inches. 4.56″ (seconds of arc) is the angle between two barely separable images seen in a 1-inch telescope. The number can be computed from a formula (see page 50, formula 4–10) obtained from the theory of optics and involves the wavelength of the light which is being received. We may also consider this formula to have been obtained by observation. A law or formula obtained by observation alone, and not by theory, is said to be empirical.

While the eye is an optical instrument, its resolving power cannot be determined by the formula, because the retina of the eye is made up of rods and cones, which are the light-sensitive elements. Because of the distances between these elements, the eye cannot resolve objects as close together as theory demands. As an illustration of the use of this formula, the largest refracting telescope, the 40-inch at the Yerkes Observatory, can resolve two stars only 0.11″ (seconds of arc) apart. In other words, two mountains on the moon which are 0.11″ apart can just barely be seen separately. That is, two features on the moon less than 240 yd apart cannot be seen separately with the 40-inch telescope. (Figure 4–3)

With the 200-inch telescope the minimum separation on the moon is 48 yd or about 150 ft

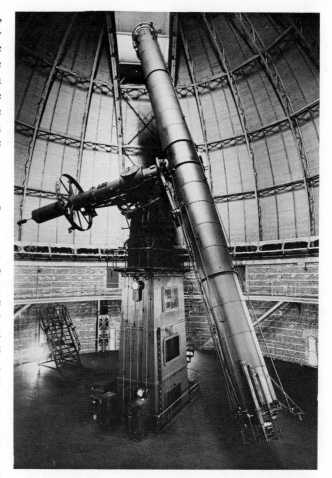

Fig. 4–3  The 40-inch telescope of the Yerkes Observatory. (Yerkes Observatory Photograph)

(half the length of a football field). On the other hand, the eye alone should be able to see distinctly two stars about 18″ apart. However, in the double-double star, ε Lyrae, there is an angular distance of 207″ between the two pairs. They can be separated with difficulty, if at all, with the unaided eye. Compare these figures with craters 3-feet wide (angular separation 0.0005″) observed from Ranger VII.

### 4.5    The Reflecting Telescope

We have seen that a parallel beam of light may be brought to one focus by using the principle of refraction through glass by a double-convex lens. A parallel beam may also be brought to a focus by the principle of reflection. This principle is used in reflecting telescopes. Instead of passing light through a refracting medium, the reflecting telescope brings the beam to a focus by the use of a concave mirror. In this case, the telescope is so built that the light passes through the telescope tube, strikes the mirror which changes its direction by reflection, and forms an image at the focus located in the upper end of the tube. (Figure 4-4)

If the surface of the mirror is a section of a concave sphere, not all the rays will come to the same focus. This is spherical aberration as in the spherical lens. If the surface of the mirror is a section of a paraboloid, all the rays in a parallel beam will meet in a common focus. Thus spherical aberration is eliminated. The mathematical principle is as follows:

If a right circular cone† is cut by a plane parallel to one side of the cone, the intersection is called a parabola. Another definition of the parabola

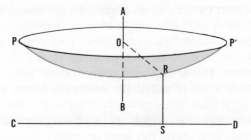

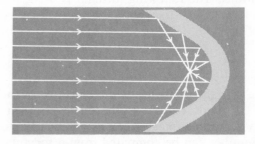

Fig. 4-5    Definition of a parabola or paraboloid (upper figure). Every point, $R$, on the parabola is equidistant from $O$, the focus, and the directrix, $CD$. The lower figure shows that all parallel rays come to the same focus of a parabolic mirror.

is that it is a plane figure so drawn that any point on the parabola is equally distant from a point inside, called the focus, and a straight line, called the directrix. In Figure 4-5, $CD$ is the directrix and $O$ is the focus. For any point, $R$, on the parabola, $OR = RS$. If a parabola is rotated about its axis, $AOB$, a three-dimensional figure is generated. This figure is called a paraboloid of revolution.

In the mathematical theory of a parabola, any line parallel to the axis of the parabola (or paraboloid) will be reflected at equal angles to the perpendicular at the point of reflection. All rays of a parallel beam of light coming from the direction of the axis will meet in a common point and this point

Fig. 4-4    Formation of two star images by a concave mirror.

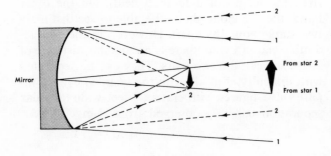

† A right circular cone is a cone that has a circle for its base; its altitude, which is the perpendicular line drawn from the vertex to the plane of the base, goes through the center of the circle.

is the focus *O* of the parabola (paraboloid). Hence in a parabolic reflector there is no spherical aberration.

Since the mirror of the reflecting telescope forms an image in the direction from which the light is coming, an eyepiece may be used in the focus. Or, a photographic plate may be placed there and a photograph of the object made. This form of telescope is called the *direct-focus reflecting telescope.* It should be noted that the eyepiece or the photographic plate must be held in position at the upper end of the tube. This of course obstructs the beam of light and some of the beam is stopped before it reaches the mirror. This is not a serious difficulty, since only a small percent of the light is lost. It does not produce a "hole" in the center of the image as many people think should happen. Only the largest telescopes are used in the direct focus.

The 200-inch telescope has a "cage" at the upper end of the tube where the observer sits to make his observations. In spite of the large size of the observer's cage, the 200-inch mirror is so large that only about 15 percent of the light is lost by the obstruction. (Figure 4–6)

Fig. 4–6  The 200-inch Hale telescope on Mount Palomar. (Photograph from the Mount Wilson and Palomar Observatories)

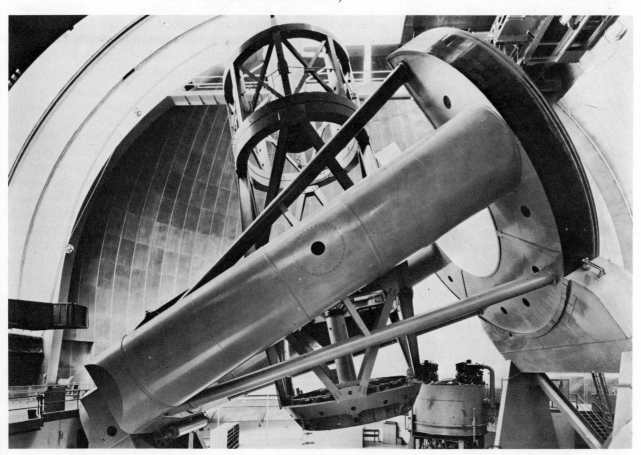

In the reflecting telescope, since the light of all colors is reflected equally, there is no chromatic aberration. However, as has been pointed out, the 200-inch telescope is troubled by coma.

In smaller instruments, it is necessary to deflect the beam of light before it reaches the focus. This is done by placing a plane mirror in the converging beam. If this mirror is set at an angle of 45° to the axis of the telescope, the focus is formed by passing the light through a hole in the side of the tube. The focus is conveniently located for visual or photographic observation, except that it is necessary to place the eyepiece at the upper end of the tube. In large telescopes, such as the 100-inch telescope, there is an observing platform which can be raised and lowered. It runs on a track attached to the observatory dome and the observer may be 50 ft or so above the floor. This form of telescope was first used by Sir Isaac Newton and is called a *Newtonian reflector*, or Newtonian telescope.

Sir William Herschel and others used the direct focus of their telescopes by tipping the mirror slightly so the image was formed at one side of the open end of the tube. This, however, introduced a slight amount of coma, because the observations were made off the axis of the telescope. So the Newtonian form is to be preferred. Many amateur astronomers own and use the Newtonian type of reflector. The small secondary, diagonal mirror blocks out usually about 10 percent of the incoming light. This can be compensated for by increasing the exposure time of a photograph by 10 percent, but no compensation is possible for visual observations—except to get a larger telescope.

Another type of reflecting telescope is called a *Cassegrain reflector*. In this form a small secondary convex mirror is placed, not at 45° as in the Newtonian form, but at right angles to the beam. This mirror reflects the light back again toward the objective below. If used alone, the convex mirror would diverge the light. But, as in the case of the second component of the achromatic lens, the combination of a converging and a diverging beam produces an image at any selected distance below the secondary mirror. Usually the beam is allowed to pass through a hole in the primary mirror and the image is formed in a convenient location at the lower end of the tube. Here it can be reached from the floor and the handling of auxilliary apparatus can be done much more easily than from the upper end of the telescope.

The 100-inch and 60-inch telescopes at the Mount Wilson Observatory do not have holes in the primary mirrors. But they are used in a modified Cassegrain form by placing a third mirror just above the primary mirror in each telescope. This mirror, set at 45°, again deflects the light, this time at right angles, where it can be examined at the side of the lower end of the telescope. In modern forms of the reflecting telescope, the primary mirror may be spherical and the secondary some other form, such as an elliptical mirror. Figure 4–7 shows the various types of reflecting telescopes.

## 4.6   Telescope   Mirrors

At the time of Sir William Herschel, telescope mirrors were made of speculum metal. This is a combination of copper and tin. Herschel cast his own mirrors. The difficulty with speculum metal was that the proportions of copper and tin—about ⅓ tin, ⅔ copper, and a little arsenic, antimony, or zinc added for whiteness—had to be almost perfectly correct or the metal was too hard or too soft. Also, if the whiteness deteriorated with time, the only way to improve the mirror was to start all over with a new casting. The term *speculum* is still used by some amateur astronomers to mean the mirrors of their telescopes, even if the mirrors are made of glass and coated with metal.

Later, plate glass was used because it could be ground and polished to the desired shape, usually a paraboloid, and then coated with silver, which became the reflecting surface. Notice that the silver is not deposited on the back of the glass as in the usual mirrors used in the home, but is on the front

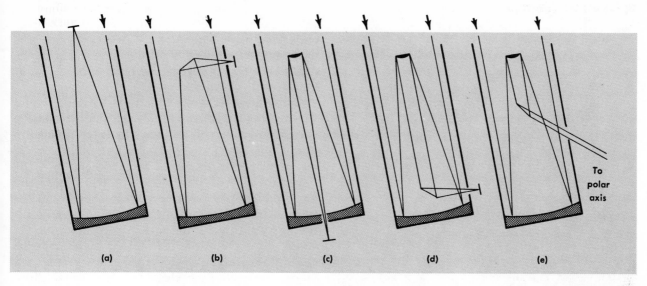

To polar axis

(a)        (b)        (c)        (d)        (e)

Fig. 4–7   Five forms of reflecting telescopes: (a) direct focus; (b) Newtonian, with flat secondary mirror; (c) and (d) Cassegrain and modified Cassegrain, with convex secondary; (e) Coudé with beam directed down polar axis. (d) and (e) each have third flat mirror.

surface. If the silver tarnishes, as it does in the presence of sulfur in natural gas or in the air, it can be removed easily and a new surface deposited on the glass by chemical processes. This is necessary several times a year and is a troublesome process and relatively expensive. Still later, aluminum was used in place of silver, since it lasts longer and has even greater reflectivity in the violet region of the spectrum. However, it must be deposited on the glass by exploding aluminum foil in a vacuum. This requires special equipment, including a vacuum tank and vacuum pumps. The aluminizing of a 200-inch telescope mirror is a difficult process, but is necessary only about every five years.

Still more recently, a glass resistant to heat has been substituted for plate glass. Experiments with fused quartz, which had failed before the casting of the disk for the 200-inch telescope was attempted, have now proved successful. The cost of this material is almost prohibitive, except for governmental projects. A 150-inch quartz mirror for the National Observatory on Kitt Peak in Arizona was ordered in 1965 at a cost of $1,000,000!

There were also plans for casting mirrors of aluminum instead of using aluminum for coatings on glass mirrors. These plans apparently have been superseded by the use of quartz.

## 4.7  The Schmidt Camera

In 1930 another type of reflecting telescope was invented by Bernhard Schmidt, a German optician.

The Schmidt telescope uses a spherical mirror, which is relatively easy to make but produces spherical aberration. To correct for this, Schmidt used a special thin plate of glass, called a correcting lens, placed in the upper end of the telescope tube. This lens is so shaped that it corrects for spherical aberration by bending the entering rays by the proper amount before they strike the spherical mirror. It does not have to be as large as the mirror, but is quite difficult to figure correctly. It is so thin that no chromatic aberration is introduced. However, the field of focus of the telescope is not flat, but curved. Therefore it is necessary to use a curved film, which is located between the mirror and the

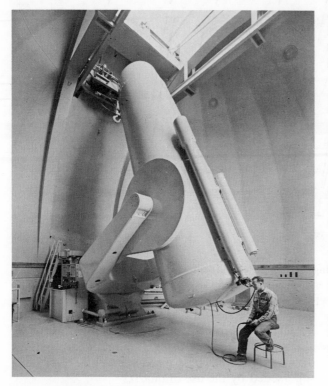

correcting plate. This type of telescope, which perhaps should be called a *camera* since it cannot be used with an eyepiece, can be built with very short focal length. (See Figure 4–8.)

The large Schmidt camera on Mount Palomar has a spherical mirror of 72-inch diameter and a correcting plate of 48-inch diameter. Its focal ratio is 2.5, which makes it very fast, and therefore an excellent instrument for photography. The Palomar Sky Atlas was made with this instrument. The photographic plates are 14 in square and the images are sharp out to the edges. Times of exposure run from 10 min to 1 hr, depending on the speed of the emulsions used on the plates, and the color filter through which the photographs are taken. The field of the telescope is 6.6°, so the entire sky visible from Mount Palomar can be covered in less than 100 hr. It is used in conjunction with the 200-inch telescope. It photographs the general area of the sky in which an interesting object is located and the larger telescope is used for fine details.

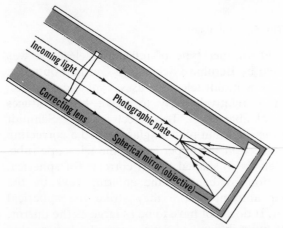

Fig. 4–8   The 48-inch Schmidt camera at the Mount Palomar Observatory (top); and a diagram showing the optical principles of a Schmidt camera (bottom). (Photograph from the Mount Wilson and Palomar Observatories)

## 4.8   Image Formation

The size of an image at the focus of a telescope can be computed by the use of plane geometry. In Figure 4–9, let the angle between two stars, $S_1$ and $S_2$, be equal to $A°$ at the point where the light passes through the telescope objective. The angle is unchanged and is the angle subtended by the image, $S$, from the objective. Let $F$ be the focal length of the objective. Then,

$$A° = \frac{S}{F} \text{ radians} = 57.3° \times \frac{S}{F} \text{ degrees.} \qquad (4–8)$$

**Solving** for $S$:

$$S = \frac{F \times A°}{57.3°}. \qquad (4–9)$$

By this formula, the distance between the images of two stars, which are $A°$ apart in the sky, at the focus of the telescope can be calculated, as can the size of image of the sun or the moon.

▶ *Example:* What is the diameter of the sun at the focus of the 150-foot telescope on Mount Wilson?

**Substituting** in equation 4–9 and assuming the angular diameter to be 0.5°, we have

$$S = \frac{150' \times 0.5°}{57.3°} = \frac{75'}{57.3} = 1.31 \text{ ft} = 15.7 \text{ in.}$$

▶ *Example:* Calculate the distance between the images of two stars, which are 6.6° apart, on a plate taken with the Palomar Schmidt camera. The focal length of the camera is 120 in.

**Solution:**   $S = \dfrac{120'' \times 6.6°}{57.3°} = 13.8 \text{ in.}$

It is therefore seen that these two images will be near the opposite edges of the 14-inch photograph.

Because of the optical properties of lenses and mirrors, there is a minimum magnification which should be used with a telescope. This minimum is four times the diameter of the objective expressed in inches. For example, if a telescope is of 15-inch diameter, the smallest magnification which should be used is 60. The reason is that with any smaller magnification, some of the light from the eyepiece will not enter the eye, but will be lost outside the pupil.

Similarly, the maximum magnification should not be greater than 50 times the diameter of the objective. This is because any greater magnification will produce blurred images, rather than points. On nights when the seeing is poor, that is, when the atmosphere is turbulent and the images unsteady, a smaller magnification than normal should be used. Most observatories have a supply of eyepieces, which can be used to fit the atmospheric conditions and can be changed according to the judgment of the observer.

Telescopes collect light and form images which can be viewed with eyepieces or photographed and otherwise examined with special equipment. A telescope permits objects to be seen which are too faint to be seen with the unaided eye. It separates objects which are too close together to be seen otherwise. The reason for building larger and larger telescopes is to take advantage of these properties of light-gathering power and resolving power. A telescope on the moon or on a space platform would not have an atmosphere to contend with. The image would always be steady, and the highest powers could be used at all times.

Radio telescopes, as will be shown later, gather and study radiation from space which is invisible to the eye or to the optical telescopes. Also, telescopes located above the earth's atmosphere can be used

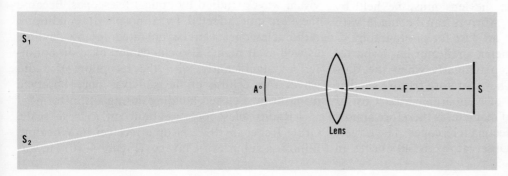

Fig. 4–9  Size of image formed by a lens of focal length, $F$.

to photograph and study the ultraviolet part of the spectrum below 2900A, which is totally absorbed by the air.

## 4.9  Refractor or Reflector?

Which is better, a refractor or a reflector? The refractor's lens is always ready for use after cleaning with alcohol and distilled water. The long focal length makes it useful where a steady image under high magnification is desirable. However, the refractor is troubled by chromatic aberration; the reflector is not. Both types do have spherical aberration, which can be corrected. The achromatic objective requires four, and sometimes more, surfaces to be figured. The reflector has only one. Light passes through a lens, but is reflected only from the surface of the mirror. Thus the lens must be made of high quality glass without bubbles. The refractor is not always suitable for photography because of its large focal ratio, but short-focus refractors are now being built. Ultraviolet light will not pass through the glass of a lens, but will be reflected from a metal surface.

The reflector's surface must be covered with a highly reflective coat. Aluminum is most widely used today, since it reflects ultraviolet light and lasts several years without deteriorating. Modern mirrors are being made of heat-resistant glass and do not change shape with dropping temperature during their nighttime use. The mirror can be supported from the back; the lens must be held by supports at the edges. Mirrors can be made with short focal length and are fast for photography.

For the same diameter, a reflector has a shorter tube than a refractor, particularly when the Cassegrain form is used. They therefore require smaller domes than refractors of comparable size. Cost of construction per unit of diameter is therefore almost entirely in favor of reflecting telescopes. The largest refractor, at Yerkes Observatory, is 40 inches in

diameter and about 60 ft long. It is housed in a dome 90 ft in diameter. The largest reflector is the Hale telescope on Mount Palomar. Its diameter is 200 in and it is 55 ft long. The dome on Palomar is 137 ft in diameter.

## 4.10  Radio Telescopes

A relatively new form of telescope is the radio telescope. It is used to detect and measure radiation from the stars and from matter between the stars which was previously not detectable. Such telescopes have now added a great deal of information about the make-up of stars and of the location and composition of interstellar matter. This branch of astronomy has now become very important and many large receivers of radio waves from space have been built and are being operated by electronic technicians.

Radio waves from space were discovered accidentally by Karl Jansky in 1931. He built a receiver which could be rotated on a circular track and proposed to investigate the causes of static interference. To his surprise, he found that certain noises were coming from a particular point in the sky and that the celestial sources from which they came moved across the sky at the rate of the daily motion of the stars. They were located at the center of the galaxy.

Radio waves are part of the electromagnetic spectrum but have longer wavelengths than the visual waves studied by optical telescopes. Because they are not affected by atmospheric conditions, radio telescopes can be operated in the daytime as well as at night; also clouds and haze do not interfere significantly with the reception of radio waves. An eclipse of the sun was once observed from inside a closed building during a rainstorm!

Radio telescopes are built on a large scale. Grote Reber in 1937 set up a receiver in Wheaton, Illinois, a suburb of Chicago. (Figure 4–10) He was the first astronomer to follow up Jansky's experiments. He had trouble avoiding electric waves generated by ignitions from passing cars, but did succeed in mapping the directions of radio-wave sources from space. The heating of his equipment by the sun on clear days was also a source of trouble. In 1943 Reber discovered radio waves from the sun by tuning his receiver to a wavelength of 187 cm. They come from the solar corona where the temperature is about 1,000,000°K.

Fig. 4–10   The first radio telescope; Wheaton, Illinois, 1937.

A map of radio radiations from the Milky Way is shown in Figure 4–11.

It should be emphasized that radio waves are not sound waves but are electrical waves. They vary in length from about 8 mm to about 17 m. These are the wavelengths of the spectrum which can penetrate the earth's ionosphere. They must therefore be detected by receivers tuned to those wavelengths. They have the properties of electromagnetic induction, have very low intensities, and must therefore be amplified and recorded.

Radio waves can be reflected and refracted like light waves. The radio telescope, therefore, consists primarily of a large parabolic dish which collects the waves and brings them to a focus. This dish may be a solid surface or a mesh of wires. In the focus is an antenna in which an electric current is induced that goes to a receiver where it is amplified. The amplifier is similar to one in a home radio set, except that the signal is usually not converted to sound, but is recorded on a recording meter. If a signal from space is received, it appears as a rise above the line formed by background "noise." (Figure 4–12) When radar signals are bounced off the moon, they return to earth in about 2.5 sec and are recorded as pips. The time between the sending of the wave and its reception on the earth can be used to determine the distance to the moon, since the velocity of radio and radar waves is the same as that of light waves.

Since the signals from space are so weak, the radio receivers must be very large. Their resolving

Fig. 4–11   A radio map of the Milky Way shows intense radiations along the galactic equator. Some of the sources are known to lie outside the Milky Way system. The area indicated as Cygnus A is an example of an extragalactic source. Only a small part of the sky is shown here.

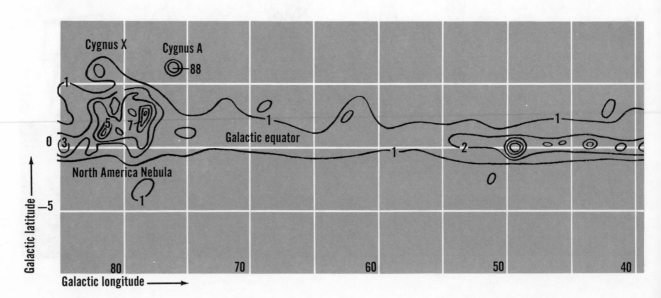

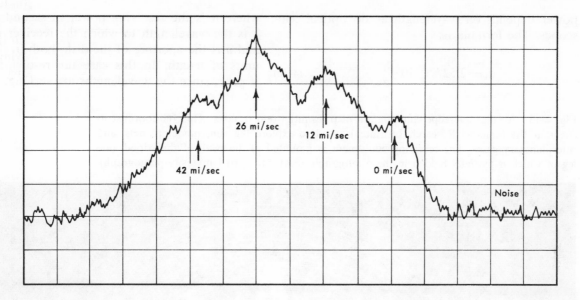

Fig. 4–12 Drawing of a radio signal from space, adapted from an actual tracing from a source on the galactic equator. The velocities have been determined from measures of the Doppler shifts of the rises above the background noise.

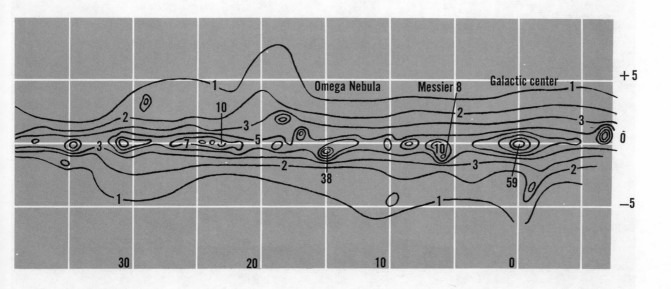

power depends on wavelength as do optical telescopes. The formula is:

$$\alpha = 2.52'' \times 10^5 \frac{\lambda}{a} \qquad (4\text{–}10)$$

where $\alpha$ is the resolving power in seconds of arc. $\lambda$ is the wavelength to which the receiver is tuned and $a$ is the aperture of the dish, both in the same units of length. In this case the resolving power is poor, since the wavelengths are so long. That is,

Fig. 4–13   A radar telescope combination of transmitter and receiver. This 160-foot instrument at the Stanford Research Institute is used to explore the sun, moon, planets, and interplanetary gases. The receiving equipment is mounted at the peak of the tripod, one leg of which is partially hidden in the photograph. (SRI, Stanford University photograph)

the smallest detectable angle between two radio sources is large. A 50-foot dish tuned to 21 cm has a resolving power of about 1.0°. This is less than the resolving power of the eye, which is another reason for building very large radio telescopes.

The largest steerable radio telescope is 250 ft in diameter. It is located at Jodrell Bank, near Manchester, England. (Figure 1–5) An earlier instrument at the same observatory was composed of a mesh of wires strung near the ground in the shape of a paraboloid and with its antenna at the top of a pole placed vertically to the dish. This instrument was steerable by tilting the pole slightly.

A more recent, large radio telescope is in Puerto Rico and is operated by Cornell University. Its surface is spherical rather than parabolic because the dish is stationary and the beam can be swung over a wider range of angles. It is to be used for radar studies of the planets.

A radar telescope is a special kind of radio telescope which directs powerful radio beams at celestial objects and receives them when they return to the earth. It was with such an instrument that the United States Army Signal Corps in 1946 bounced a signal off the surface of the moon and accurately determined its distance. Radar is also used to detect and measure the speeds of meteors, since the signals are reflected by the meteor trails. A radar telescope was also used to determine the distance to Venus. Radar signals have even been reflected from the sun. (See Figure 4–13.)

## 4.11 Telescope Mountings

There are two principal methods of mounting telescopes. They are the alt-azimuth and the equatorial mountings. In order to reach all parts of the sky, it is necessary to be able to turn the telescope in any direction. This is done by using two axes, which are rigidly connected and about which it is possible to move the telescope in two independent directions. The alt-azimuth form has a vertical axis about which the telescope can be turned in a direction

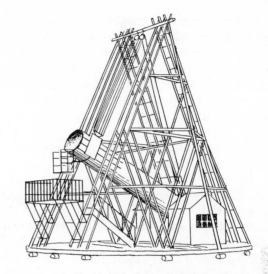

Fig. 4–14  Sir William Herschel's 40-foot telescope. It was a 48-inch reflector mounted as an alt-azimuth telescope, and operated by man power.

parallel to a level surface. A second axis permits the telescope to be turned in a vertical direction. This is the principle of the surveyor's transit. To keep a star in the field of the telescope, it is necessary to keep the telescope moving slowly in the proper direction by the use of the two axes. This cannot be done by a simple mechanical device. (For example, see Figure 4–14.)

A much better way is to point one axis, called the *polar axis,* toward the celestial poles. There are two points in the sky that are on a continuation of the earth's axis of rotation. It is the turning of the earth about this axis that makes all the stars and other bodies appear to move across the sky. If the polar axis of a telescope is rotated by a clock mechanism at the same rate at which the earth rotates, but in the opposite direction, a star will always remain in the center of the field of view.

To find a star, it is desirable to have another axis, which is perpendicular to the polar axis, about which the telescope can be moved north or south. This form is called the *equatorial telescope.* The second axis is called the *declination axis*. It usually carries a circle which is divided into degrees and fractions of degrees and reads zero when the telescope is pointed to a position 90° from each pole. There are an infinite number of such points, all of which lie on a circle, called the celestial equator. The declination circle reads the angular distance of a star north or south of the celestial equator. This angle is called the star's declination. (See Chapter 7 for a more complete discussion.)

There are several ways of mounting an equatorial telescope. The older forms used a central column, which was placed on a structure of stone or cement that extended into the ground. This was for stability and to prevent vibrations inside the observatory from being transferred to the telescope. The central column was not in contact with the building at any point.

On top of this column was the mounting head, which contained the polar axis. This was a short axis and was rotated by a clock mechanism or, later, by

an electric motor moving exactly at the rate of the earth's rotation. Attached at right angles to the polar axis was the declination axis. The telescope was hung on one end of this axis; and, since its position brought the telescope off the center of gravity, it had to be counter-balanced by a heavy weight at the opposite end of the axis. There were several ways of mounting the clock either inside or outside the central column. The 40-inch telescope at the Yerkes Observatory is this type (see Figure 4–3).

A better and more modern way of mounting a large telescope was used in the 100-inch telescope. There are two vertical piers placed some distance apart. Each pier supports part of the weight of the moving telescope and its declination axis. The polar axis, which is supported by the two piers, extends between them and points toward the north celestial pole. It is rotated by a motor beneath the observatory floor at the lower end of the axis. The 200-inch telescope is similarly mounted. But there is one notable improvement over the 100-inch installation.

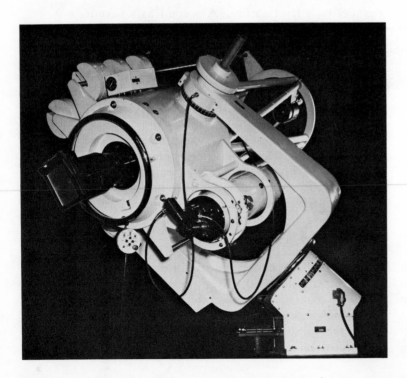

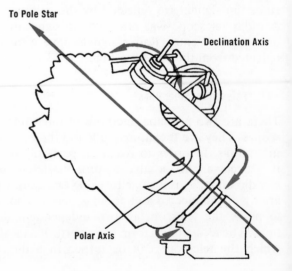

Fig. 4–15 The equatorial fork-type telescope mounting, showing the polar and declination axes. The declination axis is graduated in degrees north and south; the polar axis in hours east and west. (Competition Associates of Boston photograph)

In the latter case, the telescope cannot be pointed directly at the pole, since the axis is in the way. In the 200-inch mounting the upper end of the polar axis is cut in the form of a horseshoe. The telescope can be depressed inside this U-shaped axis and the polar stars can be reached for observation.

Another type of modern mounting is the fork type, shown in Figure 4–15. Here only one pier is used on which the two axes and the telescope tube are mounted.

## QUESTIONS AND PROBLEMS

1. The Palomar 200-inch telescope has a focal ratio of 3.3. (a) What is its focal length? (b) Compute $7\frac{1}{8}''$ its magnifying power, if a ½-inch eyepiece is used. (c) Compute its resolving power. **Ans:** (a) 55 ft.

2. The 36-inch Lick refractor has a focal length of 60 ft. What is its (a) focal ratio, (b) magnifying power with ½-inch eyepiece, and (c) resolving power? (d) Compare its light-gathering power with the 200-inch telescope.

3. In Figure 4–9, suppose the rays from $S_1$ and $S_2$ are coming from two edges of the moon. Calculate the size of the image formed at the focus of the (a) 36-inch and (b) 200-inch telescopes.

4. What are two ways for correcting a reflecting telescope for spherical aberration? Why is it not necessary to correct for chromatic aberration?

5. Discuss the ways in which the diameter and focal length of a telescope objective affect its ability to detect faint objects.

6. (a) How many times greater would the diameter of a telescope objective need to be to increase its light-gathering power by a factor of 25? (b) How would this change affect the resolving power and magnification? **Ans:** (a) 5.

7. If the secondary mirror in the Cassegrain form of a 100-inch telescope has a circular shape, what percentage of the incoming light does it obscure if it is (a) 25-inch and (b) 20-inch diameter? **Ans:** (a) 6.25 percent.

8. How would the image be affected if the lower half of the lens in Figure 4–9 were covered? (Hint: What would be the effect of removing the light rays that pass through the lower half of the lens?)

9. If the mirrors of the 100-inch telescope each reflect 90 percent of the incident light, what percent of the original light is reflected by the last mirror in the modified Cassegrain form?

10. What are the maximum and minimum magnifications that should be used in a (a) 6-inch telescope, and (b) 15-inch telescope?

11. The moon subtends an angle of about 0.5° as observed from the earth. What is the diameter in inches of its image at the focus of (a) the 200-inch telescope; (b) the 100-inch telescope; and (c) an $f/16$ 6-inch telescope?

12. Where on the earth would an alt-azimuth mounting be equivalent to an equatorial mounting?

13. In some photographs, symmetrical "spikes" radiate from the stellar images. (See, for example, Neptune in Figure 14–9.) Is this because stars are shaped that way, or is it due to some characteristic of some telescopes? Explain.

14. How large would the dish of a radio telescope need to be to have the same resolving power as the 200-inch telescope? Assume the radio telescope is tuned to 21 cm and the optical telescope to 4000 A (angstroms) wavelength.

15. Compute the effective focal length of the 200-inch telescope when used as a Cassegrain reflector. Assume the secondary mirror to be 20 in. in diameter and 35 ft from the eyepiece and that the light beam exactly fills the secondary mirror.

16. Compare the distance between the images of two stars on plates taken with the 200-inch telescope and the large Schmidt camera. Assume the two stars are 10 min of arc apart and the focal lengths is 55 and 10 ft, respectively. **Ans:** about 2″ and ⅓″.

# Chapter Five

## Auxiliary Instruments of Astronomy

Since ancient times, astronomy has been useful in religious and civil affairs. In some periods of history the calendar was based on the motions of the sun; in others, on the motions of the moon. The sun was used thousands of years ago for a determination of time.

It is agreed that the beginning of the Egyptian year was based on the times of rise of the Nile River, an important event in the Egyptian economy. The rise of the Nile also coincided, during early Egyptian history, with the visibility of the bright star Sirius in the dawn. This is known as the heliacal rising of Sirius, a star which was also personified as the goddess Sothis.

### 5.1 Ancient Instruments

The Egyptians also used their pyramids as observing stations for the determination of time. In the Great Pyramid there was a Grand Gallery which was oriented north and south. Times of passage of stars across this gallery, which was open to the sky before the pyramid was finished, served as a clock at night. During daylight, the Egyptians used a vertical shaft called an obelisk. It cast a shadow that

served as a sundial to mark the hours. These were among the first instruments of astronomy. In Figure 5–1 is shown an Egyptian obelisk, now in New York, and the massive structure at Stonehenge, England.

Very early in the history of England, two circles of large stones (dated between 2000 and 1500? B.C.) were used at Stonehenge for religious and, almost certainly, for astronomical purposes. Summer began when the sun could be seen to rise approximately over the Heel Stone as seen from the Altar Stone. This marked what today we call the summer solstice. Other alignments marked further positions of sunrise, sunset, moonrise, and moonset. The arrangement of stones served as an astronomical observatory.

By the end of the sixteenth century, Tycho Brahe was observing the sky from an observatory on the island of Hven off the coast of Denmark. Among his instruments were the sextant and wall quadrant. (See Chapter 1, Figure 1–2.) The sextant was a sixth of a circle fastened to a frame. It was provided with an arm pivoted at a point about which it could be turned. The movable arm had an arrangement for sighting on an object in the sky. The vertical direction was marked by a plumb bob. As a

Fig. 5–1  Ancient timekeepers included the Egyptian obelisk and the prehistoric arrangements of stones, called Stonehenge, in England. (Photograph of obelisk taken in 1918, Courtesy of the Metropolitan Museum of Art; Stonehenge courtesy C. M. Huffer)

star was sighted along the arm, the angle between the zenith, the point overhead, and the direction of the star was read off. This angle we now call the zenith distance. The sextant could also be rotated in direction, and the angle between some fixed point and the direction of the star could be determined. This is called azimuth. The two angles are basic angles for determining the position of a star on the celestial sphere.

Tycho's wall quadrant was a quarter of a circle mounted on a wall in a fixed direction, probably north and south. With this quadrant, the altitude of a star could be accurately determined when it was exactly south, or north, on the meridian. Tycho had the arc of his circle graduated accurately in degrees and invented a way of measuring fractions of degrees—the forerunner of the modern vernier.

With these instruments, Tycho measured the positions of the planets. His observations were the most accurate which had been made up to that time.

They served Johannes Kepler as a basis for his three laws of the motions of bodies in the solar system. Tycho also constructed a celestial sphere on which he plotted the positions of about 1000 stars. His observations were the beginning of modern astronomy of position. From them Kepler was able to compute the distances of the known planets, particularly Mars, in terms of the distance from the sun to the earth, which was not known at that time.

All instruments before the time of Galileo were, of course, built without optical assistance. When Galileo adapted the telescope to the study of astronomy, it became possible to use it also with the auxiliary instruments then in use.

## 5.2   Transits and Sextants

In the surveyor's transit, a telescope is mounted on two axes with graduated circles reading to less than one minute (1′) of arc. There is a fundamental plate that can be rotated about a vertical axis for measuring azimuth. The telescope turns in altitude about a horizontal axis. This instrument is similar to Tycho's sextant equipped with a telescope. (Figure 5–2)

The mariner's sextant has a small telescope mounted on a frame which can be held in the hand of a ship's officer. It is used to measure the angle between an astronomical body and the sea horizon. Methods have been developed by which a skillful navigator can determine his position from a moving ship with an accuracy of about 2 mi. The sextant has been modified for use in the air. The so-called bubble octant makes use of a bubble in a fluid which marks the horizontal position. The position of an aircraft can be determined to within about 10 mi with a bubble octant.

Similar methods are used in space vehicles,

Fig. 5–2   The surveyor's transit (top); and the mariner's sextant (bottom). (Courtesy of Keuffel & Esser Co.; U.S. Navy)

but the technique is quite different. The signal from a space satellite, called a navigational satellite, can also be received with a radio sextant, in which a radio receiver takes the place of the lenses and mirrors in the optical instrument. This device will be a great help to navigation, since it can be used even though the sky is covered with clouds.

The astronomical transit is a telescope mounted on one axis placed in a horizontal east-west position. The telescope is thus so directed that it can be used only for stars on the meridian. It is therefore similar to Tycho's wall quadrant, except that it is equipped with a telescope and very accurately graduated circles with verniers. With this instrument the latitude of an observatory can be determined to about 0.1″ of arc, or about 10 ft.

An even more accurate instrument is the meridian circle, a special form of transit, but usually with a larger telescope and still more refinements for reading angles. It is also used in a north-south position (on the meridian) and the positions of stars can be determined with the greatest precision—about 0.01″ of arc. With the astronomical transit and the meridian circle the sun, moon, and planets are kept under observation and their orbits determined from these observations with great accuracy. Work of this nature is one of the principal tasks of the United States Naval Observatory in Washington.

## 5.3  Astronomical Photography

The use of photography was adapted to astronomy about the middle of the nineteenth century. The advantage of photography is that a section of the sky can be recorded at one time instead of observing

Fig. 5–3  Two photographs of the same region of the Milky Way taken with the 48-inch Schmidt camera; left in blue light, right in red light. Notice the difference in number and brightness of stars and nebulae in the two colors. (Photographs from the Mount Wilson and Palomar Observatories. © Copyright 1957 by the National Geographic Society—Palomar Observatory Sky Survey)

each star separately, as with the transit and meridian circle. A photograph shows the relative positions and brightness of the stars in the telescope field, including those which are below the limit of visual observation. The photographic film, usually on glass, is placed at the focus of the telescope. The exposure times can be varied according to the judgment of the astronomer and depending on the purpose for which the photograph is being made.

For example, in the Palomar survey of the sky made with the 48-inch Schmidt camera, exposures of 10 min were made through a yellow filter and about 50 min through a red filter. These photographs give the positions of the stars with respect to each other or some central star whose exact position can be determined with the transit or meridian circle. Also the brightness can be measured by the amount of darkening of the silver grains on the film. The colors of the stars can be found by comparing the brightness as measured on the yellow and red photographs. The plates were then copied and printed by ordinary photographic processes. Then the original plates were stored for future reference. In Figure 5–3 the blue stars are recorded on the blue photograph and the red stars on the red photograph. Colors are determined by the ratios of the intensity of the star images.

Before 1959 all photographs in astronomy were necessarily limited to black and white, except under special conditions when color film was available for some problem such as an eclipse of the sun. In 1959 the first successful color pictures of nebulae and galaxies were made by William Miller of the Mount Wilson and Palomar Observatories with the 200-inch Hale and 48-inch Schmidt telescopes. Six of these photographs are reproduced in the color section.

## 5.4 Astronomical Photometry

The instrument used to measure the brightness of an object is called a *photometer*. Modern photometers use photoelectric cells. The cell generates a small current of electricity when exposed to light. It must be amplified and can then be measured by a sensitive meter. Such an instrument, called a photoelectric photometer, is easily attached to a telescope. The amount of current is strictly proportional to the amount of light admitted to the cell and thus can be used to measure the brightness of a star. Photometers are also equipped with colored filters of glass or other material which transmit light of different wavelengths. They are used for the measurement of the colors of stars and other objects.

Formerly the eye was used as a sensitive light meter. This is called visual photometry and has been largely superseded by photographic photometry which is very important and is widely used for faint sources. Photographs can be made of many stars at the same time, while the photoelectric photometer is limited to one object at a time. While most photocells are sensitive only in the blue region of the spectrum, red-sensitive cells have been developed. Also, cells with lead sulfide as the sensitive surface permit measurement of radiation in the infrared region of the spectrum.

In the early 1960s a device called the image-converter tube was developed and successfully put into operation. This tube uses a photoelectric surface in the focus of the telescope. Light striking the surface releases electrons, which are focused on a sensitive photographic surface. These electrons act on the silver grains which are then developed into a photograph. Ordinarily it takes about 50 times more light intensity to produce a photograph directly than it does with the image tube. Thus the telescope is being made more efficient than formerly by increasing the effectiveness of its equipment rather than the size of the telescope.

There are several ways of adapting photography to the problems of photometry. If a photograph of a portion of the sky is made with the images of the stars in focus on the plate, the blackness of the image is proportional to the brightness of the star. The silver grains are affected at greater distances from the centers of the images of bright stars than of faint ones. Hence the stars will show as round, black spots on the plate and the sizes will be proportional to the brightness of the stars. Figure 5–4 shows this effect. The magnitude of a star can thus be determined by comparing the size of its image with that of a star of known magnitude.

Visual photometry for many years used Polaris, the Pole Star, as the standard of magnitude. It was selected because it could be seen throughout the night. It always remained in a nearly fixed position and was always in reach of observers in the northern hemisphere. All other stars could be compared with Polaris by a special double telescope at the Harvard Observatory. Unfortunately, it was shown by accurate photoelectric observations that the standard is not constant in brightness, but varies by about 4 percent. Thereafter, the magnitude of Polaris at average brightness was used as the standard.

For photographic photometry, a series of stars, called the Polar Sequence, near the north celestial pole is now used. This sequence includes Polaris.

Fig. 5–4  A photograph of a star cluster showing the effect of a star's magnitude on the size of its image. (Yerkes Observatory photograph)

The images of stars in other parts of the sky are compared with those of the Polar Sequence taken with the same exposure times and with the same equipment. This photometry is accurate to about 0.01 magnitude or about 1 percent. Secondary standards have also been set up in selected areas of the sky. The stars in these areas have been carefully compared with the Polar Sequence. A similar series has also been set up in the southern hemisphere.

## 5.5  The Spectrograph

A *spectroscope* is an instrument for producing a spectrum and permitting it to be examined visually. If such an instrument is equipped with a plateholder on which the spectrum is photographed instead of viewed through an eyepiece, it is called a *spectrograph*. This instrument is provided with a narrow adjustable slit through which the light of a luminous object is allowed to pass. The slit is placed in the focus of the telescope objective. The light diverges after passing through the slit and then is passed through a lens which makes the beam parallel. This lens is called the collimating lens, or collimator.

The light then passes through a prism, which is made of glass or some other refracting material, where it is dispersed into its component colors. It then goes through a small telescope composed of an objective lens and an eyepiece, where it can be viewed by the eye. The eyepiece may be replaced by a photographic plateholder and the spectrum permanently recorded by photography. Figure 5–5 shows the optical principles of the spectrograph and the production of spectra.

The prism may be replaced by a grating, which has two advantages over the prism. First, the dispersion is greater; that is, the spectrum lines are farther apart and can be measured with greater accuracy. Secondly, in the grating spectrum, the dispersion is the same for all colors, while in the prism spectrum the dispersion changes continually from red to violet.

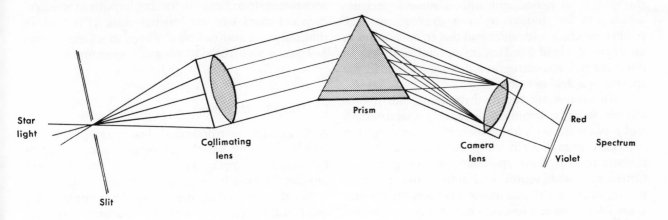

Fig. 5–5 Optical principles of a single-prism spectrograph.

Several hours of exposure time are sometimes required to get a good photograph of the spectrum of a star. Since it is usually cold in the dome of an observatory and the temperature drops during the course of an exposure, it is necessary to keep the spectrograph at a constant temperature to prevent a change in the refraction produced by the optical parts. For that reason, the entire spectrograph is housed in a specially insulated case equipped with an electric heater and controlled by a thermostat.

It is also desirable to compare the spectrum of a source under investigation with the spectra of various comparison elements, each of which has its own set of spectral lines. This comparison with a known source makes it possible to determine whether or not the element is present in the atmosphere of the star, to measure the Doppler effect which determines the amount of motion (radial velocity) of a star, and many other effects which are investigated by the astrophysicist. The light from the comparison source is allowed to pass through the two ends of the slit to form two spectra, between which is photo-

graphed the spectrum of the source under investigation. Having the spectra of star and comparison source side by side provides a very accurate and direct method of measurement.

Astronomical spectrographs are built with one, two, or more prisms or with gratings which have as many as 30,000 rulings per inch. Individual spectral lines that cannot be separated with a series of prisms can be detected with the grating spectrograph. With modern gratings it is no longer necessary to confine observations to only the brightest stars.

For many years, research was done to develop methods by which the spectra of stars could be obtained with spectrographs without slits. This was successful to some degree, but it was impossible to measure the Doppler effect except roughly by introducing a liquid which gave a broad absorption line in the stellar spectra, but which did not give accurate velocities.

By placing a thin prism in front of the telescope objective, it is possible to photograph a field of many stars at the same time. Instead of a round image for each star as in direct photography, the starlight is stretched out into a short spectrum which can be studied under a microscope. The prisms are made with sides inclined to each other at an angle of about 5°. This instrument is called an objective prism spectrograph. Figure 5–6 shows the spectra of a field of stars.

An even more recent instrument, the photoelectric scanner, combines a grating spectrograph and a photoelectric photometer. Here the spectrum is passed through a slit which eliminates all except a short region of the spectrum. As the grating is turned by a small motor, each part of the spectrum in turn falls on a photoelectric photomultiplier and is then recorded as a line on a meter. The lines in the spectrum show as dips in the tracing. The width and depth of each line can then be measured directly

without the use of photography. This method is somewhat slow, but is becoming important in astrophysical studies of the brighter stars. It is obvious that only one star can be observed at a time. Figure 5–7 shows an artist's drawing of a spectrum scan.

### 5.6   The Filar Micrometer

Still another astronomical instrument, but one which no longer has the importance it once had, is the filar micrometer. This is a device by which the angular distance between two stars can be measured. It can also be used for measuring the position of the head of a comet or of a planet or asteroid with respect to stars whose positions have previously been determined.

Fig. 5–6   A photograph made with a transmission grating—a grating placed in front of the telescope objective. Spectra of a number of stars can be taken at one time. The spectra have been artificially widened by moving the plate during the exposure. (Courtesy of Fritz Zwicky)

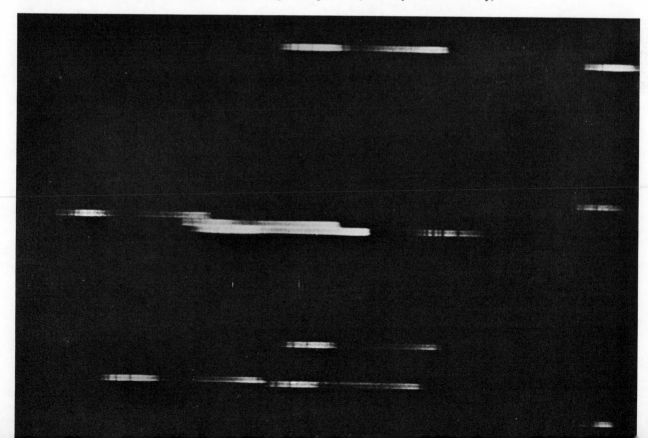

Fig. 5–7 Artist's drawing of a photoelectric scanner tracing of a spectrogram. *A* is a strong, but broad and diffuse, absorption line; *B* a weak, sharp line; *C* a stronger, somewhat diffuse line; and *D* a still weaker, slightly broadened line.

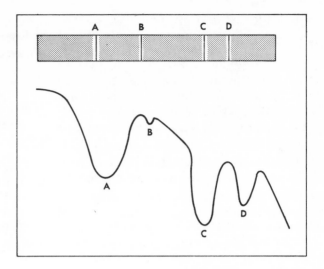

The micrometer is provided with a pair of movable hairs, or with very thin spider webs, which can be separated by moving a finely graduated screw. Also, the wires can be rotated. By bisecting the two stars, one with each wire, and knowing the value of one turn of the screw in seconds of arc at the focus of the telescope, the angular distance between the stars can be measured with great accuracy. And, by letting the stars trail along one of the wires, due to the rotation of the earth, the east-west direction can be found. Then, by rotating the micrometer until the wire bisects both stars at the same time, the angle between them and the east-west direction (and hence north-south, 90° away) can be determined. Of course such readings can also be made by measuring the positions of these objects on photographic plates.

The micrometer has been in use for more than a hundred years for the measurement of the motions of pairs of stars, known as visual binary stars. These measurements can also be made by photography, unless the stars are too close together for their images to be seen separately on the plate. Here the eye is superior to the photograph for stars near the resolving power of the telescope. Figure 5–8 shows the method of measurement.

Fig. 5–8  Method of measurement of the distance apart and direction between two stars. Line *f* is a fixed wire and *m* is a movable wire in a micrometer. The entire micrometer can be rotated. $S_1$ and $S_2$ are bisected by a fixed wire perpendicular to *f* and *m*. The distance between $S_1$ and $S_2$ is read off a scale (not shown). The direction angle in the drawing is about 38° measured from north towards east.

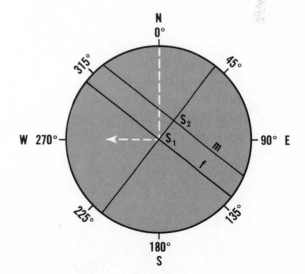

## QUESTIONS AND PROBLEMS

1. What is the derivation of the terms "sextant" and "bubble octant"?

2. Why might the altitude of a star measured with a mariner's sextant be slightly larger than when measured with a bubble octant?

3. Why is it not possible to use a bubble octant or a mariner's sextant in a space craft?

4. List the advantages and disadvantages of photography over visual observations in astronomy.

5. What are two ways of measuring the brightness of stars that are more accurate than by visual observation?

6. Gratings with low dispersion are used to obtain spectra of very faint stars. Why cannot gratings with greater dispersion, which are more accurate, be used for these stars?

7. In photographic studies of star brightness, the Polar Sequence is used as a reference. Why is it desirable to photograph it each time a comparison is made, rather than use the same photograph over and over?

8. Verify the statement that 0.1″ of arc along the earth's surface corresponds to a distance of about 10 ft. (Assume the earth to be a perfect sphere 25,000 mi in circumference.)

# Chapter Six

# Theories of Planetary Motion

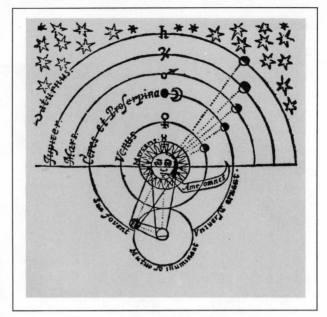

## 6.1 Apparent Motions

Everybody knows that the sun and the moon appear to rise in the east and set in the west. It may not be so well known and obvious, however, that the stars do likewise. The explanation is simple, if it is assumed that the earth rotates on an axis and that the motions we see of the heavenly bodies across the sky are a result of the earth's motion. This apparent motion would be the same if the earth were motionless and the stars were fixed on a sphere which rotated around the earth. Since the earth seemed stationary, the ancient astronomers assumed that it was the stars which moved.

The ancient astronomers were well aware of the phenomena of the rising and setting of the stars and had studied their motions on the celestial sphere for centuries. They recognized groups of stars which kept their shapes. These groups were called *constellations,* of which 48 had been named before A.D. 150. The stars in the constellations even today are called fixed stars. The ancient astronomers also noticed that there are some bodies which move among the constellations. These they called *planets,* from a Greek word meaning wanderer. Since the sun and moon also appear to move, they were classified as planets, of which there were seven in all: the sun, the moon, Mercury, Venus, Mars, Jupiter, and Saturn.

Viewed from the earth, the sun and moon always are seen to move among the stars from day to day in an easterly direction. This motion is called *direct motion.* The other five of the ancient astronomers' planets also move in direct motion most of the time, but occasionally they stop moving eastward and move westward—this is called *retrograde motion*—for a short distance and over a period of a few weeks. If the apparent paths of the five planets are plotted on a star map, they make loops which may be open or closed. Figure 6–1 shows the loop made by Mars in 1965. These loops were difficult to explain and it was not until the time of Copernicus and, later, of Kepler that they were fully understood.

## 6.2 Planetary Systems

In the Greek astronomy, the earth was considered to be the largest body in the universe and fixed in

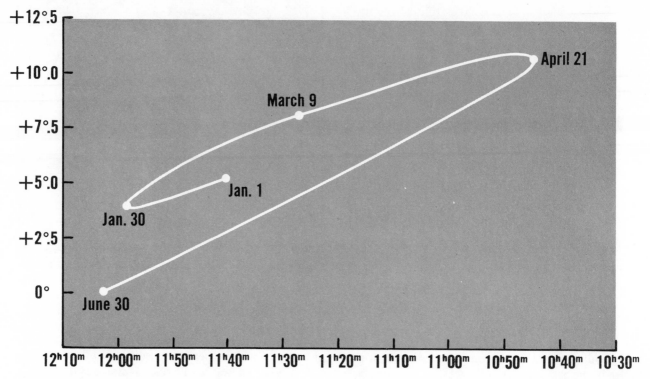

Fig. 6–1   The loop on the celestial sphere traced by the planet Mars in 1965. January 30 and April 21 were stationary points; March 9 was in opposition. *(point farther away from the theory)*

space. There were various ways to explain how the earth was supported, most of which were quite fantastic. To explain the motions of the planets, each of the seven was thought to be fixed on a separate sphere, which rotated around the earth once a day. This system explained the daily motions but did not quite explain the motions of the planets among the stars. There was an eighth sphere, to which the stars were fixed, that also rotated around the earth in one day. These spheres were of course transparent, so the remainder of the sky could be seen through them.

One very complicated system was proposed by a Greek astronomer named Eudoxus, who lived between 409 B.C. and 356 B.C. His system used 27 spheres to explain both the daily motions and the direct and retrograde motions of the planets. This system was later modified to 34 spheres by Callippus.

The most famous system has been called the *Ptolemaic System,* because it was published by Claudius Ptolemy in his book *Megale Syntaxis tes Astronomias,* or *Almagest* for short. (*Almagest* means the greatest book.) It was published about A.D. 140. The theory was based on the work of two men who lived in Asia Minor, Apollonius in the third century B.C. and Hipparchus, about 150 B.C.

In the Ptolemaic System, as in an earlier one, the earth was spherical, but stationary. Each planet had its own circle, a *deferent,* whose center was the earth. The smallest deferent was that of the moon, then increasingly larger ones for Mercury, Venus, the sun, Mars, Jupiter, and Saturn in that order. (See Figure 6–2.) The seven planets circled the earth in one day, the moon and sun in direct motion on their deferents.

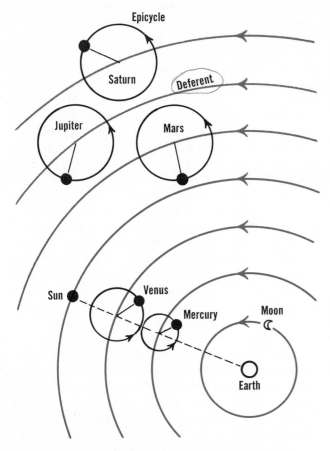

Fig. 6–2  The Ptolemaic System of the Universe, later called the Solar System.

In order to explain the motions of the other five planets, the star-like planets, each was assumed to move, not in its *deferent*, but in a smaller circle, called an *epicycle*, whose center moved eastward along the deferent. The sun and moon did not need epicycles, since their motions were always direct. Since Mercury is never more than 28° from the sun and Venus never more than 46°, the centers of their epicycles stayed in line with the sun.

To explain the direct motion, all five planets when farthest from the sun moved in their epicycles in the same direction as that of the epicycle on the deferent; that is, in direct motion. But when nearest the earth, the planets were moving in the opposite direction. The backward motion in the epicycle exceeded the forward motion along the deferent resulting in retrograde motion. During the retrograde part of the motion, the planets were on the side of the epicycle nearest the earth and were therefore the brightest. Mercury's fastest retrograde motion coincided with the time when it was closest to the earth, in the center of the retrograde loop. This position, sometimes called perigee, occurred for Mercury once in about 116 days. Venus described a similar, but larger loop once every 586 days (1½ years).

For Mars, Jupiter, and Saturn, the epicycles did not stay in line with the sun; and the planets came to the middle of their retrograde loops every 780, 399, and 378 days, respectively. At those times each planet was on the opposite side of the deferent from the sun. Mars is conspicuously brighter at those times. We now call this position *opposition*. The loop of Mars is very long, sometimes as long as 19°, and may take almost three months to complete. Saturn's loop is 6.5° long and takes almost five months.

The biggest difficulty with the Ptolemaic System was that the loops made by the planets are not always the same. Sometimes they are closed, like the one made by Mars in 1965. Sometimes they are open. Also they are not always the same size. In order to explain these irregularities, smaller epicycles were added to the rims of the larger ones, until, according to some historians, there were 55 in all. This system was so cumbersome that King Alphonso X of Spain remarked that if he had been consulted at the creation of the universe, he would have designed it on a simpler plan. The fault was not with the creation, but with the interpretation. The Greeks thought of the planets as perfect bodies and the circle as the perfect geometrical figure. Therefore the planets could move only in circles. However, this system was not improved upon for over 1500 years.

The ancient universe consisted of the earth at the center, the seven planets, and an eighth sphere of the stars. Few distances were known, although Aristarchus, a Greek scholar of the third century B.C., calculated the distance to the moon at 240,000 mi and the sun at 4,800,000 mi. Kepler increased this latter distance to about 14,000,000 mi.

## 6.3   The Copernican System

The first change in the theories of the universe came in the sixteenth century. Nicholas Copernicus was a Polish mathematician and astronomer. He discovered that Aristarchus had suggested a universe with the sun at the center—a *heliocentric*, instead of a *geocentric* universe. Copernicus adopted this system, which simplified the problem of explaining the motions of the planets by having them describe orbits around the sun. Our present heliocentric solar system is called the Copernican System, although it was changed and improved almost 100 years later by Johannes Kepler.

Aristarchus' plan had other advantages besides its simplicity. It also explained why the planets vary in brightness during the year. If the earth is assumed to be in motion, its distance from the other planets continually changes, causing them to change in brightness.

Copernicus also believed that the planets had to move around the sun in circles. To explain some of the irregularities, such as the sizes and shapes of the loops, he placed the sun slightly out of center. This could also explain why Mars showed a difference in brightness at oppositions from year to year. But Copernicus also used some epicycles. Some writers think that he reduced the number, but recent research seems to indicate that the number may have been increased.

While the Copernican System was widely adopted, Tycho rejected it. Thomas Digges, an English astronomer and mathematician, had suggested that the stars are not all at the same distance on the eighth sphere, but are scattered throughout space. Probably he thought the brighter stars are bright because they are near. Accepting this concept, Tycho tested the theory by looking for stellar *parallax*, an apparent movement of the nearer stars with respect to the more distant stars when viewed from different positions in the earth's orbit. Tycho could not detect any parallax, because the stars are too far away to have shown the effect with his instruments. It was not until about 1830 that such motions could be observed, and then only with large telescopes.

It remained for Galileo's invention of the telescope to give astronomy a big assist, and for Kepler's work to really explain the apparent complexities of the solar system. When Galileo looked at the sky with his first telescope, two discoveries became of great importance for the heliocentric theory. First, he showed that Jupiter has a family of four moons circling it as the planets were assumed to circle the sun. Then he found that Venus shows all the phases which the moon exhibits. This was in contradiction to the Ptolemaic System, as an examination of that system easily shows. That is, since Venus and Mercury were always between the earth and the sun in the Ptolemaic System, they should show only new and crescent phases. But Galileo showed that Venus also shows gibbous and full phases and therefore must at times be more distant than the sun. In fact, Venus shows a phase greater than quarter for 445 days in its phase period of 584 days. Galileo announced to the world his discovery of the phases of Venus by an anagram in Latin, which, when the letters were rearranged, said: The Mother of Loves imitates the form of Cynthia. This means: Venus imitates the moon.

With the adoption of a heliocentric system,

the sun was no longer considered to be a planet, but the earth became the third planet from the sun, and the moon was called a satellite of the earth. The system of circles and epicycles was retained, but it was not until the time of Sir Isaac Newton that the explanation of planetary orbits under the force of gravitation was possible.

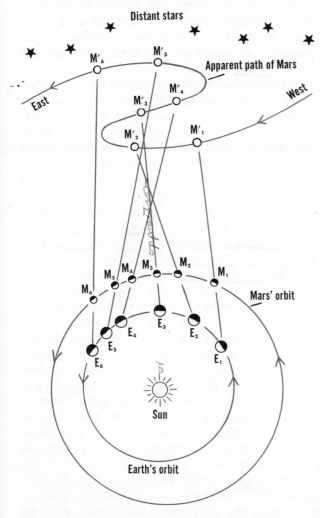

Fig. 6–3 Explanation of the retrograde motion of Mars.

In the heliocentric theory the retrograde motions can be explained easily. The planet nearest the sun moves most rapidly in its orbit. Thus Mercury moves faster than Venus, which moves faster than the earth. All the others move more slowly, the speed decreasing with increasing distance. Figure 6–3 shows the reason for the apparent motions of Mars. When the earth catches up with Mars, as it does during the oppositions, Mars seems to move backwards, just as from a faster car a slower car seems to drop back when it is passed on the road. The open or closed loops depend on the planes in which the planets move, and the shape of the loop depends on where the earth and the planet happen to be at the time of opposition. The variation in size of the loops and the apparent change of brightness of the planet from one opposition to another was explained by means of eccentric circular orbits and small epicycles.

### 6.4 Elongations and Phases

*Elongation* is the angle between the centers of two astronomical bodies as seen from the center of the earth. But since the earth is so small compared to the distances between the sun and the planets, elongation may be observed from any station on the earth's surface without appreciable error. The elongation of a planet is usually taken as its angular distance from the center of the sun. When the elongation is zero, the planet is said to be in *conjunction*. Since Mercury and Venus are closer to the sun than the earth, they come to conjunction when they are between the earth and the sun—this is called *inferior conjunction*; and when they are beyond the sun, it is called *superior conjunction*. (See Figure 6–4.)

When these two planets are in inferior conjunction, their illuminated faces are turned away from the earth and their *phases* are said to be new. At superior conjunction, the illuminated faces are toward the earth and their phases are full.

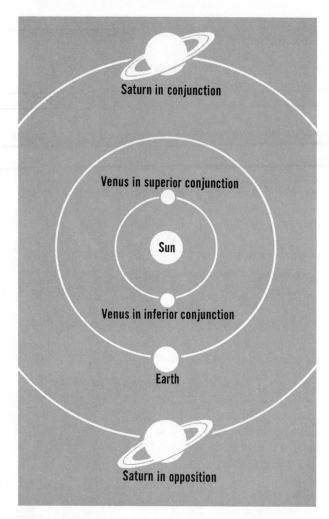

Fig. 6–4 Diagram showing conjunctions and oppositions of planets.

bous. They show the same phases in reverse after superior conjunction. Thus the phases of these two planets are like the phases of the moon.

All the other planets are outside the earth's orbit and come to conjunction only on the far side of the sun. After conjunction their elongations increase. An elongation of 90° is called *quadrature*, and one of 180° is called *opposition*. Their phases change very little from full, except Mars which shows a slightly gibbous phase when near quadrature. When two bodies are in conjunction or opposition as seen from the earth, they are said to be in *syzygy*.

The definitions of conjunction and opposition should be changed slightly. For example, when Venus is in inferior conjunction, its elongation may be as large as 7°, because the inclination of its orbit puts it above or below the line joining the earth and the sun. The planet is said to be in conjunction when its elongation is a minimum. The same may be said of opposition, where the elongation may not be quite 180°. Quadrature, however, is always exactly 90°. Elongation is the shortest angular distance, measured on the arc of a great circle, between two bodies.

The *synodic period* of a planet is the length of time between two successive conjunctions of the same kind, or between two successive oppositions. It is possible to determine the times of opposition or conjunction by observation. At conjunction, Mercury and Venus are not visible, but by interpolations carried out over many years (or even centuries) these times have been computed and the synodic periods are known with great accuracy. Because of the elliptical orbits, the times of conjunction or opposition do not occur with exact regularity. The average (mean) synodic periods are given in Table 14–1.

The synodic periods result from the differences between the sidereal periods of the planets and that of the earth. The more distant the planet is from the sun, the slower it travels and the longer is its *sidereal period*, which is the time required for a planet

The greatest elongations of Mercury and Venus are 28° and 46°, respectively. At those times the phases are like the quarter moon, because we see only one-half of the illuminated face. Between inferior conjunction and greatest elongation, the phases are crescent, and between greatest elongation and superior conjunction the phases are gib-

to complete one orbit around the sun. The inner planets, Mercury and Venus, gain a lap on the earth between similar conjunctions, while the outer planets lose a lap between oppositions. The relation between sidereal and synodic period can be developed by determining the fraction of a lap gained or lost each day.

Let $Sy$ stand for the synodic period of a planet, $Si$ the sidereal period, and $E$ the sidereal period of the earth—all expressed in days, or years for the most distant planets. Then $1/Si$ is the fraction of its orbit that a planet travels in one day and $1/E$ is the fraction of its orbit that the earth travels in one day. $1/Sy$ is the fraction of a lap the planet gains or loses on the earth each day.

For the inner planets:

$$1/Si - 1/E = 1/Sy. \tag{6-1}$$

*Subtract to show gain on earth*

For the outer planets:

$$1/E - 1/Si = 1/Sy. \tag{6-2}$$

*Subtract from earth to show loss*

▶*Example:* The sidereal period of Venus is 225 days. Compute its synodic period.

**Solution:**  Substituting in the first of the above formulas:

$1/Sy = 1/225 - 1/365 = 0.00444 - 0.00274 = 0.00170.$

**Solving** for $Sy$,

$$Sy = 1/0.00170 = 588 \text{ days.}$$

A more accurate value is obtained by substituting the exact values of the periods of Venus and the earth.

## 6.5  Kepler's Three Laws

In 1600 Kepler went to Prague, which was then the residence of the emperor of the Holy Roman Empire, to become a student of Tycho Brahe. Tycho had been forced to leave his observatory on the island of Hven and had gone to Prague as official astronomer. There he spent the rest of his life refining his tables of planetary motion. After Tycho's death in 1601, Kepler had access to the storehouse of Tycho's observations of the planets, in particular those of Mars. His main object in the study of the motions of Mars and the other planets was to try to improve his model of the solar system.

Kepler had the firm conviction that the planets move in orbits whose distances could be represented by the following geometrical concept. He wished to use the five regular solids, or polyhedrons, of geometry: the four-faced tetrahedron; the six-faced hexahedron; the eight-faced octahedron; the twelve-faced dodecahedron; and the twenty-faced icosahedron. This was a compromise between the Greek idea of circles and the Copernican System.

Inside and outside of each solid, a sphere could be placed touching all corners of the solid. Kepler's model contained the five solids in a sequence such that the distances between the successive tangent spheres were in approximately the same ratio as the distances between the planets. In other words, the radii of the spheres were proportional to the distances of the planets from the sun. He found, however, that this system would not fit the facts. But he did arrive at three laws which revolutionized the theories of the solar system. Figure 6–5 shows Kepler's original model of the universe, using the five spheres.

Kepler's first two laws were published in his book *Commentaries on the Motions of Mars* in 1609, eight years after Tycho's death. The third law followed in 1619 in a book called *The Harmony of the Worlds*.

In the three laws Kepler abandoned the Greek idea of circles and turned to the ellipse for an explanation of the apparent irregularities found in the speeds with which the planets move across the sky, and particularly in the size of their retrograde motions. The ellipse is a closed curve in a plane in which the sum of the distances from any point on

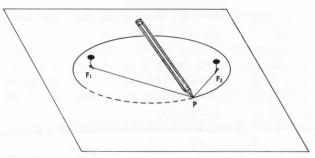

Fig. 6–6   Drawing an ellipse.

the curve to two internal points is always the same. The two internal points are called foci (singular, focus). An easy way to draw an ellipse is shown in Figure 6–6. A string is attached to tacks at the foci of the ellipse, leaving some slack, so that a pencil can be moved around the tacks while keeping the string taut. This keeps the sum of the distances from the pencil to the foci equal to the length of the string. Notice that the shape of the ellipse depends on the separation of the foci and the length of the string. Another way is to use a loop of string stretched around the two tacks and the pencil.

The long diameter of the ellipse, called the *major axis*, is equal to the length of the string. For a fixed major axis, if the foci are moved apart, the ellipse becomes long and narrow; if they are moved closer together, it becomes more nearly circular, and if the foci coincide, the ellipse becomes a circle. Thus, the circle is a special form of ellipse. The ellipse is as fundamental, or as perfect, as the circle.

The ellipse is one of the conic sections, which

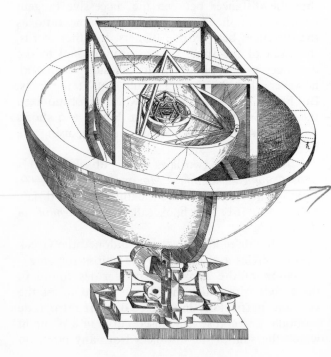

Fig. 6–5   Kepler and his model of the universe, which used five regular solids tangent to five spheres. The radius of each sphere was proportional to the distances of the planets from the sun. This model did not fit the facts. (Yerkes Observatory photograph; N.Y. Public Library, Science and Technology Division, From Kepler's original works)

are curves produced by the intersection of a plane with a hollow cone. If the plane is parallel to the base of the cone, the curve is a circle. If the plane makes an angle with the base, the figure is an ellipse until the plane becomes parallel to one edge of the cone. In that special case, the figure is a parabola. Finally, if the angle is still greater, the figure is a hyperbola. All of these types of conic section are important in astronomy. Figure 6–7 illustrates the definition of these types of curve.

① Kepler's first law can be simply stated as: The orbits of the planets are ellipses with the sun at one focus of each ellipse. Each planet and the sun are always in a plane. However, the planes for the six planets known in Kepler's time, and all nine known today, are not all the same, but are inclined to each other and thus to the plane of the earth's orbit around the sun.

Figure 6–8 shows the elliptical orbit of the earth with the sun at one focus. The other focus is empty. Since the orbit is an ellipse, the distance from the sun to each planet changes continually. The size of

Fig. 6–7 Three of the four types of conic sections.

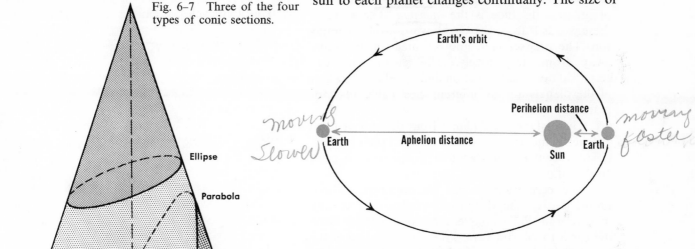

Fig. 6–8 The elliptical shape of the earth's orbit with the sun at one focus.

each orbit is measured by the mean distance, which is the average (mean) of the greatest and smallest distances. In the case of the earth's orbit, the mean distance is just short of 93,000,000 mi. This distance is called the *astronomical unit* and in 1965 was given as 92,976,000 mi or 149,598,000 km. It is extremely difficult to measure exactly, but is now known with an accuracy of about 500 km, or 300 mi. Its determination will be discussed in Chapter 12.

The shape of an ellipse is given by its eccentricity, a number which expresses the amount of flattening. It is determined by dividing the distance between the two foci by the length of the major axis, the longest diameter of the ellipse. For the earth the eccentricity, $e$, is

$$e = \frac{3{,}111{,}000 \text{ mi}}{185{,}952{,}000 \text{ mi}} = 0.01673.$$

The size and shape of the ellipse are determined, therefore, from a knowledge of the distance from the sun to the planet at various points in the orbit.

The point in each orbit where the planet is closest to the sun is called the *perihelion*. The point of greatest distance is the *aphelion*. The stem of these words is from the Greek word *helios* meaning sun. The prefixes *peri-* and *ap-* mean near to and away from, respectively. The mean distances, eccentricities, and perihelion and aphelion distances of the planets are all different. See Table 14–1 for planetary data.

The distance of a planet from the sun or from another planet is the distance between their centers. It is the center of a planet that describes an orbit around the sun.

The eccentricity $e$ can be obtained without knowledge of the distance in miles, but in any relative unit. For example, since the distance from the earth to the sun varies, the apparent size of the sun also varies. If the apparent angular diameter of the sun at perihelion is 32.49′ and at aphelion is 31.42′, the average diameter is 31.955′. The eccentricity is the difference between the largest and smallest angle divided by their sum: That is,

$$e = \frac{1.07'}{63.91'} = 0.0167.$$

The proof of this and the determination of the angles by measurement is a good problem to work on, provided accurate results are not expected.

Kepler's first and second laws were discovered by the use of geometry, based entirely on observation, and had no theoretical foundation. The unifying physical principle basic to these laws, the law

of gravitation, had not yet been discovered, but Kepler's work was fundamental to Newton's law. His three laws can be proved by the law of gravitation, or the law of gravitation can be derived from Kepler's laws. For these proofs, the student is referred to any standard book on celestial mechanics.

Kepler's second law may be stated as follows: The line joining each planet to the sun (called the *radius vector*) sweeps over equal areas of space in equal intervals of time. This law cleared up some unexplained variations in the planetary motions and made it unnecessary to use the cumbersome system of epicycles. It can be seen from Figure 6–9

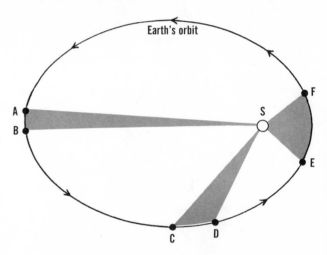

Fig. 6–9    Kepler's second law of areas explains why the earth's orbital velocity varies. The three shaded sections are equal in area and represent periods of 15 days each.

that, since the areas are equal for a given time interval, the speed of the planet must vary. That is, a planet moves fastest in its orbit at perihelion and slowest at aphelion. This can be demonstrated by watching the motion of the sun along the ecliptic. It appears to describe a longer arc in one day in January than it does in July. The earth's perihelion occurs in early January and aphelion in early July.

Kepler's third law is sometimes called the

harmonic law. It may be stated in several ways. The usual form is: The squares of the sidereal periods of any two planets are proportional to the cubes of their mean distances from the sun. This period cannot be determined directly. It is necessary to compute it from the synodic period by solving equations 6–1 or 6–2 for $Si$.

The third law may be stated in mathematical form as:

*planet*
*sidereal*
*period*
$$\frac{P_1^2}{P_2^2} = \frac{A_1^3}{A_2^3} \quad \text{mean distance} \quad (6\text{--}3)$$

where $P_1$ and $P_2$ are the sidereal periods of two planets expressed in days or years, but both in the same units; $A_1$ and $A_2$ are their mean distances in units of distance, miles or astronomical units. If $P$ is expressed in years and $A$ in astronomical units, and if the second planet is the earth, the denominators are both equal to one, and the equation may be written as:

$$P^2 = A^3. \qquad (6\text{--}4)$$

▶*Example:* Compute the sidereal period of Mars, if its mean distance is 1.52 a.u.

**Solution:** Substituting in the formula

$$P^2 = (1.52)^3 = 3.51$$
$$P = \sqrt{3.51} = 1.88 \text{ years} = 686 \text{ days.}$$

It should be noted that as $P$ increases, $A$ also increases. *described the motion at the earth's surface*

## 6.6　Galileo and Mechanics

In addition to his work with the first telescope, Galileo made some important contributions to the field of mechanics. It is said that he discovered the principle of the pendulum by timing the swings of a chandelier in the cathedral at Pisa by using his pulse as a timepiece. Galileo also studied the prob-

lem of falling bodies. Aristotle had taught that the time of fall of heavy bodies depended on their weights. It is said that Galileo dropped weights from the Leaning Tower of Pisa and found that there was a small difference in the times, but much smaller than Aristotle had predicted. It was not until the problem could be tested in a vacuum that the small difference was found to be due to the resistance of the air. Galileo also reasoned that the laws of falling bodies should also apply to bodies rolling down an inclined plane. By changing the angle of the plane, it was possible to slow down the motion to where it could be timed by a clock. The results were:

1. The vertical distance through which a body falls (or rolls down an inclined plane) is directly proportional to the square of the elapsed time.
2. The acceleration (rate of change of velocity) of a falling (or rolling) body is constant.

Expressed as a formula:

$a = 32 \text{ ft/sec}^2$

*distance fallen* $s = \dfrac{1}{2} at^2 \qquad (6\text{--}5)$

where $s$ is the distance the body falls in the time $t$, and $a$ is the acceleration, which is constant. To this it could be added that the velocity, $v$, is directly proportional to the time, or

$$v = at \qquad (6\text{--}6)$$

▶*Example:* A rock falls from a cliff and strikes the earth below 5 sec later. The acceleration due to gravity is 32 ft/sec$^2$. The usual symbol for gravity is $g$ and the formula is:

$$s = \frac{1}{2} gt^2. \qquad (6\text{--}7)$$

(a) What is the rock's velocity when it lands?
**Ans:** $v = (32 \text{ ft/sec}^2) \times (5 \text{ sec}) = 160 \text{ ft/sec.}$
(b) How far does the rock fall in 5 sec?
**Ans:** $s = \frac{1}{2} gt^2 = \frac{1}{2} (32 \text{ ft/sec}^2) \times (5 \text{ sec})^2 = 400 \text{ ft.}$

Both acceleration and velocity are vector quantities which involve both magnitude and direction.

## 6.7  Newton's Laws

The work of such scientists as Tycho, Galileo, Kepler, and others paved the way for Sir Isaac Newton, who was called by the French geometrician and astronomer, Lagrange, "the greatest genius that ever existed." Newton was born on December 25, 1642 (old style calendar), or January 4, 1643 (present calendar), and made great contributions to the field of astronomy, optics, mechanics, and mathematics before he was twenty-four years old. However, he did not publish his work until twenty years later, when his famous book, usually called the *Principia* (*Philosophiae Naturalis Principia Mathematica*) was printed at the expense of Edmund Halley in 1687.

In the *Principia,* Newton stated three laws of motion, which are the basis of mechanics. Newton's first law of motion may be stated: A body remains at rest or continues to move with constant velocity in a straight line unless it is acted on by an unbalanced outside force. This fundamental property of all matter is called *inertia*. There are two important consequences of this law:

1. It is obvious that if a body at rest is pushed by equal forces from opposite directions, it will remain at rest. Also, balanced forces do not change the uniform velocity of a body. But if the forces are unbalanced, the body will change its speed or direction, or both.

For example, a car travels at constant velocity if the retarding frictional forces are balanced by the driving force of the wheels. Increasing the driving force so it exceeds the retarding forces increases the velocity. To change the direction of the car's motion, another force must be applied at right angles to the car. This force is exerted by the road on the front wheels when they are turned to follow a curve in the road. If the road is icy, it will not exert the force needed and the car continues in a straight line.

2. Since the planets continually change their directions, some unbalanced force must be acting on them to counteract their inertial tendency to move in a straight line.

Newton was able to show that the force changing their speeds and directions is directed toward the sun. This law is completely incompatible with Ptolemy's epicycles, because it requires a force directed towards the center of each of the loops. The Greeks thought the planets' motions were an intrinsic part of their nature. Figure 6–10 shows how a force changes the speed or direction of a moving body.

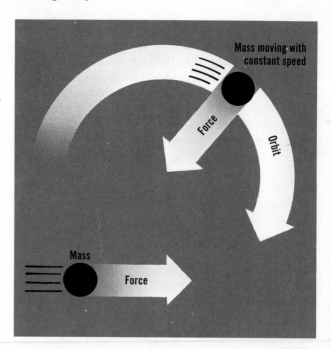

Fig. 6–10   Diagram showing a change of speed by a force (bottom) and a change of direction (top).

Newton's second law of motion states: The change of speed or direction of a body is directly proportional to the external force producing the change, inversely proportional to the mass of the body, and takes place in the direction of the external force. This law may be written: $a = f/m$, or its equivalent $f = ma$, where $f$ is the external force, $m$ is the mass of the body, and $a$ is the acceleration produced by the force.

To use this law, it is necessary to define a standard amount of matter, or a unit mass. In the metric system, the unit mass is the kilogram, a cylinder of platinum-iridium kept in the International Bureau of Weights and Measures near Paris. In the English system, the standard of force is the pound.

*Weight* is a measure of the amount of attraction between the earth and a given mass. It will be shown later that on the surface of the earth, the acceleration due to gravity changes slightly with location. Therefore, the weight of a given mass varies over the surface of the earth. Thus, if the distance of a body from the center of the earth changes, the attraction by the earth also changes, and so does the weight. Similarly, the weight of a body on the moon or a planet is different from its weight on the earth, provided we extend the definition of weight to include the attraction for the body by the astronomical body involved. The use of the word weight in this sense will be continued in this book. It can now be seen that Newton's second law of motion can be used to define mass, or it can be used to calculate a force, if the other two terms of the equation are known.

*Mass* is a measure of inertia, the resistance to a change in motion. This property of an object never changes, regardless of its location. For example, a space ship far removed from any gravitational source, such as the earth, would not have any weight. Yet the force required to impart a given acceleration would be exactly the same as on the earth, because its mass is still the same. Inside the space ship, objects would be weightless while the ship was in uniform motion (no acceleration) even though the ship were traveling at a high velocity with respect to the earth. There would be no up nor down. If the ship were accelerated forward by its rocket engine, the rear of the passenger compartment would overtake the occupants and press against them, exerting the necessary force to accelerate them at the same rate as the ship. The occupants would have the impression that they had fallen toward the rear of the ship. There would seem to be a force, just like gravity, holding them against the rear compartment wall. The sensation would be the same as that of a person inside a ship standing on its base on the earth. The rear compartment wall would seem to be the floor. The "weight" would be proportional to the rocket's acceleration.

Newton's third law of motion may be stated: To every action there exists an opposite and equal reaction. This says that actions are never alone, but exist in pairs. For example, if the earth pulls on a given mass, the mass pulls on the earth with an equal force, but in the opposite direction. However, because the mass of the earth is so much greater, the force on the small mass accelerates the mass by 32 ft/sec². The acceleration of the earth is infinitesimally small. The effect of the pull between the earth and the moon is to swing the moon around the center of mass between the two bodies in an orbit which is nearly a quarter of a million miles in radius. But the opposite pull of the moon moves the earth in an orbit only 2900 mi in radius.

Newton realized that the planets are pulled in orbit around the sun by a force which he called gravitation. He stated the *law of gravitation* as follows:

Every particle in the universe attracts every other particle with a force which is directly proportional to the product of their masses and inversely proportional to the square of the distance between them. Expressed as a formula:

$$F = G\frac{m_1 m_2}{d^2} \quad or \qquad F \propto \frac{m_1 m_2}{d^2} \tag{6-7}$$

where $F$ is the gravitational force, $m_1$ and $m_2$ are the masses of the two bodies, $d$ is the distance between their centers. $G$ is a universal constant, a factor of proportionality between the two sides of the equation to balance the units. In the metric system, if the force is measured in dynes, the mass is measured in grams, and the distance in centimeters,

$G = 6.67 \times 10^{-8}$ units (dyne-cm²/g²). A dyne is a unit of force of such magnitude that it would accelerate a particle of one gram by one centimeter per second per second.

It has been shown in various ways that this law holds true for all bodies in the solar system and probably in the universe, although this has not been definitely proved. The constant $G$ is therefore called the universal constant of gravitation and the law is called the universal law of gravitation.

This equation can be applied to the calculation of the weight of an object on the earth by rewriting it in the following form. Let $m$ be the mass of the object, $E$ the mass of the earth, and $r$ the radius of the earth. Then

$$W = G \frac{mE}{r^2}. \qquad (6\text{–}8)$$

Notice that the weight is proportional to the mass of the attracting body, in this case the earth. Since the masses of the planets differ, the weight of an object depends on the planet on which it is located. The weight is also proportional to the mass of the object and thus heavier objects have more inertia than lighter ones. This agrees with common experience.

In modern practice the units used in the metric system are the meter, the kilogram, and the second (MKS), instead of the older centimeter, gram, and second (cgs) units. In MKS units, the unit of force is the newton, a force which produces an acceleration of 1 m/sec² on a mass of 1 kg. Then the value of $G$ is $6.67 \times 10^{-11}$ nm²/kg².

Kepler's first law places the sun at one focus of each of the orbits of the planets. Kepler knew this as an observational fact, but he did not know why it should be so. Newton's universal law gave the reason. It is possible to show that if the sun were at the center of the orbits, the force of attraction would be directly proportional to the distance between them. This is of course not so, otherwise the force would decrease to zero as the two bodies approach each

other. But since Newton showed that the force is inversely proportional to the square of the distance, the force should increase as the bodies approach each other. Furthermore, Newton showed mathematically that the force had to be located at the focus, thus proving Kepler's first law.

Kepler's third law is only approximately true, but gave a satisfactory result with the known data of the time. It remained for Newton and the law of gravitation to refine it. There are several ways of stating Newton's modification of this law. One way is:

$$\frac{P_1^2}{P_2^2} = \frac{A_1^3 (M + m_2)}{A_2^3 (M + m_1)}. \qquad (6\text{–}9)$$

where the symbols are the same as for Kepler's statement, except for $M$, the mass of the sun, and $m_1$ and $m_2$, the masses of the two planets. Since the mass of the largest planet, Jupiter, is only ¹⁄₁₀₀₀ that of the sun, it can be seen easily that no serious error is made by neglecting the masses, $m_1$ and $m_2$, as Kepler did.

Another way is to let the second planet be the earth, as before. Then

$$P^2 (M + m) = A^3 \qquad (6\text{–}10)$$

where $P$ is the sidereal period of a planet expressed in sidereal years, $A$ is its distance from the sun in astronomical units, and $(M + m)$ is the combined mass of the sun and the planet. The earth's mass has been neglected, since it is only about ³⁄₁,₀₀₀,₀₀₀ of the mass of the sun.

## QUESTIONS AND PROBLEMS

1. Complete Figure 6–2 and show the phases of the planets. If Ptolemy had observed them with a telescope, would he have found that his theory correctly predicted the phases he observed? *Yes* –

2. Which planets can be at (a) inferior conjunc-

tion; (b) superior conjunction; (c) quadrature; and (d) opposition?

3. If a hunter were deposited on the middle of a frozen lake covered with frictionless ice, how could he get to shore? He has a loaded shotgun and two dead ducks. State the laws of Newton that apply.

4. Is it correct to say that an astronaut in an orbiting space vehicle is weightless? Explain.

5. Galileo is said to have found a very slight difference in the times of fall of light and heavy weights from the Leaning Tower of Pisa. (a) What caused this difference? (b) Should not a heavy weight fall faster than a lighter one, since it is accelerated by a greater force? Explain.

6. Is the gravitational attraction between two bodies affected by the presence of matter between them? Illustrate with an example.

7. Rockets used to launch satellites consist of several stages that drop off in succession during launch. Why does the final stage have a higher velocity than a single stage rocket of the same total weight and fuel?

8. A ball starting from rest rolls 10 ft down an inclined plane in 2 sec. (a) What is its acceleration? (b) What is its velocity at the end of the 2 sec? (c) How far will it have traveled after a total time of 5 sec?

9. Neglecting air resistance, (a) what velocity will a rock acquire during 10 sec of free fall? (b) How far will it have fallen?

10. Compute the weight of a 200 lb man in each of the following situations: (a) In space 4000 mi above the earth's surface; (b) On a planet 10 times the mass of the earth, but of equal radius; (c) on a planet of equal mass but radius twice that of the earth.

11. (a) Compute the sidereal period of Mercury from its mean distance (Table 14–1) by using Kepler's third law. (b) Compute its synodic period.

12. Why do the synodic periods of planets decrease from Mars to Pluto?

13. The velocity of a planet is inversely proportional to its distance from the sun at perihelion and aphelion. Show that Mercury's perihelion velocity is about 1.5 its aphelion velocity.

14. Compare the forces between (a) Jupiter and the sun, and (b) between Jupiter and Saturn, with the force between the earth and the sun.

*15. Verify equation 6–9 from the tabular data for Jupiter and Saturn.

# Chapter Seven

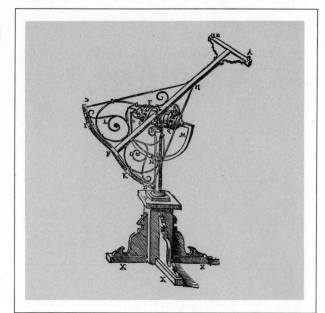

# Celestial Coordinates

## 7.1  Coordinate Systems

As a convenience for locating objects in the sky and especially for transmitting information about their locations (a new comet for instance), it is desirable to set up one or more systems of coordinates. A *coordinate system* is a set of numbers that may be used to locate an object. It must have a frame of reference to define direction, and initial reference points from which measurements are made. For example, a straight line has only one dimension: length. If it has an initial point, such as the end of a ruler, only one coordinate is needed to describe the location of any point on the line. A straight line is said to be one dimensional.

A flat surface is two dimensional, having length and width. Thus two coordinates are required to locate a point on a surface. An address in a city requires a coordinate system of two dimensions: the street and the number of a house on the street. The frame of reference is established by the streets where the house numbers begin.

The surface of a solid, such as a cube, requires three coordinates: length, width, and height. Points on the surface of a sphere can also be located by three dimensions, but it is easier to use a two-dimensional system in which angles, circles, and points are used. Such a system is called a polar coordinate system. Several sets of polar coordinates on the apparent sphere of the sky have been devised.

## 7.2  Terrestrial Latitude and Longitude

A familiar set of polar coordinates is that used to describe positions of points on the earth. The fundamental circle is the earth's equator with two poles 90° away. Secondary circles perpendicular to the equator and running through the poles are called meridians. The distance in angle from the equator to any point, measured on a meridian, is called *latitude,* which is measured north and south from the equator. The second coordinate is *longitude.* For this, it is necessary to choose a point on the equator as the initial point of reference. The meridian, called the prime meridian, through the observatory in Greenwich, England, was chosen because this observatory was set up to aid British navigators and England was the principal maritime nation of the time. The intersection of this meridian with the equator is the initial point from which longitude is measured. This system is shown in Figure 7–1.

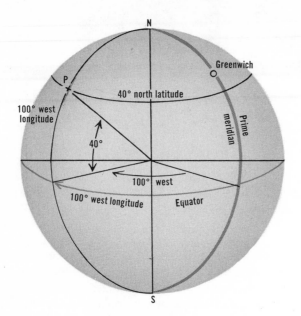

Fig. 7–1  The system of terrestrial latitude and longitude.

Longitude is therefore defined as the distance in angle between the meridian of Greenwich and any other meridian measured both east and west. Continental United States lies in the western hemisphere from about 65°W to 125°W longitude and from 25°N to 50°N latitude.

## THE HORIZON SYSTEM

### 7.3  The Celestial Sphere

The ancient astronomers, as has been pointed out, thought of the stars as set in a crystal sphere beyond the spheres of the planets. Today the stars are not thought of as fixed on a sphere, but a hypothetical surface, called the celestial sphere, is set

up onto which all the stars can be projected.

Since it is now known that the stars are at various distances from the earth, and since the galaxies are still more distant, the celestial sphere must be large enough to include all the bodies in the universe. Its radius is therefore infinite in length. The center may be anywhere we wish, but since the earth is so small compared with the size of an infinite sphere, it may just as well be the point where the observer is located. In other words, each person has his own celestial sphere, but it is essentially the same as that of a person nearby, or even a traveler in space. The *celestial sphere* is, therefore, a sphere of infinite size with its center at the eye of the observer, and on which all objects in space seem to be projected.

In a simple system of celestial coordinates, direction only is considered. Distance is not included, as it is not needed at first. Thus the stars are located only by their directions with respect to each other. We may say that two stars are so many degrees apart and talk about their angular distances from each other or from some initial point or points —a bright star, for example.

Two initial points may be determined by the direction of gravity. If a heavy weight is hung on a nearly weightless string, called a plumb line, and hypothetically extended to infinity in both directions, it will intersect the celestial sphere in two points. The point overhead is called the *zenith* and the point underneath is the *nadir*.

The angular distance between two stars, $S_1$ and $S_2$ in Figure 7–2, is defined by the angle between them as seen from the observer at the center, $O$; that is, the angle $S_1OS_2$ = angle $S_1'OS_2'$; or, $S_2OG_1 = S_2'OG_1'$. It is seen that the distances to the stars are not considered. They will seem to be projected onto the celestial sphere at $S_1'$, $S_2'$, and $G_1'$.

The zenith $Z$, the point at the top of the sphere, is located by the upward direction of a plumb line. Similarly, the nadir, at $N$, is located by the downward direction.

*disadvantage - every person has a different celestial horizon*

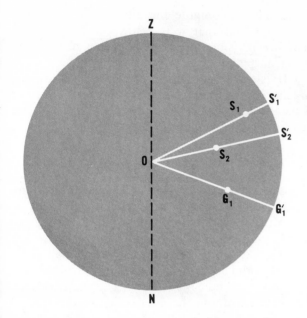

Fig. 7–2  The celestial sphere, showing angular measurements.

## 7.4  The Great Circle — *used alot in Navigation*

Each point on a sphere (actually two points on opposite sides) has one great circle 90° away. A great circle is the largest circle which can be drawn on a sphere. It has the following properties:

1. Its center is located at the center of the sphere.
2. It divides the sphere into equal parts, called hemispheres.
3. Each point on the great circle has a corresponding point on the opposite side of the sphere, which also lies on the great circle. *180° away*
4. It has two poles that are 90° (equidistant) from all parts of the circle.
5. All great circles drawn through the poles of a great circle are perpendicular to it.
6. Only one great circle can be drawn through any two points on a sphere, unless they are 180° apart.
7. An infinite number of great circles can be drawn on a sphere.
8. The shortest distance between two points on the surface of a sphere is measured along the arc of a great circle.

Any circle on a sphere that is parallel to a great circle is therefore smaller. Such a circle is called a small circle. The earth's equator and meridians are great circles. Parallels of latitude are small circles.

### 7.5  Celestial Reference Circles

The zenith and nadir are poles of a great circle called the *celestial horizon*. If great circles are drawn through the zenith and nadir, they will therefore be perpendicular to the celestial horizon and are called *vertical* (perpendicular) *circles*. The zenith and nadir are 90° from all points of the horizon.

Two starting points on the celestial sphere have now been located by the direction of a plumb line. Thus each point on the earth has its own zenith and nadir, and therefore its own horizon. This is because the direction of gravity is different for all points on the earth. Because of the irregularities of the landscape, the terrestrial horizon does not always coincide with the celestial horizon, which is a perfect circle. The sea horizon is more than 90° from the zenith because of the "dip of the horizon" due to the curvature of the earth.

If a camera is loaded with high-speed film, pointed toward the North Star, and the shutter left open for an hour or so (not so long that the film will be fogged), it will be found that the stars trace arcs of circles on the film, as shown in Figure 7–3. These arcs are parts of small circles, which increase in size away from Polaris, the North Star. They are all centered at the north celestial pole.

If a great circle is drawn from the zenith through the north celestial pole and continued completely around the sphere, it will intersect the horizon in two points, called the north point and the south point. This great circle, called the *celestial meridian*, is one of the fundamental circles of astronomy and navigation. It is evident that each point on the earth will have its own meridian concentric with the terrestrial meridian which passes through the terrestrial poles and the place of observation.

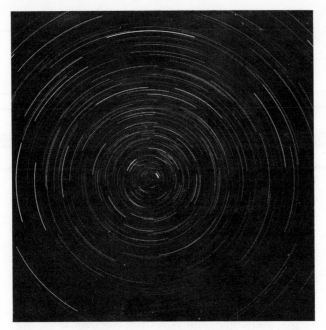

Fig. 7–3   Star trails around the north celestial pole. The bright overexposed object near the center is Polaris. (Yerkes Observatory photograph)

## 7.6   Altitude and Azimuth

Any celestial body can be located by means of two coordinates based on the horizon and meridian as references. One of these coordinates, called *altitude,* is the arc of a vertical circle from the celestial horizon to the object, as shown in Figure 7–4. It is also the smallest angle at the eye of the observer between the celestial horizon and the object. It can be measured by an instrument, such as the surveyor's transit.

Altitude is plus if the object is above the horizon and minus if it is below the horizon. Usually negative altitudes mean that the body is not visible, but refraction by the air bends the light from a body just below the horizon, making it visible even though its true altitude is negative by a small angle. The rising and setting sun and moon appear to be on the horizon, but are actually a little below. Also it

is possible to compute the altitude of a celestial body and find that it is below the horizon and therefore invisible at a time when an observation had been planned.

It is sometimes more convenient to use the angular distance of a star from the zenith instead of its altitude. This is called the *zenith distance* and each is the complement of the altitude:

$$z = 90° - h \text{ and } h = 90° - z \qquad (7\text{–}1)$$

where $z$, the zenith distance, and $h$, the altitude, are the standard symbols.

Altitude is only one coordinate. There are an infinite number of points on the celestial sphere with the same altitude, all lying on a small circle parallel to the horizon. To locate a particular body, a second coordinate is necessary. The angle between the north point and the intersection of the vertical circle through the body with the horizon is called

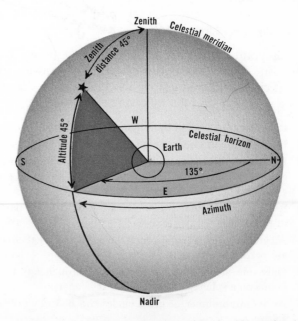

Fig. 7–4   Diagram showing altitude 45° and azimuth 135° of a star.

its *azimuth*. Azimuth is measured as an arc of the celestial horizon from the north point toward the east to the intersection of the vertical circle with the horizon. This angle may have any value from 0° to 360°. For example, north is 0°, east 90°, south 180°, and west 270°. These are the four cardinal points. Southeast is 135,° northwest 315°, and so on.

Sometimes other angles are used instead of azimuth. *Bearing* is the angle between a cardinal point and a point on the horizon. For example, SE = E 45° S, or S 45°E, and so forth.

As seen from a given place on the earth, there is only one point on the celestial sphere which has a given altitude and azimuth. That is, altitude and azimuth uniquely determine a position. If the north point can be determined as described, the two co-ordinates of a star can be determined easily with a surveyor's transit. It is equipped with a horizontal plate, which can be set in the plane of the horizon by accurate bubbles and serves as the horizon which is the altitude reference plane. Zero point of an azimuth scale on the horizontal plate is aligned with the north point, which locates the celestial meridian (hereafter just referred to as the meridian) and serves as the azimuth reference point. (See Figure 5–2.)

However, the horizon system has certain disadvantages. At a given instant both coordinates are different from those for the same object at other observing stations. For example, the sun may be overhead in the tropics, but at the same instant it may be several degrees from the zenith at a station farther north. Also the azimuth and altitude of a body change continually. It is not possible to write a friend to look in a certain position for a planet or a comet, if this system is used, without making complicated computations beforehand.

But there are also advantages of this system which outweigh its defects. The very fact that altitudes and azimuths change continually makes it possible to determine latitude and longitude, provided certain fundamental data are available. This is a basic problem of navigation. Tables of planetary positions for every day of the year are published in advance, giving the data needed. The problems of navigation are too involved for this text, but there are many books on navigation available to the interested student.

## THE EQUATOR SYSTEM

### 7.7  Equator and Poles

Fortunately, there is another system, the equator system, which can be used in any part of the world. And it is possible to convert the coordinates of one system into those of the other through the use of spherical trigonometry. Since the equator system is used on star charts and for the setting of telescopes, it is important that the student of astronomy become familiar with it.

The fundamental points in the equator system are the two celestial poles in place of the zenith and nadir in the horizon system. They are directly above the north and south terrestrial poles, and are therefore in line with the earth's axis of rotation. For an observer at the terrestrial pole, the celestial pole is at his zenith, and the Pole Star is overhead.

If a camera is pointed toward the zenith and the film exposed for 24 hr during the long polar night, each star describes a small circle parallel to the horizon. The great circle 90° from the pole, called the *celestial equator*, is the fundamental circle, and, in this case, coincides with the horizon. The celestial equator is the projection of the terrestrial equator onto the celestial sphere. The apparent motion of the stars, which is due to the rotation of the earth, is called *diurnal motion* (diurnal means daily).

For an observer on the terrestrial equator, the celestial poles are on the horizon and the celestial equator is an east-west vertical circle. All the diurnal circles are perpendicular to the horizon and are bisected by it. Therefore the sun, moon, and all the stars rise and set at right angles to the horizon.

Each star is above the horizon for 12 hr out of each 24-hour day. All the stars are visible from the terrestrial equator at some time during the year.

From the north or south terrestrial pole only half of the stars can be seen, the other half being permanently below the horizon. At intermediate latitudes, the diurnal circles all make angles with the horizon which depend on the latitude of the place of observation. The angles decrease from 90° at the equator to 0° at the poles. They are equal to 90° minus the latitude. Figure 7–5 shows the diurnal circles as seen from the north pole (parallel sphere), the equator (right sphere), and an intermediate latitude (oblique sphere).

The statement that the sun rises in the east and sets in the west is not strictly true. At all latitudes the celestial equator cuts the celestial horizon in exactly the east and west points. Therefore when the sun is on the equator at the beginning of spring and autumn, when its declination is 0°, it rises at the east point and sets at the west point. It can be seen that when the sun is north of the celestial equator, as it is from the beginning of spring to the beginning of autumn, it rises to the north of the east point, describes its diurnal circle, a small circle parallel to the equator but north of it, and sets to the north of west. From autumn to spring, the sun is south of the equator, rises to the south of east and sets to the south of west. The exact directions

of sunrise and sunset depend on both the sun's declination and the latitude of the observing station. Their calculation is a problem in spherical trigonometry.

The reason the days are longer in summer than in winter is that more than half of the sun's diurnal circle is above the horizon from March to September. During the other half of the year, the larger part of the diurnal circle is below the horizon.

## 7.8  Right Ascension and Declination

An infinite number of great circles can be drawn through the poles. From property 5, they will all be perpendicular to the celestial equator. They are therefore similar to the vertical circles in the horizon system. These great circles are called *hour circles*, because they are related to time. (See Figure 7–6.)

Only one hour circle can be drawn through a given point—the sun, moon, a planet, or a star. That is, each body on the celestial sphere has its own hour circle, as it did a vertical circle. The angular distance of a body from the celestial equator, measured along the hour circle, is called *declination*. Declination is defined with respect to the equator and poles as altitude was defined with respect to the horizon and the zenith. Similarly, there is an infinite number of points with the same declination.

Fig. 7–5   Position of diurnal circles as seen from the terrestial pole (parallel sphere), equator (right sphere), and intermediate latitude (oblique sphere).

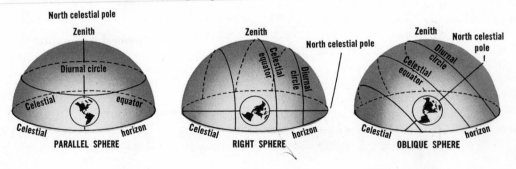

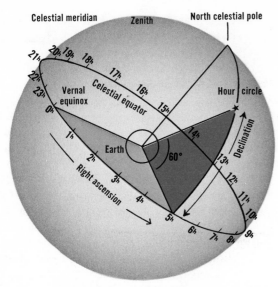

Fig. 7–6   The system of right ascension and declination.

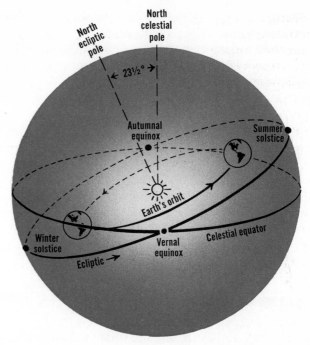

Fig. 7–7   The ecliptic and the celestial equator, showing their intersections at the two equinoxes. The two circles are inclined to each other by an angle of 23½°.

Therefore it is necessary to find a reference point on the celestial equator, and to define another coordinate, as was done with azimuth in the horizon system. The point selected depends on the motion of the sun during the course of one year.

Centuries of observation have shown that the sun seems to describe a great circle as seen from the moving earth. This circle, which the sun describes in a period of one year, is called the *ecliptic*. The word comes from the fact that the sun and moon must be on this circle for an eclipse to occur.

The ecliptic is inclined to the celestial equator at an angle of about 23½°. It will be seen later that this is responsible for our seasons. There are two intersections of the ecliptic and the equator. The one where the sun crosses the equator when it is moving northward in March is called the *vernal equinox*. The other, where the sun crosses the equator moving southward in September, is the *autumnal equinox*. Vernal means spring, and autumnal means fall. Equinox means that the day and night are of equal length. Figure 7–7 shows the ecliptic and its two intersections with the celestial equator.

The vernal equinox is the starting point for the coordinate called *right ascension*. Its right ascension is 0° and, since it is on the equator, its declination is also 0°. Declination is measured in degrees from the equator, plus to the north and minus to the south up to 90° at the celestial poles. Right ascension is measured eastward beginning at the vernal equinox and up to 360°. But since right ascension is related to time, it is customary to measure it in hours, up to 24 hr (written 24$^h$).

The point of highest declination of the ecliptic is +23½° and the lowest is −23½°. The former point is called the *summer solstice* and the latter is the *winter solstice*. Solstice means "sun stands still." Summer begins when the sun reaches the summer solstice about June 21, and winter begins when the sun reaches the winter solstice about December 21.

Spring begins when the sun is at the vernal equinox around March 21, and autumn begins about September 23 when the autumnal equinox is reached.

The right ascensions and declinations of the four principal points of the ecliptic are:

TABLE 7–1

| Name | Right Ascension | Declination |
|---|---|---|
| Vernal equinox | $0^h = 0°$ | $0°$ |
| Summer solstice | $6^h = 90°$ | $+23½°$ |
| Autumnal equinox | $12^h = 180°$ | $0°$ |
| Winter solstice | $18^h = 270°$ | $-23½°$ |

Since $24^h = 360°$, it is easily seen that:

$$1 \text{ hr of time} = 15° \text{ of arc}$$
$$1 \text{ min} = 15'$$
$$1 \text{ sec} = 15''$$

The student is referred to Chapter 8 for illustrations of the uses of these coordinates in star maps.

### 7.9  Sidereal Time

The hour circles are numbered toward the east. As the earth rotates (from west to east), successively numbered hour circles come into coincidence with the celestial meridian, as the celestial sphere appears to rotate from east to west. Thus time and right ascension are related.

If a clock is set to read zero hours when the hour circle through the vernal equinox coincides with the meridian, and if it is rated to read zero hours or 24 hr whenever the vernal equinox is on the meridian, the clock will also read the hours successively as the 1-hour, 2-hour, and following circles cross the meridian. Such a system of time-keeping is called *sidereal time*. Sidereal time can therefore be defined as the right ascension of the meridian.

The angle between the meridian and an hour circle, measured toward the west, is called the local hour angle and equals the time since any point on the hour circle was on the meridian. The hour angle of the meridian is of course always zero. Hour angles measured toward the east are negative.

Sidereal time may be defined as the angle between the meridian and the hour circle through the vernal equinox; that is, sidereal time is the hour angle of the vernal equinox. It is also the time since the vernal equinox crossed the meridian. All these three definitions of sidereal time are identical in meaning.

The hour angle of a star is equal to the difference between the sidereal time at any instant and the right ascension of the star; or, H.A. or $t =$ S.T. $-$ R.A. It is customary for all observatories to keep one or more clocks rated to show the sidereal time. The hour angle of a star can then be computed, if its right ascension is known. Figure 7–8 shows the relation between the right ascension of a star and its hour angle.

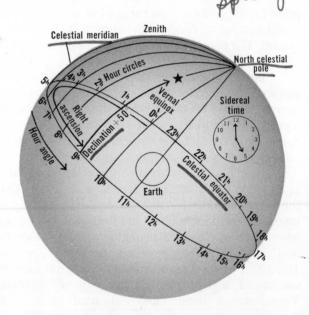

Fig. 7–8  The position of a star whose right ascension is $9^h$ and declination is $+50°$, for sidereal time $5^h$.

►*Example:* Compute the hour angle of Vega at sidereal time $15^h 27^m$. The right ascension of Vega is $18^h 35^m$.

**Substituting** in the formula,

$$t = 15^h 27^m - 18^h 35^m = -3^h 08^m.$$

Vega is therefore east of the meridian. The hour angle may be converted to degrees by the relations given on page 88: $3^h = 45°$; $08^m = 120' = 2°$. Adding, $-3^h 08^m = -47°$.

The sun always moves eastward along the ecliptic and its right ascension is known for any time. Sidereal time, the hour angle of the vernal equinox, is therefore continually changing with respect to *solar time,* which is defined as the hour angle of the sun. The two kinds of time do not coincide except on March 21, when the sun's right ascension is $0^h$.

*Apparent noon* is defined as the time when the sun is on the local meridian. The sidereal time at apparent noon is equal to the right ascension of the sun, as can be seen by substituting in the formula. Because the length of the year is not exactly 365 days, the sun is not at the vernal equinox at the same time by our clocks every year. Table 7–2 gives the approximate sidereal time for noon and 9:00 P.M. for different times of year.

TABLE 7–2
**Sidereal Time at Different Times of Year**

| Date | Noon<br>(Standard Meridian) | 9:00 P.M. | Date | Noon<br>(Standard Meridian) | 9:00 P.M. |
|------|------|-----------|------|------|-----------|
| Jan. 21 | $20^h$ | $5^h$ | July 21 | $8^h$ | $17^h$ |
| Feb. 21 | 22 | 7 | Aug. 21 | 10 | 19 |
| Mar. 21 | 0 | 9 | Sept. 21 | 12 | 21 |
| Apr. 21 | 2 | 11 | Oct. 21 | 14 | 23 |
| May 21 | 4 | 13 | Nov. 21 | 16 | 1 |
| June 21 | 6 | 15 | Dec. 21 | 18 | 3 |

## 7.10 Computing Sidereal Time

It is desirable to be able to compute the sidereal time at night for the use of a star map. To aid the student

in this computation, the following explanation is given, by which the sidereal time may be computed to within five minutes, which is sufficiently accurate for the use of a star map.

►*Example:* Suppose it is required to compute the sidereal time for San Diego at 10:30 P.M. Pacific Standard Time on February 1.

It can be seen from Table 7–2 that the sidereal time increases at a rate of 2 hr per month, or 24 hr = 1440 min in one year. Dividing 1440 min by 365¼ days, the gain is $3^m 56^s$ per day (roughly $4^m$).

In the example, February 1 is 11 days after January 21. At the rate of $4^m$ per day, in 11 days the sidereal time gains $11 \times 4$, or 44 min. Adding $44^m$ to the tabular value for January 21, the sidereal time at noon on February 1 is $20^h 44^m$, and at 9:00 P.M. $5^h 44^m$. At 10:30, $1^h 30^m$ later than 9:00, the sidereal time is $5^h 44^m + 1^h 30^m = 7^h 14^m$. This would be accurate to within a few minutes if San Diego were on a standard meridian. For Pacific Standard Time, the standard meridian is the 120th, $8^h$ behind the meridian of Greenwich, or $3^h$ behind the 75th meridian of Eastern Standard Time.

San Diego is $3°$ or $12^m$ of time east of the 120th meridian and the sun and vernal equinox cross its meridian (the 117th) $12^m$ before they do the 120th. Hence 12 minutes must be added to $7^h 14^m$, and the sidereal time at 10:30 P.M. P.S.T. on February 1 for San Diego is $7^h 26^m$.

*Summary* for procedure in computing sidereal time:

1. Look up the tabular value for the date just before the required date. Use either noon or 9:00 P.M. as desired.

2. Add 4 min per day (4 min/day) for the number of days following the tabular date.

3. Add the interval of time that has elapsed between noon, or 9:00 P.M., and the time of observation.

4. Correct for the number of minutes from the nearest standard meridian, plus if east, minus if west. For daylight saving time, subtract one additional hour.

5. Result: the desired sidereal time for the given date.

If a more accurate computation is required, for example to the nearest second, consult a standard almanac, such as the *American Ephemeris and Nautical Almanac,* published by the U.S. Nautical Almanac Office. Follow the procedure outlined in the almanac.

## 7.11  Meridian Altitudes

It may be desirable to compute the altitude of the sun or other body when it is on the meridian. This requires that the declination of the object be known; also the latitude of the place where the observation is to be made. It is easy to show that the latitude of the place of observation is equal to the altitude of the celestial pole. This is done as follows:

It is necessary first to define the required terms. In Figure 7–9, the latitude, $L$ = angle $ECO$ or arc

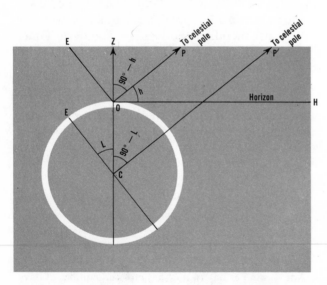

Fig. 7–9  Illustration proves that the altitude of the celestial pole, $h$, is equal to the latitude of the observer, $L$.

$EO$, is the angle between the terrestrial equator and $O$, the place of observation. It is determined from a map or a survey. Neglecting the fact that the earth

is not exactly a sphere, the zenith is on a line from the center $C$ through $O$ projected to the celestial sphere. Even considering the true shape of the earth, this statement is correct if $C$ is on the plane of the terrestrial equator and the astronomical latitude (to be defined later) is used.

The horizon is perpendicular to the direction of the zenith, which is defined by the plumb line. Hence angle $ZOH = 90°$. Also, the polar axis is perpendicular to the equator and angle $ECP' = 90°$. The altitude of the pole, $h$, is the angle between the horizon and the direction to the pole; $h$ = angle $HOP$. Since the celestial sphere is infinitely far away, the lines through $C$ and $O$, which are parallel, will appear to meet on the celestial sphere at the pole.

It is now necessary to prove that the angle $h$, the altitude of the pole, is equal to the latitude $L$. This is a simple problem in plane geometry.

1. The angles $ZOP$ and $ZCP'$ are equal, because $OC$ is a transversal (straight line) cutting two parallel lines. Therefore, corresponding angles, $ZOP$ and $ZCP'$, are equal.
2. $h = 90° - ZOP$, since $ZOP + HOP = ZOH = 90°$.
3. $L = 90° - ZCP'$, since $ECZ + ZCP' = ECP' = 90°$.
4. $L = h$, since they are complements of equal angles.

There is an even simpler geometric proof: $HOP$ and $OCE$ have mutually perpendicular sides. They are therefore equal.

This is a very convenient relation and is used in many different problems of astronomy, navigation, engineering, etc. It can be used to calculate the noon altitude of the sun or the meridian altitude of any other astronomical body.

Let $SZN$ in Figure 7–10 be the meridian from the south point $S$ to the north point $N$. It passes through the zenith $Z$ and the pole $P$. It has just been proved that the altitude of the pole, angle $NOP = h$, equals the latitude, angle $ECO = L$, of the place of observation. Since the direction of the pole is perpendicular to the equator, and that of the zenith is perpendicular to the horizon, angle $EOP = 90°$ and angle $NOZ = 90°$. Also angle $EOZ$ = angle $NOP$

since they are complements of the same angle, *ZOP.* As before, angle *NOP,* which is *h,* is equal to *L,* which must therefore be *EOZ.*

To compute the altitude of the center of the sun or any other body at *A,* angle *SOA* (the altitude) = *SOE + EOA.* But *SOE* = 90° − *L* and *EOA = d,* the declination of the body, which is its angular dis-

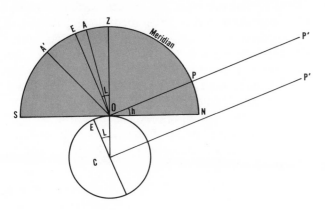

Fig. 7–10   Meridian altitudes of stars A and A′.

tance from the celestial equator. Similarly, angle *SOA′ = SOE − EOA′,* if the body is south of the celestial equator. Writing this relation as an equation:

$$h = 90° − L + d. \qquad (7\text{–}1)$$

If the body is above the equator, *d* is plus; if below the equator, *d* is minus.

▶*Example:*   Compute the meridian altitude of the bright star Sirius as seen from San Diego.

**Solution:**   From a table of bright stars (Chapter 17), the declination of Sirius is −16° 39′. The latitude of San Diego is 32° 45′N. Substituting in equation 7–1, the altitude of Sirius is:

$$h = 90° − 32° 45′ − 16° 39′ = 40° 36′.$$

## 7.12   The Astronomical Triangle   ~~Impt.~~

The equator and horizon systems of coordinates are related by the *astronomical triangle,* where the altitude and azimuth of a star can be determined by computation, if its declination and hour angle are known.

Let Figure 7–11 represent the celestial sphere with its center at *C.* The astronomical triangle is the

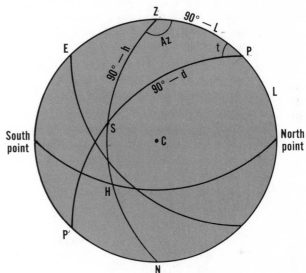

Fig. 7–11   The astronomical triangle.

spherical triangle *ZPS,* where *Z* is the zenith, *P* is the pole, and *S* is any star or other astronomical body. A spherical triangle is so drawn on the surface of a sphere that its three sides are arcs of great circles and the vertices are the intersections of the three sides in pairs. In the case of the astronomical triangle, it can be seen from the figure and the discussion of the systems of coordinates in this chapter, that the three sides are 90° − *L,* 90° − *d,* and 90° − *h,* where *L, d,* and *h* have been defined previously. The three angles are the hour angle, *t,* at the pole; the azimuth *Az* at the zenith, and the third angle at the star, called the *parallactic angle,* which is not used in this problem.

If any three parts of a spherical triangle are given, the other three parts can be found, except in some indeterminate cases, which are not possible in this case. The solution depends on spherical trigonometry.

For the benefit of the student who has studied plane trigonometry, the formulas are given here for two cases. The trigonometric functions are those used in plane trigonometry, and a suitable table of functions can be used for the solution of any problem.

**Case 1:**    Given $L$, $t$, and $d$. To find $h$ and $Az$:

$$\sin h = \sin L \sin d + \cos L \cos d \cos t. \qquad (7\text{-}2)$$

$$\cos Az = (\sin d - \sin L \sin h) \sec L \sec h. \qquad (7\text{-}3)$$

It will be noticed that it is necessary to compute $h$ first, and use the result in the second equation to find $Az$. It is assumed that the latitude is known and that the right ascension and declination of the body can be found in the proper tables and that $t$ can be found from the sidereal time and the right ascension.

**Case 2:**    Given $L$, $h$, and $Az$. To find $d$ and $t$:

$$\sin d = \sin h \sin L + \cos h \cos L \cos Az. \qquad (7\text{-}4)$$

$$\cos t = (\sin h - \sin L \sin d) \sec L \sec d. \qquad (7\text{-}5)$$

It is assumed that the altitude and azimuth have been measured with a surveyor's transit or other instrument.

Equation 7–2 reduces to equation 7–1 if the body is on the meridian.

## QUESTIONS AND PROBLEMS

1. Does each point on the earth's surface have a unique celestial horizon? Explain.

2. A person located at 45°N latitude and 90°W longitude observes a star at his zenith. What would be the altitude and azimuth of the star as observed at the same time from: (a) the equator at 90°W longitude; (b) at 45°N latitude, 90°E longitude; (c) at 45°S latitude, 90°W longitude? **Ans:** (a) $h = 45°$; $Az = 0°$.

3. Draw a circle representing the earth and a concentric larger circle representing the celestial sphere. Show that no stars within 45° of the south celestial pole would be visible from latitude 45°N.

4. What are the altitude, azimuth, declination, and hour angle of the sun on the following dates and local times for an observer at 45°N latitude? (a) Noon, June 21; (b) 6 P.M., March 21; (c) Noon, December 21; (d) Same times at your latitude? **Ans:** (a) $h = 68\frac{1}{2}°$; $Az = 180°$: decl. $= +23\frac{1}{2}°$; hour angle 0°.

5. The right ascension of Sirius is $6^h$ $43^m$. At sidereal time $5^h$ $13^m$, what is its hour angle expressed in time and in degrees? Is Sirius east or west of the meridian?

6. Assuming the sky to be dark and stars visible between 6 P.M. and 6 A.M. standard time, what would be the minimum and maximum right ascensions of stars at the observer's zenith between those hours on (a) March 21, (b) Sept. 21, and (c) Nov. 15? **Ans:** (a) $6^h$ and $18^h$.

7. Compute the sidereal time at (a) 10:30 A.M. on May 30 and (b) 11:30 P.M. on December 10. Assume standard meridian and daylight time for (a), standard time for (b). **Ans:** (a) $2^h$ $06^m$.

8. Compute the sidereal times for the following: (a) 8:00 P.M. P.D.T. on July 5 in Portland, Oregon, longitude 123°W; (b) 7:30 A.M. E.S.T. on December 31 in Pittsburgh, Pennsylvania, longitude 80°W. **Ans:** (a) $14^h$ $08^m$.

9. (a) How much of the meridian is above the horizon? (b) Is this answer the same for all great circles on the celestial sphere? (c) How much of the meridian is between the pole and the zenith at your latitude?

10. Compute the altitudes of Sirius and Vega when they are on the meridian of an observer at 45°N latitude, and for your latitude. Their declinations are $-16°39'$ and $+38°44'$, respectively.

11. Equation 7–1 reads: $h = 90° − L + d$ for computing the altitude of a star. (a) Show that this equation does not hold for stars north of the zenith. (b) Derive the correct formula for stars between the zenith and the pole. (c) Derive the corresponding formula for a star below the pole. Use a diagram.

12. Show that the sides of angles $HOP$ and $OCE$ in Figure 7–9 (see page 90) are mutually perpendicular.

# Chapter Eight

## Constellations and Star Maps

—Perseus and Andromeda.—After a Miniature of the Fourteenth Century, "Liber de Locis Stellarum Fixarum."—Spanish Manuscript.—In the Arsenal Library, Paris.

### 8.1 The Constellations

The first astronomers carved in stone the forms of several well-known and easily identified constellations. Among them are Ursa Major (Big Dipper), Ursa Minor (Little Dipper), and the Pleiades (Seven Sisters). The stars are represented by small depressions in the stone. Several dozen of these rock carvings have been found in France. They are prehistoric, dating from near the end of the Stone Age.

It is not definitely known how the constellations were named. Some of their shapes resemble animals, such as a serpent or a scorpion; but others do not bear any resemblance to their names, such as the constellation Aquarius, shown in Figure 8–1.

It is certain that the first constellations were named by people living north of the equator, since there is a lion, two bears, several dogs, some sea creatures, a ram, a bull, and others; but there is no elephant or hippopotamus. There is, however, a centaur. The giraffe was added later. There is also a gap around the south celestial pole, which is not visible in the Mediterranean regions, where there were no named constellations in Ptolemy's list published in A.D. 150. Southern constellations were

named after the beginning of the seventeenth century. We now recognize 88 constellations in all. They are listed in Table 8–1.

The old star maps, published in the 1800s, had drawings of the supposed creatures and mythological figures in the neighborhood of the constella-

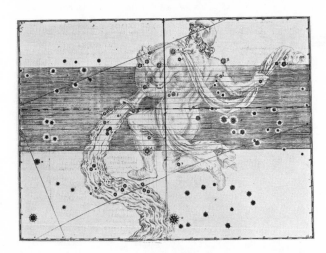

Fig. 8–1 The constellation Aquarius, the "Water Bearer." (Courtesy of the American Museum of Natural History)

## Table 8-1
### A List of Constellations

| Name in Latin[a] | Name in English | Abbr. | Approx. Position | Bright Star(s) (if named) |
|---|---|---|---|---|
| Andromeda | Princess | And | 1ʰ +40° | (Galaxy) |
| Antlia | Air Pump | Ant | 10 −35 | |
| Apus | Bird of Paradise | Aps | 16 −75 | |
| Aquarius | Water Bearer | Aqr | 23 −15 | |
| Aquila | Eagle | Aql | 20 + 5 | Altair |
| Ara | Altar | Ara | 17 −55 | |
| Aries | Ram | Ari | 3 +20 | |
| Auriga | Charioteer | Aur | 6 +40 | Capella |
| Bootes | Herdsman | Boo | 15 +30 | Arcturus |
| Coelum | Graving tool | Coe | 5 −40 | |
| Camelopardalis | Giraffe | Cam | 6 +70 | |
| Cancer | Crab | Cnc | 9 +20 | (Praesepe) |
| Canes Venatici | Hunting dogs | CVn | 13 +40 | |
| Canis Major | Big dog | CMa | 7 −20 | Sirius |
| Canis Minor | Little dog | CMi | 8 + 5 | Procyon |
| Capricornus | Sea goat | Cap | 21 −20 | |
| Carina | Keel of ship | Car | 9 −60 | Canopus |
| Cassiopeia | Queen | Cas | 1 +60 | |
| Centaurus | Centaur | Cen | 13 −50 | (Nearest star) |
| Cepheus | King | Cep | 22 +70 | |
| Cetus | Whale | Cet | 2 −10 | Mira |
| Chamaeleon | Chameleon | Cha | 11 −80 | |
| Circinus | Compass | Cir | 15 −60 | |
| Columba | Dove | Col | 6 −35 | |
| Coma Berenices | Bernice's hair | Com | 13 +20 | |
| Corona Australis | Southern crown | CrA | 19 −40 | |
| Corona Borealis | Northern crown | CrB | 16 +30 | |
| Corvus | Crow | Crv | 12 −20 | |
| Crater | Cup | Crt | 11 −15 | |
| Crux | Southern cross | Cru | 12 −60 | |
| Cygnus | Swan, N cross | Cyg | 21 +40 | Deneb |
| Delphinus | Dolphin | Del | 21 +10 | |
| Dorado | Swordfish | Dor | 5 −65 | |
| Draco | Dragon | Dra | 17 +65 | Thuban |
| Equuleus | Little Horse | Equ | 21 +10 | |
| Eridanus | Po River | Eri | 3 −20 | Achernar |
| Fornax | Furnace | For | 3 −30 | |
| Gemini | Twins | Gem | 7 +20 | Castor, Pollux |
| Grus | Crane | Gru | 22 −45 | |
| Hercules | Hercules | Her | 17 +30 | (Cluster) |
| Horologium | Clock | Hor | 3 −60 | |
| Hydra | Sea serpent | Hya | 10 −20 | |
| Hydrus | Water snake | Hyi | 2 −75 | |
| Indus | Indian | Ind | 21 −55 | |
| Lacerta | Lizard | Lac | 22 +45 | |
| Leo | Lion | Leo | 11 +15 | Regulus |

| Name in Latin[a] | Name in English | Abbr. | Approx. Position | | Bright Star(s) (if named) |
|---|---|---|---|---|---|
| Leo Minor | Little lion | LMi | 10 | +35 | |
| Lepus | Hare | Lep | 6 | −20 | |
| Libra | Balance (scales) | Lib | 15 | −15 | |
| Lupus | Wolf | Lup | 15 | −45 | |
| Lynx | Lynx (bobcat) | Lyn | 8 | +45 | |
| Lyra | Lyre (harp) | Lyr | 19 | +40 | Vega |
| Mensa | Table mountain | Men | 5 | −80 | |
| Microscopium | Microscope | Mic | 21 | −35 | |
| Monoceros | Unicorn | Mon | 7 | − 5 | |
| Musca | Fly | Mus | 12 | −70 | |
| Norma | Carpenter's level | Nor | 16 | −50 | |
| Octans | Octant | Oct | 22 | −85 | (South pole) |
| Ophiuchus | Holder of serpent | Oph | 17 | 0 | |
| Orion | Hunter | Ori | 5 | + 5 | Betelgeuse, Rigel |
| Pavo | Peacock | Pav | 20 | −65 | |
| Pegasus | Winged horse | Peg | 22 | +20 | |
| Perseus | Perseus (hero) | Per | 3 | +45 | Algol |
| Phoenix | Legendary bird | Phe | 1 | −50 | |
| Pictor | Easel | Pic | 6 | −55 | |
| Pisces | Fishes | Psc | 1 | +15 | |
| Piscis Austrinus | Southern fish | PsA | 22 | −30 | Fomalhaut |
| Puppis | Stern of ship | Pup | 8 | −40 | |
| Pyxis | Compass of ship | Pyx | 9 | −30 | |
| Reticulum | Net | Ret | 4 | −60 | |
| Sagitta | Arrow | Sge | 20 | +10 | |
| Sagittarius | Archer | Sgr | 19 | −25 | |
| Scorpius | Scorpion | Sco | 17 | −40 | Antares |
| Sculptor | Sculptor's tools | Scl | 0 | −30 | |
| Scutum | Shield | Sct | 19 | −10 | |
| Serpens | Serpent | Ser | 17 | 0 | |
| Sextans | Sextant | Sex | 10 | 0 | |
| Taurus | Bull | Tau | 4 | +15 | Aldebaran |
| Telescopium | Telescope | Tel | 19 | −50 | |
| Triangulum | Triangle | Tri | 2 | +30 | |
| Triangulum Aus. | Southern triangle | TrA | 16 | −65 | |
| Tucana | Toucan | Tuc | 0 | −65 | |
| Ursa Major | Big Bear | UMa | 11 | +50 | Mizar |
| Ursa Minor | Little bear | UMi | 15 | +70 | Polaris |
| Vela | Sail of ship | Vel | 9 | −50 | |
| Virgo | Virgin | Vir | 13 | 0 | Spica |
| Volans | Flying fish | Vol | 8 | −70 | |
| Vulpecula | Fox | Vul | 20 | +25 | |

[a]Carina, Puppis, Pyxis, and Vela were originally a single constellation, Argo Navis, the ship of the Argonauts, commanded by Jason.

tions which carried their names. Some modern maps have lines drawn between certain stars in a group to help outline the figure which is supposed to be represented, as in Figure 8–2.

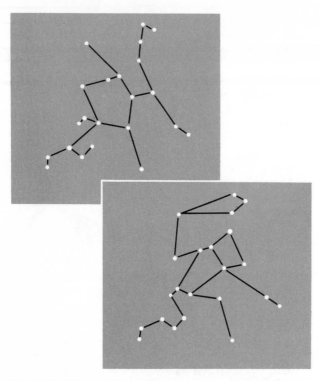

Fig. 8–2 The customary way of representing the constellation Hercules (upper) and a modern re-arrangement of lines to help recognize the figure (lower).

A chart that shows the positions and brightness of the stars is called a *star map*. Ptolemy published one of the first star maps. He used a system of co-ordinates which was based on the ecliptic, not on the celestial equator as is customary today. He also noted in his catalog of stars their positions in the constellations, such as the shoulder of the hunter or the knee of the giant. Hipparchus and Ptolemy also used numbers to indicate the brightness of the stars. The brightest stars were called *first magnitude,* the

next brightest were *second magnitude,* and so, on down to sixth for the faintest stars which could be seen in the dark, clear Egyptian sky.

On the star maps of today, the same system of magnitudes is used, although the system has now been put on a definite mathematical basis, as will be shown in Chapter 20. On the star maps in this book, the brightness is indicated by the size of the filled circles used to locate the stars. The scale is shown at the bottom of each map. Also, star positions are indicated by a grid of lines with scales for right as-cension at the top and bottom and for declination at the sides. Lines connecting the stars in their re-spective constellations are used to help in the iden-tification. Most of the stars in each constellation are designated by Greek letters, with usually the bright-est star having the letter alpha, the next brightest beta, and so on. One exception to this is that in the Big Dipper the stars are lettered beginning with alpha, the Pointer star in the Bowl nearer the pole, and running along the configuration to the end of the Handle. The Big Dipper is a portion of the con-stellation Ursa Major (Great Bear). A group of stars inside a constellation, such as the Little Dipper, the Pleiades, or others, is called an *asterism.*

Sometimes several stars are given the same Greek letter, such as $mu_1$ and $mu_2$ in the Scorpion and $pi_1$ to $pi_6$ in Orion. Sometimes, however, Latin letters or numbers are used, such as *G* in the Tail of the Scorpion and numbers 41 and 43 in Eridanus. All of these and others will be found on star maps. Letters beginning with *R* are used to designate variable stars—those whose light varies either peri-odically or irregularly. In the maps of this book, variable stars also carry the word variable and, if known, occasionally the period of variation is given.

The ancient astronomers paid particular at-tention to 12 constellations along the ecliptic. A zone about 8° on each side of the ecliptic is called the *zodiac* and the 12 constellations are called the signs of the zodiac. They are shown in order in Figure 8–3. About 2000 years ago, the vernal equinox was in Aries but since that time has moved into Pisces. In some terminology, the vernal equinox

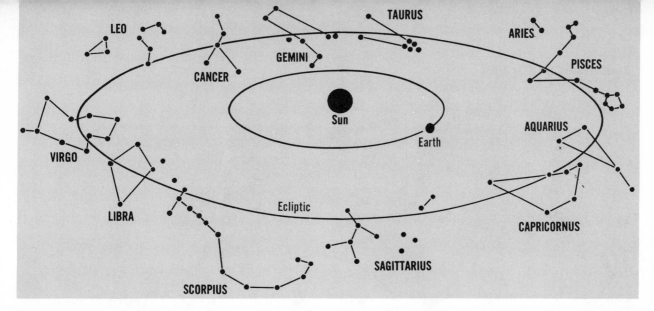

Fig. 8–3   The twelve signs of the zodiac.

is still called the first point of Aries. Because of the motion of the earth around the sun, the sun appears to be in Pisces at the beginning of spring and then moves through the zodiac at the rate of one constellation per month, in the order Pisces, Aries, Taurus, and so forth.

In addition to Greek letters, the brightest stars have names. The brightest star(s) in some constellations are listed in Table 8–1 of the 88 constellations. The brightest star in the sky is Sirius (alpha Canis Majoris).

## 8.2  The Milky Way

There is a very noticeable region in the sky where the stars are more numerous than in any other part. This has long been called the *Milky Way*, because of its whitish appearance. In 1609 Galileo examined the Milky Way and found that it contains great numbers of faint stars which were invisible without the telescope. In the Milky Way, the number of stars increases greatly towards the south, where they are so thick these regions have been called *star clouds*. The sun is a star in the Milky Way system, now called the *Galaxy,* from a Latin word meaning milk. The region where the stars are most numerous and where there are great clouds of gas and dust is now known to be the center of this

great system, containing some 100 billion stars. It is the location of an axis about which the sun moves in a period of about 220 million years.

It is also easily apparent that the stars have a tendency to group together. Such groups are called *star clusters*. Some, like the Pleiades which were known in the Stone Age, are loosely formed, so-called open clusters. Others, like the Great Star Cluster in the constellation Hercules, contain thousands of stars, most of them invisible without the aid of a telescope. They are closely packed in a spherical shape and are called *globular clusters*. The brightest cluster of this type is in the constellation Centaurus and is marked with the Greek letter omega, since it appears to the unaided eye as a faint star of about the fourth magnitude. (See Map 3.)

The Milky Way is shown on the maps in this book as an irregular, shaded area, part of which appears on all the maps. The Milky Way follows a great circle around the sky, which is now called the galactic equator, which is shown as a curved line in Figure 8–4. Also, see Table 8–2 on page 107.

## 8.3  North Circumpolar Star Map

For the beginner, who is just learning the constellations, the first map to use is the map in Figure 8–4,

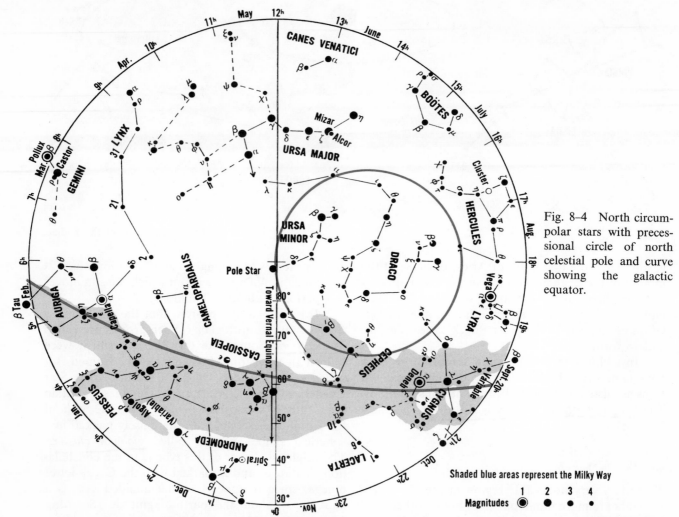

Fig. 8–4 North circumpolar stars with precessional circle of north celestial pole and curve showing the galactic equator.

Shaded blue areas represent the Milky Way

Magnitudes    1    2    3    4

which shows the North Circumpolar Stars. This region of the sky is always above the horizon for observers north of 60° latitude. For observers farther south, the zone of circumpolar stars decreases in size to zero at the equator. For any observer, it has a radius equal to his latitude. For example, for an observer in San Diego in Southern California, the circumpolar circle has a radius of 32¾°, in Chicago, 40°, and so forth.

To use this map in Figure 8–4, the observer should face north and hold the map so the center is in line with Polaris, the Pole Star. Polaris is most

easily located by using the two Pointer Stars in the Big Dipper. They are marked alpha and beta in Ursa Major and on the map are connected by a line tipped with an arrow pointing toward the Pole. Polaris is about 30° from alpha, and alpha is about 5° from beta. Also the length of the Big Dipper is about 30°. These angular distances should give the beginner a good idea of the scale to be used in estimating angles in the sky. Alpha and beta Ursae Majoris, and Polaris, which is alpha Ursae Minoris, are all three about equally bright and are second magnitude.

The next step depends on the time of year and the time of night the observations are being made. Perhaps the best way is to turn the map until the Big Dipper is in its proper place with respect to the Pole Star. The Figure 8–4 map is designed for 8:00 P.M. standard time or 9:00 P.M. daylight saving time. So if the time is 9:00 DST in May, the map is to be held with the top straight up. If the month is November, the map is to be turned upside down. Other months are marked and the map must be turned until the given month is up. The constellations will be in the positions shown for 8:00 P.M.

If the time is not 8:00 P.M. standard time, the map is to be turned further by 15° for each hour. Fifteen degrees equals one hour, as marked on the map. It is to be turned to the left, counterclockwise, if the time is later than 8:00, or to the right, clockwise, if earlier. By checking the months and hours on the edge of the map, the observer will be able to turn it more exactly after the Dipper has been found.

Sidereal time was defined in Chapter 7. If the hours marked on the map coincide with the meridian, the line from north through the zenith, they will show the sidereal time. For example, at 9:00 DST, in May, the 12$^h$ circle will pass from north through the pole to and beyond the zenith. The meridian will then run through the Pole Star and between the stars gamma and delta in the Dipper (Ursa Major), which will be in the north above the pole, and also through the east corner of Cassiopeia below the pole.

In the old maps, the Dipper is shown as the back of the bear with the Handle as the bear's tail. The stars are about second and third magnitudes; but with modern meanings of magnitude, they run from epsilon, the fifth star, at magnitude 1.68 to delta at magnitude 3.44. Translated into light, this means that epsilon is five times brighter than delta. It is an interesting experiment to see if the observer can distinguish between the stars in the Dipper by brightness and arrange them in order, not of position, but of magnitude. Also, there are slight differences in color.

In addition to the seven bright stars, there is

a fainter one close to zeta (Mizar), the middle star in the Handle. These two stars, Mizar, the brighter, and Alcor, the fainter, form an optical double star. They are sometimes called the Horse and Rider and are supposed to have been used by the Indians and other peoples as a test for vision. Mizar itself is composed of two stars very close together, but visible separately in a telescope. It was the first binary star to be discovered. The brighter component of Mizar is also double, as is proved by observations with the spectrograph. So Mizar is at least a triple star, with Alcor a companion star close by. It has been recently discovered that Mizar and Alcor form a seven-star system.

Another important constellation shown on the map in Figure 8–4 is Ursa Minor, the Little Bear, which contains the asterism called the Little Dipper. This asterism contains the same number of stars as the Big Dipper, but the shape is slightly different and the stars are not as bright. The most important star, Polaris, is the last star in the Handle of the Little Dipper; and is near the pole.

Across the pole from Ursa Major is the W-shaped constellation Cassiopeia. This constellation lies in the Milky Way about 30° from the celestial pole. A fainter constellation, Draco the Dragon, winds around the Little Dipper with its tail between the two Dippers. The star marked alpha on the map was the pole star at the time of the building of the pyramids in Egypt. It is between Mizar and the two end stars in the bowl of the Little Dipper. Marked alpha, its name is Thuban, and it was very close to the pole in 2800 B.C. A passage in the Great Pyramid of Cheops was pointed toward Thuban. This astronomical fact helps to date its construction.

Cassiopeia was represented by the Queen sitting in a chair and the constellation is sometimes called Cassiopeia's Chair. A nearby group, Cepheus, represented the King. Their daughter, Andromeda, is also nearby. Andromeda does not have any very bright stars; but inside its boundaries can be found the Great Galaxy, a system of stars similar to, but larger than, the one of which the sun is a part. It is marked "Spiral" on the map in Figure 8–4 and Map 1 on the front end papers. It is very faint, but visible to the unaided eye on a dark sky and appears as a fuzzy patch of light with binoculars and small telescopes.

## 8.4 The Stars of Autumn

Suppose a study of the constellations overhead and in the south is to be made in early October and that the time is 9:00 DST. Then the map in Figure 8–4 will turned until the hour circle marked 21$^h$ is held up toward the zenith. That is, the sidereal time will be 21 hr. This can be checked from the table for computing sidereal time in Chapter 7. Now Map 1 on the front end papers is to be used. Face south and hold the map in such position that the 21-hour circle is on the meridian and the top of the page is toward the zenith, The declination of the zenith is equal to the latitude of the observer, as can be seen from Figure 7–9.

At 9:00 P.M. DST on October 7, the bright star Deneb, at the top of Cygnus (the Northern Cross), will be nearly overhead. The Cross may be identified by its shape, with Deneb the most northerly star of four in the upright and three stars forming the cross-arm, It will be tipped slightly with the north part to the left and the bottom to the right. It lies in the Milky Way where the stars are closely packed together except for a dark area, called the Coalsack, which is in Cygnus. The Coalsack is at the northern end of a long section of the Milky Way, which seems to split near Deneb and continues to below the horizon, where the two parts of the Milky Way seem to join again near the Southern Cross in the southern hemisphere. In a telescope, the star beta Cygni (Albireo) at the foot of the Northern Cross is a double star with two components of slightly different colors.

To the right of the center of Cygnus is the bright star Vega in the constellation Lyra. Vega is the brightest star in the summer sky and is blue or white. The constellation Lyra, meaning the Lyre or Harp, is composed of an equilateral triangle with

Vega as the brightest star. The eastern corner is a well-known double-double star, epsilon. Some people with especially keen vision can see it with the naked eye as two stars. With binoculars two stars are easily seen. In a larger telescope, each star of the pair can be seen as two distinct stars only a second or two apart.

The third star in the triangle of Lyra is zeta, another third magnitude star. It also forms one corner of a parallelogram with beta, gamma, and delta as the other three stars. One object of interest in this configuration is the Ring Nebula, invisible except with telescopes larger than 3 inches in diameter. A nebula is a mass of diffuse gas in space. This one is a luminous, so-called planetary nebula and is illuminated by a star at its center (see Figure 8–5). A planetary nebula is not like a planet, except that is has a disk-like shape which shows some detail, as the figure shows. It is believed that the material in this object was ejected from the central star by a violent explosion, which was first visible in the year 1054. The ring is actually a sphere which appears as a ring from a distance of 1800 light-years. Its color is greenish when seen visually and the central star is not visible except in photographs, because of its low luminosity and blue color. (In addition to a strong green line in the spectrum, there is also a blue line which is not visible to the human eye.)

The Milky Way runs in the same direction as the upright of the Cross; that is, southwesterly in October. Its apparent division into two parts is not real, but the effect is produced by the absorption of light from the background stars by enormous clouds of dust and gas in space.

Lying in and along the Milky Way are several other constellations. The one with the first magnitude star, Altair, is Aquila (the Eagle). This constellation is easily identified by the bright star with a fainter star on each side. Near Aquila in the Milky Way is Sagitta (the Arrow), a faint group of four stars. Forming the third angle of a triangle with Aquila and Sagitta is Delphinus (the Dolphin,

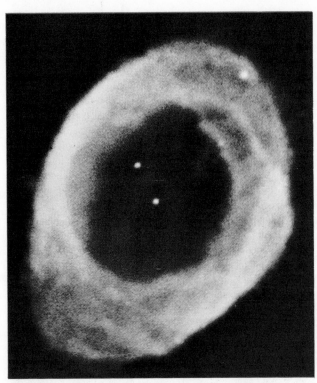

Fig. 8–5  The Ring Nebula, a planetary nebula in Lyra. (Photograph from the Mount Wilson and Palomar Observatories)

sometimes called Job's Coffin), which lies alongside the Milky Way. This little group looks something like a kite with a short tail. The Arrow is aimed toward the east side of Cygnus. Still farther south is an inconspicuous constellation, Scutum (the Shield) and below that, in and along the Milky Way, is Sagittarius (the Archer). This constellation is the most populated area of the sky and is in the direction of the center of our galaxy, which is hidden by thick clouds of dust and gas. The center of the galaxy cannot be seen with optical instruments, but is being probed by radio instruments.

To the west of Sagittarius is Scorpius (the Scorpion), a long, winding constellation, which somewhat resembles the scorpion for which it is

named. The first magnitude star in Scorpius is Antares, which means Rival of Mars. It is one of the largest stars visible to the unaided eye. It is definitely reddish in color, about the same as Mars, but is a little fainter when Mars is seen alongside in opposition. Antares is about 500 times the diameter of the sun; its redness is caused by its temperature, which is about 3000°K lower than that of the sun. Its average density is comparable to a high vacuum obtained in the physics laboratory; that is, about 1 mm of pressure or about 1/1000 of one atmosphere.

East of Antares, the stars of the Milky Way are so thick that they resemble a luminous cloud, which is called the Great Star Cloud in Sagittarius. (See Figure 8–6.)

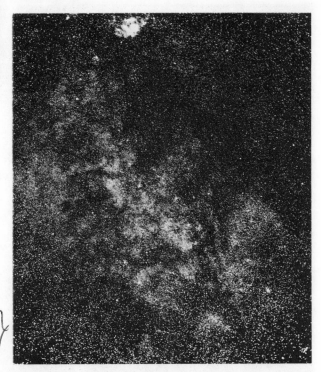

Fig. 8–6  The Great Star Cloud in Sagittarius. (Yerkes Observatory photograph)

West of Lyra are some faint constellations which belong to the stars of summer (see Map 3). There is Hercules, named for the famous hero of mythology. This constellation is composed of four central stars in the Keystone, which forms the central part of Hercules' body. On the western side of the Keystone is the Great Cluster, which is marked on the map. This is a globular cluster which contains so many stars that it cannot be resolved at the center with even the biggest telescopes. It may be barely visible to the unaided eye in a dark sky and should be visible in a pair of binoculars. It probably contains more than 100,000 stars, most of the visible ones being brighter and hotter than the sun, but seen at a distance of over 30,000 light-years. (Figure 8–7) There are other clusters of this type near the southern part of the Milky Way, particularly in Sagittarius, but none are found in the Milky Way itself. They surround the stars of the galaxy, but are seen mostly in the Sagittarius region because of the eccentric position of the sun.

East of overhead in October are some other faint constellations. To name a few: There is Pegasus (the Winged Horse), which has a central square 15° on a side—of which one star is in the constellation Andromeda. (See Map 1.) There is the constellation Pisces (the Fish), represented by two fish tied together by their tails in the old star

Fig. 8–7   The globular cluster M13 in Hercules. (Photograph from the Mount Wilson and Palomar Observatories)

maps. Below Pisces is Aquarius (the Water Bearer), and in the southeast is the first magnitude star Fomalhaut in Piscis Austrinus (the Southern Fish). Between Aquarius and Sagittarius is Capricornus, (the Goat), also one of the signs of the zodiac.

## 8.5 Winter and Spring Skies

Maps 1 and 4, on the end papers, show the stars of winter and spring. Suppose the time is early February and the time 8:00 P.M. The sidereal time on February 7 is $5^h 00^m$ and the brightest stars of the winter sky are near the meridian at the time of observation. A conspicuous feature of the sky at this time is the Winter Triangle. The three stars, the vertices of the triangle, are in three different constellations. Sirius, the Dog Star in Canis Major (the Big Dog), is the brightest star in the sky.

The next brightest star in the Winter Triangle is Procyon, in Canis Minor (the Little Dog), which is only one-sixth as bright as Sirius and only slightly less blue. (See Map 4.) The third star is the decidedly reddish star Betelgeuse, which is about the color of Antares and of about the same brightness. Its light varies a small amount, but is not detectable by visual observations. Betelgeuse is a very large star, but its diameter is not easy to measure. It may be nearly 1000 times larger than the sun and varies in size.

The Winter Triangle is used by navigators for their star fixes because the stars are very bright and therefore easily identified.

Probably the most beautiful and certainly the best-known constellation in the winter sky is Orion (the Great Hunter). It is located near the winter branch of the Milky Way, which is not very bright in this part of the sky, but can be seen as patches of luminosity much fainter than the part visible in the fall. Orion has many hot, blue stars which form an "association." The stars in this association are now thought to be young stars that are using up their internal energy at a relatively fast rate and in a few million years will have lost their ability to

shine. Also the long exposure photographs show a great deal of bright gas and dust in this region of space. (See Chapter 1, Figure 1–1.)

The central part of Orion is composed of three second magnitude stars in line, which represent the belt of the hunter. Extending south from the belt are three fainter stars called the Sword. The central star in the Sword is marked theta on the star maps. It is actually composed of many parts, about six of which are listed, but there are many more faint stars very close to what appears to the eye to be one star. Here is the Great Nebula, which is luminous because it is close to and illuminated by these hot, bright stars. It is easily visible with binoculars and in a telescope shows considerable detail, as shown in Figure 8–8.

Fig. 8–8 The Great Nebula in Orion. (Yerkes Observatory photograph)

The summer solstice is located at right ascension 6$^h$, declination +23.5°, about 15° north of Betelgeuse.

Just north and a little west of Orion is Taurus (the Bull). Its brightest star is Aldebaran, a slightly reddish giant star, whose color has been described as orange. It is a little hotter than Betelgeuse, about 4000°K, and has a diameter about 25 times that of the sun, or 22,500,000 mi. Aldebaran is found at one tip of a V-shaped cluster, called the Hyades, which contains about 200 stars. It is not actually a member of the cluster, but is at a different distance and is not moving at the same speed.

Taurus also contains an even better-known cluster, the Pleiades or the Seven Sisters. There are six bright stars easily visible to the unaided eye, but two or three more may be visible in the dark sky at a mountain station. It is possible that the seventh bright star has faded to below naked eye visibility. There are 250 or more members of this cluster visible in large telescopes. Twenty-five of them are perhaps visible with a good pair of binoculars. The cluster is embedded in glowing gas, which can be detected by long-exposure photography. (See Chapter 20.)

North of Taurus is Auriga (the Charioteer), with the first-magnitude star Capella. This star is sometimes called the sailor's star, since it is visible in late summer in northern latitudes and was supposed to warn sailors of stormy weather to come. Capella has the same temperature as the sun, but it has a diameter about ten times that of the sun and is 100 times brighter. The constellation Auriga consists of a pentagon of naked-eye stars. Of particular interest are two of the three stars in a triangle near Capella. The star at the vertex nearest Capella is epsilon Aurigae, a long-period eclipsing star. It is composed of one super-giant, hot star and an even larger star which is so cool it only radiates infrared light and is therefore detectable only when it eclipses its companion every 27 years. The infrared component is probably at least 3000 times the diameter of the sun and is the largest star known.

The fainter of the other two stars is zeta, which is also composed of two stars which eclipse each other. The period of their motion around each other is two and two-thirds years and the fainter star is about 40 times larger than the other. The eclipses of this pair last about one month, while the eclipses of epsilon last two years!

Directly north of Procyon are the celestial twins, Castor and Pollux, in Gemini. Castor is a well-known double star and has a ninth magnitude star accompanying it, all three visible in a telescope of moderate size. Castor is actually composed of six stars.

## 8.6  Stars of Spring and Summer

Following Gemini comes Leo (the Lion). It consists of a group of stars called the Sickle with the bright star Regulus at the end of the handle. This group forms the forepart of the lion, his head, mane, and front legs. Then come the back and hind legs and finally the tail, which is marked by a naked-eye star Denebola ($\beta$ on Map 4). With a little imagination, this constellation probably looks more like the object it is supposed to represent than any other. When it is visible in the evening sky, it is certain that spring is not far away.

Following the Lion are other, mostly fainter constellations seen in the evenings of spring and early summer. The autumnal equinox is about 15°, almost directly south of Denebola. It is in Virgo (the Maiden), which contains one bright star, Spica (see Map 3). South of the autumnal equinox are Crater (the Cup), and Corvus (the Crow), and north of it is the Little Lion (Leo Minor), which is not on the map because its stars are faint. North of Virgo are Coma Berenices (Bernice's Hair), and Canes Venatici (the Hunting Dogs). Their stars are also quite faint.

One more first magnitude star worth mentioning is Arcturus, the bright star of Bootes (the Herdsman), sometimes called the Driver of the Bears, which are to the northwest. Arcturus was the star selected to open the World's Fair in Chicago in 1933. Its light left the star 40 years earlier at the time of the first Chicago fair; and reaching the earth in 1933, it was focused onto a photoelectric cell which operated relays and turned on the lights of the fair every evening when the sky was clear.

Following Bootes (pronounced with three syllables, Bo-o-tes) is the semicircle of stars called Corona (the Northern Crown). It is easily identified, since it has a second magnitude star on one side. Below Corona is Serpens, the long, winding constellation which runs down to the east of Antares in Scorpius. These constellations are followed by the stars of summer, which were described at the beginning of Section 8.4.

## 8.7  Other Maps

The student who has a telescope and wishes to have more detailed star maps will find them in the monthly magazine *Sky and Telescope* or the bimonthly *Review of Popular Astronomy*. Both magazines print star maps in each issue with instructions for their use and also positions of the sun, moon, and planets, which are constantly changing.

An even more detailed set of maps is found in *Norton's Sky Atlas*, which also lists objects of interest such as clusters, nebulae and galaxies, double stars, and variable stars. A more recent set, still more detailed, is the *Skelnate-Pleso Atlas*, which is published in Czechoslovakia and is available at moderate cost. The newest issue of this set of maps has been done in color to indicate the color-temperature of the stars. An older and still more complete set of maps with magnitudes down to below naked-eye visibility is the *Bonner Durchmusterung* also with a catalog of positions. This set was published in Germany almost a century ago, but has recently been reissued. They show positions of stars for 1855 or 1875 and considerable computation is necessary to bring the star positions up to date.

Finally, the most complete of all (and the most expensive, costing about $2000!) is the *Palomar Sky Atlas*. This is a set of photographic prints of the negatives taken with the Mount Palomar 48-inch Schmidt camera. It shows all stars down to about 18th magnitude taken in red and blue light. Each print has its companion in the other color. It is useful for observatories with large telescopes.

## 8.8  The Planetarium

The planetarium is an instrument with which star images can be projected onto the inside surface of a spherical dome. It is a very useful device for instruction in constellation study and in teaching the system of right ascension and declination. In the modern instruments, the motions of the sun, moon, and planets can be shown. It is also possible to simulate a shower of meteors, which is very spectacular, and to project a comet onto the sky among the stars. There are several large planetariums in the United States and others of smaller size are being installed in schools, colleges, and universities. In many planetariums it is possible to show the appearance of the sky for any date in the past, present, or future.

TABLE 8–2
**Right Ascensions and Declinations of Galactic Equator**

| Right Ascension | Declination | Right Ascension | Declination |
|---|---|---|---|
| 0ʰ | +62.1° | 12ʰ | −62.1 |
| 1 | +62.6 | 13 | −62.6 |
| 2 | +61.4 | 14 | −61.4 |
| 3 | +58.3 | 15 | −58.3 |
| 4 | +52.4 | 16 | −52.4 |
| 5 | +41.6 | 17 | −41.6 |
| 6 | +22.2 | 18 | −22.2 |
| 7 | −5.4 | 19 | + 5.4 |
| 8 | −30.5 | 20 | +30.5 |
| 9 | −46.3 | 21 | +46.3 |
| 10 | −55.0 | 22 | +55.0 |
| 11 | −59.8 | 23 | +59.8 |
| | | 24 | +62.1 |

### QUESTIONS AND PROBLEMS

1. If you wanted to describe the size of an object in the sky to a friend, would it be better to compare it to a familiar object, such as a golf ball, or in terms of the full moon? Explain.

2. Look up the derivation of the word *zodiac* in the dictionary. Why do you suppose this name was chosen?

3. It is often helpful to estimate angular distances on the sky by comparing them with the known angle between familiar stars. Using the angle between the two pointers in the Big Dipper as a reference, estimate the following angles: (a) distance between Polaris and Alpha Ursae Majoris; (b) length of Orion's belt; (c) length of the Northern Cross.

4. Which of the following stars are circumpolar for your latitude? (a) Deneb; (b) beta Cassiopeiae; (c) gamma Ursae Majoris.

5. What day of the year is the vernal equinox on the meridian at 10:00 P.M. standard time for your longitude?

6. Assuming that the map in Figure 8–4 is properly oriented for 8:00 P.M., standard time, how many degrees should it be rotated, and in which direction, for the following times on the same night? (a) 10:40 P.M. standard time; (b) 6:28 P.M. daylight time.

7. In which month is a part of the Milky Way at the zenith of an observer at 40°N latitude, at 9:00 P.M., standard time?

8. Show that the radius of the zone of circumpolar stars is equal to the latitude of the observer. Use a diagram.

9. Draw a diagram, like Figure 8–3, showing the zodiac and the earth's orbit around the sun. Indicate the position of the earth on March 21. Then show the position of the earth on November 21 and explain why $0^h$ on Map 1 corresponds to this date.

10. Show that the declination of the zenith is equal to the latitude of the observer. Draw a diagram.

11. Draw a large diagram showing the orbits of Mercury, Venus, Earth, Mars, Jupiter, and Saturn as a series of concentric circles with the sun in the center. Also draw one still larger circle for the zodiac as in Question 9, but label the right ascensions from a star map. Place the vernal equinox half-way between Pisces and Aquarius at the top of the chart. Then indicate the position of each planet in its orbit based on the following data (as seen from the earth): The date is March 21; Mercury is in Aries; Venus is in Aquarius; Mars is in Leo; Jupiter is between Aries and Taurus; and Saturn is in Sagittarius. Fill in the table:

|  | Aspect | Phase | Rises | Sets | Crosses Meridian |
|---|---|---|---|---|---|
| Mercury | eastern elongation | half | 8 A.M. | 8 P.M. | 2 P.M. |
| Venus |  |  |  |  |  |
| Mars |  |  |  |  |  |
| Jupiter |  |  |  |  |  |
| Saturn |  |  |  |  |  |

# Chapter Nine

## Planet Earth

### 9.1 The Shape and Size of the Earth

It is important to think of the earth as a planet early in a course in astronomy, since it is frequently used as a standard for size, mass, structure, and other things. How does it compare in size with the other planets? Is it the only planet on which life is possible or are there others in the solar system or in orbit around other stars, which are capable of sustaining life?

First of all, what are the proofs that the earth is round? By 2500 B.C. the Egyptians had explored southward up the Nile River beyond what is now Aswan, near the first cataract of the river. By 2000 B.C. the Phoenicians had sailed out of the Straits of Gibraltar and northward to the British Isles. In 300 B.C. Pytheas, a Greek sea captain, had explored northward from Gibraltar. He had noticed that the Pole Star rose higher in the sky as he sailed north. This would be the case only if the earth were round.

Other explorers sailing south along the west coast of Africa noticed that the Pole Star dropped lower in the north and that formerly unknown constellations rose above the southern horizon. Since all believed the earth to be flat, none of the explorers could explain these movements of the stars.

A similar change in the altitude of the sun with change of latitude led Bion, a Greek philosopher, in the fourth century B.C. to predict that the sun should be visible for 24 hr in the summer, if an explorer could go far enough north. This was the first prediction of the "midnight sun."

Today we are all familiar with the fact that the lower part of a ship disappears below the horizon before the upper part does. Also we are aware of the fact that the shadow of the earth, which falls on the moon during a lunar eclipse, is always curved and is the shape expected when the shadow of one sphere falls on another. And, the most convincing proof of all, photographs of the earth taken from great heights in rockets and satellites show the curvature of the horizon very clearly.

In order to answer questions about other planets, the first thing to do is to measure the size of our own earth and to study its composition and construction in order to compare it with other planets within reach of our telescopes. Not only the size, but the exact shape is one of the fundamental facts which must be obtained.

The question now arises: Is the earth a perfect sphere or is it only approximately a sphere?

In about 200 B.C. Eratosthenes, a Greek astronomer living in Egypt, assuming that the earth is a sphere, proceeded to determine its circumference. It was noticed that on the day of the year when the sun was highest at noon, its rays fell directly down a vertical well at Syene in Egypt. On the same day in Alexandria, about 500 mi north, it was seen that a vertical post cast a shadow, which made an angle of 7.2° with the vertical. Since 7.2° is 1/50 of 360°, the number of degrees in a circle, the distance between Syene and Alexandria must be 1/50 of the circumference of the earth. (See Figure 9–1.) The unit of measurement of distance used in Egypt was the stadium, about 1/10 mi in length, though its exact length is not known to us today. The distance between the two places in Egypt was 5000 stadia, which would make the circumference 250,000 stadia or about 25,000 mi—very close to the correct figure as measured today.

From the circumference, the diameter of the earth can be calculated from the familiar formula in plane geometry, $C = \pi D$. The diameter of the earth from Eratosthenes' figures is hence 25,000 mi divided by 3.14159 or 7960 mi.

In about A.D. 30 Strabo, a Greek geographer, deduced that the earth was round and that its circumference was about 18,000 mi. This figure, some 7000 mi too small, was the accepted figure in 1492, and was the distance used by Columbus when he made his famous attempt to sail from Spain to India. It is possible that if Columbus had known the real size of the earth, he might have hesitated to make such a long journey across many thousands of miles of unknown ocean. Perhaps the course of history owes a great debt of thanks to the error of a scientist!

It was shown in Chapter 7 that the altitude of the celestial pole is equal to the latitude of the observer. This provides us with a way of calculating

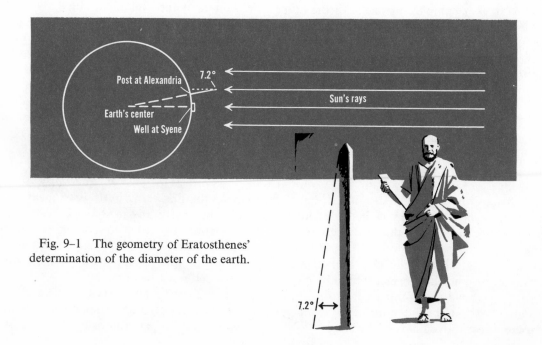

Fig. 9–1   The geometry of Eratosthenes' determination of the diameter of the earth.

the circumference and diameter of the earth from the measure of a north-south arc of a meridian. The measurements are made by a process called triangulation used by surveyors. Without going into the details, the results are as follows:

If the earth were a perfect sphere, the length of a degree of latitude should be a constant value. Or, a change of altitude of the pole by one degree should occur at equal distances on the surface of the earth. For a change of 1° in the latitude, the distance should equal ¹⁄₉₀ the distance from the equator to the pole, and each degree of latitude should give the same result. This is not the case, as Table 9–1 shows.

TABLE 9–1

| At Latitude | Miles per Degree of Latitude |
|---|---|
| 0° (equator) | 68.7 |
| 20 | 68.8 |
| 40 | 69.0 |
| 60 | 69.2 |
| 90 (poles) | 69.4 |

From these figures, and others for intermediate latitudes, the shape of a slice of the earth through the poles can be calculated. This shows that the curvature of the earth varies from place to place on the earth and that the shape of a north-south cut is an ellipse.

East and west measures, however, show that the earth's equator is a circle (neglecting such irregularities as mountains and valleys). In other words, the equator at sea-level is a circle and the earth is an oblate spheroid, a figure obtained by rotating an ellipse about its minor axis.

Also by computation, the diameter of the earth through the poles—the polar axis about which the earth rotates—is 7899.98 mi, and the equatorial diameter is 7926.68 mi. The difference of 26.70 mi divided by the equatorial diameter is called the oblateness of the earth. That is, 26.70/7926.68 = 1/297.

The oblateness of the earth, as it is for all the planets, is caused by rotation. Each part of the earth travels in a circle around the polar axis. To maintain this motion a centripetal (center-seeking) force must be exerted on each part to continually divert it from its natural tendency to travel in a straight line. In accordance with Newton's third law of motion, there is an opposing inertial reaction away from the axis of rotation. A similar inertial reaction would be observed by a person standing on a turntable; the faster the rotation, the greater the inertial reaction away from the center. Since this acts as a real force in the frame of reference of the observer in circular motion, it is often called centrifugal (center-fleeing) force. To indicate that it is the inertial reaction to the centripetal force, it will be referred to as the centrifugal reaction force.

The directions of the gravitational force and the centrifugal reaction force on parts of the earth's crust are shown in Figure 9–2. Any force may be resolved into components, which, when added to-

Fig. 9–2 The centrifugal reaction force, *PA*, and its two components: *PB* opposes the force of gravity and diminishes the weight of an object; *PC* is in the direction of the equator and produces the earth's oblateness.

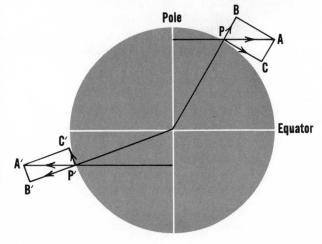

gether, are equivalent to the force they replace. In the case of the rotation of the earth, the centrifugal reaction force, *PA*, may be broken down into a component directed away from the center of the earth, the other at right angles to it; that is, along a tangent to the earth's surface.

---

A vector is a quantity which has size (magnitude) and direction. It can be represented by a straight line with an arrow to represent direction and length proportional to the magnitude of the vector. A velocity, an acceleration, or a force may be represented by a vector. If two forces act in the same direction, their resultant is a force that acts in the same direction and whose magnitude equals the sum of the magnitudes of the two original forces. If they act in opposite directions, the resultant acts in the direction of the larger force and its magnitude equals the difference of the two.

Any vector may be resolved into two vectors, usually, but not always, at right angles to each other. If they act at an angle, the two forces may be represented by the sides of a parallelogram. The resultant acts in the direction of the diagonal and is proportional to its length.

---

In Figure 9–2 the component, *PB*, acts opposite to the direction of gravity and decreases the weight of a body at point *P*. The other component, *PC*, is directed toward the earth's equator in both hemispheres. It is this component that produced the bulge at the earth's equator at a time when the earth was somewhat plastic and the particles of the crust were free to move. The following table shows the magnitude of the outward force of rotation and its two components at four latitudes:

TABLE 9–2

| Latitude | Outward Force on 100 lb | | Vertical Component | Horizontal Component |
|---|---|---|---|---|
| 0° | 0.37 lbs | = 6 oz | 6 oz | 0 oz |
| 30 | 0.30 | = 5 | 4.3 | 2.5 |
| 60 | 0.18 | = 3 | 1.5 | 2.6 |
| 90 | 0 | = 0 | 0 | 0 |

The American satellite, Vanguard, in 1958 showed orbital variations at the poles of the earth. These variations were interpreted to mean that since the earth bulges a little at the north pole and is a little flatter at the south pole, the earth is not a regular spheroid. The amount is only about 50 ft up or down. That is, the earth is slightly pear-shaped. It is thought that this deformation is caused by the greater weight of the antarctic continent, which pushes toward the center of the earth, and by the lack of a continent at the north pole.

### 9.2  Latitude

The fact that the earth is shaped like an oblate spheroid, with minor variations, requires that latitude be redefined. There are several kinds of latitude. If the earth were a sphere, latitude could be defined as the angle between the plane of the equator and the direction from the center of the earth to the zenith. This would equal the number of degrees in the arc of a meridian between the equator and the place of observation.

*Astronomical latitude* is now defined as the angle between the plane of the equator and the direction of gravity. The plumb line does not point toward the center of the earth, but is perpendicular to a level surface, which is tangent to the earth's surface at the point *P* in Figure 9–3. This does not change the proof that the altitude of the celestial pole is equal to the latitude, if the new definition of astronomical latitude is used. This unit is used because it is determined by measures of the altitude of the celestial pole above a horizontal surface. *Geocentric latitude* is defined, as for a sphere, as the angle between the plane of the equator and a line from the center of the spheroid to the observer.

*Geographical latitude* is astronomical latitude corrected for station errors. Since gravity is used for astronomical latitude, it is possible that the plumb line may be disturbed and its direction changed by an irregularity in the density of the earth's crust nearby. The difference between the

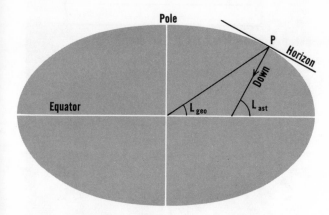

Fig. 9–3 Astronomical latitude ($L_{ast}$) differs from geocentric latitude ($L_{geo}$) because of the oblateness (greatly exaggerated for clarity). Arrow shows direction of gravity.

actual direction of gravity and its direction if the earth were a smooth spheroid is called a *station error*. These errors are small, at most a few seconds of arc.

___

The difference between astronomical and geocentric latitudes may amount to more than 11′ (minutes of arc) occurring at about 45° latitude, both north and south. The equation for computing the difference is:

$$L_{ast} - L_{geo} = + 11' \ 35''6635 \sin 2L_{ast} - 1''1731 \sin 4L_{ast} + 0''0026 \sin 6L_{ast}$$

___

## 9.3 The Earth's Interior

The structure of the earth's interior is studied by means of earthquake waves; this branch of science is called seismology. An earthquake center sends out waves in all directions. One type of wave, the primary $P$ wave, is compressional, like sound waves, and travels through both solid and liquid parts of the interior of the earth. Another type, the secondary $S$ wave, is a transverse wave, like light waves, and vibrates at right angles to the line of travel. The

$S$-wave travels only through solids. The speed of each type varies with depth. The $P$-waves are refracted as they pass from one medium to another of different density. These facts permit the seismologist to study the structure of the interior by means of the elapsed time for each wave to travel from the point of the earthquake to various stations on the surface where they are recorded by seismographs. (See Figure 9–4.)

Fig. 9–4 Paths of earthquake waves from the quake center to seismological observing stations on the surface.

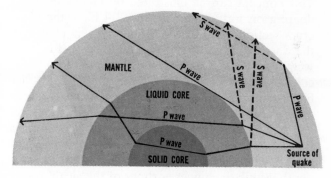

The internal structure of the earth, after many years of study, is estimated to be as follows:

1. The crust is a shallow layer a few miles thick with average density 2.7 g/cm³.
2. The mantle is 1800 mi thick and of average density 5.0 g/cm³. It meets the crust in an irregular boundary, called the Mohorovicic discontinuity.
3. The outer core is liquid, about 1300 mi thick, density 11.0 g/cm³.
4. The inner core is solid, with radius 800 mi, and density 14.0 g/cm³.

The crust is not uniform in density or thickness. Its composition is studied by means of samples of rock from different depths. The rocks in the crust vary in density from 2.5 g/cm³ for the lightest sedimentary rocks to 3.4 g/cm³ for the heaviest. The crust is thinnest under the oceans, which cover more than 70 percent of the earth's surface. The density of the ocean water is slightly more than the density of pure water, which is 1 g/cm³. This is because of the salt it contains. The thickness under the ocean may be as small as 3 to 5 mi. Under the mountains it may be as much as 30 mi.

According to the theory of isostasy, the earth adjusts itself so the weight of all columns of material are the same. The theory assumes that the earth's crust floats on the denser rock of the mantle, which, due to the higher pressure and temperature at that depth, is plastic and flows like a very viscous liquid. This concept can be illustrated by blocks of wood floating on water. Suppose they all have the same cross-section, but vary in height. When placed in the water, each block sinks until it displaces its own weight of water; each is then supported by the column of water beneath it. Since the taller, heavier blocks sink deeper, their supporting water columns are correspondingly shorter. Consequently, the total weight of each block and its supporting column is the same as that of any other. The block rising highest above the surface also extends to the greatest depth. Similarly, higher portions of the earth's crust extend deeper into the mantle to equalize the weight and a mountain has a root of the crust beneath it.

The boundary between the crust and the mantle was named for a Yugoslav scientist, Andrja Mohorovicic. It is called the Moho for short. An American project, called Mohole, was proposed for drilling through the crust under the ocean in an attempt to probe into the mantle. Experimental drillings have been made off Mexico, in the West Indies, and near Hawaii. It is also believed that the Russians are attempting to reach the mantle under the continent, where the thickness of the crust may be as much as 20 mi. Figure 9–5 shows a drawing of the Mohole project and the structure of the crust, the Moho, and the top of the mantle. It has been announced that the American Mohole project was discontinued in 1966.

Fig. 9–5   A schematic diagram of the Mohole project.

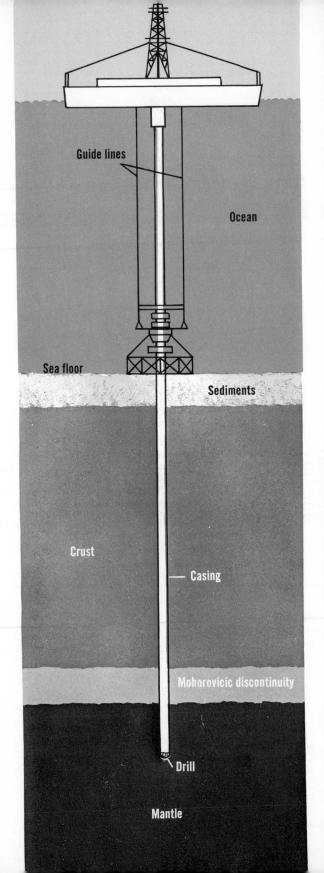

Studies of the crust are far from complete, but indicate that the composition under the continents is mostly of granite, which contains aluminum and other elements. The floors of the oceans are deficient in granite, but contain rocks rich in magnesium. This discovery is contrary to the old belief that the continents were lifted out of the seas. It also appears that the composition of the moon is different from that under the oceans. This is opposed to one theory that the moon originally came from the earth out of the region now occupied by the Pacific Ocean.

Figure 9–6 shows the relative abundance of the crustal elements. This is of course an estimate, since the exact composition of the crust is still unknown.

Fig. 9–6   The estimated abundance of elements in the earth's crust.

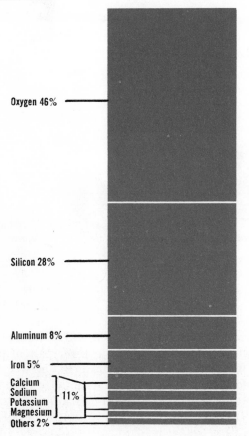

Oxygen 46%

Silicon 28%

Aluminum 8%

Iron 5%

Calcium
Sodium
Potassium    11%
Magnesium
Others 2%

Oxygen, the most abundant element, is in compound with hydrogen in water, and it is also one of the elements in other compounds which make up the rocks. So it is not surprising that the crust is thought to contain 46 percent oxygen.

Silicon is abundant in sand and indeed in most rocks. So its abundance is estimated as 28 percent. This is followed by aluminum and iron, and smaller amounts of all the other elements. Because of erosion, all elements are being washed from the continents into the sea. It is likely that in the near future a project will be organized to recover valuable minerals from the ocean bottom.

The theory of isostasy also helps explain the production of earthquakes. These are movements of the earth due to natural causes, although earthquake waves can be produced by man-made explosions. If for any reason, such as seepage of rainwater or deposits of heavy materials by run-off into the oceans, the crust becomes unbalanced, a sudden movement may restore the balance. Sometimes very large isostatic pressures build up and the shift is very sudden, thus producing very severe quakes. Such earth slippages send out strong waves which may cause a great deal of damage, as happens frequently around the rim of the Pacific Ocean and in other parts of the world.

Before it is possible to make an intelligent guess about the earth's interior, it is necessary to compute the density, the mass per unit volume, of its various parts.

From the dimensions of the earth already given in this chapter, it is easy to compute the volume. But, since density is best expressed in grams per cubic centimeter (g/cm³), the figures for the dimensions, which have been given in miles, must be converted to the metric system. From the table in the appendix, 1 mi = 1.6093 km.

Since the earth is an oblate spheroid, its average diameter can be used as approximately the diameter of a sphere of equal volume. To find the average, the polar diameter is taken once and the equatorial diameter twice. We then have:

Average diameter $= \dfrac{(7899.98 + 2 \times 7926.68) \text{ mi}}{3}$

$= 7917.78 \text{ mi.}$

Multiplying by 1.6093 km/mi, we find

Average diameter $= 1.2743 \times 10^4 \text{ km} = 1.2743$
$\times 10^9$ cm (since 1 km $= 1000$ m $= 100{,}000$ cm
$= 10^5$ cm).

Therefore the volume, from the formula of solid geometry, is

$$\text{Vol} = \tfrac{1}{6}\pi d^3 = \tfrac{1}{6} \times 3.14159 \times (1.2743 \times 10^9 \text{ cm})^3 = 1.0834 \times 10^{27} \text{ cm}^3.$$

### 9.4    The Mass and Density of The Earth

The first determination of the mass of the earth was made in 1774 by Nevil Maskelyne, one of the British astronomers royal. His method was to study the attraction of a mountain, Schehallion, in Scotland, by suspending a plumb line in various positions and at different distances around the mountain. As Figure 9–7 shows, the plumb bob was

Fig. 9–7  Maskelyne's method of measuring the mass of the earth. The plumb bob is deflected from the vertical by the attraction of the mountain.

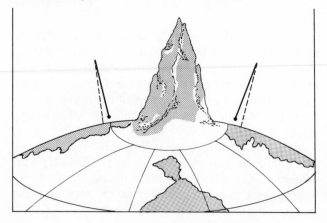

attracted toward the mountain. The deviation from the vertical was small, but measurable. By estimating the mass of the mountain and its distance from the various positions of the plumb bob, Maskelyne computed the mass of the earth. However, because of the difficulty of estimating the mass of the mountain and the location of its center of mass, the result was inaccurate.

Two other more accurate methods are now available. The older was used by Henry Cavendish in England in 1798 and the other by P. von Jolly in Germany in 1881. Since the Jolly balance method is easier to understand, it is given first.

The balance was built of large size (Figure 9–8) and the pans were suspended by long cables. Actu-

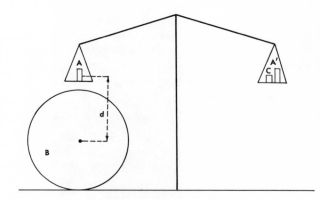

Fig. 9–8  A schematic diagram of the Jolly balance method of determining the mass of the earth.

ally (although not shown in the figure), four pans were used, one with a short cable and the other with a long cable on each side. If the system was in balance and two equal masses $A$ and $A'$ were placed in each of either the upper or lower pair of pans, there would again be a balance. But if weight $A$ was placed in a lower pan and $A'$ in the opposite upper pan, $A$ would be more strongly attracted by the earth than $A'$ and the system would be out of balance by a small amount. A small weight in the upper pan would restore the balance. Suppose this had been done and that the system was in balance.

Next, a large mass of several tons was placed just below the lower pan. The attraction between $A$ and the large mass $B$ upset the balance obtained before. This attraction was again balanced by placing a small weight $C$ in the upper pan. The attraction of the earth on mass $C$ equaled the attraction of mass $B$ on mass $A$. Equating these two attactions:

$$G \frac{M_A M_B}{d^2} = G \frac{M_C M_E}{R^2} \qquad (9-1)$$

from which
$$M_E = \frac{M_A M_B}{M_C} \cdot \frac{R^2}{d^2} \qquad (9-2)$$

where $M_A$, $M_B$, and $M_C$ are the three masses, $M_E$ is the mass of the earth, $d$ is the distance between the centers of masses $A$ and $B$, and $R$ is the distance from $C$ to the center of the earth. The three masses and the two distances are known and the mass of the earth can be computed.

A more accurate mass of the earth can be obtained by the Cavendish experiment. Here a pair of small masses is suspended from a very fine wire, as shown in Figure 9–9. The deflection of the small masses toward a pair of heavy ones is measured by the torsion (twist) of the wire. The mass of the earth can be deduced from the masses and the amount of torsion.

The value of the mass of the earth accepted today is $5.977 \times 10^{27}$ g or $5.977 \times 10^{21}$ metric tons of 1 million grams each, or 2200 lb per metric ton. The uncertainty is 4 in the third decimal place.

From the mass and the volume given previously, the density of the earth is:

$$\text{density} = \frac{5.977 \times 10^{27} \text{ g}}{1.0834 \times 10^{27} \text{ cm}^3} = 5.52 \text{ g/cm}^3. \quad (9-3)$$

This is the average density, since it is based on the volume and mass of the entire earth.

Compare this figure for the average density with the density of some common substances: water, 1 g/cm³; rock, about 3 g/cm³; copper, 8.9 g/

Fig. 9–9   The Cavendish torsion balance method of determining the mass of the earth.

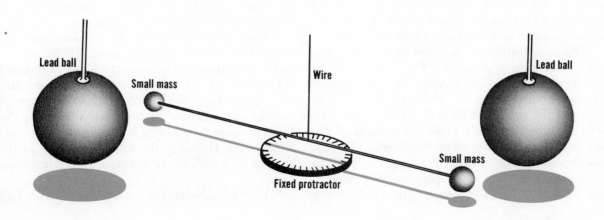

cm³; lead, 11.3 g/cm³; mercury, 13.6 g/cm³. It is obvious that, since the crust has a density between that of rock and water, there must be material inside the earth which has a density greater than average to compensate for the lighter crust.

The high density at the center of the earth may be assumed to be the result of pressure from above. Since the crust is composed of sea water of density slightly greater than 1.0 g/cm³, and rock, its average density is assumed to be about 2.7 g/cm³. The density at the top of the mantle is about 3.5 g/cm³ at the Moho and increases to 5.5 g/cm³ at its inner boundary some 1800 mi below the crust. It is thought to be composed of basic rocks containing large quantities of silicates.

The most probable composition of the outer core is liquid iron; that of the inner core is still unknown. The densities are 11.0 g/cm³ and 14.0 g/cm³, respectively. The body of the earth responds to tides as the oceans do, but the amount is much less due to its rigidity. At the time of the highest spring tides, the surface rises about nine inches. From this it is estimated that the earth is almost perfectly elastic, although its rigidity is greater than that of steel.

Pressures increase from an estimated 12,000 lbs/in² (6 tons/in²) at the bottom of the Pacific Ocean to 50 tons/in² at a depth of 20 mi in the crust. At the base of the mantle, the pressure is estimated to be 10,000 tons/in², and at the center of the earth, 25,000 tons/in². Estimates of the central temperature vary so much that it can be said that the temperature at the center is still unknown.

The temperature of the crust increases downward at the rate of about 1.8°F for every 100 ft. Heat flows from the core through the solid mantle and crust, but since the conductivity is very low, cooling of the core must be at a very low rate. Calculations show that only about 20 percent of the heat in the crust comes from the interior. The remainder comes from radioactive elements, such as uranium and thorium, that spontaneously disintegrate through a chain of various other radioactive elements, such as radium and radon gas, finally becoming stable lead. During this process some of the mass is converted to heat.

The age of the earth can be estimated in several ways. There is, of course, the rate of deposit of materials in the oceans from erosion of the continents. Probably a more accurate estimate is from the above-mentioned decay of radioactive elements. The half-life of an element is the length of time it takes for one-half of its atoms to decay. The half-life of uranium is 4.5 billion years; thorium, 13.9 billion, and radium, 1620 years. While investigations by different methods give quite a variety of results, the probable age of the earth is now estimated at around 5 billion years.

## 9.5 The Atmosphere

The "ocean of air," the atmosphere, around the earth can be studied by a variety of methods. The oldest method was that of taking samples from different levels up to the highest mountain which could be climbed. The next method was by balloons, both captive and free. Free balloons are sent up regularly from weather stations to determine the direction and velocity of winds. Manned balloons have gone up to about 15 mi. Free balloons can be equipped with radio apparatus to help in locating them when they come down. They have been sent up to about 19 mi with equipment for taking samples of air and for making records of radiation, temperature, and other conditions at various levels.

Information about the extent of the atmosphere comes from meteor trails to about 100 mi or more and by triangulation of northern lights (auroras) to about 600 mi. Most recently satellite launchings have given more data, including the fact that the atmosphere extends farther from the earth than formerly thought and that it mingles with the solar atmosphere. However, the density is so low at 1000 mi that it is difficult to say where the atmosphere ends.

For convenience, the atmosphere is divided into

layers and there are many systems of classification. Only the most important layers will be discussed here and the student is referred to advanced texts on meteorology for details.

The lowest layer is called the *troposphere*. (See Figure 9–10.) This layer is most important to life on the earth, since it contains all the elements necessary to support life and because nearly all the weather is determined by it. It extends to five miles above sea level at the poles and ten miles at the equator. The rotation of the earth may be the cause of this difference, since rotation causes flattening of the air mass as well as the central mass of the earth. It may be that the seasons with their different temperatures also affect the height of the troposphere.

The pressure at the bottom of the troposphere averages 14.7 lbs/in$^2$; and the density of air at sea level is about $\frac{1}{800}$ that of water. The density varies with pressure, because air is compressible. There are about $2.6 \times 10^{19}$ molecules per cubic centimeter at sea level in the troposphere.

The composition of the troposphere is: nitrogen 78 percent, and oxygen 21 percent. Water vapor, carbon dioxide, argon, neon, and so forth make up the remaining 1 percent. Smog is not considered part of the true atmosphere, because it is composed of solid particles. Moist air contains about 2 percent of water vapor by weight.

In the upper part of the troposphere are streams of high-speed particles. Westerly winds, called *jet streams,* have velocities which at times reach 300 mi per hour. Discovered accidentally during World War II, they are now both useful and bothersome to long distance air travel. If a plane is eastbound, it is advantageous to fly in the jet stream, which adds to the plane's velocity. Westbound planes should fly at levels which avoid these contrary winds.

It has been discovered that jet streams are associated with the air masses in the lower atmosphere. When cold air masses move south, the jet streams move south also and mark the boundary between masses of cold and warmer air. They have been called the heat exchangers for the world's weather. If the air did not circulate between the equator and the poles, one would get hotter and the other colder. The jet streams equalize them.

The theory was once held that hot air rose above the equator and moved gradually to the poles where it cooled and then descended. Now it is believed that cold air from the north pole moves south high in the troposphere and the currents of the

Fig. 9–10 The important layers of the earth's atmosphere. The heights are not to scale.

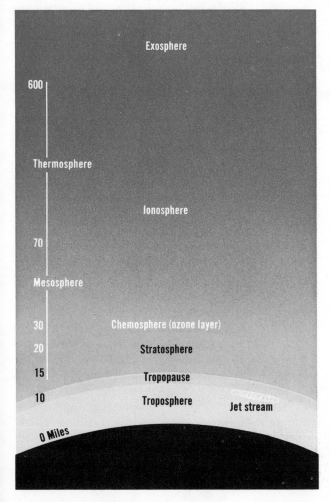

troposphere and stratosphere mix. High-speed westerly winds blow along gaps in the upper troposphere, producing the polar front jet. There is also a southern jet stream, which is not as high or fast as the polar jet. The polar jet blows over the densely populated regions of the earth where they are accessible to commercial aviation during most of the year. However, in summer this stream moves north with the polar front and cannot be used by aviators.

Jet streams may also determine the location and severity of typhoons and hurricanes. Study of these streams, therefore, may be of great help in the prediction of destructive storms, and also help decide whether the earth is getting colder or warmer.

The average temperature at the bottom of the troposphere is about 56°F, although temperatures well over 100°F and down to −125°F have been recorded. At the top, the temperature has dropped to about −85°F. The upper boundary of the troposphere is marked by the *tropopause,* a thin layer of somewhat higher temperature, which makes it possible for a pilot to determine when he has reached that level by reading a thermometer on the outside of his plane.

The layer just above the troposphere is the *stratosphere,* which extends upward to about 20 mi. Here the temperature is fairly constant at about −65°F, except in the ozone layer, where it is near +32°F. Its low density makes it difficult for clouds and storms to develop. Therefore the stratosphere has little effect on the weather except at its lower levels where air currents mix with those of the troposphere to form the jet streams.

Above the stratosphere is the *ionosphere,* which extends upward from about 20 mi to over 500 mi. This layer is named from the great number of ions, which are present at that altitude. An ion is a remnant of an atom or molecule after an electron has been removed, or to which an extra electron has been added. The former is therefore positively charged and the latter has an excess negative charge. The energy required to ionize the nitrogen and oxygen atoms is supplied by the more energetic portion of the solar radiation. The energy of the photons is inversely proportional to their wavelengths and only the shorter wavelengths (gamma rays, X rays, and short ultraviolet rays) have enough energy to remove electrons. Many free electrons are present in the ionosphere, the electron density ranging from some 10,000 electrons per cubic centimeter at the bottom to about 1 million in the middle.

Another process, the splitting of oxygen molecules into atoms, requires less energy and absorbs the long ultraviolet wavelengths. The free oxygen atoms unite with the diatomic (two-atom) oxygen molecules to form ozone, a molecule of three oxygen atoms. This results in an ozone layer (also called the *chemosphere*) beginning in the stratosphere at about 15 mi altitude and extending into the ionosphere. This layer is very beneficial to animal life, because it converts the remaining ultraviolet light from the sun into harmless heat (infrared) rays. It therefore protects us from too much sunburn.

The lowest layer of the ionosphere is also called the *mesosphere,* meaning middle sphere. Here the temperature is about 32°F at the bottom, rises to perhaps 170°F and drops to about −85°F at the top.

The pressure decreases very rapidly above the stratosphere. One-half the mass of the atmosphere is below 3.5 mi. At 60 mi it is only $\frac{1}{400,000}$ the density at sea level. The number of particles per cubic centimeter here is $7 \times 10^{13}$.

The Kennelly-Heaviside layer is another useful layer of the ionosphere. Radio waves are reflected from this layer. It is further divided into levels named D, E, $F_1$, and $F_2$. They reflect radio wavelengths longer than about 17 m and make long-range radio communication possible. Radio waves can travel around the earth by successive reflections alternately between the ocean or the ground and the ionized layers. Wavelengths shorter than 17 m, however, penetrate the ionosphere and make possible the reception of short radio waves from space.

The ionosphere is not stationary, but moves up and down because of the solar influence. The D-layer at about 50 mi reflects the radio broadcast band, the E-layer at 75 mi turns back the short waves, and the F-layers, which vary from about 120 mi by day and 200 mi by night, also turn back short waves. Wind velocities, studied by meteor trails and aurora curtains, are estimated at about 100 mi per hour at 50 mi to over 1000 mi per hour at 400 mi. The temperature is above 2000°F. The hot layer at the top of the ionosphere is sometimes called the *thermosphere.*

In addition to the light of the moon and bright stars, the night sky glows with the faint light of unresolved stars. Also the atoms and molecules store up energy during the day and radiate it at night. More spectacular are the auroras—luminous bands and streamers of light that sporadically appear over the northern and southern parts of the earth. There is also a permanent aurora, which radiates in the infrared region of the spectrum. Auroral streamers do not exist below 60 mi and curtains have been triangulated up to about 600 mi. They are therefore confined to the ionosphere. Figure 9–11 is an example of a bright aurora with streamers.

The topmost layer of the atmosphere is called the *exosphere,* or, freely translated, the escape sphere. The lightest atoms, particularly hydrogen and helium, have velocities greater than the velocity of escape, which is just under 7 mi/sec at the earth's surface. The helium is escaping from the atmosphere at about the rate it is being released from natural gas wells in the crust.

The satellites launched since 1957 have given much information about the ionosphere and exosphere and also permitted the discovery of the Van Allen radiation belts. These belts are almost certainly produced by radiation from the sun and vary considerably in height and intensity with the sunspot cycle. They were discovered in 1958 during the IGY when the sun was extremely active. Later they decreased to about one-fifth their 1958 intensity during the following solar minimum. There is a region near the poles where no radiation belts exist. It is through these "escape cones" that astronauts

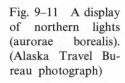

Fig. 9–11   A display of northern lights (aurorae borealis). (Alaska Travel Bureau photograph)

are expected to be launched to the moon.

The radiation belts consist mostly of a mixture of electrons and protons, which is called plasma. Dr. Van Allen believes that the belts are caused by streams of plasma particles from the sun. As the plasma reacts with the earth's magnetic field, a shower of charged particles is produced.

At the end of 1961 a new picture of the structure of the atmosphere was announced by Robert Jastrow, director of the theoretical division of the National Aeronautics and Space Administration (NASA) at the Goddard Space Flight Center in Greenbelt, Maryland. This was based on a new discovery of a thick layer of helium gas surrounding the ionosphere and extending to 1500 mi. The discovery of this helium zone came originally from France. Data from Explorer VIII confirmed it.

The distribution of the various gases in Jastrow's proposed structure of the atmosphere is as follows:

nitrogen and oxygen to 72 mi;

oxygen to 600 mi;

newly discovered helium layer from 600 to 1500 mi;

hydrogen to 6000 mi;

interplanetary gas and particles of solar origin beyond 6000 mi.

## QUESTIONS AND PROBLEMS

1. Give two reasons why a person's weight at the North Pole would differ from his weight on the equator. Where on the earth's surface would he weigh the most?

2. When a rock is whirled on a string, it pulls outward on the string, away from the center of rotation. This outward force would break the string if whirled fast enough. (a) Explain in terms of Newton's laws; (b) Describe the motion of the rock, if the string breaks.

3. Describe the seasons on the earth if (a) its axis were perpendicular to the plane of the orbit and (b) if the axis were in the plane of the orbit, but

remained parallel to itself in space.

4. Suppose the earth were shaped like a football with the poles at the two ends. At what locations on the surface would there be (a) the smallest number and (b) the greatest number of miles per degree of astronomical latitude.

*5. Compute your approximate geocentric latitude and compare it with your geographic latitude.

*6. Using the diameters of the earth through the poles and the equator, calculate the eccentricity of a section through the poles. Draw a figure. **Ans:** 0.08.

7. About what percentage of the earth's crust is composed of metals?

8. What are two possible sources of error in estimating the age of the earth from the rate of deposition of erosion materials?

9. Compare the advantages and disadvantages of digging a Mohole on land or on the ocean.

10. Why does removing an electron from an atom make it positively charged?

11. Why are ions not produced in the earth's atmosphere below 20 mi?

12. If the temperature of the earth increased uniformly with depth from the surface to the center, compute the central temperature. Assume $T = 0°C$ at the surface. Is your answer reasonable? Explain.

13. (a) How does the height of the troposphere vary with location on the earth? (b) The mean atmospheric pressure at sea level is about the same over the entire surface of the earth. Is this consistent with the variation in the height of the troposphere?

14. In the Jolly balance experiment, compute the mass of $C$, if mass $A$ is 1 kg, mass $B$ is one metric ton, and their distance apart, $d$, is 10 ft. **Ans:** $10^{-6}$ g.

15. Explain why an object dropped from a high tower on the equator will strike the earth slightly east of the base of the tower.

# Chapter Ten

# Time and Position

## 10.1 Latitude and Longitude

The determination of time is one of the major problems of astronomy. Navigation, whose major problem is the determination of position, depends on astronomy for accurate time. The Royal Greenwich Observatory was established in England, near London, for the express purpose of determining time and the accurate positions of stars, the sun, the moon, and the planets for use in navigation.

The position of a place on the earth requires calculation of its latitude and longitude. If both are known, the location is uniquely determined.

Astronomical latitude was defined in Chapter 9 as the angle between the plane of the terrestrial equator and the direction of gravity. The celestial meridian is that great circle through the celestial poles and the zenith of a given place. The terrestrial meridian is one-half of a great circle concentric with the celestial meridian, but on the earth itself. Since all celestial meridians converge at the celestial poles, so also the terrestrial meridians pass through the terrestrial poles, which are on the earth under the celestial poles. The meridian through Greenwich, called the prime meridian, was selected as the fundamental meridian from which longitude is meas-

ured. Thus *longitude* is defined as the angle between a given meridian and the prime meridian through Greenwich.

For example, since the longitude of San Diego is 117°, the angle between its meridian and the prime meridian is 117°. This angle may be measured either as an angle at the pole or as an arc of the equator. Longitudes east or west of Greenwich are measured up to 180°. The longitude of Rome is 12° 5′ E. New York is 74° 0′ W. There is no point on the earth except New York whose longitude is 74° 0′ W and latitude 40° 25′ N. Fig. 7–1 shows the location of a point at latitude 40°N, longitude 100°W.

It has been shown in Chapter 7 that the altitude of the pole is equal to the astronomical latitude of the place of observation. This suggests a simple way of determining latitude. However, there is no bright star exactly at the pole, so latitude cannot be determined directly. But it is possible to determine the altitude of Polaris by measurement of two positions and use the average altitude as the altitude of the pole and hence the latitude. For this observation, Polaris or any other star in the neighborhood of the pole, must be observed at intervals of exactly 12 hr, once on each side of the pole. It is easier to make the observations when the star is on the meridian. Polaris is bright enough to be seen when the sky is not perfectly dark. Table 10–1 gives the declination and distance of Polaris from the pole for various dates.

TABLE 10–1
**Declination of Polaris**

| Date | Declination | Polar Distance | Date | Declination | Polar Distance |
|------|-------------|----------------|------|-------------|----------------|
| 1900 | 88°46′ | 1°14′ | 1960 | 89°05′ | 0°55′ |
| 1910 | 88 50 | 1 10 | 1970 | 89 08 | 0 52 |
| 1920 | 88 53 | 1 07 | 1980 | 89 11 | 0 49 |
| 1930 | 88 56 | 1 04 | 1990 | 89 14 | 0 46 |
| 1940 | 88 59 | 1 01 | 2000 | 89 17 | 0 43 |
| 1950 | 89 02 | 0 58 | 2010 | 89 20 | 0 40 |

The reason for the change will be discussed later in this chapter.

## 10.2  Effect of Refraction

There is one correction which must be made to the observed altitude. The air above the earth refracts the light from the star (see Chapter 3) in such a way that the star appears to be higher in the sky than it would be if the earth had no atmosphere. The amount of refraction, and therefore the amount of correction necessary, depends on the altitude. The change of refraction with altitude is shown in Table 10–2.

TABLE 10–2
**Refraction at Various Altitudes**

| Altitude (degrees) | Refraction (min of arc) | Altitude (degrees) | Refraction (min of arc) |
|--------------------|-------------------------|--------------------|-------------------------|
| 0° | 34′ 50″ | 50° | 0′ 48.3″ |
| 5 | 9 45 | 60 | 33.2 |
| 10 | 5 16 | 70 | 20.9 |
| 20 | 2 37.0 | 80 | 10.2 |
| 30 | 1 39.5 | 90 | 0.0 |
| 40 | 1 08.6 | | |

Refraction increases approximately as the secant of the zenith distance. It also depends on temperature and barometric pressure. For a more complete table of refraction, an advanced text on navigation or the tables in *Bowditch's American Practical Navigator* should be consulted. The corrections should be applied separately for all observations.

## 10.3  Meridian Altitudes

Formula 7–1 gives the relation between altitude and declination of a star and the latitude of the place of observation for stars on the meridian south of the zenith. This formula can be restated to find the latitude by a single observation, as follows:

$$L = 90° + d - h. \qquad (10\text{–}1)$$

The altitude, $h$, must be corrected for refraction before the computation of the latitude is made.

For a star between the zenith and the pole, a similar formula is:

$$L = h + d - 90°. \qquad (10\text{–}2)$$

For a star below the pole

$$L = 90° + h - d. \qquad (10\text{–}3)$$

Thus the easiest and most accurate way of determining astronomical latitude is by observing the altitudes of stars as they cross the meridian. Geographic latitude requires a slight correction for station errors. Of course the declinations must be known from the *American Ephemeris and Nautical Almanac* or some other table of star positions. The astronomical transit or meridian circle (see Chapter 5) will show a difference of latitude of two stations only about 10 ft apart.

▶*Sample Problem:* On November 26, 1965, at 6:00 P.M., the altitude of Polaris was measured at 33° 40.0′ and on November 27, 1965, at 6:00 A.M. its altitude was observed to be 31° 52.9′. In both cases the star was on the meridian. What was the latitude of the place of observation and what was the declination of Polaris?

**Solution:**   Interpolating from Table 10–2, for altitude 33.7° the refraction is 1′ 28.1″ or 1.5′. For 31.9° it is 1′ 33.7″ or 1.6′. The corrected altitudes are 33° 38.5′ and 31° 51.3′. The mean is 32° 44.9′, which is the latitude.

The polar distances of the star are the differences of their altitudes from the mean or 0° 53.6′. This is easily shown from a figure. The declination equals 90° minus the polar distance or 89° 6.4′. This can be checked from Table 10–1, which gives 89° 6.5′ for the average between 1960 and 1970.

▶*Sample Problem:* Sirius was observed on the meridian at the observatory of the preceding problem on November 26, 1965. The position of Sirius was: R.A. 6$^h$ 41$^m$; Decl. −16°36′. What was the latitude of the observatory if the star's measured altitude was 40° 40′?

**Solution:**   Correct the measured altitude for refraction from the table. Since the declination and altitude are given only to the nearest minute, use 1′ from the table for the refraction. Hence the corrected altitude was 40° 39′.

**Substituting** in the formula, $L = 90° + d − h$,

$$L = 90° + (−16° 36′) − 40° 39′ =$$

$$90° − 16° 36′ − 40° 39′ = 90° − 57° 15′ = 32° 45′$$

as in the preceding problem. The student is advised to draw a figure and check the results.

## 10.4   Timekeepers

The determination of the other coordinate, longitude, is based on the relation between time and longitude, which it is now necessary to consider.

Time is the measure of the instant when something happens or it is the interval between two events. For example, it is noon when the sun is highest in the sky. Or, it is 8:00 A.M., four hours before noon. In this chapter it will be assumed that time is so familiar that it is not necessary to define it carefully, but it is desirable to show how time is determined and how it is related to the problem of determining one's position on the earth. Today, time can be obtained by observation to a small fraction of a second and it may be indicated by clocks which have an accuracy of a millisecond—1/1000 of a second—or less.

Time has been kept by astronomers for thousands of years. At first its determination and the time services were in the hands of the soldiers or of the priests, but later was given to astronomers in their observatories, because they had the instruments necessary for its accurate determination.

Centuries ago the day was divided into hours and the night into watches, the latter because it was necessary to keep watch for security. The Hebrews had three equal night watches, the Greeks five, and the Romans four. Timekeeping in the daytime was fairly simple by observing the sun in the clear skies of the Middle East. The Egyptians developed a system based on the direction and motion of shadows. A stake called a *gnomon* was set vertically in the ground. When the shadow cast by the stake was shortest it was noon. The hours could be marked off on a horizontal area (the ground), or a plate which could be graduated into equal divisions. This was a sundial. Herodotus said, ". . . the sundial and the gnomon and the twelve divisions of the day came into Greece from Babylon."

The shadow at noon points to the north in the northern latitudes and to the south in southern latitudes. The Egyptians eventually set up ornate obelisks and sundials for timekeeping. Figure 5–1 shows an Egyptian obelisk, now in New York. Naturally this method was fine for clear days, but would not work on cloudy days or at night. So, sandglasses and, later, water clocks, or clepsydras, were built which could be used at all times. Sandglasses had to be turned over at the end of an hour and hence were called hourglasses. The water clock had to be kept filled, but an automatic reservoir to maintain constant level was later invented. Also, candles which burned at a given rate were marked into equal intervals to show the hours. Three of these devices are shown in Figure 10–1.

The Egyptians also used a series of stars at night as time indicators. In the Great Pyramid of Cheops there was a "grand gallery" which was open to the sky before the pyramid was capped and finished. The hours were determined by observing the passage of certain stars across the opening of the gallery, but an intricate table of correlating data was necessary because of the changing position of the stars with respect to the sun during the course of a year.

The first mechanical clocks were run by weights; but there was no satisfactory way of regulating the rate at which these mechanisms ran, so time by these clocks was not very accurate. In 1360 there were only about 20 mechanical clocks in Europe, most of them in churches and monasteries. Timekeeping was in the hands of the priests in Egypt and in Europe for the purpose of announcing the times of the various religious offices and services. Clocks were not used in public buildings until about 1450.

Fig. 10–1 The hour candle, sand glass, and water clock were ancient instruments for keeping time.

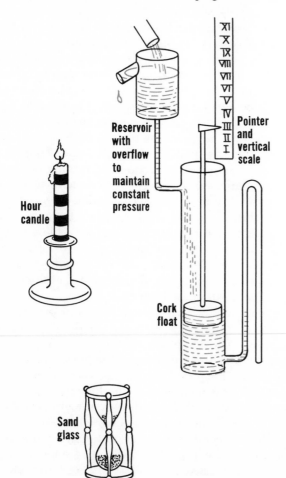

### 10.5   The Principle of the Pendulum

The first observatory to be equipped with a clock was in Nuremberg about twenty years before Copernicus. It later became necessary for observatories to be equipped with accurate timekeepers for making accurate observations of the positions and motions of the sun, moon, planets, and stars. The invention of the pendulum and its adaptation to the regulation of mechanical clocks provided the needed accuracy. Galileo had studied the pendulum and in 1656 Christian Huygens published a treatise, *The Pendulum Clock*, stating the principle of the pendulum, and adapted it to use in mechanical clocks.

The formula for the time of one swing of a pendulum is:

$$t = 2\pi \sqrt{\frac{l}{g}} \qquad (10\text{--}4)$$

where $t$ is the time of the entire swing back and forth of the pendulum, $l$ is its length and $g$ is the acceleration due to gravity. This principle has been used in the gravimeter, an instrument for measuring $g$, in various parts of the world. The length, $l$, is kept constant and, by measuring $t$, the constant $g$ is determined. It turns out that $g$ is not quite constant on the earth's surface, but varies because of the shape and rotation of the earth. From such measures the exact dimensions and variations of shape have been determined.

▶*Sample Problem:* Compute the time of a complete swing of a pendulum whose length is 1.00 m. Assume the acceleration of gravity to be 980 cm/sec².

**Solution:** 1.00 m = 100 cm. Substituting in equation 10–4,

$$t = 2 \times 3.14159 \times \sqrt{100 \text{ cm}/980 \text{ cm/sec}^2}$$

$$= 6.28318 \times 0.3195 \text{ sec} = 2.005 \text{ sec.}$$

One meter is the length of a platinum-iridium bar kept near Paris. It was originally intended to be 1 ten-millionth of a meridian from the equator to the pole, but later measures of the size of the earth showed that the meter is not quite equal to that distance. A pendulum whose length is 1 m will have a half-swing of about one second, as the above problem shows. Since $g$ varies from one latitude to another, the length of a seconds pendulum will also vary. Its length for the latitude of Greenwich is 99.40 cm or 39.1398 in and 99.32 cm or 39.0968 inches in Washington. The acceleration of gravity is 980.621 cm/sec² at sea level at latitude 45°.

Time is measured by something moving—the sand in an hourglass, the water in a water clock, the shadow on a sundial, the hands on the face of a clock. But the most important moving object for timekeeping is the earth itself. The earth rotates about an axis and revolves in an orbit around the sun. Its rotation provides a definition of the day and its revolution defines the year. We now examine in detail the various kinds of day and the different kinds of year.

## 10.6 Sidereal Time

As the earth rotates all the visible stars appear to cross the celestial meridian. This is called a *transit*. An instrument which is set up so stars can be seen only when they are on the meridian is also called a transit. A meridian circle is a transit with a slightly larger and more accurate circle for measuring altitudes. If a clock is set to run perfectly and to read zero when a certain star is visible at the center of the transit instrument, that is, when it is on the meridian, the length of time between successive transits of the star or any other star is called one *sidereal day*. This is the length of time it takes the earth to rotate once on its axis.

If the clock is reset to read zero when the vernal equinox—the point in the sky where the sun crosses the celestial equator in the spring—is on the meridian, the time kept by the clock is called *sidereal time*. Sidereal time is also the time which has elapsed since the vernal equinox was on the meridian. Since the meridian is local, each place keeps it own sidereal time. Each observatory with a transit instrument can determine its sidereal time by observation; but if there is no transit instrument, the sidereal time must be obtained by computation.

*Hour angle* has been defined as the number of degrees between the celestial meridian and the hour circle of any object in the sky, measured westward from the celestial meridian. The hour angle of the vernal equinox is the angle between the meridian, marked by the transit instrument, and the hour circle which passes through the vernal equinox. Sidereal time is also, therefore, the hour angle of the vernal equinox.

Right ascension is the angle between the hour circle through the vernal equinox and the hour circle of a star, measured to the east. Since the earth rotates toward the east, the hour circles transit the meridian in succession. Now if the sidereal clock is graduated to read up to 24 hr between transits of the vernal equinox and the hour circles are read in hours to the east, each hour circle will read the same as the sidereal clock when it is on the meridian. Sidereal time may, therefore, be defined also as the right ascension of the meridian. This provides a simple method of determining sidereal time.

Suppose the right ascension of a star has been determined. Sirius, for example, has right ascension 6$^h$ 41$^m$. If the sidereal clock reads 0$^h$ when the vernal equinox is on the meridian (that is, if it reads sidereal time), it will read 6$^h$ 41$^m$ when Sirius is in the center of the transit field. In this way sidereal time may be determined by setting the reading of a sidereal clock to be equal to the right ascensions of stars when they are on the meridian, provided the right ascensions are known.

The United States Naval Observatory publishes the right ascensions and declinations of several hundred stars every year. A selected number of them, eight for example, may be observed on a given night and the sidereal time determined to within a small fraction of a second. It is seen that the vernal equinox is the timekeeper and the earth is the timepiece.

However, for civil affairs it is customary to use the sun as the timekeeper. The interval of time between successive transits of the sun is called a *solar day*. When the sun is on the meridian, it is said to be apparent noon. If time is referred to a given meridian, the sun transits the meridian at local apparent noon. The hour angle of the apparent, or real, sun is called local apparent solar time. It is abbreviated as L.A.T. or L.A.S.T. Each meridian therefore has also its own local solar time. Each day is divided into hours, minutes, and seconds.

The sidereal time is also divided into hours, minutes, and seconds, but the lengths of the solar and sidereal days are not equal.

### 10.7   The Day and the Year

Since the earth revolves around the sun, the difference between times of transit of the vernal equinox and the sun across each meridian change

continually. If both are on the meridian on March 21 at noon, on March 22 the sun will have moved about 1° to the east and will transit the meridian after the vernal equinox does. Each day the sun moves farther to the east and the vernal equinox crosses the meridian earlier by solar time. In one year it gains an entire lap of 360° or 24$^h$ over the sun. In other words, there are about 365 solar days and 366 sidereal days in a year. The gain of a reference star or the vernal equinox over the sun is shown in Figure 10–2.

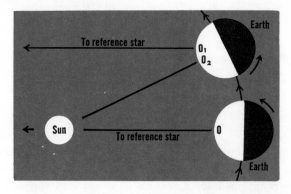

Fig. 10–2   For an observer at $O$, the sun and a reference star or the vernal equinox are in conjunction. One sidereal day later, the observer is at $O_1$, because the earth has made a complete rotation. But the sun is not overhead until the observer arrives at $O_2$. The interval of time from $O$ through $O_1$ to $O_2$ is one solar day.

Stated in another way, the earth requires about four minutes longer to complete one rotation with respect to the sun than it does with respect to the vernal equinox. A sidereal day of 24 sidereal hours is equal to only 23$^h$ 56$^m$ 4.091$^s$ of solar time. Or, the sidereal day is about 236 sec shorter than the average solar day. One sidereal second = 1/86,400 sidereal day = 0.9972 average solar second.

According to Kepler's second law, the earth's rate of speed around the sun is variable. Also the sun does not appear to move along the celestial equator. When the ecliptic and celestial equator are shown on a flat surface as in Figure 10–3, with the equator as a straight line, the ecliptic is curved. It can be seen from the diagram that even if the earth moved at a constant speed, so the apparent motion of the sun along the ecliptic was uniform, the apparent motion relative to the equator would not be uniform. For example, a displacement along the ecliptic at *A*, where it is parallel to the equator, results in an equal displacement relative to the equator. The same displacement along the ecliptic at *B*, where it is inclined to the equator, results in a smaller displacement relative to the equator.

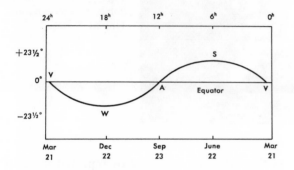

Fig. 10–3   The ecliptic and celestial equator drawn on a flat surface.

For these reasons, the solar days are not all equal in length. Table 10–3 shows the length of the apparent solar day at four times of year. The days are longer in both January and July because in each of these months the sun is near one of the solstices, where its apparent speed relative to the equator is

TABLE 10–3
**Variation in Length of Apparent Solar Day**

| Date | Length of Day | | |
|---|---|---|---|
| January 1 | 24$^h$ | 00$^m$ | 29$^s$ |
| April 1 | 23 | 59 | 42 |
| July 1 | 24 | 00 | 12 |
| October 1 | 23 | 59 | 41 |

greater, thus increasing the angle between $0_1$ and $0_2$ shown in Figure 10–2. The other effect, the earth's variable speed, causes the days to be longer in January than in July, because the earth is at perihelion in January.

## 10.8   Mean Solar Time

For the same reasons the lengths of the seconds of apparent time are also variable. It would be difficult to build a clock to keep this kind of time. So it has been the custom for many years to use a fictitious sun, called the *mean sun*, by which our clocks can be regulated. The mean sun is an imaginary sun, an average sun which is assumed to move eastward along the celestial equator at a uniform rate such that it makes a complete circle around the sky in exactly the same time it takes the apparent sun to move around the ecliptic. The hour angle of the mean sun is called *local mean time*. It is the interval of time since the mean sun was on the local meridian.

Because each meridian on the earth has its own mean time, when the railroads became important in our economy, it became necessary to standardize the time. Standard meridians were chosen and each city and town in a zone began to keep the same time, which was called standard time. The standard meridians are spaced 15° apart beginning at Greenwich, and a standard time zone keeps time exactly one hour from that in the neighboring zone. The four familiar time zones in continental United States are based on the 75th meridian for eastern time, the 90th for central time, the 105th for mountain time, and the 120th for Pacific standard time. These are five, six, seven, and eight hours from Greenwich, respectively. However, later it became customary for individual states or parts of states to adopt zone times out of their normal zones, which therefore became somewhat irregular, as shown in Figure 10–4.

When daylight saving time is adopted, usually from the last Sunday in April to the last Sunday in

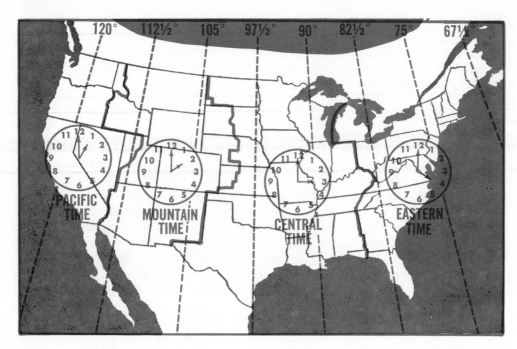

Fig. 10-4    Time zones in continental United States.

October, each zone using daylight time adopts the time of the zone adjacent to the east. That is, central time adopts eastern time, mountain time becomes central time, and so on for all the time zones.

It also became apparent that if a person sailed or flew around the world, his date on the completion of the journey would not agree with that of the place he had sailed from. To cite an extreme case, suppose a plane left New York on Monday flying westward. If it took 24 hr to make the flight, the pilot would need to set his clock back 1 hr for every hour of the trip to agree with the time zones over which he was flying. In other words, when he got back to New York, his clock would show no elapsed time but it would be the next day, Tuesday, on landing.   To remedy this, it is customary to omit one day if sailing westward—that is, to turn the calendar ahead one day—when about half-way around the world from Greenwich. This meridian of longitude 180°, both east and west, is called the international date line. When traveling eastward

across this line, one day must be repeated in order to keep the date in agreement with the date of the landing places. The line is also irregular by agreement as shown in Figure 10-5.

A favorite conundrum of a well-known teacher of astronomy at an eastern university in the nineteenth century was as follows: What is the greatest number of Sundays possible in February? Answer: 10, in a leap year when there are five Sundays, by a ship crossing the international date line weekly from west to east.

The fact that the apparent sun moves irregularly along the ecliptic means that it does not come to the meridian at equal intervals of time. The mean sun does, which was the reason for inventing this imaginary sun. The difference in time between transits of the mean sun and the apparent sun—that is, the difference between their hour circles—is called the *equation of time*, which is defined as apparent time minus mean time.

Figure 10-6 is a graph of the equation of time

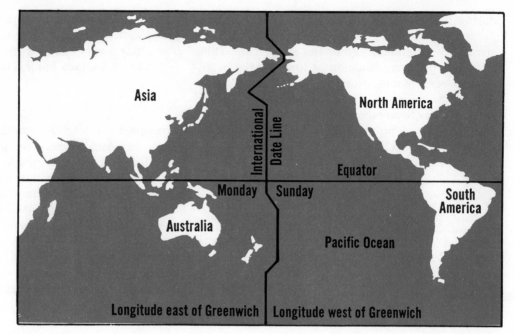

Fig. 10–5 The international date line, which is near longitude 180°.

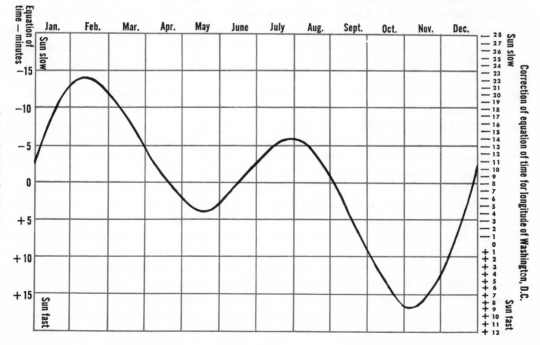

Fig. 10–6 Variation of the equation of time in one year. It must also be adjusted for a difference of longitude as shown at the right for Washington, D.C.

during the year. The plus sign means that the apparent sun is ahead of the mean sun; that is, it crosses the meridian before the mean sun. Table 10–4 also gives the equation of time for the beginning of each month. Notice that it is zero 4 times during the year—about the middle of April and June, in early September and late December—when the two suns are on the meridian at the same time, although their declinations are different.

TABLE 10–4

**The Equation of Time**

| Date | Appt. − Mean | Date | Appt. − Mean |
|---|---|---|---|
| January 1 | − 3m 21s | July 1 | − 3m 31s |
| February 1 | −13 36 | August 1 | − 6 14 |
| March 1 | −12 35 | September 1 | − 0 11 |
| April 1 | − 4 08 | October 1 | +10 05 |
| May 1 | + 2 53 | November 1 | +16 19 |
| June 1 | + 2 27 | December 1 | +11 09 |

On many sundial plates and terrestrial globes a figure shaped roughly like the figure 8 is shown. It is called an analemma and shows the sun's declination and the equation of time for one year.

From the graph and the table, it can be seen that in December the apparent sun is ahead of the mean sun until late in the month. The equation of time changes from +11m on December 1 to −3m on January 1. Since the earth is traveling faster than average, the apparent sun gains on the mean sun, moving eastward by 14 min with respect to the mean sun during the month of December. The shortest day, the day when the sun is above the horizon for the shortest time, comes about the 21st of December at the time of the winter solstice. It is usually thought that the sun sets earliest and rises latest at that time. This is not the case. The sun sets earliest about December 5 and rises latest about January 5. The reason is that the real sun is moving eastward with respect to the mean sun as shown by the equation of time. This motion cancels the effect of shortening evenings and after December 5 the sun sets later

than it would otherwise. For the same reason, the sun continues to rise later until about January 5. These dates vary because of a latitude effect, which is greater in Canada but less in Mexico.

## 10.9  Determination of Longitude

Longitude must be determined as the difference of angle between a given meridian and a reference meridian of known longitude. Latitude is the angle between the given position and the equator, which is the fundamental circle in a system of latitudes. Similarly, the meridian of Greenwich is the fundamental circle for the system of longitude.

Celestial and terrestrial meridians have been defined as concentric circles. Thus the longitude of Washington, for example, can be determined by measuring the angle between either its celestial or terrestrial meridian and the corresponding meridian of Greenwich. Sidereal time is equal to the right ascension of the celestial meridian and can be measured by observing the transit of a star whose right ascension is known, as previously described. The difference between the sidereal times at Washington and Greenwich is equal to the difference between their meridians and therefore of their longitudes.

Suppose it was agreed in advance to observe certain stars on the same night as they crossed the meridians of Greenwich and Washington. This would happen when the sidereal clocks at each place read the same—for example, 6h 41m for Sirius—but each star would cross the meridian of Greenwich some 5 hr before it reached the meridian of Washington. Suppose a signal is sent to Washington when Sirius is on the meridian at Greenwich, and that 5h 08m 16s later Sirius is on the meridian at Washington. This interval is equal to the longitude of Washington. Any star bright enough to be observed with the instruments at the two observatories can be used for a determination of the difference in longitude.

Washington serves as the standard meridian for the determination of longitudes in the United

States and if the difference between transits of stars is determined for each observatory, the longitude of each is found by adding the time difference to the longitude of Washington. The accuracy of the determination of longitude is therefore exactly the same as the accuracy of the determination of time; that is, to about 0.01 sec or less.

Longitude is expressed either in hours or degrees and fractions. From Table 10–5, the conversion from time to arc, or the reverse, is possible to whatever accuracy is desired. On maps it is customary to express longitude in degrees. In astronomy, it is usually expressed in units of time.

TABLE 10–5
**Relation between Time and Angle**

| | |
|---|---|
| 24 hours = 360° of arc | 1° = 4 min of time |
| 1 hour = 15° | 1′ = 4 sec |
| 1 minute = 15′ | 1″ = 1/15 sec |
| 1 second = 15″ | |

To recapitulate, there are several kinds of day, each dependent on a different timekeeper:

1. *Sidereal day:* the interval between successive transits of the vernal equinox. Length: $24^h$ of sidereal time equals $23^h 56^m 4.091^s$ of mean solar time.
2. *Mean solar day:* the interval between successive transits of the mean sun. Length: exactly $24^h$ of mean solar time.
3. *Apparent solar day:* the interval between successive transits of the apparent sun. Length: approximately $24^h$ of mean solar time, but irregular in length.

## 10.10   The Motions of the Earth

The earth turns about an axis. This motion is called *rotation*. It also moves in an orbit around the sun in accordance with Kepler's laws. The orbit is an ellipse and the sun is at one focus. This motion is called *revolution*. As the earth rotates and revolves, its axis remains nearly parallel to itself. The time of rotation is one sidereal day. The period of revolution, from one position in the orbit back to the same position, is called one sidereal year. Its length is $365^d 6^h 9^m 10^s$ of mean solar time or 365.25636 mean solar days. The sidereal year may also be defined as the length of time between two successive conjunctions of the sun with a star as seen from the earth, or two successive conjunctions of the earth with a star as seen from the sun.

The stability of the earth during its revolution around the sun is characteristic of rotating bodies, the inertia of their moving parts resisting a change in direction, as well as speed of rotation. However, the orientation of the axis will change, if it is subjected to a twisting force, or torque. The toy top is a familiar example. The weight of a top that is leaning away from the vertical exerts a torque tending to topple it. But when it is spinning, the top does not fall; instead, the combined inertial reaction of all the top's whirling parts moves the axis at right angles to the force producing the torque. As a result, the axis moves in a cone around the vertical line passing through the pivot point. This conical motion is called *precession*. The period of precession depends on the size and mass of the top and the rate of spin. The top would precess at the same angle indefinitely, if friction did not slow it down.

The earth is also subjected to a torque, tending to change the direction of its spin axis. This is due to the gravitational pull of the sun, the moon, and the planets on its equatorial bulge. To illustrate the origin of the torque due to the moon's gravitation, the bulge is greatly exaggerated and shown superposed on the spherical portion of the earth in Figure 10–7. Only the forces on the bulge need be considered, as gravitational force on a sphere does not produce torque because of its symmetry. It can be seen in the diagram that the torques oppose each other. The torque due to the force on the far side tends to rotate the earth counter-clockwise, while the one due to the force on the near side tends to rotate it clockwise. Thus, the resultant torque depends on the difference of the forces. Since gravitational force is inversely proportional to the square of the distance, the force on the near side is stronger

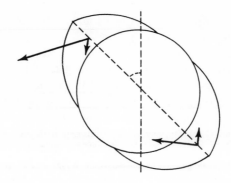

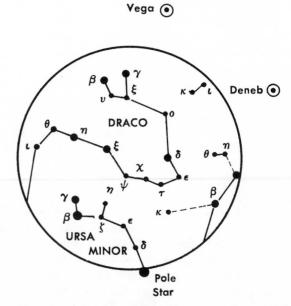

Fig. 10–7 Precessional force of the moon's gravitation on the oblate earth.

as indicated by the lengths of the arrows. The resultant clockwise torque tends to pull the bulge into the plane of the moon's orbit.

The sun also tries to pull the earth's bulge into the plane of its orbit, the ecliptic. This reinforces the torque due to the moon, since there is only a 5° angle between the planes of their orbits. Although the sun's force of attraction on the earth is about 200 times stronger than that of the moon, the moon is the principal cause of precession. This is because the closer the source, the more rapid is the rate at which the differential gravitation effect changes. Tides are also a differential effect, as discussed in Chapter 11.

Because of the large size and mass of the earth, its rate of precession is very slow—once around in 25,900 years. This has been known since the time of Hipparchus in the second century B.C. When the Great Pyramid was built in Egypt, the pole star was Thuban, alpha Draconis, a faint star in the tail of the Dragon. See page 101. At the time of Hipparchus, Thuban was about 11° from the pole. At the present time, it is about 25° distant. It would be better to say that the pole is 25° from Thuban, since it is the pole which moves.

The equatorial plane of the earth is tipped about 23½° to the plane of the orbit. The north celestial pole, which is defined by the direction of the axis, is thus 23½° from the pole of the ecliptic. The right ascension of the north pole of the ecliptic is 18 hr and its declination is 66½°. Precession causes the north celestial pole to describe a small circle

23½° in radius about the pole of the ecliptic in a period of 25,900 years.

Precession of the earth's axis would be uniform if the forces on its equatorial bulge were constant. But the moon's orbital plane is also changing due to the attractions of the other bodies in the solar system. The consequent variation in the direction of the moon's pull is noticeable as a slight nodding of the earth's pole. This is called *nutation*,

Fig. 10–8 The path of the north celestial pole among the stars due to precession. The pole of the ecliptic is at the center of the circle.

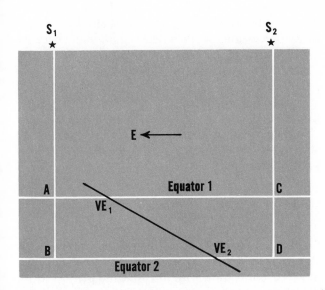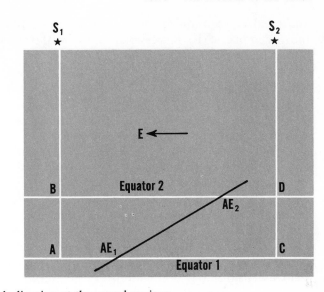

Fig. 10–9   The effect of precession on right ascension and declination at the vernal equinox (left) and autumnal equinox (right).

which means nodding. The period of nutation is 18.6 years and is related to the regression of the nodes of the moon's orbit. The result is that the circle of precession is not a smooth curve, but is a wave superposed on the circle. The height of the wave is only about 9.2″, above and below the circle.

Figure 10–8 shows the path of the north celestial pole among the constellations. The changing declination of Polaris (Table 10–1) is a result of precession. It will be noticed that in about 12,000 years the bright star Vega will be some 5° from the pole and will then be the pole star. Nutation is too small to show on a map of this scale.

If the earth's pole is shifting, its equator must change also. The vernal equinox and the autumnal equinox are sliding westward along the ecliptic. This is called the precession of the equinoxes. The period is also 25,900 years in which the equinoxes move over 360° of the ecliptic. Thus the rate is about 50″ per year. The equator is changing position with respect to the stars and the celestial coordinates of all stars are changing, as shown in Figure 10–9.

In Figure 10–9 let $S_1$ and $S_2$ be two stars near the vernal equinox on the left diagram and at the

Fig. 10–10   Aberration of starlight. A telescope must be tipped 20.5″ in the direction of the moving earth.

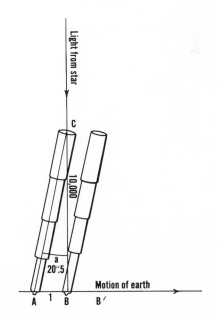

autumnal equinox on the right. The arrow shows the direction east (E). Precession is to the west (right in the figures). The diagonal line is a section of the ecliptic. At the beginning of the year, the vernal equinox ($VE_1$) and the autumnal equinox ($AE_1$) will be at the intersection of Equator 1 with the ecliptic. The equinoxes move from $VE_1$ to $VE_2$ and from $AE_1$ to $AE_2$, about 50″ of arc, in one year.

The right ascension of $S_1$ is $VE_1A$ and its declination is $AS_1$ at the beginning of the year. At the end of the year they will be $VE_2B$ and $BS_1$, respectively. The same is true for the right-hand figure except that 12 hr must be added to the right ascension. The autumnal equinox is 12 hr from the vernal equinox. Similarly, the hour circle of $S_2$ intersects Equator 1 at $C$ and Equator 2 at $D$, points to which right ascensions and declinations are measured.

It can be seen from the figure that the right ascensions of all four stars have increased near each equinox. The declinations increase near the vernal equinox, but decrease near the autumnal equinox. The amounts and directions of these changes depend on the location of the stars involved.

## 10.11  The Sidereal and the Tropical Year

The *sidereal year* is the length of time of one revolution of the earth in its orbit. It is the interval between successive passages of the sun through any point on the ecliptic. The length of the sidereal year is 365.25636 days of mean solar time. The *tropical year* is the length of time between successive passages of the sun through the vernal equinox. But because of precession, since the vernal equinox moves westward, the length of the tropical year is less than that of the sidereal year by the time it takes the sun to move along the ecliptic from $VE_1$ to $VE_2$, which is 50″ of arc. This takes about 20 min of time. Thus the length of the tropical year is only 365.24220 mean solar days. It is the year on which our calendar is based.

To recapitulate: Precession is caused by the rotation of the earth and the pull of the sun and moon on the equatorial bulge. The planets also have a part in the precession, but the effect is quite small because of their great distances. The planetary effect is included in an accurate determination of the rate of precession.

The effects of precession are: the changing position of the poles, the motion of the equinoxes, the changing right ascensions and declinations of all stars, and the difference in the lengths of the two kinds of year.

## 10.12  Proofs of the Earth's Motion

Tycho Brahe would not accept the Copernican theory of a moving earth. Instead, he proposed the theory that the earth is stationary, that the sun moves around the earth, but that the planets move in orbits around the sun. He reasoned that if the earth were in motion, it should be possible to detect retrograde motions of stars when in opposition to the sun. This would be true if the stars were close to the planet Saturn, which was the most distant planet known in Tycho's time. The length of Saturn's retrograde loop is about 12°, an angle which could be measured easily by Tycho. If a star were twelve times farther away than Saturn, its loop would still be 1° long. Tycho could find no evidence of such motion. Of course, we know the answer today. The stars are much more distant, the nearest star being some 27,000 times the distance of Saturn.

At the present time it is possible to measure changes of position of the nearest stars with respect to the background stars, but a long-focus telescope is needed. Photographs taken at the proper times are measured under microscopes with special measuring machines, something which Tycho did not have. The largest apparent shift of position with respect to the most distant stars on a photograph is only about 1.5″ or only 0.13 mm for a telescope 60 ft long. Angles as small as 0.005″ have been measured.

This apparent motion of the nearest stars is due to the motion of the earth. It can be used to determine the distances of 2000 or more stars. This is one proof that the earth is moving through space and is not stationary. The first *stellar parallax,* as it is called, was measured in 1838.

A second proof of the revolution of the earth was discovered in 1727. It is called the aberration of starlight. To illustrate: Suppose it is raining with the rain coming straight down. An umbrella held upright will keep off the rain. But everybody is familiar with the fact that a moving person must tip his umbrella in the direction in which he is walking or running to keep the rain from his clothes. The greater the speed, the greater the angle of tip.

Light travels at a speed of 186,000 mi per second; the earth's speed in its orbit is about 18.5 mi per second, almost exactly ¹⁄₁₀,₀₀₀ the speed of light. Hence, if an observer wishes to see a star in his telescope, he must turn it a slight amount to take account of the motion of the earth. The amount of turn is equal to ¹⁄₁₀,₀₀₀ of a radian or 20.5″ as shown in Figure 10–10. This is due to the fact that as light comes down the telescope tube, the lower part of the tube has moved during the time the light travels from the upper to the lower end.

As the earth moves in its orbit around the sun, the telescope must be turned in a circle to keep a star at the pole of the ecliptic in the center of the telescope. In other words, in one year the star seems to describe a small circle about the pole. The radius of this circle can be measured and is 20.5″. If the speed of light is known, as it is, the amount of tip of the telescope can be used to determine the speed of the earth in its orbit. Multiplying the speed by the number of seconds in a year, the circumference of the earth's orbit is found and therefore the radius, the distance from the earth to the sun. The trouble with this method is that the angle cannot be measured with sufficient accuracy.

▶ *Sample Problem:* Assuming the aberrational constant to be 20.5″, compute the distance from the earth to the sun.

**Solution:** (See Appendix for definition of radian measure.) Write as a proportion:

$$\frac{\text{speed of earth}}{\text{speed of light}} = \frac{\text{aberrational constant}}{1 \text{ radian}}$$

or $\frac{\text{speed of earth}}{186,000 \text{ mi/sec}} = \frac{20.5''}{206,265''}.$

Solving,
$$\text{speed of earth} = \frac{20.5 \times 186,000}{206,265} \text{ mi/sec.}$$

Multiplying by $31.5 \times 10^6$ sec/yr and dividing by $2\pi$, the radius of the earth's orbit is:

$$\text{radius} = \frac{3.15 \times 10^7 \times 20.5 \times 186,000}{2\pi \times 206,265}$$
$$= 92,700,000 \text{ mi.}$$

For stars not at the pole of the ecliptic, the apparent motions due to aberration are not circles, but ellipses. The major axis of each ellipse is 20.5″, with a small variation due to the changing speed of the earth. On the ecliptic a star appears to move back and forth along a straight line whose length is 2 × 20.5″. This is because the earth is moving directly toward or away from the star.

A third method to demonstrate the revolution of the earth is the radial velocity of stars. When the earth is moving toward a star, assuming the star is stationary, the lines in the star's spectrum are shifted towards the violet end of the spectrum according to the Doppler effect. When the earth is receding from the star, the lines are shifted toward the red. Since all stars, including the sun, have their own motions, the Doppler shift due to the earth's orbital motion is superposed on the effects due to the stellar motions. If a star is on the ecliptic, the periodic variation in the measured velocity of the star is due to the motion of the earth in its orbit. By making many measures of many stars, a fairly accurate velocity of the earth, 18.5 mi/sec, may be found and can be used to determine the distance to the sun, as in the case of aberration. Again, this method is not sufficiently accurate, but is a proof of the earth's motion through space.

These three methods are entirely different, but give the same result. They prove that the earth is in motion around the sun. A further discussion of parallax and radial velocity will be found in later chapters on stellar astronomy.

## 10.13    The Calendar

Herodotus said that "the Egyptians by their study of astronomy discovered the solar year and were the first to divide it into twelve parts. . . . their method of calculation is better than the Greeks; for the Greeks, to make their seasons work out properly, intercalate a whole month every other year, while the Egyptians make the year consist of 12 months of 30 days each and every year intercalate 5 additional days, and so complete the regular circle of the seasons."

The Egyptians divided their year into three seasons: Inundation, Winter, and Summer. So it was actually an agricultural year based on the rise of the Nile River and the resulting seasons of growth and nongrowth.

The Hebrew calendar was—and still is—based on the phases of the moon. Their year has 12 months of what should be 29½ days each, which came to only 354 days in a year. This meant that extra months had to be added every two or three years. The months began when the new moon was first visible in the western sky after sunset. The weeks consisted of six days followed by the seventh, the Sabbath. There were four seasons, which were probably borrowed from the Greeks, since the eastern Mediterranean region knows only two seasons—a hot and dry summer and a cold and wet winter. The lunar calendar is very irregular because of the incommensurability of the phases of the moon with the motions of the sun. Also the new moon is seen in varying positions with respect to sunset, which changes the interval of time at which the moon can be seen after it passes the sun.

When Julius Caesar came to power in Rome, the Roman calendar of 12 months had fallen into a sad state with spring in December. Caesar with the help of Sosigenes, a Greek astronomer in Alexandria at the time (45 B.C.), reformed the calendar by making the year 365¼ days in length. That is, he went back to the common year of 365 days, with a leap year every four years, as in the Egyptian calendar. This calendar is called the Julian calendar. It went into effect on January 1, 45 B.C., the year before Caesar was assassinated. Table 10–6 gives the origin of the names of the months.

Since the tropical year is a little shorter than the 365¼ days of the Julian calendar, spring came progressively earlier by the calendar. Near the end of the sixteenth century, spring began on March 11. Pope Gregory XIII in 1582 signed a decree dropping 10 days. The day after October 4, 1582, became October 15. This brought spring back to March 21. The Gregorian calendar was not universally adopted immediately. England adopted it in 1752 and Russia not until after the revolution in 1917.

TABLE 10–6
**Origin of Names of Months**

| | |
|---|---|
| January: | Janus, the two-faced god |
| February: | from Latin *Februarius*, feast of purification; month of sacrifices |
| March: | Mars |
| April: | (Unknown) |
| May: | Maius Jupiter, the great (god) |
| June: | a Roman clan |
| July: | Julius Caesar |
| August: | Augustus Caesar |
| September, October, November, December: | 7th to 10th months in the old Roman calendar |

The Gregorian calendar is based on the tropical year of 365.2422 days. Each common year has 365 days, with a leap year every fourth year, as in the Julian calendar. But leap years are omitted in the century years which are not divisible by 400. 1800, 1900, 2100, and so on are not leap years; but 2000 will be. Thus the length of the average year of the Gregorian calendar is 365.2425 days, as follows:

$$365 + \tfrac{1}{4} - \tfrac{1}{100} + \tfrac{1}{400} = 365.2425.$$

Therefore the year is too long by 365.2425 — 365.2422, or 0.0003 day, or three days in 10,000 years. The perpetual calendar explained in the Appendix makes it possible to determine the day of the week for any year in history after the year A.D. 1.

The Russian calendar is the same as the Gregorian calendar until 2800, which will be a leap year in the Gregorian but not in the Russian calendar. The error in the Russian calendar is only one day in 44,000 years.

The Gregorian calendar is not entirely satisfactory for several reasons. The months are not of equal length and the year begins on a different weekday in successive years. Christmas, for example, may come on any day of the week. Easter is a movable feast day, which always falls on Sunday. The date of Easter is computed by a complicated formula, approximately as follows:

Easter falls on the first Sunday after the first full moon on or after March 21. The earliest date of Easter is therefore March 22 and the latest is April 25. If the full moon after March 21 falls on Sunday, Easter is the following Sunday. Labor Day and Thanksgiving fall on Monday and Thursday, respectively.

It has been suggested that the present calendar with its variable holiday dates be replaced by another which fixes the days of the week so the calendar will remain the same from year to year. There have been two proposals, both based on the tropical year and using the formula for the length of the year for the Gregorian calendar.

The first proposal was for a calendar of 13 months of 28 days each. The length of the year would then be only 364 days and an extra day or two would have to be intercalated. If the first day of each month fell on Sunday, the extra day would be inserted after the 13th month between Saturday and Sunday. Similarly a second day would be added in leap years. This calendar has not been favorably received. According to one source, the reason is partly that it would contain 13 Fridays on the 13th!

The World Calendar, which is reproduced in the Appendix, has had more success and was approved by most of the countries of the old League of Nations before World War II. The United States did not join the nations in favor of this calendar. It contains the present 12 months, but rearranged to have successively 31, 30, and 30 days for a total of 91 days or exactly 13 weeks in each quarter of the year. The first day of January, April, July, and October would fall on Sunday. The first day of every other month would always begin on the same day of the week each year. As in the 13-month calendar, the extra days would be intercalated at the end of December, or June in leap years, and would not be weekdays, but added between Saturday and Sunday.

The advantages of the World Calendar are that it would be perpetual with all holidays falling on the same day of the week every year. The quarters would all be the same length, which is desirable for business statistics. The extra days could be declared church feast days, but this would violate the old Jewish sequence of six days followed by the Sabbath. Even Easter could be fixed, if the full-moon rule were to be given up. It is suggested that January begin on Saturday so there would be no Fridays on the 13th and Christmas would always fall on Sunday.

There is no strong organization backing this calendar, although the World Calendar Association of New York and the Association for Calendar Reform have been in existence since before the breakup of the League of Nations.

The astronomers use a perpetual calendar which has many advantages. There are no weeks or weekdays. Each day is numbered and a particular date is merely the number of the day since January 1, 4713 B.C. This scheme includes all the dates of recorded history. It is therefore possible to calculate the number of days between two events by a simple subtraction. This is very useful in periodic events, such as the study of eclipses and periodically varying stars. The calendar is called the Julian-day Calendar. Each day begins at noon Greenwich mean time. Lists of numbers of days are published and are readily accessible to astronomers.

As an example, January 1, 1964 was day number 2,438,396. The astronomers usually record the time of an observation as the day followed by a decimal, the fraction of a day after noon G.M.T. Care must be taken to change the date at the proper time, after allowance has been made for the difference of longitude. For example, 6:00 P.M. P.S.T. on January 1, 1964 was J.D.2,438,396.5825. 4:00 P.M. P.S.T. occurs at Greenwich midnight. This method of computing time intervals eliminates the need of calculating the number of leap years betwen two dates.

## QUESTIONS AND PROBLEMS

1. If calendars were devised for Jupiter, Mars, and Venus, how many days would there be in a year in each case? See Table 14–1.

2. Why is the declination of Polaris continuously changing?

3. How much are the centers of the sun and moon displaced by refraction (a) when rising, and (b) when 5° above the horizon?

4. Does refraction cause a star to rise faster or slower than it would if the earth had no atmosphere?

5. When would a gnomon cast no shadow at noon in latitudes (a) 0°, (b) 23½°N, and (c) 23½°S? **Ans:** (a) March 21 and Sept. 21.

6. Is the aberration of light greater on Mercury or Mars?

7. Is it possible for an observatory to measure the same altitude of Polaris at 6 P.M. and 6 A.M. on the same night? Explain.

8. Show why the latest possible date of Easter is April 25.

*9. How would time kept by a pendulum clock on Mercury compare with the time it would keep on earth? Would a wristwatch, which keeps time by an oscillating balance wheel driven by a spring, be similarly affected? Assume gravity on Mercury is 0.4 $g$.

10. If the earth rotated at the same rate in the opposite direction, (a) how many sidereal days would there be in a sidereal year? (b) What would be the length of a sidereal day in solar time?

11. Compute the length of a regressional loop of a star 27,000 times the distance of Saturn from the sun.

12. Show from the data in Table 10–2 that the sun and moon should appear flattened when rising.

13. At local apparent noon, what is the (a) Pacific Daylight Time in San Francisco (122½°W longitude) on July 15? (b) Eastern Standard Time in Boston (71°W longitude) on November 20? Give the answer to the nearest minute. **Ans:** (a) 1:15 P.D.T.

14. Using the data from Table 14–1, (a) what is the orbital velocity of Mars, assuming the orbit is circular? (Hint: The earth's orbital velocity is 18.5 mi/sec.) (b) What is the aberrational constant for Mars? **Ans:** (a) 15 mi/sec.

*15. During 1950 an observatory measured the altitude of Polaris on the meridian at 5:30 P.M. and at 5:30 A.M. The measured altitudes were 19°59.1′ and 21°54.9′, respectively. Compute the latitude of the observatory and the declination of Polaris. (Note: The altitudes should be corrected for refraction.)

16. Show how the right ascensions and declinations of stars change near (a) the solstices and (b) the celestial poles.

# Chapter Eleven

# The Moon

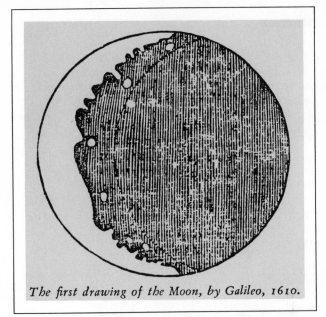

*The first drawing of the Moon, by Galileo, 1610.*

## 11.1 The Moon's Distance

The moon was probably the most discussed object in the universe during the middle 1960s. Will we be able to land on it? Who will be first? What will it be like when we get there? These were among the questions asked.

There are many technical details to study before an attempt can be made to actually land a team of scientists on the lunar surface. It is desirable first to learn the condition of the surface. Is it hard or soft? Can it support the weight of a space ship? Is it covered with dust? If so, how thick a layer will be found? These questions are difficult to answer.

The first question which must be answered is: How far is the moon from the earth? All computations of size, density, amount of atmosphere, and dimensions of surface features depend on this fundamental piece of information. The approximate distance has been known for many years, even centuries; but it is desirable to find the distance with the utmost precision. Fortunately, it was known to an accuracy of about one mile before the start of space flights.

The old methods depended on the determination of the moon's parallax. Parallax is the angle formed by two lines drawn from the ends of a base line to a distant point. The parallax of the moon is the angle formed at the center of the moon by one-half the diameter of the earth, as shown in Figure 11–1.

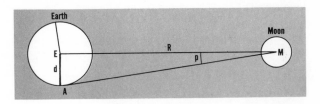

Fig. 11–1 The parallax of the moon.

The problem of finding the moon's distance is similar to the determination of the distance across a body of water where the distance cannot be measured directly. In that problem a base line can be set up, its length measured accurately, and the angles to a point whose distance is to be found measured from both ends of the base line. The computation depends on trigonometry. In Figure 11–2 the base line is $AB$ and the angles $BAC$ and $ABC$ are measured from the ends of the line $AB$. The distances $AC$ and $BC$ are then computed.

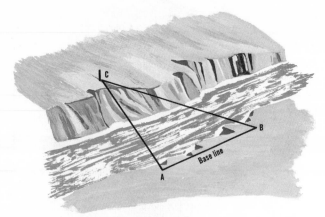

Fig. 11–2  Determination of the distance to an inaccessible point by triangulation.

However, the triangle formed by the two ends of a radius of the earth and the center of the moon is very slender. Consequently, it is not necessary to use trigonometry. In this discussion, the solution of a slender triangle by the use of radian measure will be used. The method is discussed in the Appendix.

In the Appendix, the following formula is developed:

$$\text{angle (in radians)} = \text{parallax} =$$

$$\frac{\text{length of base line}}{\text{length of radius.}} \qquad (11\text{–}1)$$

Adapting this equation to the problem of the moon's parallax, the angle is $p$, the parallax; the length of the radius is $EM$ or $R$, the distance to the moon; and the base line is $AE$, the radius of the earth, $d$. Hence, rewriting equation 11–1, we have

$$R = \frac{d}{p} \text{ where } p \text{ is in radians,} \qquad (11\text{–}2)$$

or,
$$R = 57.3° \times \frac{d}{p°} = 3437.8' \times \frac{d}{p'} =$$

$$206{,}265'' \times \frac{d}{p''} \qquad (11\text{–}3)$$

where the first form is to be used if $p$ is in degrees, the second if $p$ is in minutes and the third if $p$ is in seconds. These equations are not restricted to the parallax of the moon, but may be used for any distances and parallaxes in the solar system.

Also if $p$ is small, less than about 4°, the arc of the circle is so nearly equal to the chord that the small difference in length may be neglected.

If $A$ and $B$ are two points on the earth, for simplicity assumed to be at opposite ends of a diameter, the distance $AB$ is known, and, if the angle $p$ can be measured, the distance to the moon, $R$, can be calculated. In practice, it is not possible to observe the moon simultaneously from two ends of a diameter. But if $A$ and $B$ are as far apart as convenient, the distance between them can be calculated from their latitudes and longitudes.

As can be seen from Figure 11–3, the angle between two points, $S_1$ and $S_2$, on the celestial sphere

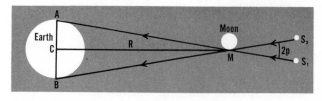

Fig. 11–3  The parallax method of determining the moon's distance.

is also equal to twice the parallax. Because the sphere is infinitely large, one-half the angle between $S_1$ and $S_2$ as seen from the earth and from the moon is essentially the same. It averages 57.04', but varies constantly because of the changing distance from the earth to the moon.

## 11.2  The Moon's Diameter

Assuming the average parallax is 57.04' and the equatorial radius of the earth is 3963 mi, the distance from the center of the earth to the center of the moon may be calculated by substituting in equation 11–3:

$$R = \frac{3438' \times 3963 \text{ mi}}{57.04'} = 238,860 \text{ mi.}$$

By using the most accurate data available, the average distance to the moon is 238,857 mi with an uncertainty of 1.3 mi. This distance is called the *mean distance*. This distance was checked by a radar echo from the moon in 1946.

Knowing the mean distance and measuring the moon's apparent angular diameter, the same formula may be adapted to the determination of the moon's diameter. (Figure 11–4) The mean angular diameter is 31.09'. Hence the diameter

$$AB = \frac{238,857 \text{ mi} \times 31.09'}{3437.8'} = 2160 \text{ mi.}$$

The most accurate value available is 2160.03 mi, with an uncertainty of 0.09 mi or about 465 ft. This figure may be used to determine the size of the lunar features.

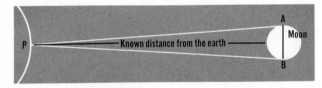

Fig. 11–4   Determination of diameter of the moon.

Since the parallax and distance of the moon vary, its angular diameter must also be a variable quantity. This can be shown to be the case by measuring the apparent diameter with an instrument, such as the surveyor's transit.

Since the earth and the moon are so nearly the same size, the moon's diameter being 27½ percent that of the earth, the two together make up what is called the *earth-moon system*. Their center of mass moves in an elliptical orbit around the sun. The earth departs from this orbit by nearly 3000 mi. The determination of this distance leads to a determination of the mass of the moon.

## 11.3   The Moon's Mass

The center of mass between two bodies is so located that the mass of one body times its distance from the center of mass equals the mass of the other body times its distance from the center. This may be expressed by the following equation:

$$m_1 d_1 = m_2 d_2. \qquad (11\text{–}4)$$

The distance between the center of the earth and the center of mass of the earth-moon system, called the *barycenter*, has been carefully determined at the United States Naval Observatory by observations of the planets and minor planets. These bodies have a small east or west displacement in their orbits, which are produced by the changing position of the earth with respect to the barycenter. This distance is 2903 mi and hence the center of the earth-moon system lies inside the earth.

The distance of the moon from the barycenter is 238,857 − 2903 mi. Substituting in equation 11–4:

$$M_E \times 2903 \text{ mi} = M_M \times 235,954 \text{ mi.}$$

From this equation:

$$\frac{M_E}{M_M} = \frac{235,954}{2903}$$

$$= 81.28.$$

Thus the mass of the moon is 1.23 percent of the mass of the earth. The moon is the only satellite in the solar system that has as large a ratio of mass and diameter to those of its planet, and the earth-moon system is sometimes considered to be a double planet.

Expressed in tons, the mass of the moon is $7.351 \times 10^{19}$ metric tons of 2204.6 lb each or $8.10 \times 10^{19}$ short tons of 2000 lb. From this and the volume calculated from the moon's diameter, its density is

3.343 g/cm³. This is comparable to the density of rocks in the earth's crust. It is not likely that the moon is as compressed at its center as the earth and has been assumed to be fairly uniform in density throughout.

The density of the moon may also be calculated as a proportion of the earth's density. Density is mass divided by volume, which is proportional to the cube of the diameter. Expressing each in terms already found, the density of the moon, $d_M$, is:

$$d_M = \frac{\text{mass of moon}}{\text{mass of earth}} \bigg/ \frac{(\text{diameter of moon})^3}{(\text{diameter of earth})^3}$$

$$= \frac{1}{81.28} \bigg/ \frac{(2160 \, \text{mi})^3}{(7917 \, \text{mi})^3} = 0.605 \, d_E.$$

That is, the density of the moon is 0.605 times the density of the earth or $0.605 \times 5.51$ g/cm³ = 3.343 g/cm³ as before.

## 11.4   Moon's Surface Gravity and Velocity of Escape

The surface gravity of the moon is found similarly, except that it is proportional to the square of the radius, and is:

$$g_M = \frac{1}{81.28} \bigg/ \frac{(\frac{1}{2} \times 2160 \, \text{mi})^2}{(\frac{1}{2} \times 7917 \, \text{mi})^2} = 0.1653 \, g.$$

or about one-sixth the gravity on the surface of the earth.

The velocity of escape also depends on the mass and size of a body. The moon's velocity of escape is equal to the square root of the mass divided by the square root of the radius. Both mass and radius can be expressed in terms of those of the earth. The velocity of escape from the moon's surface is:

$$\sqrt{\frac{1}{81.28}} \bigg/ \sqrt{\frac{1080 \, \text{mi}}{3908 \, \text{mi}}} = 0.212$$

times that from the surface of the earth, or 0.212 times 6.95 mi/sec = 1.475 mi /sec.

## 11.5   The Moon's Path

The apparent path of the moon among the stars as seen from the earth is a great circle which roughly follows the ecliptic. The moon moves in direct motion (from west to east) from night to night, but of course appears to rise and set as other bodies do because of the rotation of the earth. The period of time between successive conjunctions with a star, called the *sidereal month,* is about 27⅓ days. It is somewhat variable because of the attractions by the sun, the bulge at the earth's equator, and the planets. The average sidereal month is 27.3216615 mean solar days and the amount of the variation is as much as seven hours.

As shown in Figure 11–5, the path of the moon crosses the ecliptic in two points, called *nodes.* At

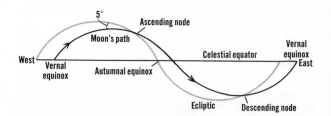

Fig. 11–5   The path of the moon and the ecliptic, showing the ascending and descending nodes and inclination of 5°.

the ascending node, the moon moves from south to north and at the descending node from north to south of the ecliptic. Because of attractions by other bodies, these nodes are not stationary, but move completely around the ecliptic from east to west in about 18.6 years. This motion is called the *regression of the nodes.*

Since the sun is also moving along the ecliptic in an easterly direction, the intervals between new moons, when the moon is in conjunction with the sun, is longer than the sidereal month. This month of the phases is called the *synodic month* and averages about 29½ days in length. A more accurate value is 29ᵈ 12ʰ 44ᵐ 2.8ˢ or 29.53059 mean solar days. The increase in length of the synodic month over the sidereal month is the time it takes the moon to move from the position of the sun at one new moon to its position at the next new moon.

The inclination of the moon's path to the ecliptic is about 5°, but this is also variable from 4° 59′ to 5° 18′ because of the external attractions. Its average is 5° 08′.

The relation between sidereal and synodic month can be found from the formula:

$$\frac{1}{Sy} = \frac{1}{Si} - \frac{1}{E} \qquad (11\text{-}5)$$

or

$$\frac{360°}{Sy} = \frac{360°}{Si} - \frac{360°}{E} \qquad (11\text{-}6)$$

where $Sy$ = synodic month, $Si$ = sidereal month, and $E$ = 1 year. This is sometimes called the "stern chase" formula. In equation 11-6, it is seen that the first term on the right is the number of degrees the moon moves on its path in one day. The second term is the number of degrees the sun moves on the ecliptic in one day. The difference is the gain of the moon on the sun. Substituting the values of $Sy$, $Si$, and $E$,

$$\frac{360°}{29.5^d} = \frac{360°}{27.3^d} - \frac{360°}{365^d},$$

$$12.2° = 13.2° - 1.0°.$$

That is, if the moon gains 12.2° per day over the sun, it will gain a complete lap in 29.5 days (360° divided by 12.2° per day), or one synodic month.

## 11.6   The Moon's Orbit

The parallax of the moon and its apparent diameter change continually due to the variation in the distance to the moon. Both distance and apparent diameter are inversely proportional to the parallax. Hence, relative distances can be plotted on a convenient scale, which is inversely proportional to either the parallax or the apparent diameter. When they are correlated with the direction of the moon

as seen against the background of stars, it can be deduced that the moon's orbit is an ellipse with the earth at one focus. Also, since it is gravitation which holds the two bodies together, it can be deduced mathematically that Kepler's laws, restated for satellites, should hold for the moon and all artificial satellites in orbit around the earth.

The period of the moon in its orbit around the earth is 1 sidereal month of 27⅓ days. The eccentricity of the orbit is about 0.055, but is quite variable because of external attractions. These attractions are called *perturbations*, which are defined as the disturbances due to such forces as the attraction of the sun and the planets on the normal elliptical orbit. These perturbations in the case of the moon and the artificial satellites are very numerous and very difficult to compute. The principal perturbations are from the sun and the bulge at the earth's equator.

Perturbations affect the eccentricity of the orbits by causing them to vary by small amounts, but the averages remain about the same. For the moon, the average eccentricity, $e$, is 0.0549. They also cause the regression of the nodes and the changes in the inclination of the orbit to the plane of the ecliptic. The average inclination, $i$, is 5.145° = 5° 8.7′.

The point of closest approach of the moon to the earth is called *perigee;* that of greatest recession is *apogee*. The line joining these two points is the major axis of the ellipse, or the line of apsides. The center of the major axis is also the center of the ellipse. (See Figure 11-6.)

Because of perturbations, the line of apsides rotates from west to east, that is in the opposite direction to the regression of the nodes. This is called the *advance of the perigee*. The perigee point makes a complete circle around the sky in about nine years (8.85 years). Because of this advance of over 3° per month, the moon reaches perigee at intervals of 27.55455 days. This is known as the anomalistic month.

The distance of the earth from the center of the ellipse is found by multiplying the mean distance

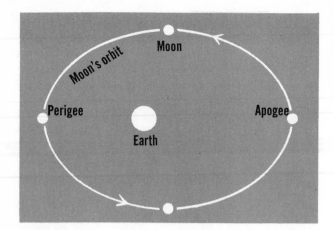

Fig. 11–6    The elliptical orbit of the moon around the earth.

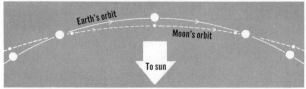

Fig. 11–7    Since the sun's gravitational pull is greater than that of the earth or the moon, both bodies follow orbits which are continually concave toward the sun.

by the eccentricity. It is 13,100 mi. Therefore the average perigee distance is 225,757 mi and the average apogee distance is 251,957 mi. But because of perturbations, the smallest actual perigee distance is 221,463 mi and the largest apogee distance is 252,710 mi.

Professor E. W. Brown of Yale University spent many years in his computation of lunar perturbations. He calculated 155 periodic terms in the equation to determine the position of the moon in its orbit with coefficients greater than 0.1″ and more than 500 smaller terms. The exact computation of the lunar parallax requires almost 150 terms. The equation needed to determine the position of the moon above or below the ecliptic (its celestial latitude) requires about half as many as for the determination of its east-west position (its celestial longitude).

## 11.7    Phases and Elongations

As Figure 11–7 shows, the moon's orbit is everywhere concave toward the sun. This can only be seen by drawing the path of the earth-moon system to the same scale as the distance to the sun.

The phases of the moon are produced by the changing positions of the three bodies, as shown in Figure 11–8. At new moon, the elongation of the moon can vary between 0° and 5°, because of the inclination of the orbit. If the inclination were 0° and the moon always moved in the ecliptic, there would be an eclipse of the sun at every new moon. But because of the 5° inclination, the moon may be as far as 5° from the sun at new moon. Thus eclipses are only occasionally possible.

Fig. 11–8    Production of phases of the moon.

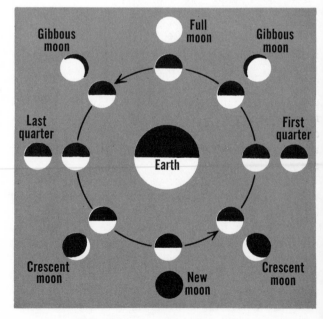

The age of the new moon is zero and increases through the 29½ days of the synodic period. After new moon, the elongation increases and the moon shows a crescent phase until it is 90° from the sun, at quadrature. It is then at first quarter and the moon's age is about seven days, or one-fourth of its synodic period. After quadrature, the moon is gibbous and we can see more than one-half of its illuminated surface. At full moon—age 15 days—the elongation is between 175° and 180°. Elongation is always measured as the shortest distance between two bodies, and so the full moon can never have an elongation greater than 180°. Lunar eclipses occur at full moon when the moon is at a node. At full moon, the moon rises as the sun sets. After full moon, the phases occur in reverse order until at age 29½ days the moon is new again.

The edge of the moon is called the *limb*. There are both bright and dark limbs, except of course when the moon is new or full. The line between the bright and dark areas, the sunrise or sunset line, is called the *terminator*. It is roughly the arc of a circle, but is very irregular because of the rough surface features. Just after new moon, when the crescent is very narrow, the dark surface can be seen faintly illuminated. This is sometimes called "the old moon in the new moon's arms." The reason for this is that from the moon the earth would appear fully illuminated—a "full earth." Light reflected from the earth's atmosphere returns toward the sun and the moon. Since the reflecting power of the moon, its albedo, is only 7 percent and the earth's albedo is about 40 percent, the earth at full phase would appear 77 times brighter from the moon than the full moon seen from the earth. Thus the light reflected from the earth is bright enough to faintly illuminate the dark part of the moon.

The average interval between moonrises or moonsets is about 24ʰ 50ᵐ. However, because of the variations in the declination of the moon (see Figure 11–9), which run from −28½° to +28½° when the ascending node coincides with the vernal equinox, the times of moonrise, for example, are strongly

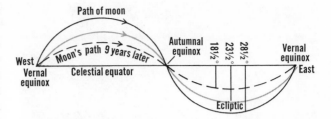

Fig. 11–9   The changing position of the moon's path with the position of the nodes. Note particularly the change of declination.

affected. They also depend on the latitude of the observer. At the north pole when the moon is above the celestial equator, as it is one half of the time, it is always above the horizon. If below the equator, the moon never rises. As one moves south from the pole, there comes a time when the moon just barely rises or sets. From the equator, the moon is above the horizon for exactly 12 hr at a time, except for its daily eastward motion.

At intermediate latitudes, the most noticeable change in the intervals between successive moon-rises is at full moon in autumn. When the full moon is near the vernal equinox and rises at sunset, its northward motion carries it above the equator and this makes it rise earlier. The eastward delay and the northward speed-up in time of rising nearly cancel each other. There are several nights when the moon rises only a few minutes later than on the previous night. This effect nearest the autumnal equinox is called the *harvest moon*. One month later, it is called the *hunter's moon*. They are much more noticeable in the northern parts of the United States than in the south. (See Figure 11–10 for an explanation of the harvest and hunter's moon.)

The ascending node and the vernal equinox will coincide in March, 1969 and again in October, 1988. The harvest and hunter's moons will be most conspicuous during those years. Halfway between those

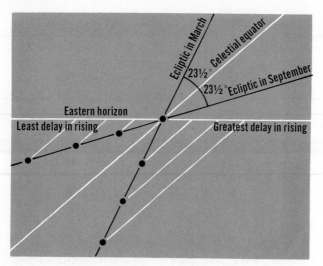

Fig. 11–10   Explanation of the harvest and hunter's moon. The moon's path is near the ecliptic, which is nearly parallel to the horizon in September and again in October.

dates, the ascending node will coincide with the autumnal equinox and the moon's declination will vary from only $-18.5°$ to $+18.5°$. The harvest and hunter's moons will not be as noticeable at that time.

### 11.8   The Moon's Rotation

As the moon revolves around the earth, it is quite obvious that it does not rotate rapidly. The same surface features, the "man in the moon," are always visible except for a few near the limb which can be seen to disappear and reappear during a month's time when viewed through a telescope. This is because the moon always presents approximately the same face to the earth. However, if the moon could be viewed from a distant planet, all parts could be seen each month. So the moon does rotate. The period of rotation is equal to the period of revolution—one sidereal month.

This situation has been produced by tidal action of the earth during the billions of years the two bodies have been in existence. When the moon was less solid than it is at present, the earth raised

tides in the mass of the moon in directions toward and away from the earth, similar to the tides in the earth's oceans raised by the moon. Since the moon's material was viscous, there was a great deal of friction, which slowed up the moon's original rotation until the tides remained fixed toward and away from the earth. When they solidified there remained a bulge in the figure of the moon. The maximum and minimum diameters differ by less than 2 mi.

The far side of the moon has been called the dark side. This is not actually true. When the moon is new, the dark side faces the earth and the far side is completely illuminated. The duration of sunlight on any part of the moon is one-half of one synodic month, or about 15 days. The length of time a star is above the moon's horizon is one-half of one sidereal month, or about 14 days.

### 11.9   Lunar Librations

The disappearance and reappearance of features near the moon's limbs can be explained by four effects called *librations*. They are as follows:

1. Diurnal librations. These are parallax effects. When the moon rises, an observer on the earth can see over the top limb. As the earth rotates, he is carried to a position where he can see beyond the other limb, which he sees as the upper limb of the setting moon. The total effect is equal to the moon's parallax, or about 1° at both moon-rise and moonset.

2. Latitudinal librations. The moon's equator is tipped about 6½° to the plane of the orbit. This permits alternately 6½° of the northern and southern limbs to be visible from some part of the earth during each month.

3. Longitudinal librations. The moon rotates uniformly on its axis. This is because there is no known force to cause the rotation to slow down or speed up. The moon's revolution is not uniform, as stated by Kepler's second law. Hence the rotation and revolution get out of step. At perigee revolution is ahead, and a few degrees of the following limb become visible. At apogee the preceding limb becomes visible by a similar amount, about 8° at each limb.

4. Physical librations. There is a slight shift of the moon due to its bulge in the earth's direction. These librations move the features of the moon by about one mile as seen from the earth.

The result of librations is that 41 percent of the moon's surface can never be seen from the earth. Forty-one percent is always visible, and the remaining 18 percent is visible at times from some place on the earth. This area is along the limb and is very irregular in shape.

## 11.10  The Moon's Atmosphere

The moon has little or no atmosphere. The most powerful argument for this is that the velocity of escape from the lunar surface is so low that, if the moon ever had an atmosphere, it has now all escaped, except for a very thin trace which is likely to be from atoms of the solar wind which are held temporarily captive by the moon's gravitation. The velocity of escape is only 1.475 mi per second, as we have shown. This is very near the velocity of molecules in an atmosphere of oxygen and nitrogen at moderate temperatures, such as we have on the earth. Since this is the case, at some time each atom or molecule of the original atmosphere must have reached the escape velocity and therefore must have left the moon's gravitational field.

As the atmosphere becomes thinner, the temperature rises and the molecular speeds increase. It has been calculated that, if the average molecular velocity were as high as 0.5 mi per second, the moon's atmosphere would have escaped in a few weeks.

In 1958 a Russian astronomer, N. A. Kozyrev, reported that he had seen carbon gas escaping from the region of the central peak in the crater Alphonsus. This would indicate that some molecules are coming from cracks in the floor of the moon. Kozyrev failed to mention that black areas are visible near the crater walls and that they have depressions in them. Ranger 9, which landed in Alphonsus, relayed back to the earth photographs of the crater including the dark areas, but failed to show any trace of carbon gas. Figure 11–11 shows the crater, the central peak, and the black areas. See also Figure 1–7, a Ranger 9 photograph of Alphonsus.

Fig. 11–11  The surface of the moon around the crater Alphonsus (white arrow). The central peak and black areas near the walls are easily visible.

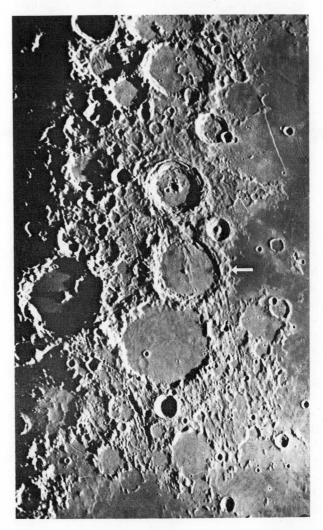

Observational confirmation of the lack of a lunar atmosphere have been cited for many years. They are as follows:

1. No clouds have ever been observed on the moon. The illuminated surface is always distinctly visible through a telescope. This shows that there is no water vapor above the surface.
2. During an occultation of a star (when the moon passes in front of a star), it disappears very suddenly. It does not fade out slowly as would be the case if the moon had an atmosphere. Automatic photometric traces of the light of a star as it passes behind the moon's limb show only a diffraction pattern such as would be the case in the passage of the star's light behind a sharp edge. This pattern disappears in about ⅟₅₀ sec.
3. There is no twilight on the moon. The terminator is a sharp line between the bright and dark areas without the diffusion of light which would be present with an atmosphere.
4. There is a sudden change of temperature across the terminator. If the moon had an atmosphere, the dark side would be warmer and the bright side cooler because of the blanketing effect such as is the case on the earth.

The temperature on the lunar surface can be estimated from the earth by the use of a thermocouple. If two small strips of different metals are welded together at both ends, and if one joint is heated while the other is kept cold, a current of electricity will flow through the metals. When one joint of a thermocouple is placed at the focus of a telescope and moonlight allowed to fall on it, the amount of radiation can be measured, since it is proportional to the amount of the current generated. Then the temperature of the moon's surface can be calculated. A thermocouple placed in the focus of the 100-inch telescope was used to measure the very small amount of heat from stars as well as from the moon.

The results for a region of the moon directly below the sun showed a high temperature of 110°C or 230°F, slightly above the boiling point of water. The dark side measured −173°C or −280°F. Away from the subsolar point a beam of sunlight covers a greater area and the temperature is not quite as high. However, since the sun is above the lunar horizon for two weeks at a time, the surface temperature rises to somewhat higher levels. The temperature at the lunar poles would be uncomfortably, but not unbearably, high.

Sufficient protection for a landing team must be provided, including protection from the ultraviolet rays of direct sunlight. Also, at night lack of solar radiation requires protection from cold. The lack of a lunar atmosphere is particularly striking during a total eclipse of the moon. At those times, sunlight is intercepted by the earth; the lunar temperature drops very rapidly, then rises immediately when the moon moves out of the earth's shadow. The rise in temperature may be as much as 200°C or 360°F in one hour. Under the extreme changes, rocks should be shattered by alternate expansion and contraction unless they are protected by a layer of dust. Before the Surveyor I landing in 1966, the thickness of the dust layer was entirely unknown. Present estimates run from an inch or two to one mile.

Because of the absence of atmosphere, the moon has no water and no clouds. The extremes of temperature result from rapid heat radiation after sunset. The moon has no twilight and no auroras. The sky is black and stars should be visible even in daytime by shielding the eyes from direct sunlight. Blue sky on the earth is caused by scattering of the blue light in the spectrum by particles of air.

On the moon there would be no sound, since sound requires a medium for transmission. Meteors would not be visible, although it is certain that both large and small meteoroids are hitting the moon all the time. Ranger 7 photographs showed the effects of meteoric bombardment on the small surface craters (Figure 1–6). Their sides appeared to be eroded, and, there being no water or wind for erosion, must have been struck by small meteoroids or ultraviolet radiation, which would not get through an atmosphere.

## 11.11 Surface Features

There are several types of features on the lunar surface, all of which, except the smallest, can be observed from the earth. The following is a list of features each of which will be described more fully in following paragraphs:

1. Seas. These are relatively smooth, dark, and large areas which are conspicuous in small instruments.
2. Craters. Hundreds of thousands of depressions in the lunar surface are called craters. They vary from 146 mi to 3 ft in diameter.
3. Mountains and mountain ranges. Through the telescope they are much like the mountains on earth in appearance.
4. Rays. Rays are bright streaks which radiate from some craters. They may be as long as 2000 mi.
5. Rills. These are cracks in the surface, probably produced by faulting when the moon was in the cooling stage.
6. Domes and calderas. These are evidences of a swelling of the surface with resulting subsidence. Occasionally a crater is seen on the top of a mountain peak.

Galileo was the first to observe the dark areas which he called seas, or *maria* in Latin. There are about 20 maria, which cover nearly half the surface. The largest is the Mare Imbrium, the Sea of Showers, which is some 700 mi across. Others have similar fanciful names, such as Tranquility, Serenity, Fertility, Crises, Clouds, Nectar, and the Bay of Rainbows. Most of the seas were named by Hevelius, a Polish astronomer, who published a book on selenography (a term similar to geography, but applied to the moon; Selene was the goddess of the moon).

The seas are not as smooth as they look at first glance, but are pitted with craters and surrounded by mountain ranges. Their dark appearance is due to their low albedo—a reflecting power of only 2 percent or 3 percent compared to 7 percent for the average and 40 percent for Aristarchus, the brightest spot on the moon. The curvature of the moon is so great that the walls around the seas are not visible from the centers. For example, the highest peak in the lunar Appenines is Mt. Huygens, which is 3.4 mi high. This peak cannot be seen from a distance greater than 86 mi, which is only about one-eighth of the distance across the Mare Imbrium.

The rays are nearly straight lines of higher albedo extending outward from certain craters. The most conspicuous ray system radiates from the crater Tycho, which is near the lunar south pole. During full moon, these rays are easily seen and it is possible to trace one across the Sea of Serenity almost to the northern limb. Allowing for the moon's curvature, the length of this ray is more than 2000 mi. It can be traced on Figure 11–12, the Western Hemisphere of the Moon.

Another easily seen system of rays extends radially from the crater Copernicus (see Figure 11–13). Others radiate from Kepler, Herodotus, Aristarchus, and so on. Ranger 7 landed in Mare Nubium (Sea of Clouds) in a relatively smooth area on a ray from Tycho and possibly one from Copernicus. This region was selected as a test site for possible manned spacecraft landings in 1970, because of its apparently smooth surface. Ranger 8 landed in the Sea of Tranquility and found conditions there very similar to those in the Sea of Clouds. The name of the latter sea was changed after the Ranger 7 landing to Mare Cognitum (the Known Sea).

Surrounding many of the seas are ranges of mountains. They are named for mountain ranges of the earth, such as Appenines, Alps, and Caucasus. Other mountain ranges are located in the southern hemisphere. The highest are the Doerfel Mountains and the Leibnitz range, which reach heights of some 30,000 ft. Other mountains are single, such as Pico and Piton, which rise out of the Mare Imbrium. The height of Piton can be calculated from measurements on a photograph taken near the quarter moon, since its shadow is sharp and easily measured. (See Figure 11–13.)

## 11.12 Height of a Lunar Mountain

To measure the height of a mountain from the earth, at least two methods are available. The first requires a knowledge of the altitude of the sun above the

Fig. 11–12 Photograph of the western hemisphere of the moon and drawing (on opposite page) showing principal features of the western hemisphere of the moon. (Lick Observatory Photograph)

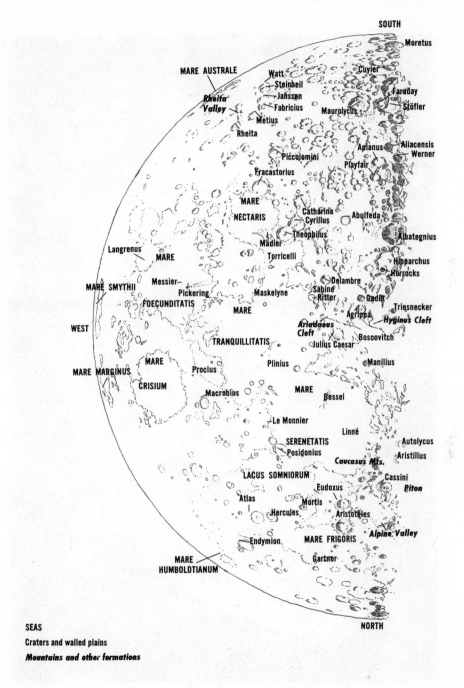

SOUTH

Moretus

MARE AUSTRALE

Watt
Steinheil
Janssen
Fabricius
Metius

Cuvier

Faraday
Stöfler

Maurolycus

Rheita
Valley

Rheita

Aliacensis
Werner

Apianus

Piccolomini

Playfair

Fracastorius

MARE
NECTARIS

Catharina
Cyrillus

Abulfeda

Theophilus

Albategnius

Mädler

Langrenus

Torricelli

Hipparchus
Horrocks

MARE

Messier

Delambre

MARE SMYTHII

Pickering

Sabine
Ritter

Godin

Triesnecker

Maskelyne

Agrippa

Hyginus Cleft

FOECUNDITATIS

MARE

WEST

Ariadaeus
Cleft

Boscovitch

TRANQUILLITATIS

Julius Caesar

Plinius

Manilius

MARE MARGINUS

Proclus

MARE
CRISIUM

MARE

Bessel

Macrobius

Le Monnier

Linné

SERENETATIS

Autolycus

Posidonius

Aristillus

Caucasus Mts.

LACUS SOMNIORUM

Cassini

Eudoxus

Piton

Atlas

Mortis

Hercules

Aristoteles

Endymion

MARE FRIGORIS

Alpine Valley

MARE
HUMBOLDTIANUM

Gartner

NORTH

SEAS

Craters and walled plains

*Mountains and other formations*

Fig. 11–13 Photograph of the eastern hemisphere of the moon and drawing (on opposite page) showing principal features of the eastern hemisphere of the moon. (Lick Observatory Photograph)

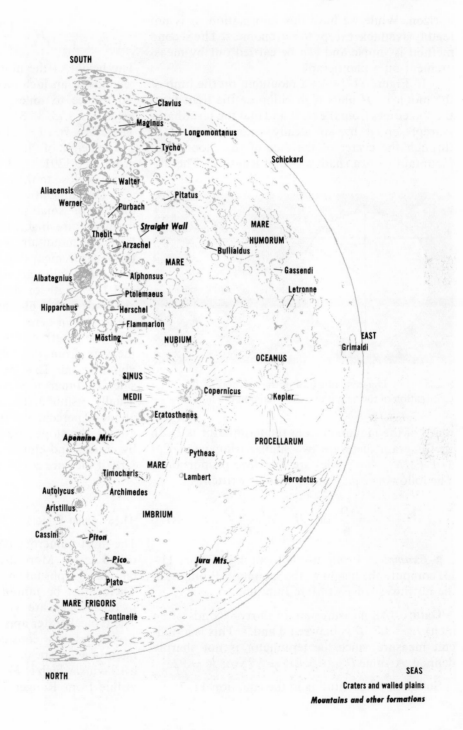

SOUTH

Clavius

Maginus

Longomontanus

Tycho

Schickard

Walter

Aliacensis

Pitatus

Werner

Purbach

MARE

Straight Wall

HUMORUM

Thebit

Arzachel

Bullialdus

MARE

Alphonsus

Gassendi

Albategnius

Ptolemaeus

Letronne

Hipparchus

Herschel

Flammarion

NUBIUM

Mösting

EAST

Grimaldi

OCEANUS

SINUS

MEDII

Copernicus

Kepler

Eratosthenes

PROCELLARUM

Apennine Mts.

Pytheas

MARE

Timocharis

Lambert

Herodotus

Autolycus

Archimedes

Aristillus

IMBRIUM

Cassini

Piton

Pico

Jura Mts.

Plato

MARE FRIGORIS

Fontinelle

NORTH

SEAS

Craters and walled plains

Mountains and other formations

horizon. While we have this information, it is not readily available except to astronomers. The second method is simple and can be carried out by measurement on a photograph.

In Figure 11–14, let a mountain on the limb of the moon be $H$ units high. Suppose the light from the sun comes from the right and that the terminator is represented by an ideally straight line $AOB$ through the center of the face of the moon. The mountain casts a shadow $NT$ of length $L$. The dis-

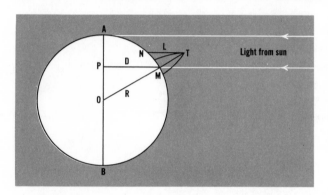

Fig. 11–14   Diagram illustrating the method of determination of the height of a mountain on the moon.

tance of the mountain from the terminator is $D$. In the diagram there are two similar triangles, $OPM$ and $TMN$, whose sides are therefore proportional. The following equation can then be written:

$$\frac{H}{L} = \frac{D}{R} \quad \text{or} \quad H = \frac{L \times D}{R} \qquad (11\text{–}7)$$

▶*Example:*   From the photograph in Figure 11–13, compute the height of the mountain Piton, near the northwest edge of Mare Imbrium.

**Data:**   (All measures are in thirty-seconds of an inch) $L = 1.7$; $D$ is between 6 and 7. This is a difficult measure, since the terminator is not sharply defined. Assume $D = 6.5$; $2R = 5.75$ in; $R = 92$.

**Solution:**   Substituting in the equation 11–7:

$$H = \frac{1.7 \times 6.5}{92} = 0.1201$$

The height of the mountain is, then, 0.1201 thirty-seconds of an inch on the scale of the photograph. To reduce to miles, the moon's diameter, which measures $5.75 \times 32 = 184$ 32/nds, is 2160 miles. Therefore, $\frac{1}{32}$ in = 2160 mi/184 = 11.75 mi.

The height of Piton by measurement of the photograph is $0.1201 \times 11.75$ mi = 1.41 mi, or 7440 ft, which is close to the published height of 7670 ft.

The difficulties of this measurement are obvious. On the small scale of the photograph, all measurements are inaccurate, particularly the distance from the mountain to the terminator. In practice, this measurement should be done directly at the telescope and with varying positions of the terminator and the length of the shadow. The measurements are made with a filar micrometer, but the principles are as shown here.

The length of the mountain is also difficult to measure from this photograph, but seems to be about 15 mi. This indicates that the slopes of the sides of lunar mountains are not as great as is usually assumed. The steepest gradient on Piton is about 40 percent. On the basis of the Ranger photographs, the slopes are probably quite badly scarred by craters and climbing might be difficult, particularly if they are covered with a yard of volcanic ash.

### 11.13   Lunar Craters

The most numerous type of lunar feature is the so-called crater. More than 30,000 have been counted on photographs taken from terrestrial observatories. There must be millions, if the photographs taken by the Rangers are typical of the entire lunar surface. The typical crater apparently is a pit surrounded by a wall, usually considered to be quite steep, frequently with a peak in the center. The largest crater is Clavius, which is 146 mi in diameter. The smallest visible from Ranger 7 was about 3 ft across and

18 in deep. No crater visible with a telescope on the earth is less than a few hundred feet across. While they are found on all parts of the lunar surface, they are most numerous in the southern hemisphere. Many are visible on the seas, but the seas are relatively free of craters compared with the southern areas. Even on the rays in the Mare Nubium (Cognitum) Ranger 7 found a vast network of small craters.

Craters are named for philosophers and astronomers of the past, a custom started by Riccioli, an Italian astronomer, in 1651. A glance at the charts facing the two photographs of the quarter moon in this chapter will give the student a good idea of the famous people represented. More detailed lunar maps have been published.

The floor of the typical crater is below the average level of the surface, sometimes several thousand feet lower. And the walls are piled up above the average level. It has been estimated that the volume of material in the walls is about the same as the volume of the crater, indicating that the material was somehow dug out of the crater and deposited around the rim. Running outward from some of the prominent craters are systems of rays, as mentioned previously. Where did this material come from and why is it brighter than that of the crater floor? The answer seems to be related to the problem of crater formation.

Rills are cracks in the lunar floor. The usual rill is about one-half mile wide, of unknown depth, and usually many miles in length. They are sometimes straight (for example, the Great Wall, which is some 60 mi long) but many are curved and run across other types of features. Ranger 9 photographed beautiful rills on the floor of the crater Alphonsus with small craters strung along the rims. (See Figure 1–7.) Rills are apparently faults in the lunar surface. It is possible that when the moon cooled it contracted and the rills were formed by slippage during the process.

The first American soft landing on the moon was made by Surveyor I on June 2, 1966. The Soviet scientists had engineered the first successful landing with Luna 9 on February 3, 1966. However, the Surveyor I photographs showed much better resolution and have given a much better understanding of the lunar surface.

Surveyor I landed on the Oceanus Procellarum (Ocean of Tempests) near the east limb of the moon and inside a large partially buried crater, which has the smaller crater Flamsteed on its southern rim. (See map, Fig. 11–15.) Photographs of the horizon show low mountains on the crater rim about 12 km

Fig. 11–15 Lunar chart showing the landing site of Surveyor I. Area I designates the site as deduced from horizon features in sections A through F, while area II was deduced from trajectory tracking data. (NASA)

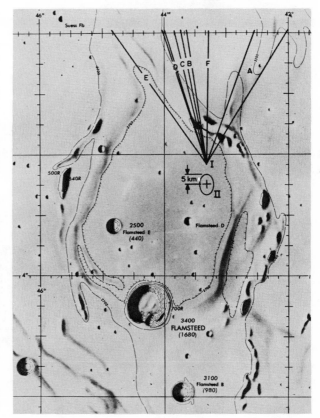

(7 mi) distant. They project up to 100 m (330 ft) above the ordinary near horizon. The ancient crater has been almost buried beneath the covering material of the Ocean. It is about 60 mi in diameter. About 20 small craters, ranging from about 10 to 300 ft in diameter are in sight of the cameras on board the spacecraft. One crater, about 35 ft away, is 10 ft wide and 2 ft deep.

The narrow-angle photograph (Figure 11–16) shows one of the footpads of the vehicle and indi-

cates that the lunar surface is quite hard. The pad sank about 2 inches into the surface on landing. The close-up photo (Figure 11–17) shows that the surface is covered with granular material down to at least 1/30 inch in diameter with large boulders 20 inches long. These boulders are pitted and cracked. The result of a brief study indicates that the surface consists of a hard material with a weaker material on top, which has a depth of about 1 in. It apparently can withstand a pressure of at least 10 lb/in². The

Fig. 11–16   Surveyor I photo of the moon with a portion of the spacecraft landing gear at the upper right. The construction of the foot pads made it possible to obtain data about the load-bearing capacity of the lunar surface. (NASA)

Fig. 11–17  One of 4000 photos taken from Surveyor I during its first five days on the moon. The distance along the horizon (from upper left to lower right) is about 30 yd. (NASA)

coarse blocks and fragments are scattered at random. There apparently is no appreciable layer of dust in this region of the lunar surface. Most of the smaller visible craters are shallow and have low, rounded rims or are apparently rimless.

## 11.14  Formation of Lunar Features

The question of the formation of the craters and other lunar features has never been answered satisfactorily. One school of thought says that the moon

was once a molten mass which solidified, producing the craters by volcanic action. However, since the moon's density is about the same as rock on the earth and since it is believed that there is no dense core, as is the case inside the earth, the central temperature is probably not over 2000°C and the interior is solid rock, very dry, and rigid to the center. If the moon were once a hot, molten mass, it is difficult to see how it could have cooled to its present temperature. Observations from a Russian space rocket which crash landed on the moon, showed no trace of a magnetic field above a height of 30 mi. These observations confirm the theory that the moon does not have a magnetic core.

Another, and probably more widely accepted theory, is that the craters were formed by bombardment of meteors. A meteoroid coming from an orbit around the sun would strike the moon with a velocity as high as 45 mi/sec, or even higher. The kinetic energy of motion would be mostly transformed into heat, raising the temperature to a high degree, enough to melt the surface material. The sudden rise in the temperature, possibly to as much as 1,000,000° Kelvin, would vaporize at least a portion of the lunar rock and result in an explosion, which would be most efficient in a direction perpendicular to the surface. Since the surface gravity is only one-sixth the earth's surface gravity, the explosion would be six times as effective as on the earth, and, because of the lack of friction from an atmosphere, the material would be thrown to great distances. Experiments with bullets fired at a lead plate give results similar to the depths and shapes of the lunar craters, including central peaks.

Some of the kinetic energy would be dissipated into shock waves, which may have caused great destruction of already existing craters and mountains on the far side of the moon. Such effects have not yet been fully investigated. A seismograph landed on the moon would help with this problem.

The fact that craters are seen on the walls of other craters strengthens the theory. But the objection has been raised that no new craters are now being formed. However, if the moon is 5 billion years old and if there are 1 million craters visible from the earth, the rate of production is only one every 5000 years and the moon has been under observation with telescopes for less than one-tenth of that time.

The rays may have been formed from material with higher reflectivity thrown out of the craters when they were formed. Why should these rays run in nearly straight lines, if they were formed by material coming from cracks in the lunar surface? And why do some craters have rays while others do not?

Ranger 9 photographs inside the crater Alphonsus show large rills with craters along their edges. It appears that Alphonsus might have been formed by a dome which was pushed up by gases from inside the moon, a theory which is strengthened by the observations of carbon fumes made by Kozyrev. As the dome settled, the floor shrank and cracked, then later was hit by meteoroids.

One theory of the formation of the seas which has been proposed is that there were grazing collisions with low-velocity particles which produced lava by melting. Another scientist has proposed the theory that they were formed by impact with comets which released chemical energy in addition to kinetic energy. Still another thinks they resulted from internal basalt formed when the fluid interior released gaseous elements. The craters could have formed later. A close examination of the Mare Imbrium shows that there were original craters which have been almost completely filled with heated material at the time the sea was formed.

Probably a better theory is that the moon was originally covered with craters like those in its southern hemisphere and that a very large fall of meteoroids or a comet melted the surface and the material flowed into the existing craters and even into some of the neighboring seas. The smooth floor of the Mare Imbrium could have been produced as a result of the solidification of this melted lava which was later hit by other meteoroids forming the craters of smaller size visible today.

At present it is safest to conclude that the lunar features were not formed by a single kind of catastrophe, but that both impacts from outside and forces inside the moon have been at work for billions of years. Almost certainly, craters like Tycho and Copernicus and their ray systems were formed by impact. They also appear to be younger than others outside the system of seas. Alphonsus and possibly even Clavius may have been formed by the collapse of domes. Investigation by a geologist, who has landed on the moon from a space ship, would be very desirable.

In 1959 the Russians announced that the satellite Lunik III went behind the moon. When it was about 4000 mi from the lunar surface, special cameras were put into operation. The film was developed inside the rocket, stored on magnetic tape, and relayed to the earth after the rocket had returned to within about 25,000 mi of the earth. At the International Astronomical Union meeting in Berkeley, California, in 1961, Russian members of the Union gave other members a map of the far side on which they had located several seas and a few craters, which they had discovered and named. The Russians repeated this feat in 1965. A more detailed Russian map is reproduced in Figure 11–18.

## 11.15  Lunar and Solar Tides

In describing the shape of the moon, mention has been made of the tides raised by the earth on the moon and which have solidified into a permanent bulge in the direction of the earth. The moon also raises tides in the earth, which, while very small, have been measured. But the most obvious tides are those raised in the sea by a combined gravitational pull of the moon and the sun.

Tides are caused by differential forces. That is, because of a difference in distance, the force exerted by the moon and sun on the oceans is different from that on the earth itself. The gravitational pull is inversely proportional to the square of the distance, according to Newton's law. But the differential tidal force varies inversely as the cube of the distance.

Figure 11–19 shows the difference in tidal forces for various parts of the earth. Those on the side toward the moon are greater than those on the other side, because of the different distances involved. However, the tidal force on the far side acts in a direction away from the moon, but toward the moon on the near side. The result is that there are two tidal forces acting at the same time on the two sides. It might be said that the water is pulled away from the earth on the near side, while the earth is

pulled away from the water on the far side. The magnitudes of the forces are indicated in the figure by the relative lengths of the arrows.

The earth rotates under the two tides, so they appear to move westward around the earth at a rate of about 1000 mi per hour at the equator, assuming that the moon is directly above the equator and that the earth is completely covered with water. This is only an ideal case. Because of the land masses and shallow seas in parts of the earth, the actual computation of the tides is very complicated and can be done only by high-speed computers and for each port individually. On the average the high tides, which are followed by low tides, return at intervals of $12^h 25^m$. This is one-half of $24^h 50^m$, which is the average interval between transits of the moon across any meridian. This coincidence was responsible for the discovery that tides are produced by the moon.

The sun also produces tides on the earth. As indicated by the law of gravitation, tides are proportional to the mass of the attracting body as well as to the inverse cube of the distance. Therefore the ratio of the sun's tide to that caused by the moon can be calculated as follows:

$$\frac{T_{sun}}{T_{moon}} = \frac{M_{sun}}{M_{moon}} \times \frac{D^3_{moon}}{D^3_{sun}} =$$

$$\frac{333,000}{1/81.5} \times \frac{(0.239 \times 10^6 \text{ mi})^3}{(92.9 \times 10^6 \text{ mi})^3} = 0.46$$

In other words, the sun's tide-raising force is not quite one-half that of the moon. Because of changing distances, the above figure is only an average value between a high of 0.57 and a low of 0.35.

When the moon is new or full (i.e., at syzygy), the two tides reinforce each other. This is called a *spring tide*. At the times of spring tides, the high tides are unusually high and are followed by unusually low tides. At quarter moon (quadrature), the solar and lunar tides tend to cancel each other. The moon's tide being slightly greater, there is a shallow high tide followed by a moderate low tide. This is called a *neap tide*. Since the distances to the moon

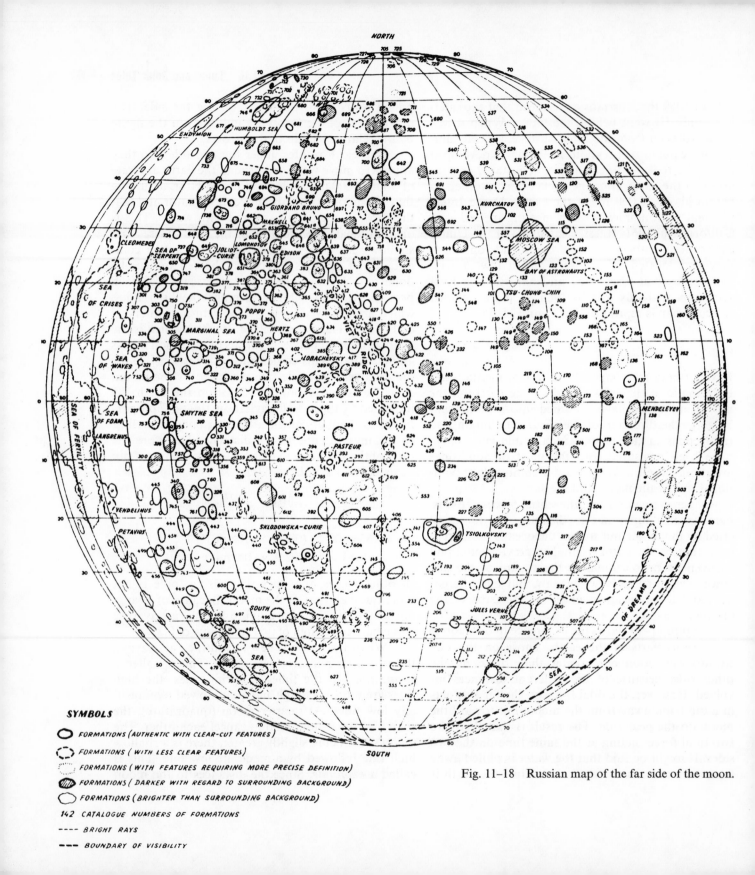

Fig. 11–18 Russian map of the far side of the moon.

**SYMBOLS**

◯ FORMATIONS (AUTHENTIC WITH CLEAR-CUT FEATURES)

◌ FORMATIONS ( WITH LESS CLEAR FEATURES)

⬚ FORMATIONS (WITH FEATURES REQUIRING MORE PRECISE DEFINITION)

⬤ FORMATIONS ( DARKER WITH REGARD TO SURROUNDING BACKGROUND)

◯ FORMATIONS ( BRIGHTER THAN SURROUNDING BACKGROUND)

142 CATALOGUE NUMBERS OF FORMATIONS

---- BRIGHT RAYS

– – BOUNDARY OF VISIBILITY

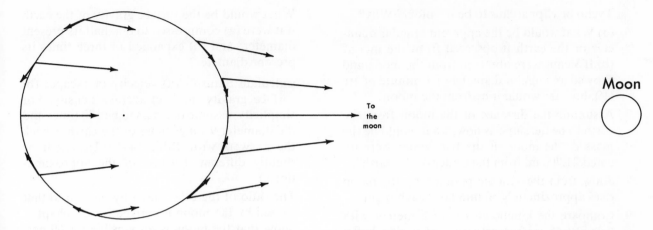

Fig. 11–19   Relative magnitude of the tide-raising force by the moon on different parts of the earth.

and sun are involved in the tide-raising forces, it is easy to see that the highest spring tides occur when the earth is at perihelion, which occurs in January, and when the moon is at perigee.

As the tides ebb and flow, there is friction between the water and the ocean floor, particularly where the depth of the water is small. The narrow Bay of Fundy in eastern Canada has tides which are sometimes as high as 50 ft. The friction is probably greatest in the Bering Straits. The effects of these forces are to slow the rotation of the earth. The amount can be calculated from the times of eclipses centuries ago. It has been deduced that the length of the day has increased by about 0.0016 sec per century, equivalent to a rate of decrease of energy of some 2 billion horsepower.

The final result of the exchange of energy between the earth and the moon will be that the earth's rotation will eventually be stopped entirely and the earth and the moon will keep the same hemispheres directed toward each other. The moon will also slow down in its revolution around the earth until the month and the day are equal to an estimated 47 of our present days. The moon will meanwhile recede from the earth.

After the lunar tides stop, the solar tides will still be acting. They will bring the moon back toward the earth and its distance will keep on decreasing until finally the moon will come so near the earth that the tidal forces will shatter the moon and the earth will acquire a ring system like that of the planet Saturn. These changes will require an immense amount of time.

QUESTIONS AND PROBLEMS

1. What is the phase of the moon when it is on the meridian at (a) 6 P.M.; (b) midnight; and (c) 3 A.M.? **Ans:** (a) first quarter.

2. What phases would the earth exhibit to an observer on the moon? Would the earth rise and set?

3. At what phases of the moon are the craters Archimedes and Kepler observable?

4. Measure the lengths of the Alpine Valley and the crater Archimedes on the moon photographs and compute their length in miles. **Ans:** Alpine Valley, about 80 mi.

5. Judging from their appearance in the moon photographs, would you estimate the crater

Tycho or Hipparchus to be the older? Why?

6. (a) What would be the apparent angular diameter of the earth if observed from the moon? (b) If Venus were observed from the moon and showed an angular diameter of 1 minute of arc (1′), how far would it be from the moon?

7. Assuming the distance of the moon from the earth to be the same as now, what would be the mass of the moon, if the barycenter were located 21,700 mi from the center of the earth?

8. Show from the synodic period why the moon rises approximately 50 min later each night.

9. Compare the kinetic energy of a meteor with velocity 45 mi/sec with that of a rifle bullet with muzzle velocity 0.5 mi/sec, if their masses are the same. (See Chapter 2 for kinetic energy.)

10. Show that in the figure for the determination of the height of a lunar mountain there are two similar right triangles.

*11. Following the procedure outlined for computing the height of Piton, compute the height of the wall of the crater Eratosthenes.

12. What would be the surface gravity of the earth if it were (a) compressed to one-half its present diameter; and (b) expanded to three times its present diameter?

*13. Calculate Saturn's (a) velocity of escape; (b) surface gravity; and (c) average density. For simplicity, assume the mass to be 100 times and the diameter 9 times those of the earth. Check the answers with Table 14–1. (They will be slightly different because of the approximations.)

14. The ratio of the tide caused by the sun to that caused by the moon is derived in this chapter. Show that the moon is responsible for 69 percent of the total tide-raising force.

15. Restate Kepler's three laws of planetary motion for satellites in orbit around the earth or around other planets.

16. Using the sidereal period of the moon and its mean distance, calculate by Kepler's third law (restated in Question 15) the distance from the earth's surface to a satellite whose period is one day.

# Chapter Twelve

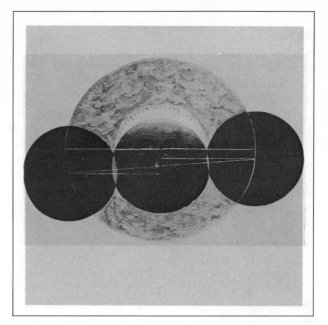

# The Sun

The sun is a star; but since the earth is at just the right distance for it to support the kind of life which exists on the earth, it is the most important star to us. It is also the only star which is near enough to be examined in detail with our telescopes. In fact it is so close that the earth is located in the solar atmosphere. Since the sun is a star, a good start can be made in stellar astronomy by a careful study of all the solar details.

The earth obtains all its heat and light energy from the sun, except for a few sources which cannot be traced directly to it. There are, for example, such sources of energy as those obtained from nuclear reactions, volcanoes and hot springs, and from lunar tides. Other sources, such as coal and oil deposits, can be traced to plant and animal life that grew in sunlight. Water power is possible since solar energy lifts the water, which then falls from higher to lower levels. Even the wind, which drives sailboats and still turns windmills, comes from a circulation of air due to solar heating. And solar tides furnish part of the tidal power, which we have not yet learned to harness satisfactorily.

## 12.1 The Sun's Distance and Size

The distance to the sun is a fundamental unit that must be known before we can determine the dimensions of solar features, and, going still further out into space, investigate the physical nature of stars and the parts of the universe to which they belong.

The problem of determining the distance from the earth to the sun has been a very difficult one for centuries; but we now have a good value, which is probably accurate to a few hundred miles. The reason for the difficulty of the problem is that the parallax method used for the determination of the distance to the moon cannot be used because no bright stars can be seen on the sky background behind the sun. Also the angle is quite small, being less than nine seconds of arc (8.8″).

However, other methods are available, particularly now that we have radar and space vehicles. The older methods were based on celestial mechanics and in 1900 a parallax of 8.8″ was adopted by international agreement as the best value at that time. Since 1900 the sun's distance has been expressed in terms of the distance defined by that parallax. The distance of about 92,890,000 mi is called *one astronomical unit*.

The method used before 1900 to determine the length of the astronomical unit was based on observations, first of Mars, but later of Venus. In 1874 and 1882 Venus passed directly between the earth and the sun. This is known as a transit of Venus, a phenomenon which occurs in pairs at intervals of about 130 years. The next transits will occur in 2004 and 2012. The transits last century were used to obtain an accurate distance to Venus by the parallax method. They also gave a quite accurate value of the astronomical unit. Later, the discovery of the minor planet or asteroid, Eros, provided an object which could be used with even greater accuracy. Eros has a starlike appearance, comes fairly close to the earth, and has a parallax which can be measured easily. The method used will now be described, but a simplification will be assumed.

Eros came to opposition with the sun in 1931 at a distance of about 14 million miles from the earth. Its parallax was about one minute (1′) at closest approach. Because of its starlike appearance—it is about 15 mi long and 5 mi wide—its position could be measured with precision. By observing it over several weeks and from different observatories, a large volume of data was collected, which was used to determine the parallax.

The calculation of the length of the astronomical unit depends on the use of celestial mechanics for a determination of the orbits of the earth and of Eros. The elements of the orbits include the sidereal period, the mean distance from the sun to Eros in terms of the earth's distance, and the eccentricity of the orbits. A simplified discussion is presented here, assuming that the fundamental data have been obtained. Complications in practice arise because of the elliptical shapes of the orbits. The solution for the solar parallax required ten years. The result was published by Sir Harold Spencer Jones, at that time Astronomer Royal of England.

Assume for a first approximation that the orbit of Eros is a circle and lies outside the earth's orbit, also considered to be a circle. (See Figure 12–1.) Suppose also that it can be observed at enough oppositions to permit the determination of the synodic

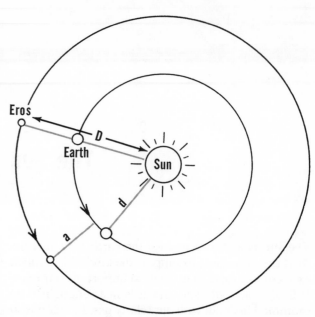

Fig. 12–1   A simplified explanation of the determination of the distance from the earth to the sun by the use of the minor planet Eros.

period. From the synodic period, the sidereal period can be calculated and used in Kepler's third law to determine the mean distance from the sun.

▶*Example:*   Let the synodic period of Eros be assumed as 2.25 years. Calculate its sidereal period and its mean distance from the sun.

The formula from Chapter 6 is:

$$1/Sy = 1/E - 1/Si.$$

**Substituting:**

$$1/2.25 = 1/Si - 1/1.$$

Solving for $Si$, the sidereal period is 1.8 years. Using Kepler's third law,

$$A^3 = P^2$$

from which $\quad D^3 = (1.8)^2 = 3.24$

and $\qquad D = \sqrt[3]{3.24} = 1.48$ a.u.

$D$ has been substituted for $A$ in Figure 12–1, and is the radius of Eros' orbit assumed to be a circle. The distance is found in terms of the earth's distance from the sun.

In the actual case, the orbit is not circular and the sidereal period cannot be determined directly; and so it is necessary to use the methods of orbit computation developed in celestial mechanics. In these methods, which cannot be described here, it is necessary to have only three positions for the asteroid to determine the entire set of elements of the orbit. With the six elements, it is possible to compute the position of the body for any past or future time. With more than three positions, the orbit is that which best satisfies all the observations.

▶ *Example:* (continued): Still assuming circular orbits, suppose the distance from the orbit of the asteroid to that of the earth ($a$ in Figure 12–1) has been determined. Kepler's third law can now be rewritten as:

$$\frac{(a + d)^3}{d^3} = \frac{P^2}{1^2} \tag{12-1}$$

Taking the cube roots:

$$(a + d) = \sqrt[3]{P^2} \times d. \tag{12-2}$$

Let $a = 44,500,000$ mi and $P = 1.8$ years. Then,

$$\sqrt[3]{P^2} = \sqrt[3]{(1.8)^2} = \sqrt[3]{3.24} = 1.48.$$

**Substituting** in equation 12–2,

$$a + d = 1.48d$$

$$0.48d = a = 44,500,000 \text{ mi}$$

and $\qquad d = 92,800,000$ mi.

After all the complications were taken care of, the 1931 distance to the sun was a little larger than the 1900 determination. Since that time, there have been still better determinations. When the distance to Venus was measured by radar in 1962, a value of 92,975,000 mi was obtained with an uncertainty of about 300 mi. This was followed by observations of Venus from Mariner 2 in December, 1962, with a still different value from the radar measure. At the International Astronomical Union general assembly in Hamburg in August, 1964, the conclusion was reached that the distance from the earth to the sun is between 149,598,000 km and 149,598,500 km (92,955,700 to 92,956,000 mi).

After the distance has been determined, the diameter of the sun can be found from its apparent mean angular diameter of 32 minutes (32′) of arc. In miles, the diameter is 864,000 with an uncertainty of about 100 mi.

## 12.2 The Sun's Mass

The sun's mass can be determined from gravitational formulas and is found to be $1.99 \times 10^{33}$ g or 2 octillion metric tons. The mass of the sun is therefore 332,930 times the mass of the earth.

---

The simplest method of computation is from mechanics: In circular motion the acceleration towards the center of attraction is equal to the square of the velocity divided by the radius of the circle. It is also known from Newton's law of gravitation that the acceleration is proportional to the mass divided by the square of the distance. Hence, adapting these two equations to the problem of determining the mass of the sun, we have:

$$a = \frac{V^2}{R} = G\frac{M_{sun}}{R^2} \quad \text{where } V = \frac{2\pi R}{P} \tag{12-3}$$

In these equations, $a$ is the acceleration toward the center; $R$ is the radius of the circle; $V$ is the orbital (circular) velocity; and $P$ is the period of revolution. In this case the orbiting body is the earth, and the orbit is nearly circular. By using the average distance and acceleration, a nearly correct value of the mass of the sun is obtained. From the equation 12–3,

$$M_{sun} = \frac{V^2 R}{G} = \frac{(2\pi R)^2 R}{P^2 G}$$

Substituting the known values,

$$M_{sun} = \frac{(6.2832)^2 (1.496 \times 10^{13}\ cm)^3}{(31,557,000\ sec)^2 \times 6.667 \times 10^{-8}}$$

$$= 1.99 \times 10^{33}\ g$$

Dividing the mass in grams by the volume in cubic centimeters, the average density of the sun is 1.41 g/cm³, which is smaller than the earth's average density of 5.51 g/cm³ and the moon's of 3.34 g/cm³.

## 12.3   The Sun's Radiant Energy

The determination of the sun's temperature depends on a measure of the amount of energy received at the earth's mean distance. The space between the earth and the sun is so empty that it can be assumed that very little solar energy has been absorbed on the way. Thus it is possible to calculate the amount of energy that one square centimeter of the solar surface is radiating into space.

One difficulty in the measurement of solar energy is that it is absorbed by the earth's atmosphere. Until recently, it was necessary to set up radiation measuring instruments at various altitudes and calculate what it would be outside the atmosphere. Now it is possible to send instruments into space and send back by radio results of the measurements.

The instrument used is the pyrheliometer, which measures the rate of increase in temperature of a solid or liquid exposed to sunlight. It is of course necessary to be sure that only solar radiation strikes the pyrheliometer and that none is lost by reradiation during the experiment.

The amount of solar radiation received outside the earth's atmosphere at the mean distance from the sun is called the *solar constant*. It is not quite constant, but varies slightly, usually not over 0.4 percent. Its value obtained by a long series of measurements is 1.96 cal (calories) per minute per square centimeter of surface at right angles to the direction of the sun.

A calorie is the amount of heat necessary to raise the temperature of 1 g of water by 1°C. It is equal to 0.003968 B.T.U. (British thermal unit) or 4.186 × 10⁷ ergs. The solar constant is thus 1.367 × 10⁶ ergs/sec/cm².

It is safe to assume that the sun radiates uniformly in all directions. If this were not so, there would be cool or hot regions in space and there is no evidence that this is so. The total amount of solar radiation can now be calculated by multiplying the solar constant by the number of square centimeters in the surface of a sphere whose radius is equal to one astronomical unit, or 1.496 × 10¹³ cm.

Since the area of a sphere is $4\pi r^2$, the area of this sphere is

$$4\pi (1.496 \times 10^{13}\ cm)^2 = 2.8124 \times 10^{27}\ cm^2$$

Similarly, the radius of the sun is 1.6093 × 10¹⁰ cm, and its surface area is 6.087 × 10²² sq cm. The rate of radiation per sq cm of the sun is the total radiation per second divided by its area, or

$$\frac{3.846 \times 10^{33}\ ergs/sec}{6.087 \times 10^{22}\ cm^2} = 6.317 \times 10^{10}\ ergs/sec.$$

This is equivalent to 84,750 hp (horsepower) of continual radiation from each square meter or more than 70,000 hp per square yard of the sun's surface.

## 12.4   Radiation Laws and the Sun's Temperature

Knowing the total radiation per square centimeter of the sun's surface, its temperature can be calculated from radiation laws formulated in the nineteenth century. It was found that all heated solids and liquids radiate energy in a similar manner. The amount of radiation emitted at a given temperature depends on the physical characteristics, such as polish and color, rather than chemical composition. Kirchhoff, who formulated the laws of spectrum analysis, discovered that at any given temperature the radiating power of a surface is directly proportional to its absorbing power. Black, which is the best absorber, is also the best emitter. Although there is no surface that absorbs all incident radiation, it was found theoretically convenient to base the radiation laws on a hypothetically perfect absorber, called a black body. The results for real surfaces with various physical characteristics can then be corrected to black-body radiation.

Black bodies emit electromagnetic radiation even when cool, but the waves are in the infrared portion of the spectrum, and are too long to be seen by the eye. When a body is heated, the first radiation apparent to the eye is a dull, red glow. As the temperature rises, the color changes to white and then to blue. However, the observed color at any temperature is a mixture of many wavelengths. The distribution of energy over the spectrum for several temperatures is shown in Figure 12–2. Although these curves are based on the theoretical black body, their general shapes were first obtained in the nineteenth century from measurements of radiating surfaces that closely approximated black-body radiation. It will be noticed that the sun's radiation curve is close to that of a black body at 6000° K.

Initially, attempts to derive a law from existing theory that completely described the shapes of these curves failed, but two laws that describe certain characteristics were derived. Stefan's law states: The total energy radiated by a black body is proportional to the fourth power of the temperature. The formula is:

$$E = 5.72 \times 10^{-5} \times T^4 \qquad (12\text{–}4)$$

where $T$ is the temperature in degrees Kelvin (absolute temperature) and the constant equates $T^4$ to the total energy in ergs per second.

The total energy radiated at all wavelengths at a given temperature is proportional to the area under the energy curve for that temperature. It is evident from Figure 12–2 that this area increases rapidly as the temperature increases. The total energy at one temperature can be compared to that at another

temperature by taking the fourth power of the ratio of the two temperatures. For example,

$$\frac{\text{total energy at } 6000^\circ \text{K}}{\text{total energy at } 3000^\circ \text{K}} = \left(\frac{6000^\circ \text{ K}}{3000^\circ \text{ K}}\right)^4 = \left(\frac{2}{1}\right)^4 = 16.$$

The temperature of the sun can be found from Stefan's law by substituting the total energy radiated per square centimeter:

$$T^4 = \frac{\text{total energy/cm}^2}{5.72 \times 10^{-5}}$$

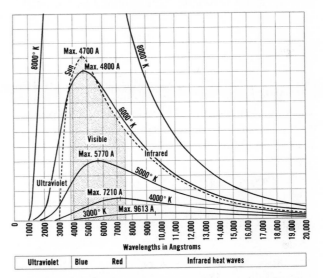

Fig. 12–2   Distribution of energy (heat) along the spectrum. The distances up from the base line to various points in the temperature curves show the amounts of heat radiated at the various temperatures. These quantities of heat (and the areas) are proportional to the fourth power of the temperatures. This is Stefan's law. Note that the maximum points in the curves move progressively toward the short-wave end as the temperature rises. Wien's law gives the relation between temperature and the wavelength of maximum energy. The dotted line is the heat curve of the sun's spectrum. It most nearly matches the 6000° K temperature curve. Note that much of the sun's ultraviolet radiation is missing. The air absorbs everything beyond wave length 2950 A.

Or,   $T^4 = \dfrac{6.317 \times 10^{10}}{5.72 \times 10^{-5}} = 1.11 \times 10^{15}$

and $T = 5760°K$.

It is also apparent from the radiation curves that, as the temperature increases, a greater portion of the energy is radiated at shorter wavelengths. This is described by a law derived by Wilhelm Wien, a German physicist: The wavelength for which the radiation is most intense, $\lambda_{max}$, is inversely proportional to the absolute temperature. The higher the temperature, the more energy is concentrated in the shorter, bluer wavelengths. Expressed as a formula:

$$\lambda_{max} = \frac{0.289}{T} \qquad (12\text{--}5)$$

where $\lambda_{max}$ is in centimeters and $T$ in degrees Kelvin.

This law affords another means of calculating the sun's temperature. The value of $\lambda_{max}$ from measurements of the solar energy curve is in the blue at 4700 A. Substituting,

$$4700\,\text{A} = 4.7 \times 10^{-5}\ \text{cm},\ T = \frac{0.289}{\lambda_{max}},$$

and   $T = \dfrac{0.289}{4.7 \times 10^{-5}} = 6150°K$.

Since Stefan's and Wien's laws are based on different data, it is not surprising that the two values of $T$ differ. It is sufficiently accurate to accept $6000°K$ as the solar temperature. This is based on radiated energy and is an average, effective observed temperature.

_____

A complete description of the curves was finally derived by Max Planck in 1900. Both Stefan's and Wien's laws can be derived mathematically from Planck's law.

The formula for Planck's law is:

$$E(\lambda, T) = \frac{c_1 \lambda^{-5}}{e\,(\exp c_2/\lambda T) - 1} \qquad (12\text{--}6)$$

where $c_1 = 3.740 \times 10^{-5}$; $c_2 = 1.4385$; and $e = 2.718$, the base of the natural logarithms.

_____

## 12.5  Observing the Sun

The sun is almost 500,000 times brighter than the moon. It was once considered to be a perfect heavenly body without blemish. But at times, when sunlight is weakened by mist, fog, or dust so the sun is still visible, its surface can be seen to show dark areas. Galileo saw these areas as spots on the sun without recognizing them for what they really are. At first they were supposed to be caused by clouds, but were soon found to be on the sun's disk.

The sun may be viewed visually, if proper precautions are taken. Never look directly at the sun, since it is so bright and emits dangerous rays which can ruin the observer's eyes very quickly. The best way with a small telescope is to project the sun through the telescope onto a piece of white paper held a few inches from the eyepiece. The eyepiece is left in place, but the focus must be adjusted until the image is sharp at the edges. The edge is called the *limb*, the same term that was used for the moon. It will be used again for the planets and stars.

Even with such simple apparatus several things about the sun's disk may be noticed. First, if there are sunspots, they will be seen easily. Next, the sun looks darker at the edge than in the center. There are spots most of the time, although there are periods when no spots are visible. Near the spot areas, particularly when they are close to the limb, there are bright areas called *faculae*. This word means little torches. They are most easily seen near the limb, because at the center they are about as bright as the solar background. Near the limb, the faculae are brighter than the background and are visible even in small telescopes. In Figure 12–3, sunspots are shown as dark areas and faculae as bright areas.

Fig. 12–3   The sun on December 25, 1957, showing sunspots and faculae. Notice that the sun is darker at the limb than at the center. (Photograph from the Mount Wilson and Palomar Observatories)

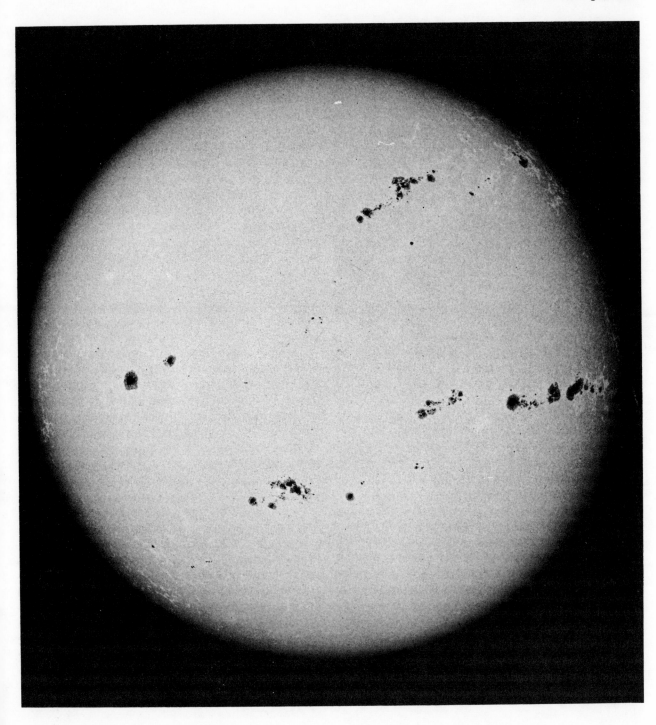

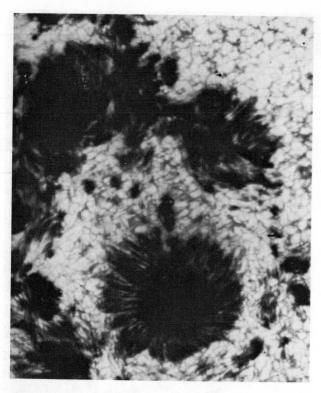

Fig. 12–4 Photograph of a portion of the sun taken from a balloon at about 80,000 ft. Granules or irregular white spots, last about 5 min; dark areas, lasting days or weeks, are sun spots. (Project Stratoscope of Princeton University sponsored by NSF, ONR, and NASA)

Outside the spot and faculae areas, the sun is not uniformly bright, but has a mottled or spotted appearance. The small areas in Figure 12–4 were originally called rice grains, but now are called *granules*. They have been photographed at high altitudes where the air is steady and the seeing good. But more recently they have been photographed with telescopes lifted above the surface of the earth to about 80,000 ft. The first (Figure 12–4) were made with a 12-inch telescope in an unmanned balloon in the northern part of the United States. The telescope was pointed at the sun by photoelectric guidance mechanisms. The photographs were taken with exposures of $1/1000$ sec at the rate of one photograph every second.

These photographs show that the granules are usually from 250 to 600 mi in diameter; but smaller and larger ones have been observed. Their lifetimes are usually from one to about ten minutes. They are hot masses of gas from the solar interior which rise, cool, and then fall back. These motions were detected and measured in balloon experiments. The temperature apparently varies between 120°K and 230°K above and below the average 6000°K of the solar disk. The granulations are visible almost to the limb.

## THE STRUCTURE OF THE SUN

For convenience, the sun is divided into four layers. They are, from the center outwards: the *interior,* the *photosphere,* the *chromosphere,* and the *corona.*

The interior contains nearly all the sun's mass; it is the part where the energy which the sun produces is radiated into space. Its nature can only be determined by computation based on the known laws of physics. This process has been called an analytical boring machine. A discussion of the interior will be delayed until the other layers have been described.

### 12.6 The Photosphere

The photosphere is that layer through which the solar energy escapes from the interior. Its name indicates that it is the layer from which light comes and is therefore the part which we see. The temperature at the top of the photosphere (formerly called the reversing layer) can be determined by the radiation formulas and is about 6000°K as derived in Section 12.4. An exact figure cannot be given, since the radiation escapes at different depths and the temperature varies from one level to another in the photosphere. This is also the reason for the darkening at the limb.

It has also been estimated that the thickness of the photosphere is about that of the diameters of the granules, perhaps 600 mi. If it could be seen by itself, its spectrum would be continuous. But at the top the cooler gases absorb some of the energy, producing the dark-line spectrum discovered by Fraunhofer. The wavelengths of more than 25,000 lines have been determined from which 60 different elements have been definitely identified with 7 more almost certain. There are still thousands of unmeasured lines, particularly in the ultraviolet and infrared regions of the spectrum.

With the development of space-borne instruments, the solar spectrum has been extended from 2900 A (angstroms), where the earth's atmosphere cuts off the ultraviolet, to 977 A. Also by the use of infrared detectors, it has been extended to 23,700 A where the atmosphere cuts off again. There is one fundamental line at 1215 A in the spectrum of hydrogen, called the Lyman-alpha line, which has been of special interest. A few lines of carbon, oxygen, and silicon have also been observed in the ultraviolet. Some lines in the X-ray region have been observed with photometers equipped with special filters.

One difficulty in observing the solar spectrum is that many of the lines are actually produced by the earth's atmosphere and it is necessary to distinguish between the two. The atmospheric lines are called telluric lines. The following methods can be used to recognize them:

1. Telluric lines are stationary, while the solar lines are shifted by the Doppler effect of the sun's rotation.
2. Telluric lines increase in intensity when the sun approaches the horizon, while solar lines do not.
3. Solar lines are affected by magnetic fields in sunspots; telluric lines are not.
4. Solar lines are broader than telluric lines, mostly because of turbulence in the sun, especially near spots.

Most of the solar lines are produced by atoms, but some molecules have now been identified. At 6000°K molecules are broken up into their funda-mental atoms. But in sunspots and high levels where the temperature is lower, molecular spectra have been known for many years. Recent reports indicate that 14 molecules are identified with reasonable certainty, with 9 others possible. Figure 12–5 shows a portion of the solar spectrum in which some of the identifications of elements are shown.

## 12.7  The Chromosphere

The chromosphere is located just above the photosphere. Its lower levels also produce some of the Fraunhofer lines. The temperature at the bottom is 6000°K and increases toward the top. It seems to be about 7000°K at the 2000-mile level, but there are differences in the computation of the temperature, depending on which spectrum lines are used. Hydrogen and helium give temperatures of between 10,000°K and 20,000°K at 2500 mi, which may be in the corona.

The division between the chromosphere and the corona is visually very sharp, but physically the changes occur gradually. Hence it is very difficult to locate the boundary exactly. One conclusion is that it is at 3000 mi.

The density at the bottom of the chromosphere is $10^{-8}$ g/cm$^3$ and at the top it has dropped to between $10^{-11}$ and $10^{-12}$ g/cm$^3$. If the chromosphere could be seen by itself, its spectrum would be a bright-line spectrum, indicating that it is a hot gas under lower pressure than in the photosphere. This spectrum is visible during eclipses of the sun. When the upper photosphere and lower chromosphere are the only parts of the sun not covered by the moon, the spectrum flashes out with bright lines occupying the places of the dark lines of the absorption spectrum. This lasts only a couple of seconds just before and just after totality and is called the flash spectrum. Clouds of hydrogen give the chromosphere (the word means color sphere) its characteristic red color, which is quite prominent during eclipses.

About 3500 mi above the photosphere, bright

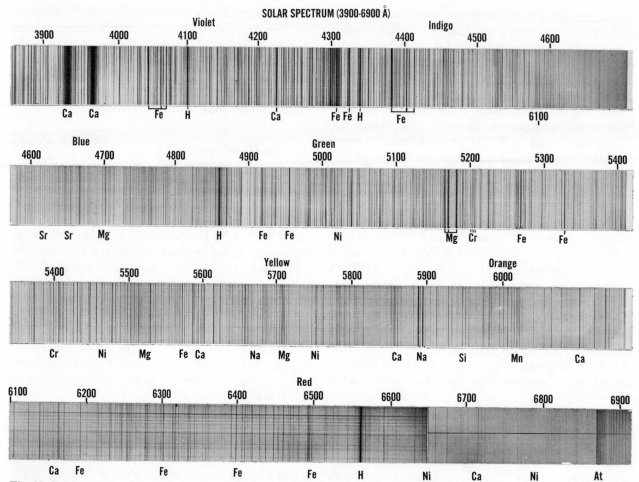

Fig. 12–5    A portion of the sun's spectrum. Wavelengths are given in angstroms and the color regions are indicated. (Photograph from the Mount Wilson and Palomar Observatories)

spicules (spikes) rise into the hot gas of the corona. They are masses of hot gas which rise to about 4500 mi at the equator and 6500 mi at the poles. They last about five minutes; their diameters are between 300 and 1200 mi; and their velocities reach 12 mi/sec to 25 mi/sec. These phenomena should be accompanied by very loud noise, which of course is not transmitted through the vacuum of space. Fifty or more spicules are visible at one time on the solar limb.

## 12.8    The Corona

The most beautiful and most publicized layer of the sun is the corona, which can ordinarily be seen only during a total eclipse of the sun. It is very large, having been seen to 7 million miles and is now thought to reach the earth and beyond. It is very faint, about as bright as the full moon, but is 500,000 times fainter than the sun, which explains why it cannot be seen at all times. Surprisingly, it is very hot, with temperature estimated at one to two million degrees Kelvin. But radiation from the corona is weak, because of its low density.

It is difficult to explain the high temperature of the corona. Probably the best explanation is that it is heated partly by the flow of hot material from the chromosphere and partly by supersonic waves from below. Kinetic energy from these waves heat the low-density gas to such a high level that it is given very high velocity. The density of the corona at 6000 mi is $10^8$ to $10^9$ atoms per cubic centimeter. At this low density and high speed, collisions would strip the electrons from the nuclei of the atoms. The speed of the electrons is 5000 mi/sec and of the protons 125 mi/sec. These particles also collide with atoms and assist in the process of splitting them. It is possible that at least some of the coronal material comes from interplanetary dust and meteoroids.

The corona has a weak continuous spectrum crossed by bright lines, not absorption lines as in the Fraunhofer spectrum. It was once thought that, since the bright lines do not correspond with the positions of the absorption lines, a new element, called coronium, had been discovered, as helium had been discovered in the solar spectrum in 1868. But in 1941 the Swedish physicist, B. Edlén, showed that the strong green line of coronium was produced by iron with 13 electrons missing, and that the red line came from iron with 9 electrons stripped from the nucleus. Other lines are due to similarly highly ionized calcium, nickel, and possibly argon. Thirty lines have now been observed in the spectrum of the corona.

The shape of the corona varies with the sunspot cycle. When there are many spots, the corona is almost spherical with streamers running out radially in all directions. At spot minimum, the corona is unsymmetrical with large lateral streamers and small polar ones.

Until all the correlations among coronal streamers, sunspots, and magnetic fields in and around the sun are made, the corona will not be completely understood. Figure 12–6 shows the changes in shape of the corona with sunspot activity.

Fig. 12–6   The changing shape of the solar corona, near sunspot minimum (left) and maximum (right). (Yerkes Observatory photographs)

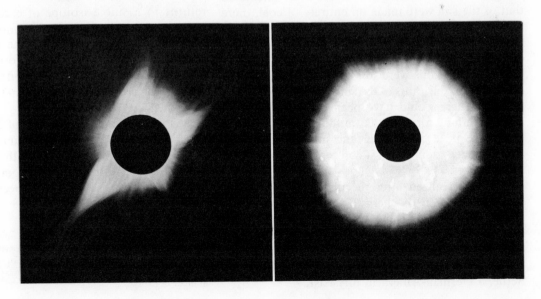

## 12.9   The Interior

Since the interior of the sun is completely inaccessible, it can be studied only by theoretical computations. They must be based on the known facts about the sun: its mass, density, temperature as observed, and the structure and motions of its atmosphere. Then the known laws of physics must be applied to investigate the interior.

Because of the great mass of the sun, the pressure at the center is estimated to be 1 billion atmospheres ($15 \times 10^9$ lb per square inch). To support this enormous pressure, the temperature at the center is computed as 15 million degrees Kelvin. It is assumed that the interior is entirely gas, so the gas laws hold, but that its density increases to between 100 g/cm$^3$ and 150 g/cm$^3$. This is some ten times that of the most dense solid known on the earth, but 1000 times less dense than some of the white dwarf stars. The spectrum is continuous and the maximum radiation, from Wien's law, is mostly X rays.

The usual idea of the source of the sun's energy is that it is produced by burning. This probably means to the average person a combination of something, like coal, with oxygen. It has been calculated that, if the sun were made up entirely of coal, there would be a sufficient supply for only 8000 years Later, it was thought that the sun may have been converting its kinetic energy, due to contraction, to heat energy. If this were so and if the sun had contracted from the limits of the solar system to its present size, there would have been enough energy to keep it shining for about 25 million years. There is every reason to believe that the sun is much older and has been radiating at its present rate for several billion years.

It was realized after the discovery of radium and the emission of energy from radioactive materials, that the solar energy probably comes from the interiors of atoms. That is, the sun is now thought of as a huge atomic reactor. Two possible chains of events were proposed in 1938 by Hans Bethe, a German-American physicist.

The *carbon cycle* (Figure 12–7) can be represented by the following nuclear equations:†

$$
\begin{aligned}
&1. \quad _6C^{12} + {}_1H^1 && \rightarrow {}_7N^{13} + \text{gamma} \\
&2. \quad \phantom{_6C^{12} + {}_1H^1} {}_7N^{13} && \rightarrow {}_6C^{13} + {}_{+1}e^0 \\
&3. \quad _6C^{13} + {}_1H^1 && \rightarrow {}_7N^{14} + \text{gamma} \\
&4. \quad _7N^{14} + {}_1H^1 && \rightarrow {}_8O^{15} + \text{gamma} \\
&5. \quad \phantom{_6C^{12} + {}_1H^1} {}_8O^{15} && \rightarrow {}_7N^{15} + {}_{+1}e^0 \\
&6. \quad _7N^{15} + {}_1H^1 && \rightarrow {}_6C^{12} + {}_2He^4
\end{aligned}
$$

arrow   = becomes
gamma = gamma ray
$_{+1}e^0$   = positron

The carbon cycle begins when a carbon nucleus captures a proton deep in the interior of the sun. The carbon is supposed to have been captured by the sun after having been formed in the interior of a star which exploded sending its heavier-than-helium atoms into space. This cycle can take place only where the temperature is around 15 million degrees Kelvin.

The combination of the carbon nucleus and the proton forms an unstable nitrogen-13 nucleus, plus a small amount of energy in the form of gamma rays. This atom immediately emits a positron and returns to a stable isotope of carbon, which combines with another proton, forming ordinary nitrogen plus more gamma rays. The nitrogen nucleus combines with another proton, forming an unstable oxygen-15 isotope. This particle decays by emitting a positron, returning to nitrogen-15, which in turn combines with a proton.

Now this particle, instead of forming a stable oxygen nucleus, splits to a helium nucleus and the original carbon which started the reaction. Thus four protons (hydrogen nuclei) combine to form one helium nucleus, energy having been released in the process.

† In a nuclear equation, the charge on the nucleus (atomic number) is written as a subscript to the left of the symbol, and the mass is written as a superscript to the right. For example, the helium nucleus is $_2He^4$, indicating an atomic mass of four and atomic number of two.

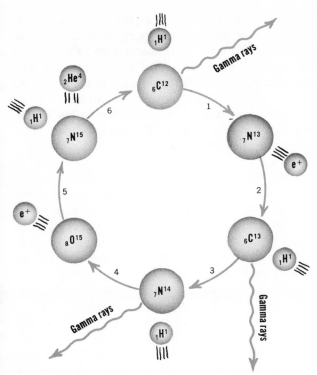

Fig. 12–7 The carbon cycle, a chain reaction inside the sun which releases energy when the nuclei of hydrogen atoms combine to form helium nuclei.

The *proton-proton reaction* takes place in three steps:

1. $_1H^1 + {_1}H^1 \rightarrow {_1}H^2 + {_{+1}}e^0$
2. $_1H^2 + {_1}H^1 \rightarrow {_2}He^3 + gamma$
3. $_2He^3 + {_2}He^3 \rightarrow {_2}He^4 + 2{_1}H^1$

In this series two protons first combine directly into a heavy hydrogen nucleus (deuteron), with the emission of a positron. The deuteron captures another proton, forming a helium isotope and some gamma radiation. Finally two of these helium nuclei combine to split and form an ordinary helium nucleus and two protons. The splitting process is called *fission*. This reaction can occur at a lower temperature than that required for the carbon cycle

and takes place above the solar center. It is estimated that the carbon cycle furnishes only 4 percent of the total solar energy and that the proton-proton reaction gives the other 96 percent. In the latter reaction, four protons combine to form one helium nucleus, as in the carbon cycle.

The atomic weight of four protons is $4 \times 1.008$ or 4.032. That of the helium nucleus is 4.004. Hence, 0.028 unit of mass has been converted in the reaction. According to the theory of relativity, mass and energy are equivalent and are related by the formula $E = mc^2$, where $E$ is the amount of energy in ergs, $m$ is the mass in grams, and $c$ is the velocity of light in centimeters per second.

From the computations in Section 12.3, the amount of energy radiated by the sun each second is $3.846 \times 10^{33}$ ergs. Substituting in the equation $E = mc^2$,

$$3.846 \times 10^{33} = m \times (3 \times 10^{10})^2$$

and solving for $m$, $m = 4.28 \times 10^{12}$g or 4,280,000 tons. This is the amount of the sun's mass which is being converted into energy *each second!*

The amount of mass lost is 0.7 percent of the mass of the protons which enter the reactions. To produce this energy, it can be calculated that about 616,000,000 tons of hydrogen are being changed into 612,000,000 tons of helium each second. Suppose the sun were composed entirely of hydrogen when these reactions started and that it has been radiating and will continue to radiate at the same rate as at present. The mass of the sun is now $2 \times 10^{27}$ tons. At this rate of mass loss, it will continue to shine for $2 \times 10^{27}/6.16 \times 10^8 = 3.2 \times 10^{18}$ sec, or 100 billion years. However, it is not thought probable that the present rate will continue unchanged.

## SUNSPOTS AND RELATED PHENOMENA

### 12.10 Sunspots

In addition to granules and faculae, the sun is marked by conspicuous dark areas, called *sunspots*.

If they are watched from day to day, they will be seen to move across the disk of the sun from the east side to the west side. If a large group lasts more than a month, it will disappear from view on the west limb and reappear two weeks later on the east limb. This apparent motion is caused by the rotation of the sun. It will also be noticed that the sun does not rotate as a solid, since spots away from the solar equator take longer to go across than those nearer the equator. The results of studies of the period of rotation are as follows:

TABLE 12–1

| Solar Latitude | Period of Rotation |
|---|---|
| 0° | 24.65 days |
| 20 | 25.19 |
| 30 | 25.85 |
| 35 | 26.62 |
| 75 | 33.00 |

Spots appear in zones, usually from 5° to 40° latitude (both north and south), although an occasional spot is seen outside these limits. The rotation can be checked by observing the Doppler effect at both limbs from the equator nearly to the poles, including latitudes where no spots are seen. The check agrees exactly with the method of spot rotation.

The center of a spot is called the *umbra*. Here the temperature measures around 4000° K, which is the reason for the dark appearance. The spectrum shows bands typical of the spectra of compounds, which can exist only at temperatures lower than that of the photosphere. The umbra is surrounded by a *penumbra* where the temperature is intermediate between that of the umbra and the photosphere.

A typical, large single spot has an umbra with diameter 10,900 mi, a penumbra 23,000 mi diameter and is surrounded by a bright ring 4000 mi wide. The intensities are 30 percent, 80 percent, and 103 percent respectively compared to the average brightness of the photosphere. A sunspot is accompanied by a magnetic field of strength 3100 gauss. By com-

parison, the strength of the earth's magnetic field is less than one gauss. There is rapid motion of the material in the spot with velocities up to about two miles per second at the level of the photosphere. The magnetic field decreases in strength as the height increases. Many single spots are accompanied by an "invisible companion," which is detectable by the magnetic field strength in the neighborhood. This companion lies completely below the visible layer of the sun.

In other words, sunspots occur in pairs, because if the invisible spot reaches the surface, two spots will be seen. The spots of a pair have opposite polarity. That is, one spot has a positive polarity like that of a north-seeking magnetic pole on the earth. The other has negative polarity. In a single sunspot cycle, if the leading spot of a pair or a group—leading in the sense that it is ahead due to the solar rotation—has a positive polarity, all leading spots in that hemisphere will have positive polarity. In the opposite hemisphere, the polarity will be reversed. At spot minimum the old-cycle spots are last seen near the solar equator and the new-cycle spots are first seen at higher latitudes. During the next cycle, the polarity will be reversed. The polarity of spot pairs is shown for the years 1942 to 1966 in Figure 12–8.

The number of sunspots is counted daily and the numbers averaged monthly and yearly. Records

Fig. 12–8    The law of sunspot polarity. The average change in latitude and corresponding magnetic polarities of spot groups from 1942 to 1966.

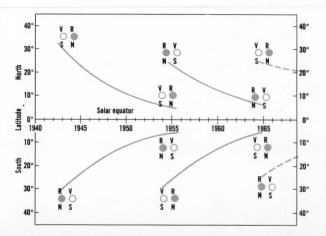

have been kept and plotted since at least 1749. Rudolph Wolf of Zurich, Switzerland, set up a formula to show the so-called Wolf sunspot numbers. The formula is:

$$\text{Wolf sunspot number, } r = k(10g + f) \quad (12\text{-}7)$$

where $g$ is the number of groups of spots and $f$ is the number of individual spots visible on a given date. $k$ is a number which depends on the size of the telescope used and conditions at the observing site. This gives a uniform number which can be plotted, as in Figures 12–9 and 12–10.

There is an approximate regularity in the times of maximum and minimum of the Wolf numbers. As the figures show, the heights of the maxima show considerable variation, while the minima are fairly uniform with few, if any, visible spots. The period is 11.1 years on the average, but the intervals vary from about 7 years to about 15 years. This period is called the *sunspot cycle*. If the change of polarity is taken into account, the period should be doubled. The spot maximum in 1958 was one of the highest on record. This was the maximum selected for the IGY, which was followed by the IQSY at a time when the sun was quiet.

Ideas about sunspots have changed radically over the years. The old books drew spots as depressions in the photosphere. Sir William Herschel thought of them as holes in the hot solar atmosphere and thought the surface underneath was cool enough to support life. But when a spot approaches the limb of the sun, it can be seen as a very turbulent region with streams of gas extending up into the chromosphere. When seen on the limb 'they are called *prominences*.

Fig. 12–9   The sunspot cycle from 1749 to 1965. Short-period fluctuations are shown below for 1933 to 1966. The upper two curves have been smoothed and the short-period fluctuations eliminated.

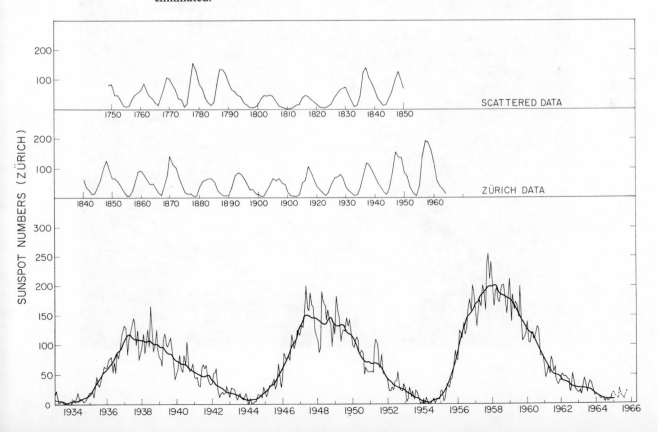

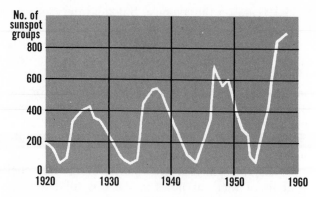

No. of sunspot groups

Fig. 12–10  A plot of Wolf sunspot numbers from 1920 to 1959. Note the increase in numbers from the maximum in 1927 to that in 1958, which was one of the highest on record.

Spots change continuously in many respects. At first a spot is seen as a small pore between the granulations in the photosphere, but with a diameter of from 1000 to 2000 mi. This small spot may soon disappear, but may last a day or longer. It may develop into a much larger spot or group of spots.

The region in which sunspots and their accompanying phenomena appear is now called a *center of activity* (Figure 12–11). This center is considered to be a result of a magnetic field deep inside the sun, which may last as long as 1000 years. Inside this field the material moves very slowly. The field itself is composed of magnetic tubes twisting into the upper layer of the sun, the convective zone. The

Fig. 12–11    An enlarged portion of a center of activity, showing bright and dark flocculi near the sun's limb. (Photograph from the Mount Wilson and Palomar Observatories)

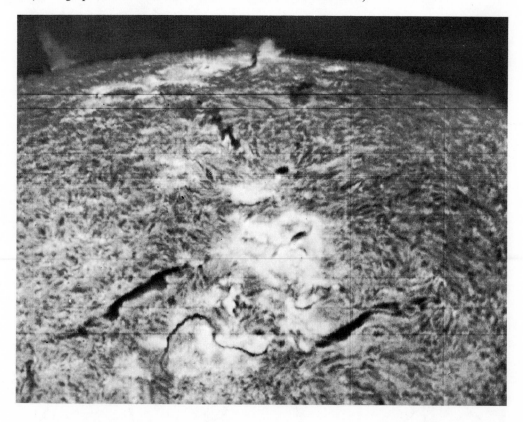

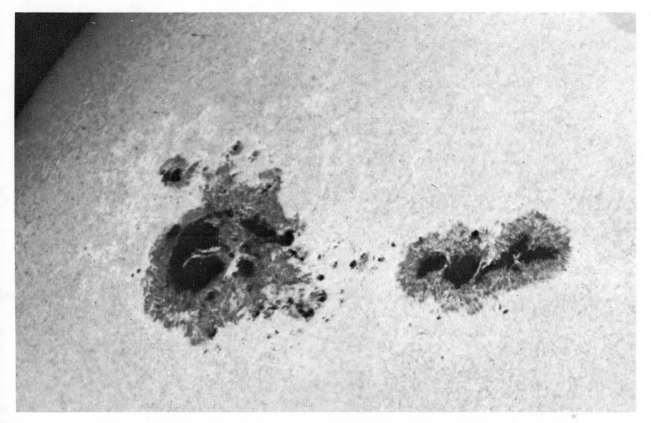

Fig. 12–12   A large sunspot group, photographed with the 60-foot tower telescope on Mount Wilson on February 2, 1946. (Photograph from the Mount Wilson and Palomar Observatories)

diameter of the tubes is the same as the thickness of the zone, perhaps 60,000 mi. When the tubes are brought to the sun's surface, by a mechanism not yet understood, the result is a spot group. This group starts as a small group of faculae followed by a visible spot 1000 mi or so in diameter. It then grows and develops into a group, which may be more than 100,000 mi in length. In 1946 and 1947 three of the largest groups ever seen were developed with intervals of about six months between them. They were visible for some two months each. The first of these groups is shown in Figure 12–12.

The maximum occurs about 11 days after the group is first seen at which time small filaments may appear. These are long string-like dark lines of hydrogen, which may reach a length of 200,000 mi. As the spot centers disappear, the filament continues to be visible, but soon stretches out in a direction parallel to the solar equator. During this time, the faculae are still visible; they are eventually cut in two by the filament, but still are present after 4 rotations of the sun for about 100 days. Finally, the filament begins to dissolve and, after nearly a year, the activity center completely disappears from the surface. It is believed that the magnetic field is still present in the interior.

### 12.11    The Spectroheliograph

Before the invention of the spectroheliograph, prominences could be seen only at times of total solar eclipses. This instrument and the spectrohelioscope have been of great importance in the study of the sun and its atmospheric details.

In the spectroheliograph, which was invented by George Ellery Hale in 1889 (Figure 12–13), an image of the sun is formed by a telescope and permitted to fall on a plate which contains a long, narrow slit (spectrograph slit). This is the slit of a spectroscope, which is built in the manner described in Chapter 5 and is equipped with prisms (or a grating) which form a spectrum. Instead of photographing the entire spectrum, only one line is permitted to pass through a second slit (right side middle). If the image of the sun is moved across the first slit at a selected, slow rate, and if a photographic plate, which is placed behind the second slit, is moved at the same rate, an image of the sun will be formed in the light of the element whose spectral line has been selected. As shown in the figure, the entire instrument is moved beneath the image of the sun and the photographic plate, and only the red line of hydrogen (for example) passes through the

Fig. 12–13    Construction of a spectroheliograph.

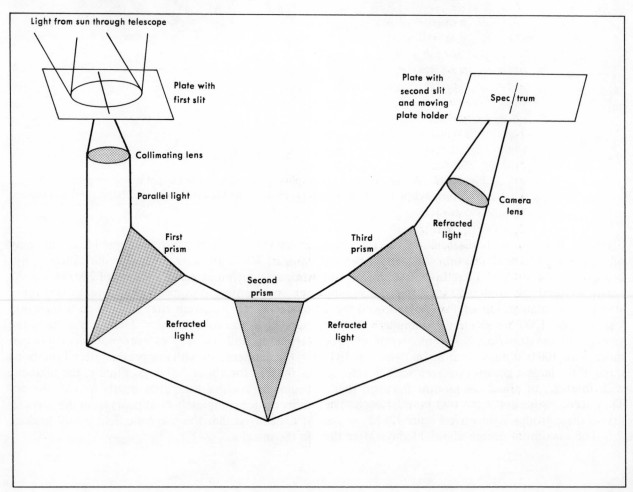

slit. In this way the hydrogen distribution over the sun's disk may be photographed.

The spectrohelioscope is similar, but is equipped with a vibrating second slit, which takes advantage of the viewer's persistence of vision. As the first slit is moved along the limb of the sun, the red shape of a prominence can be seen a line at a time. More recently, filters have been constructed that pass a very narrow portion of the spectrum. They eliminate the need of a complex and expensive spectroscope. Such filters can photograph a large part of the sun at a time with exposures of a fraction of a second. If the resulting photographs are run rapidly through a motion picture projector, the motions of the solar material can be seen. The instrument for taking such photographs is called a spectroheliokinematograph.

The best type of telescope now in use for solar studies is the coronagraph, which was invented in 1930 by Bernard Lyot, a French astronomer. This telescope uses glass for the objective which is carefully selected as free from bubbles or scratches, which might scatter the sunlight. The tube is made carefully to exclude any dust particles. The solar image is blocked off in such a way that only the light from the solar atmosphere passes through. When used with filters and placed at a high altitude station, particularly good studies can be made. The best filters pass the red line of hydrogen or one of the two lines of calcium in the blue region of the spectrum. Seven coronagraphs are now in use in the United States and in Europe.

## 12.12 Prominences

When these techniques are used, photographs of the sun show large clouds of hydrogen or calcium gas distributed over the disk, particularly in the region of centers of activity. Hale called them *flocculi*. When the centers of activity reach the limb, prominences can be seen, although prominences are also seen near the poles where there are no visible sunspots.

Prominences have been grouped by types, some of which are:

1. Quiescent. These are apparently motionless for long periods at a time, but are actually fairly active. When seen projected onto the solar disk, they are seen as filaments of hydrogen.
2. Active. This type shows much motion, rising or falling. The prominent direction is downward. Apparently the hydrogen or calcium rises in a state which does not emit light in the line being observed, particularly the H-alpha line. As the gas cools, it falls back onto the sun. Its motion is shown in the spectroheliokinematograms.
3. Eruptive. These are seen to rise at very high velocities, sometimes exceeding 300 mi per second, and are blown completely away from the sun. One of the most spectacular eruptive prominences is shown in Figure 12–14. This type plays a part in the formation of auroras.
4. Sunspot type. These are mostly arches that lie above centers of activity.
5. Coronal type. Some prominences are visible in the corona and appear to rain down onto the chromosphere.

Figure 12–15 shows a sunspot group near the limb and the same area taken in hydrogen light. Faculae are visible in the direct photograph and hydrogen clouds (flocculi) appear above the center of activity in the spectroheliograms.

Occasionally a center of activity will produce a sudden and short-lived increase of brightness called a *flare*. There may be as many as ten centers on the sun at one time, any one of which might produce a flare. One large flare and a hundred or more small ones per day may be seen near large spots. They brighten in from five to ten minutes and die out more slowly. In general it is possible to see them only in a spectrohelioscope, but the brightest flares can often be seen without special equipment. They are being looked for at several observing stations, such as the McMath-Hulbert Observatory of the University of Michigan, where the photograph in Figure 12–16 was made.

Flares emit strongly in the ultraviolet and X-ray regions of the spectrum. They also send out atomic particles with velocities of several hundred miles

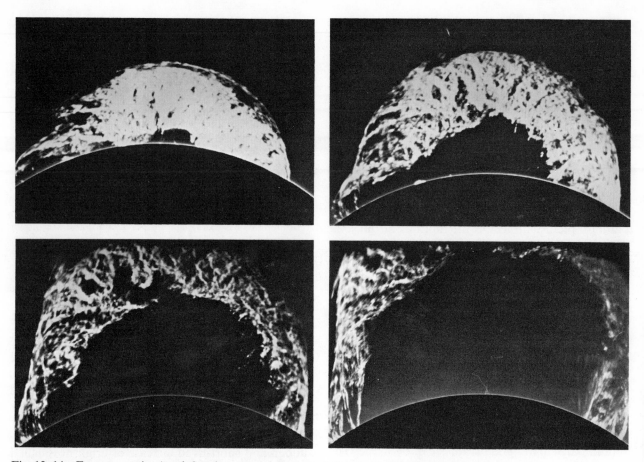

Fig. 12–14    Four successive (top left to bottom right) spectroheliograms of the great explosive prominence on June 4, 1946, taken with a coronagraph. Total elapsed time is one hour. (Harvard College Observatory photograph)

per second, and waves which are picked up by radio telescopes. Cosmic rays apparently are emitted by the large flares. The result of all this activity is that space is filled with high-energy particles and waves, which affect the magnetic field of the earth and the radiation belts around it.

It is well-known that there is a correlation between solar activity and terrestrial affairs, such as auroras, magnetic storms, radio fadeouts, and (some people believe) even the weather. Displays of auroras are more frequent in times of sunspot activity, although they have been seen when no spots are visible. They are produced by the corpuscles from the sun which have finite velocities, so there is a delay of a day or two between the ejection of the particles from a sunspot and the observation of an auroral display. However, auroras are also now thought to be the result of X-ray emission from flares. The resulting displays occur only minutes after a flare is visible. At the same time, the transmission of telegraph and radio waves is interfered with and strong magnetic storms sometimes

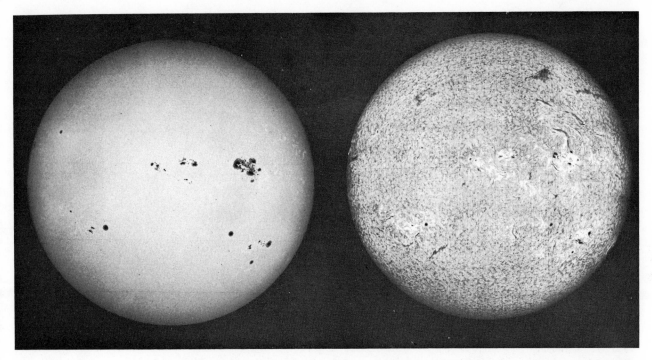

Fig. 12–15   Photograph of the sun (left) taken in ordinary light, shows sunspots and faculae. The sun on the right, taken in red hydrogen light, shows clouds of hydrogen at higher levels. (Photographs from the Mount Wilson and Palomar Observatories)

result. The enormous spot groups of 1946 had very strong magnetic storms associated with them, but those of 1947 produced only small storms. So there is no strong correlation between the size of spots and the strength of the storms in the magnetic field of the earth.

   A list of large spot groups and their correlation with magnetic storms will be found in Table 12–2.

Fig. 12–16   Spectroheliogram of a solar flare taken in a time of considerable sunspot activity. Flares are usually associated with sunspots. (McMath-Hulbert Observatory of the University of Michigan)

TABLE 12–2

**Spot Groups with Areas Greater than 0.0025 of the Sun's Visible Hemisphere**

| Central meridian passage | | Lat. | Area | | Magnetic storm began | | Character |
|---|---|---|---|---|---|---|---|
| | | | Mill.[a] | Earth = 1[c] | | | |
| 1946 Feb. | 5.4 | 27° | 5400 | 31.8 | Feb. | 7.4 | Great SC[b] |
| 1947 Apr. | 7.1 | −24 | 4500 | 26.4 | Apr. | 8.9 | Small |
| | | | | | | 17.5 | Small SC |
| 1947 Mar. | 10.2 | −23 | 4300 | 25.4 | Mar. | 2.2 | Small SC |
| | | | | | | 7.2 | Small |
| | | | | | | 12.2 | Small |
| 1946 July | 26.9 | 23 | 3700 | 21.9 | July | 26.8 | Great SC |
| 1917 Feb. | 10.0 | −16 | 3600 | 21.3 | Feb. | 16.1 | Small SC |
| 1905 Feb. | 4.7 | −15 | 3300 | 19.5 | Feb. | 3.6 | Small SC |
| 1917 Aug. | 10.6 | 16 | 3200 | 18.9 | Aug. | 9.7 | Great SC |
| | | | | | | 14.1 | Great SC |
| 1938 Jan. | 18.4 | 17 | 3100 | 18.4 | Jan. | 16.9 | Small SC |
| | | | | | | 22.2 | Great |
| | | | | | | 25.5 | Great SC |
| 1892 Feb. | 12.4 | −28 | 3000 | 17.7 | Feb. | 13.7 | Great SC |
| 1905 Oct. | 20.6 | 14 | 3000 | 17.7 | | | |
| 1938 Oct. | 12.0 | 17 | 3000 | 17.7 | Oct. | 7.4 | Small |
| 1925 Dec. | 28.6 | 23 | 2900 | 17.2 | Dec. | 27.6 | Small SC |
| 1937 July | 28.8 | 32 | 2800 | 16.6 | July | 23.6 | Small |
| | | | | | Aug. | 1.9 | Small |
| 1897 Jan. | 9.9 | −7 | 2700 | 16.0 | Jan. | 2.3 | Small |
| 1920 Mar. | 22.1 | −5 | 2700 | 16.0 | Mar. | 22.9 | Great SC |
| 1937 Oct. | 4.4 | 9 | 2700 | 16.0 | Oct. | 3.5 | Small |
| | | | | | | 7.2 | Small |
| | | | | | | 9.3 | Small |
| 1893 Aug. | 8.0 | −18 | 2600 | 15.4 | Aug. | 6.7 | Small SC |
| 1905 Mar. | 8.4 | 10 | 2600 | 15.4 | Mar. | 3.1 | Small SC |
| 1907 Feb. | 12.9 | −17 | 2600 | 15.4 | Feb. | 10.1 | Great SC |
| 1928 Sept. | 27.4 | −15 | 2600 | 15.4 | Sept. | 24.7 | Small SC |
| 1939 Aug. | 31.9 | −16 | 2600 | 15.4 | Aug. | 22.0 | Great SC |
| | | | | | Sept. | 2.9 | Small SC |

[a] The area in millionths of the sun's visible hemisphere. For example, the spot group of February, 1946, had an area of 5400/1,000,000 or 0.54 percent of the visible hemisphere.

[b] SC means Sudden Commencement of the storm. The last entry was to small to be officially classified as a storm.

[c] The area expressed in terms of the area of a cross section of the earth.

## 12.13 The Future of the Sun

The helium, which is produced by the proton-proton and carbon-nitrogen cycles discussed earlier in this chapter, is being deposited in the center of the sun. In other words, the sun is building up a helium core. As this core increases in mass, its temperature will rise and the sun will expand to take care of the resulting increase in internal pressure. This expansion stage is expected to take place in about 6 billion years. So far the sun is believed to have been in existence for about 6 billion years and to have consumed 6 percent of its original hydrogen. After another 6 billion years, when 12 percent of the hydrogen is gone, the helium core will be too hot and the pressure will be too great for the sun to remain at its present size.

The expansion stage will last perhaps 1 billion years during which the sun will expand to 30 or 40 times its present diameter and it will be a little cooler than it is now. But the increased size, even at a lower temperature, will mean an increase in the total radiation and the earth will become too hot to support life. The oceans will boil and the earth will be surrounded by a hot, steamy atmosphere. After the sun's size has become stable, it will begin to contract and heat up again, but at some stage may explode, blowing off perhaps 0.1 percent of its mass from the upper layers of the photosphere into space. It will then condense rapidly—in a few hundred million years—and become a hot, dense star of the white dwarf class. The earth will re-form its oceans, which will then freeze, and end its existence as a cold, dead planet still in orbit around a small, dying star.

### QUESTIONS AND PROBLEMS

1. Discuss two methods of measuring the distance to the sun.

2. Would a body emit as much energy in the infrared region of the spectrum when blue-hot as when red-hot?

3. Although telescopes are often located on mountains, many are used successfully at lower elevations. It is much more important, however, that coronagraphs be located at high altitudes. Why?

4. Calculate the percentage of the mass of hydrogen that is converted to energy during the formation of helium.

5. If it were possible for all the mass of the sun's hydrogen to be converted to energy, how long would the sun radiate at its present rate?

6. What is an advantage and a disadvantage of using Venus instead of Eros for determining the length of the astronomical unit?

7. Compute the solar constant if the temperature of the sun were 18,000°K instead of 6,000°K.

8. If the temperature of the sun were 4,000°K, (a) at what wavelength would the radiation be most intense, and (b) what would be the sun's color?

9. The umbra of a sunspot has a temperature of about 4,500°K. Using Stefan's law, compute the total radiation per square centimeter as a percentage of that for the average solar surface (6,000°K).

10. At the I.A.U. meeting in Germany in 1964, the ratio of the mass of the sun to that of the earth-moon system was given as 328,912. In this chapter the mass of the sun is calculated to be 332,930 times the mass of the earth. From these figures, calculate the ratio of the masses of the moon and earth. Compare your answer with the value given in Chapter 11.

11. Calculate the mass of the sun from the radius and period of Venus' orbit.

12. What differences would be expected from solar studies made during the IGY and the IQSY?

# Chapter Thirteen

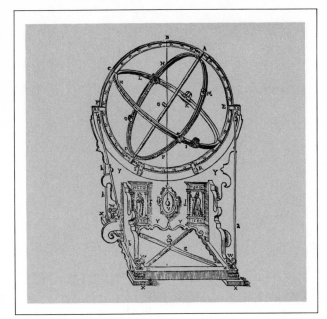

# Eclipses

Eclipses, especially solar eclipses, are among the most beautiful and awesome phenomena of nature. In ancient times, solar eclipses were seen as evil omens and have therefore been recorded for thousands of years. Ancient Chinese documents list an eclipse for October 22, 2137 B.C., and as early as the seventh century B.C. future eclipses were being predicted with considerable accuracy.

Astronomers, among them Eratosthenes, Hipparchus, and Ptolemy, knew that it was possible to determine longitude by observing the times of eclipses from widely separated stations. Ancient records have been of great value in determining the period of rotation of the earth and in showing that the earth is slowing down because of tidal action. Eclipses of the moon have been used, as previously noted, to study the rate at which the moon's surface cools when sunlight is shut off. During solar eclipses the astronomer can observe the flash spectrum, the outer corona and its spectrum, and other regions near the sun which cannot be observed even with the coronagraph.

## 13.1 Predicting Eclipses

An eclipse of the moon, a lunar eclipse, occurs when the moon runs into the shadow of the earth, which is opposite the sun. This can therefore happen only at times of full moon. Solar eclipses are possible only because the moon is at the proper distance from the earth to cast its shadow on the earth's surface. They can occur, therefore, only at times of new moon. The prediction of eclipses can be made because the relative positions of the sun, the moon, and the earth are accurately known. The moon and sun must be at or near a node; that is, the three bodies must be in or nearly in the same plane. (See Figure 13–1.)

The ancient astronomers computed the times of eclipses because they knew that both solar and lunar eclipses recur at roughly regular intervals. The method they used depended on the *saros,* which had been discovered by the Babylonians several centuries before the Christian era. After an interval of 223 synodic months, the intervals between new or full moons, the sun or the earth's shadow will be at the

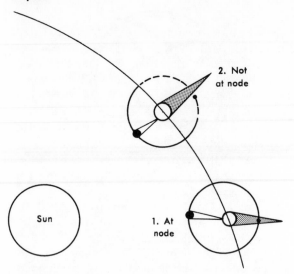

Fig. 13–1   Eclipses occur only when sun, moon, and earth are near the node (1) and are nearly in the same plane. They do not occur at preceding new or full moon when at (2) the moon is above the ecliptic (at left) or below the ecliptic (at right).

same node in the same place on the ecliptic. The time between successive passages of the sun through the same node is less than one year, because of the regression of the node. This interval, called the *eclipse year,* is 346.6 mean solar days. Two hundred twenty-three synodic months contain 6585.321 solar days or 18 years, 11⅓ days; nineteen eclipse years contain 6585.4 days. Therefore, if an eclipse occurs at a node at a certain point of the ecliptic, it will occur again in almost the same point after eighteen years. This recurrence of eclipses is called the *saros.*

The one-third day of the interval means that the next eclipse of the saros will be visible one-third of the circumference of the earth farther west. But after three saroses, an eclipse will be visible in approximately the same longitude as the first one. There will be a slight shift in latitude. As a result of these correlations, solar eclipses follow each other in a series, beginning at one of the terrestrial poles and ending at the other pole. The entire series lasts about 1200 years, during which time there will have

been 29 lunar eclipses and 41 solar eclipses, of which ten of the latter will have been total. There will be other saros series in progress at the same time.

Today it is not necessary to depend on the saros for the prediction of eclipses, because with accurate data for the orbits of the earth and the moon, the computation can be done on a more scientific and more accurate basis. This depends on a knowledge of the nature and motions of the shadows of the earth and moon. The computation of the length of the earth's shadow and of the production of lunar eclipses will be discussed first.

## 13.2   Lunar Eclipses

In Figure 13–2, three circles represent the sun, the earth, and the moon. They cannot be drawn to the correct scale, because of the differences in size and distance. The sun's diameter is 109 times larger than the earth's and 400 times larger than the moon's. Hence, if it were drawn with a diameter of one inch, for example, the earth and moon would be too small to show satisfactorily.

Since the earth is an opaque body, it will cut off sunlight completely in a cone formed by straight lines drawn tangent to both bodies. The projection of this cone is shown in the diagram as lines tangent to the circles representing the sun and the earth. These tangents are called external tangents. The geometrical cone of the earth's shadow inside of which no part of the sun can be seen is called the *umbra.* If internal tangents are drawn, as shown,

Fig. 13–2   The production of lunar eclipses.

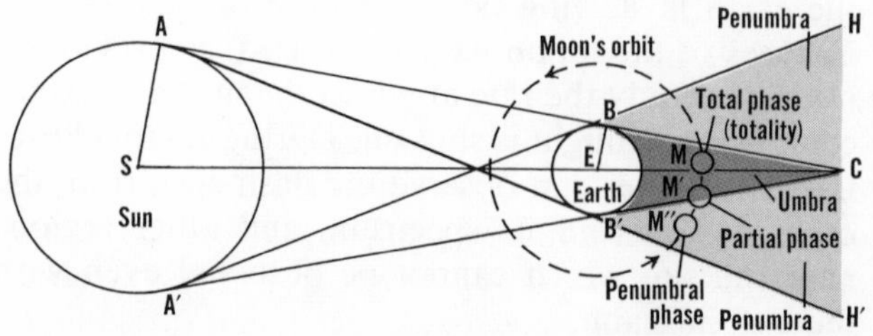

they form another cone from which a part of the sun could be seen. This is the *penumbra*. The length of the umbra from the center of the earth, *E*, to the vertex, *C*, can be calculated by plane geometry:

The radii of the two circles, *SA* and *EB*, are perpendicular to the tangents at *A* and *B*. Since the triangles, *ASC* and *BEC*, are right triangles which have a common angle, *ACS*, they are similar and their sides are therefore proportional. From this we can write:

$$\frac{SA}{EB} = \frac{SC}{EC}. \tag{13-1}$$

Let $SE = D$ be the distance from the center of the sun to the center of the earth and $EC = L$ be the length of the earth's shadow, and substitute in equation 13-1.

$$\frac{SC}{EC} = \frac{D+L}{L} = \frac{SA}{EB} = \frac{432,200\,\text{mi}}{3,963\,\text{mi}} = 109.1 \tag{13-2}$$

whence,

$$D + L = 109.1\,L \tag{13-3}$$

$$D = 108.1\,L \tag{13-4}$$

and

$$L = \frac{D}{108.1}. \tag{13-5}$$

The equation has been solved in literal form, since all the distances are variable. The average value of *D* is 92,900,000, but varies between 91,400,000 and 94,500,000 mi and must be given for the position of the earth in its orbit at the time of the eclipse.

Substituting the extreme values of *D*, the length of the earth's shadow varies from 845,000 mi when the earth is at perihelion to 875,000 mi when at aphelion.

It is also desirable to calculate the width of the earth's shadow at the distance of the moon. Again similar triangles must be set up and the proportional sides used in an equation as before. The width varies with the distance between the earth and the sun and

between the moon and the earth. Its average is about 5770 mi. This is 2⅔ the diameter of the moon. Since the moon's angular diameter is about one-half degree, the width of the earth's shadow at the distance of the moon, if it could be projected onto a huge screen, would be 1⅓° across.

Figure 13-2 shows a side view of the earth's umbra and penumbra and the production of lunar eclipses. As the moon comes to full phase and in approximately the same plane as the shadow of the earth, it passes through the penumbra, then through the umbra, and out in reverse order. As it first touches the penumbra, where part of the sunlight is cut off by the earth, there is a slight amount of darkening of the moon's surface. This increases until, when the moon nears the umbra, the darkening is noticeable. This part of an eclipse is called the *penumbral phase*.

As the limb of the moon touches the umbra, the contrast between the two parts of the shadow is so great that there is a visible division between the bright and dark areas of the lunar surface. This is the beginning of the *partial phase* of the eclipse. In a telescope, this dividing line is not sharp, but has a fuzzy appearance. The limb of the moon crosses the umbra in about one hour, but the length of the partial phase depends on how near the moon is to the node and how near the moon comes to the center of the shadow.

Finally, when the moon is completely inside the umbra, the eclipse is *total*. It would be expected that it would then be invisible, but this is not the case. Because of refraction by the earth's atmosphere, the light of the sun is bent enough for some of it to reach the moon, as shown in Figure 13-3. The blue rays of sunlight are filtered out and scattered, but the red rays get through, producing a peculiar copper color, which may be quite dark near the center of the umbra. If there are high clouds above the earth in the region where this refraction takes place, the eclipse may be very dark. This was the case in the eclipse of December 30, 1963 at which time the moon was only dimly visible.

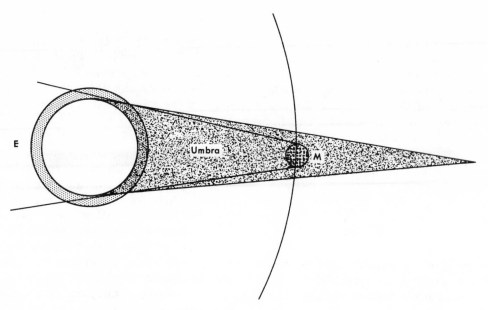

Fig. 13–3   The earth surrounded by its atmosphere at *E*. The moon at *M* in the earth's geometrical shadow (umbra) is illuminated by copper-colored light bent (refracted) by the atmosphere, the blue light being largely filtered out.

Figure 13–4 shows an end-on view of the umbra and penumbra with the production of eclipses at different distances from the node. *A* is a total eclipse nearly central; *B* is a partial eclipse; *C* is a penumbral eclipse or appulse; and *D* shows the moon barely making contact with the penumbra (no darkening would be noticed in this case).

The entire duration of a lunar eclipse may be as long as five or six hours, counting the penumbral phases. Totality can last up to $1^h 30^m$. The longest possible eclipse occurs when the moon passes through the center of the shadows. If it goes near the edge of the umbra, the totality will be of short duration. In partial eclipses the moon is not entirely covered by the umbra. Occasionally the moon passes through the penumbra only. There were five pen-

umbral eclipses between February 19, 1962 and October 29, 1966, inclusive.

Eclipses of the moon are not very important scientifically. It is possible to measure the drop of temperature as sunlight is blocked off from striking the surface of the moon. Such measures help slightly in studying the lunar surface conditions and help show that the moon lacks appreciable atmosphere.

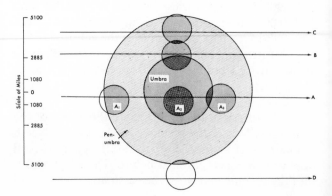

Fig. 13–4   End-on view of the umbra and penumbra of the earth's shadow, showing the path of the moon for total ($A_2$), partial ($A_3$), and penumbral phases ($A_1$) of lunar eclipses.

## 13.3 Solar Eclipses

Figure 13–5 shows the production of eclipses of the sun. The length of the moon's shadow can be calculated in a manner similar to that for the earth's shadow. As before, draw tangents from the sun (not shown in the figure) to the moon. Again there are similar triangles and the proportion becomes

$$\frac{SA}{MB} = \frac{D - d + L}{L} = \frac{D - d}{L} + 1 \qquad (13\text{–}6)$$

and

$$\frac{D - d}{L} = \frac{432{,}200 \text{ mi}}{1060 \text{ mi}} - 1 = 407.7 - 1 = 406.7 \quad (13\text{–}7)$$

hence

$$L = \frac{D - d}{406.7} \qquad (13\text{–}8)$$

where $SA$ is the radius of the sun; $MB$ is the radius of the moon; $D$ is the distance between the earth and the sun; $d$ is the distance from the earth to the moon; and $L$ is the length of the moon's shadow.

Substituting the maximum and minimum values of $D$ and $d$, the greatest length of the moon's shadow is 231,300 mi and the smallest length is 223,600 mi. Since the distance from the center of the moon to the earth's surface varies from about 221,800 mi to about 248,750 mi, the moon's shadow reaches the earth if the distance is less than average, but fails to reach the earth if greater than average.

Fig. 13–5 The production of total and partial solar eclipses.

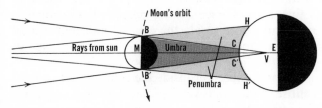

If the moon's shadow does reach the earth, the apparent diameter of the moon will be a little larger than the sun and will completely cover it, except for the corona. This is called a *total eclipse* of the sun. If the moon's shadow does not reach the earth, the moon will be too small to cover the sun, and, from the center of the umbra of the shadow extended to the earth, a perfect ring of the sun will be seen surrounding the moon. This is called an *annular eclipse*. The production of annular eclipses is shown in Figure 13–6.

The moon's shadow also has a penumbra, which is a little more than 4000 mi wide at the earth's distance. An observer inside the penumbra will see

Fig. 13–6 The production of annular and partial eclipses of the sun. The photograph shows an eclipse just before totality.

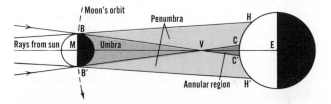

only a part of the sun's disk covered by the moon; that is, a *partial eclipse*. The amount of the eclipse will decrease for observers near the umbra to zero for those at the edge of the penumbra, which may be more than 2000 mi distant. The eclipse of July 20, 1963, was total in parts of Alaska, Canada, and Maine. The edge of the penumbra was just south of the United States in Mexico.

The earth is moving in its orbit around the sun and the moon around the earth in the same direction, west to east. The shadow also moves across the earth from west to east. The earth rotates in the same direction at about 1040 mi per hour at the equator. But the moon is traveling with respect to the sun at about 2120 mi per hour. So the moon's shadow overtakes a point on the earth's equator with a speed of 1080 mi per hour or 0.3 mi per second. At the poles where the earth's surface is not carried eastward by rotation, the shadow will move at full speed, or nearly 0.59 mi per second. At stations at other latitudes, the speed will be intermediate between the two extremes. Observers of total solar eclipses remark about the terrific speed with which the shadow can be seen to approach from the west.

The greatest width of the moon's shadow where it strikes the earth is 165 mi. The maximum duration of totality is a little more than seven minutes. This is always near the equator, as during the eclipse of 1937. The duration of totality depends on the latitude and also on the width of the moon's umbra. If the vertex of the umbra just barely touches the earth, there will be just an instantaneous total eclipse. There is a possible situation where the eclipse will be total in the center of the eclipse track and annular at each end.

An eclipse track is a narrow strip of the earth which is swept by the moon's umbra. It is curved, since it is the intersection of a straight line and a sphere. Because an eclipse track is at most 165 mi wide, total eclipses are seen in very restricted regions of the earth. This is the reason eclipse expeditions are sent to parts of the world where the eclipse is expected to be total and where weather conditions are as favorable as possible.

Many times the umbra misses the earth entirely. The eclipses at those times are partial only, varying in magnitude from near zero to nearly total. The paths of seven total eclipses between 1962 and 1970 are shown in Figure 13–7. Not included is an eclipse in the Antarctic in 1967 and inside the Arctic Circle in 1968.

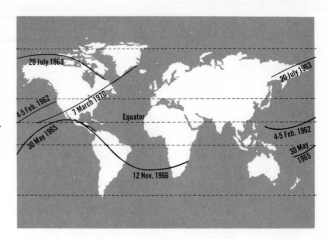

Fig. 13–7   Tracks of total solar eclipses between 1962 and 1970. The shadow moves from west to east.

The calculation of the exact time and place at which an eclipse is visible depends on the following:

1. The distance of the moon from the earth and the earth from the sun.
2. The position and motion of the umbra on the earth.
3. The latitude and longitude of the observer and his elevation above sea level.

Coming total and annular eclipses of the sun are listed in Table 13–1. Total eclipses of the moon visible in the Western Hemisphere are listed in Table 13–2. To see a total eclipse of the sun it is necessary to be inside the eclipse path, but a total eclipse of the moon may be seen from any part of the earth where the moon is above the horizon.

For an observer inside the eclipse track, a total eclipse of the sun is very spectacular. First contact is the instant when the moon begins to cover the sun's

TABLE 13–1
**Central Eclipses of the Sun**

| Date[a] | Kind | Duration | Region |
|---|---|---|---|
| 1969 Mar. 18 | annular | | Indian Ocean, Indonesia |
| 1969 Sept. 11 | annular | | Pacific Ocean |
| 1970 Mar. 7 | total | 3 min | Mexico, Atlantic Ocean |
| 1970 Aug. 31 | annular | | South Pacific |
| 1972 Jan. 16 | annular | | Antarctica |
| 1972 Jul. 10 | total | 3 min | Northern North America |
| 1973 Jan. 4 | annular | | Argentina, South Atlantic |
| 1973 Jun. 30 | total | 7 min | Atlantic Ocean, Africa |
| 1973 Dec. 24 | annular | | South America, Atlantic |

[a] Dates are in Greenwich mean time.

disk. By watching through a safe, thick dark glass or by projecting the sun on a white paper through a telescope, it is possible to estimate the time of first contact within a few seconds. The limb of the moon can be seen sharply defined at the limb of the sun. This is the beginning of the partial phase of the eclipse.

The partial phase ends in about one hour at second contact, when the sun is completely hidden by the moon. Shortly before second contact, the sky becomes noticeably darker and the colors are quite different from those at sunrise or sunset, because the light comes from the limb of the sun which is darker and more reddish than light from the center and

TABLE 13–2
**Total Eclipses of the Moon**
**Visible in the Western Hemisphere**
**Central Standard Time[a]**

| Date | Begins | Middle | Ends | Totality |
|---|---|---|---|---|
| 1967 Apr. 24 | 4:20 A.M. | 6:07 A.M. | 7:54 A.M. | 1h 22m |
| 1967 Oct. 18 | 2:33 A.M. | 4:16 A.M. | 5:59 A.M. | 0 56 |
| 1968 Apr. 12–13 | 9:06 P.M. | 10:49 P.M. | 12:32 A.M. | 0 56 |
| 1968 Oct. 6 | 3:57 A.M. | 5:41 A.M. | 7:25 A.M. | 1 02 |
| 1971 Feb. 9, 10 | 11:55 P.M. | 1:42 A.M. | 3:29 A.M. | 1 18 |
| 1972 Jan. 30 | 3:11 A.M. | 4:53 A.M. | 6:35 A.M. | 0 42 |
| 1975 May 24, 25 | 10:03 P.M. | 11:46 P.M. | 1:29 A.M. | 1 30 |

[a] For Eastern Standard Time, add 1 hr; for Mountain Standard Time, subtract 1 hr; for Pacific Standard Time, subtract 2 hr.

there is no blue and yellow light to be reflected by the earth's atmosphere.

In the instant before totality, the only visible parts of the sun are those that shine through valleys on the limb of the moon. They look like bright spots superposed on the inner corona, which is then visible. This phenomenon is called *Baily's beads,* which are shown in the bottom photograph of Figure 13–6.

The corona suddenly comes into view as Baily's beads disappear. It can usually be seen to a considerable distance from the sun and its shape changes from one eclipse to another. Totality lasts from an instant to about seven minutes, during which bright stars and planets are visible. At third contact the sun reappears, again with Baily's beads, and the partial phase repeats in reverse order until at fourth contact, the entire sun is visible again.

The type of observations made during a solar eclipse depends on the field of interest of the observatory and the astronomers making up the expedition. Among the topics of interest are:

1. Photography of the phases of the eclipse, particularly of the corona during totality. Since the invention of the coronagraph, photographs of the inner corona are not as important as previously.
2. Observations of the flash spectrum and the limb of the sun with photography.
3. Motions of the material in prominences.
4. Polarization of the solar atmosphere.
5. Radio waves from the sun when the interior is completely hidden.

## 13.4 Eclipse Seasons

Prediction of eclipses by the saros has been considered. It is now desirable to discuss in more detail the problem of calculating the production of eclipses from a modern point of view. It has long been known that the moon must be new for a solar eclipse and full for a lunar eclipse. In addition, the moon must be in the plane of the earth and the sun. That is, it must be at a node. The question to be answered now is: How near the node must the moon be and when will the eclipses be total, partial, or annular? Part of this was answered when the lengths of the shadows were computed.

First, consider eclipses of the moon. Figure 13–8 shows the positions of the earth's shadow and

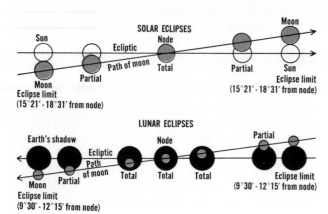

Fig. 13–8    The production of eclipses, showing the eclipse limits.

the moon near a node. The descending node is shown, but eclipses will also occur under similar circumstances near the ascending node. The following remarks apply to either node. It must be remembered that the earth's shadow (also the sun for solar eclipses) moves eastward along the ecliptic at about one degree per day, while the moon moves 13° per day or about 1° in two hours. It has already been noted that the apparent diameter of the moon is one-half degree and that the diameter of the earth's shadow is about 2⅔ times larger.

The distance between the center of the moon and the center of the shadow at the extreme positions at the left and right of the figure is one-half the sum of the two angles, or

$$\frac{1}{2}(\frac{1°}{2} + 1\frac{1°}{3}) = \frac{1}{2}(0.5° + 1.33°) =$$

$$0.25° + 0.67° = 0.92°.$$

This is shown in Figure 13–9, which is an enlargement of the lunar eclipse portion of Figure 13–8.

Both apparent angular diameters are of course variable for reasons already discussed. Here, penumbral eclipses are not considered, since they are relatively unimportant.

From the figure it is obvious that an eclipse of the moon will happen only inside the limits shown, when the moon runs through the shadow. If the moon is full outside the limits, there will be no eclipse. At the extreme right and left, the moon is just tangent to the shadow, which is the limiting case. The distance of this point from the node can be computed easily. This distance, in degrees, is called the lunar *eclipse limit*. The total distance on both sides of the node is the entire double eclipse limit.

The angle between the moon's path and the ecliptic is slightly variable, but is about 5° as shown in Figure 13–9. Assuming the angular distance from the center of the moon, *M*, to the center of the shadow, *S*, at tangency to be 0.92° from the preceding discussion, the distance, $R = NS$, can be found in the same units of angular measure from the slender triangle formula 11–3 on page 142.

$$R = 57.3° \times \frac{d}{p} = 57.3° \times \frac{0.92°}{5°} = 10.5°.$$

This is an approximate method of solving. A more accurate method gives 10° 37′. If the maximum and minimum values are used for the size of the moon and the umbra of the shadow, the eclipse limits for the moon are between 9° 30′ and 12° 15′. If internal tangents are used, as at the left and right of the center of Figure 13–7, the limiting distances from the node for total lunar eclipses can also be calculated. These limits are about 5°. That is, total eclipses of the moon occur when the full moon is within 5° of either node. If full moon occurs between this limit and the larger one, the eclipse will be partial only.

The time during which the sun or the earth's shadow is inside an entire double eclipse limit is called an *eclipse season*. The earth's shadow and

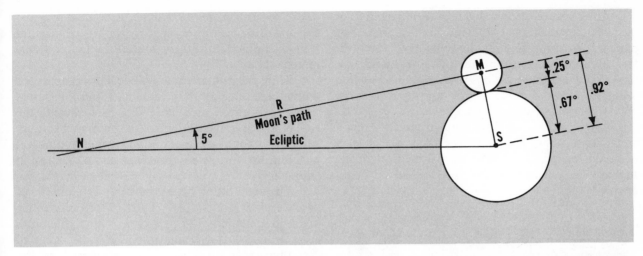

Fig. 13–9  The lunar eclipse limit showing the 5° angle between the moon's path and the ecliptic and the relative size of the moon and the earth's shadow.

the sun move around the ecliptic in 365.24 days or at a rate of about 1° per day. Therefore, in 18.7 days the earth's shadow would move completely across the smaller, double lunar eclipse limit or in 24.2 days across the larger limit. In other words, the lunar eclipse season lasts at most about 24 days. The interval between full moons is 29½ days, the synodic month. It is therefore possible for the moon to be full before it reaches the limit and again after it has passed the limit. Hence, there may be a lunar eclipse season without an eclipse.

The solar eclipse limit is about 50 percent longer than the lunar limit. It lasts between 30.3 days and 36.5 days, depending on the length of the limit. If a new moon occurs just before the limit is reached, there will be another new moon while the sun is inside the limit. In other words, there will be an eclipse of the sun at every eclipse season. In fact, there may be two eclipses during one season. For, if there is a small partial eclipse just inside the limit, there may be another 29½ days later, before the end of the same season. If there are two solar eclipses in successive months, there will be a total eclipse of the

full moon between the two, since the earth's shadow will be near the middle of the lunar eclipse limit at the other node.

There are two eclipse seasons in a single calendar year, and there may be part of a third because of the regression of the nodes. If the first season begins in early January, the second will begin in June, and the third in December. If there are two eclipses during each of the first two seasons, there is the possibility of another at the beginning of the third. That is, there may be five solar eclipses in a single calendar year. If that is the case, there will also be two eclipses of the moon, for a total of seven. However, if the first eclipse occurs in December of the preceding year instead of January, there may be one solar and one lunar eclipse before the end of the year, for a total of seven—four of the sun and three of the moon. If penumbral eclipses of the moon are counted, there will be at least two each year.

Since there are eclipse seasons without an eclipse of the moon and only one of the sun, the minimum number of eclipses in a single calendar year is two—both of the sun.

An eclipse of the moon can be seen from half of the earth's surface at one time; that is, from any part of the earth where the moon is above the horizon. Eclipses of the sun, on the other hand, are seen only from those regions of the earth where the moon's shadow falls. Since the umbra is at most only 165 mi wide, very few people have seen a total eclipse of the sun. But since the penumbra is much wider than the umbra, and since there are at least two solar eclipses each year, partial eclipses of the sun are fairly common and can be seen by many people.

## 13.5  Occultations and Transits

The passage of the moon in front of a star or a planet is called an *occultation*. This phenomenon happens frequently, since the moon is one-half degree wide. However, occultations of stars bright enough to be seen near the moon are rather rare. For example, in 1965 no bright stars were occulted, although there were occultations of several planets.

Since the moon moves eastward among the stars, when it occults a star the star disappears behind the east limb, which is the dark limb between new and full moon. To the unaided eye, the star is seen when still some distance from the lighted part of the moon and seems to disappear instantaneously for no visible reason. But in a telescope the dark part is faintly illuminated and can be seen, so the illusion is not quite as startling as it is with unaided vision. The fact that the star disappears suddenly is a proof that the moon has no atmosphere. With modern photoelectric instruments and oscilloscopes, the light of the star can be seen to vary rapidly because of diffraction by the limb. The entire phenomenon of disappearance lasts about 1/50 sec. This technique can be used to determine the angular diameter of a large star, which cannot be measured by ordinary techniques.

Occultations have been used to determine the exact location of the moon's limb and hence the center. Since the moon's motions are very complicated because of perturbations, it is impossible to calculate its position exactly. By the use of occultations, the position of the center of the moon is corrected occasionally.

The approximate times of occultation are listed annually in advance in the almanacs, but if accurate times are desired, it is necessary to substitute the exact latitude and longitude of the observing station. Methods of making the computations of times of occultations for given locations are published in advance.

The occultation of a bright star or planet is of considerable interest. (See Figure 13–10.) Binoculars are recommended, if no telescope is available. Both disappearance and reappearance of stars occur so fast that exact times should be computed beforehand. It is usually difficult to find the exact point of the moon's limb where the star will reappear. So it may be a second or two after reappearance that the star will be seen and then well separated from the limb. A planet has a visible disk, which will gradually disappear or reappear. Occultations of Venus, Jupiter, and Saturn are particularly well worth watching. Figure 13–10 shows the emergence of Jupiter and its four Galilean satellites. During occultations of Saturn, the moon can be seen crossing the ring system. And the occultations of the brilliant Venus are beautiful, particularly if both bodies exhibit their crescent phases.

An occultation of a star by a planet is very rare, but such occurances are calculated and listed in advance. The bright star Regulus was occulted by the planet Venus on July 7, 1959. Two consecutive exposures are reproduced in Figure 13–11. The star was behind the planet for about 13 min.

The planets Mercury and Venus sometimes pass in front of the sun. This phenomenon is called a *transit*. Transits of Mercury occur about 13 times per century. They always occur in May or November when the planet is near one of its nodes—the points in its orbit which lie on the ecliptic. The planet moves diagonally across the sun's disk fairly near the limb. The entire transit lasts about four hours

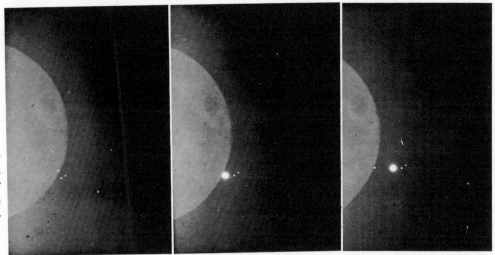

Fig. 13–10 The emergence of Jupiter and three of its satellites after their occultation by the moon. (Griffith Observatory photograph)

and must be seen in a telescope. During this time, the planet is seen as a small, very dark, round spot moving slowly from east to west. The next transits of Venus will occur on June 8, 2004, and June 6, 2012.

## QUESTIONS AND PROBLEMS

1. In a coronagraph the visible portion of the sun is occulted by a disk. During a total eclipse this portion of the sun is occulted by the moon. What observations can be made during a total eclipse that cannot be made with the coronagraph? Why?

2. Would an observer on the moon be able to make better observations of the solar corona with a coronagraph or with an ordinary telescope when the sun is eclipsed by the earth?

3. From what portions of the earth's surface can

Fig. 13–11 An occultation of the bright star Regulus by the crescent planet Venus on July 7, 1959. The star was behind the planet about 13 minutes. (Sky and Telescope)

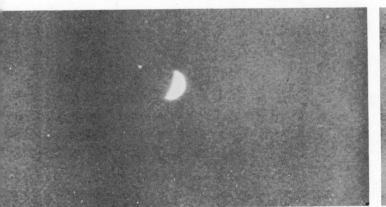
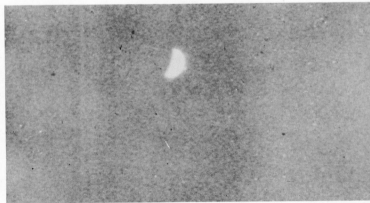

the following be observed: (a) Moon enters totality? (b) Some portion of a lunar eclipse, assuming it lasts three hours?

4. Total solar eclipses occur more frequently than lunar eclipses but few people have seen a total solar eclipse, while many people have seen a total lunar eclipse. Why?

5. What would be seen from the moon while solar and lunar eclipses are observed on the earth?

6. If the moon's node remained stationary instead of regressing, what would be the maximum number of solar and lunar eclipses in a calendar year?

7. Compute the average length of the shadows of Venus and Jupiter. (See Table 14–1.) **Ans:** Venus, 597,000 mi.

8. (a) Calculate the number of degrees the moon moves each hour at full moon, as seen from the sun. (b) Why should the synodic period be used rather than the sidereal period? (c) Using the answer to (a) and the angular size of the umbra given in the text, compute the maximum duration of a total lunar eclipse.

9. The tip of the shadow of a spherical satellite just touches the earth's surface, 100 mi below, when the satellite is in line with the centers of the sun and the earth. What is the diameter of the satellite?

10. (a) Show that during a solar eclipse the shadow of the moon travels at about 2120 mi/hr. Should the synodic or sidereal period be used in the computation? (b) If the moon revolved around the earth at the same rate but in the opposite direction, how fast would the moon's shadow overtake a point on the equator?

11. By using similar triangles, compute the width of the earth's shadow at the moon's average distance.

# Chapter Fourteen

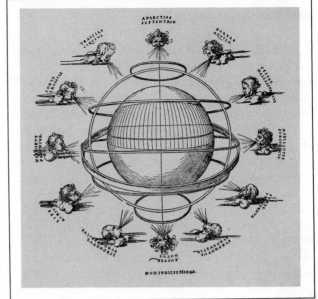

# The Planets and Their Families

The solar system consists of the sun and all the smaller bodies under its gravitational influence. Among these are the nine planets, most of which control a secondary family of satellites (moons). There are also thousands of minor planets, usually called asteroids, and an unknown number of comets, which are collections of particles loosely held together. Everywhere in between there are myriads of smaller particles, called meteoroids. Still more finely divided particles are called interplanetary dust.

The sun and one planet (the earth) and its satellite have already been described in some detail. We shall now describe the other bodies in this system and, if possible, compare them with those which can be studied in more detail. This chapter will necessarily be sketchy. It will try to summarize in brief what knowledge has been acquired since the invention of the telescope in 1609.

The solar system, or the universe as it was considered to be several centuries ago, was at first thought to be centered about the earth. The universe of Ptolemy and the modification made by Copernicus, Kepler, and Galileo have been described in Chapter 6.

## 14.1 Discovery and Classification of Planets

The first six planets in order of distance from the sun have been known since ancient times, although the earth was not recognized as a planet until the time of Copernicus. The seventh planet, Uranus, was discovered by visual observations with a telescope by Sir William Herschel in 1781. Its irregular motions led to a mathematical study which terminated in the discovery of the eighth planet Neptune, in 1846. Again mathematical computations led to a program of search that culminated in the discovery of Pluto, the ninth and last planet, in 1930. It is now believed that the system of planets in the solar system is completely known.

This system is very isolated in space. Pluto is barely 40 astronomical units from the sun. The nearest star is about 270,000 times the distance of the earth from the sun. The space between the stars and the sun is almost empty, except that there are some astronomers who believe that there are billions of comets wandering around, some of which are deflected into the region of the sun. Then there are interstellar dust particles, which are so far apart that there is only about one atom per cubic centimeter of space between the stars.

There are several ways of classifying the planets. One way calls Mercury and Venus inferior planets, meaning that they are inside the orbit of the earth. All the others are called superior planets. For convenience in classifying them by size and mass, Mercury, Venus, the earth, Mars, and probably Pluto may be called terrestrial planets, since they are much like the earth. Pluto, however, seems to be almost an unknown planet in many respects. Its size, mass, and density must be considered as uncertain, but it is certainly not in the class of the larger planets, which are called major planets. Jupiter is the largest, followed by Saturn and a pair of twins, Uranus and Neptune, of which Neptune seems to be slightly the smaller. Table 14–1 lists the known data about all nine planets, plus one of the minor planets, Ceres. Ceres was the first asteroid to be discovered and is the largest. Its orbit is typical of the average asteroid.

## 14:2    Planetary Orbits

The sidereal periods, the times required for a single revolution around the sun, increase outwards from 88 days to almost 250 years. From the sidereal periods, the synodic periods can be calculated by the formulas given in Chapter 6. The synodic periods, the intervals between conjunctions or oppositions, are in a sort of order. Mercury has the shortest. Mars and Venus have the longest, since their sidereal periods are nearly the same as that of the earth. The synodic periods then decrease to that of Pluto, which moves the slowest and advances only about 1.5° per year in its orbit, so the earth overtakes it in just a little over one year.

The mean distances are correlated with the sidereal periods by Kepler's third law. They are given in Table 14–1 in both astronomical units and in millions of miles. It is obvious from the table why the planets are placed in two groups on the basis of mass and diameter. Jupiter is the largest in both respects. The density of each planet can be computed from the mass and diameter as was done for the sun and the earth in previous chapters. The density is given in the table in grams per cubic centimeter; that is, it is compared to the density of water. It will be noticed that this figure, which is the average density, shows each planet to be heavier than water, except Saturn.

The period of rotation of each planet is given, but is subject to change, as will be noted later in this chapter. The albedo, the reflecting power, of each planet is given. Mercury's albedo is about the same as that of the moon. Both these bodies are without

TABLE 14–1

**Planetary Data**

| Name | Sidereal Period | Synodic Period | Mean Distance from Sun (astr. units) | (millions of miles) | Equatorial Diameter (miles) | Mass (earth = 1) | Average Density (g/cm³) | Period of Rotation | No. of Satellites | Albedo | Velocity of Escape | Equatorial Surface Gravity (earth = 1) |
|------|-----------------|----------------|--------------------------------------|---------------------|------------------------------|------------------|-------------------------|--------------------|-------------------|--------|---------------------|-----------------------------------------|
| Mercury | 88.$^d$0 | 116$^d$ | 0.387 | 36.0 | 3100 | 0.054 | 5.2 | 88$^d$ | 0 | 0.07 | 2.6 mi/sec | 0.36 |
| Venus | 224.69 | 584 | 0.723 | 67.2 | 7600 | 0.82 | 5.1 | 250$^d$? | 0 | 0.73 | 6.5 | 0.89 |
| Earth | 365.26 | | 1.000 | 93.0 | 7927 | 1.000 | 5.52 | 23$^h$ 56$^m$ | 1 | 0.39 | 7.0 | 1.00 |
| Mars | 686.95 | 780 | 1.524 | 141.6 | 4220 | 0.11 | 4.0 | 24 37 | 2 | 0.20 | 3.2 | 0.39 |
| Ceres | 4.$^y$604 | 467 | 2.767 | 257.3 | 480 | ? | | | | | | |
| Jupiter | 11.86 | 399 | 5.203 | 483.6 | 88,700 | 317.8 | 1.33 | 9 50 | 12 | 0.51 | 37.1 | 2.54 |
| Saturn | 29.56 | 378 | 9.561 | 888.8 | 75,100 | 95.2 | 0.68 | 10 14 | 9 | 0.50 | 22.3 | 1.06 |
| Uranus | 83.95 | 370 | 19.17 | 1782 | 29,000 | 14.5 | 1.7 | 10 49 | 5 | 0.66 | 13.9 | 1.08 |
| Neptune | 163.9 | 367 | 29.95 | 2784 | 28,000 | 17.2 | 2.2 | 15 | 2 | 0.62 | 15.4 | 1.38 |
| Pluto | 247.3 | 367 | 39.39 | 3662 | 3,600? | 0.9? | ? | 5$^d$09$^h$ | 0 | 0.16? | ? | ? |

atmospheres. Mars' albedo is intermediate, as is expected for a planet with a moderate atmosphere. All the other planets reflect sunlight from their atmospheres, which accounts for their high albedos.

The determination of the position of a planet in its orbit and with respect to the earth—its right ascension and declination at any time—is a problem belonging to the field of celestial mechanics and cannot be discussed here. However, the list of so-called elements is given because some of them are of interest in a description of the motions of the various planets and will be used in the following pages. (See Appendix.)

Because of perturbations, the elements are continually changing. February 9, 1965 was chosen for this table because of availability of data for that time. The longitude of the ascending node is the angle on the ecliptic from the vernal equinox, measured eastward. The longitude of perihelion, curly pi, is the longitude of the ascending node plus the angle along the orbit from the node to the point of perihelion. Dates of perihelion next after February 9, 1965 are listed for the first four planets only. Other dates were not computed because of their uncertainty. Pluto will be at perihelion near the beginning of the twenty-first century. All perihelion and aphelion distances can be computed from the data in the table by the formulas:

$$\text{perihelion distance} = a - ae$$
$$\text{aphelion distance} = a + ae$$

The elements of the orbits of the planets are as follows:

1. The sidereal period $P$ in tropical years is not used as an element, but is related to the mean distance.
2. The mean distance $a$ is the semimajor axis of the ellipse, in astronomical units.
3. The eccentricity $e$ of the ellipse defines its shape.
4. The inclination $i$ is the angle between the plane of the orbit and the ecliptic.
5. The longitude of the ascending node $\Omega$ is the angular distance from the vernal equinox to the point where the planet crosses the ecliptic from south to north.
6. The argument of the perihelion $\omega$ is the angular distance on the orbital plane from the ascending node to the line joining the sun and the point of perihelion.
7. The time of perihelion passage $T$ is the date at which the planet is at perihelion.

The elements of the orbits of all planets are listed in Table E in the Appendix.

## THE INDIVIDUAL PLANETS

### 14.3 Mercury

The planet nearest the sun and the smallest in the solar system is Mercury. Its mean distance from the sun is 36,000,000 mi with perihelion distance 28,600,000 mi and aphelion 43,400,000 mi. Since its synodic period is 116 days, Mercury comes into superior conjunction with the sun and afterwards into the evening sky every four months. But because its maximum elongation is only 18° at perihelion and 28° at aphelion, it is too close to the sun to be seen easily. Since Mercury and Venus are inferior planets, they show all phases from new at inferior conjunction to full at superior conjunction, as shown for Venus in Figure 14–1. The best times to see Mercury are at greatest elongation in the evening sky in March and April, when its orbit makes the greatest possible angle with the horizon, or in the morning sky in September and October. When brightest, Mercury is a little brighter than the brightest star, Sirius, but it is ten times fainter than Venus at maximum.

Since the velocity of escape is low, only 2.3 mi/sec, and the temperature is high, because of its nearness to the sun, Mercury has no appreciable atmosphere. Whatever atmosphere it has is from the solar wind (a few molecules which have been temporarily captured). The result is that the temperature on the sunward side measures between 616°K and 690°K, depending on the distance from the sun. This is above the melting point of lead.

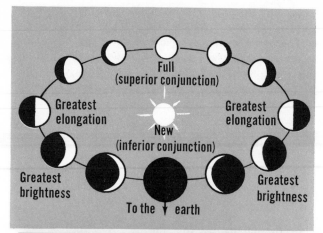

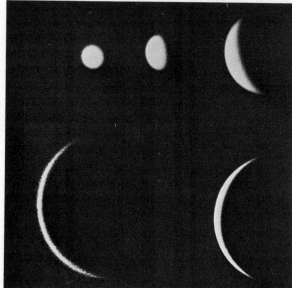

Fig. 14–1   Production of the phases of an inferior planet (top). Relative apparent size of Venus at five different phases. (Lowell Observatory photographs)

Because of tidal forces from the sun, Mercury keeps one side always toward the sun. Hence its period of rotation is the same as its sidereal period, 88 days. This means that one side is perpetually lighted and heated and the other is perpetually dark

and cold. However, because of the tilt of the axis to the orbit, which is not definitely known, and its variable speed in orbit, there are librations as in the case of the moon. About one-third of the surface is always exposed to sunlight; one-third never sees the sun; and the remaining one-third has sunlight during only part of its year.

The dark side has always been considered to have a temperature near absolute zero, perhaps 25° K. But this has been disputed and there is a possibility that the dark side has a moderate temperature. Also it is possible that Mercury rotates slowly in about 50 days.

### 14.4   Venus

The beautiful evening star, Venus, is also a conspicuous object in the morning sky. Before the two appearances were recognized as one planet only, it had different names; Phosphor, or Lucifer, in the morning and Hesper in the evening. After Venus passes superior conjunction, it remains in the evening sky for about three-fourths of a year. Then it rapidly approaches the sun, passes between the earth and the sun at inferior conjunction and into the morning sky for another nine months.

In brightness, Venus surpasses all other objects in the sky, except the sun and the moon. There are several reasons for this. When closest to the earth, the planet is only about 26,000,000 mi away and has an angular diameter slightly greater than one minute (1′). At that time, inferior conjunction, it comes closer to the earth than any other major body, except the moon. Its phase is then new, since the dark side is turned toward the earth. Venus is invisible at inferior conjunction except at rare times when it passes the sun at a distance of a few degrees and can be seen with the telescope as a thin crescent like a very new moon.

As Venus recedes from the earth after inferior conjunction, more and more of its illuminated side can be seen. After 36 days, it reaches its greatest brilliance at an elongation of about 39°. This is a compromise between phase and distance, which is then about 38,300,000 mi. It then recedes to superior conjunction at a distance of some 161,000,000 mi and is behind the sun and therefore invisible again. Its brightness has faded by a factor of about two when last seen in the bright sky just before sunrise. After about two months of invisibility, it reappears in the evening sky, going through its changes of phase and brightness in reverse order.

Another reason for its great brilliance is that Venus is nearly a twin of the earth. Since it is about the same size and mass, it therefore has nearly the same velocity of escape, 6.4 mi/sec. Its albedo is the highest of all the planets, 73 percent, indicating a very dense atmosphere, which is one of several factors that interfere with satisfactory observations of the planet. Another is that it is never more than 48° from the sun, and is observable at night only at low altitudes.

Spectrograms taken with terrestrial telescopes have shown only bands of carbon dioxide, although more recent observations show faint lines which have been tentatively identified as carbon monoxide and nitrogen. Care must be taken to distinguish between lines that have their origins in the atmosphere of Venus and those that originate in the earth's atmosphere. Observations in 1959 from a balloon high enough above the earth to be away from interference by water vapor in our atmosphere showed faint lines of oxygen and water vapor. Still more recently, on December 14, 1962 the space probe Mariner 2 passed within 21,000 mi of the planet's surface and helped settle some of the questions about the planet, which had been unanswered for many years.

The following list includes some of the findings about Venus from Mariner 2:

1. The temperature above the cloud layer is about 220°K (−60°F), but it is 700°K (800°F) on the surface. It seems to be uniform over the entire planet, except for one cold spot which may be a mountain.

2. The clouds are very dense, thick, and cold, perhaps −30°F. They lie from about 45 to 62 mi above the surface. The sun cannot penetrate the clouds, which are thought to be composed of hydrocarbons—familiarly known as smog.

3. The atmosphere below the clouds is mostly carbon dioxide. If there is oxygen, it is at least 1000 times less dense than terrestrial oxygen. The same is true of water.

4. Venus' surface seems to be composed of dust or sand.

5. Winds of solar plasma blow past Venus with speeds of 200 to 500 mi per second and temperature up to 1 million degrees.

6. Venus has no magnetic field. This may be because the planet lacks a nickel-iron core or its magnetism may have been removed by the solar wind.

The period of rotation of Venus is still in some doubt; but, from radar observations, it appears to be about 250 days. This means that Venus rotates slowly backwards. Neither Mercury nor Venus has a known satellite. Since the direct determination of the mass of a planet depends on a formula which includes the period and distance of a moon, the mass of these two planets cannot be determined except by the effect of their perturbations on other bodies. This method is very difficult and the results were uncertain for many years. The most recent values are quoted in Table 14–1.

## 14.5   Mars

Mars has probably attracted more attention than any other planet since the discovery of its so-called canals in 1877, the same year in which its two little moons were discovered. Much speculation about the possibility of life and the artificial nature of the canals has led to the publication of many books about the planet. Percival Lowell, an American astronomer, built his own observatory on "Mars Hill" on the edge of Flagstaff, Arizona, for the express purpose of observing the planet. While the Lowell Observatory has studied Mars almost continually since its founding, its work also led to the discovery of the ninth planet, Pluto, and to much other astronomical work of importance. Lowell's book entitled *Mars* is a classic. Earl C. Slipher continued Lowell's work, photographed Mars from a location in South Africa where the planet was nearly overhead at favorable oppositions, and, just before his death, published a book about his latest findings.

Mars is usually not as easily recognized as Venus and Jupiter because it is ordinarily not as bright; but its reddish color and its rapid motion among the constellations help in identifying it. Mars is absent from the evening sky for about a year near the times of conjunction with the sun. Then it brightens up as it nears the earth, stops its eastward motion and makes a long loop toward the west, which takes three months. It then resumes its eastward motion, fading slowly until conjunction again about a year later. The loops are described every 26 months. They have slightly different sizes and shapes because of the eccentricity of the orbit and the position relative to the earth. Each loop is some 30° east of the preceding loop.

Because of the eccentricity of the orbit, 0.093, the opposition distances from the earth vary from about 35,500,000 mi to 62,600,000 mi, as shown in Figure 14–2. The closest oppositions unfortunately occur when the planet is nearly 30° south of the celestial equator, which was the reason for Slipher's expeditions to Africa to photograph it. The favorable oppositions in 1954 and 1956 were disappointing in that they failed to reveal anything new about the nature of the surface. In 1956 Mars developed a veil of haze or dust, which almost completely obscured the surface features for about a month at the most favorable time.

At a distance of 35,500,000 mi the angular diameter of the planet is only 24.5″. Surface features can be seen only with the best optical equipment and under the most favorable atmospheric conditions. The best observing stations are therefore on mountains where the air is steady and free from dust and moisture.

Photographs of Mars from the earth (Figure 14–3) show a broad pattern of bright and dark areas with usually a conspicuous white cap at one of the poles. The south polar cap is best seen from the

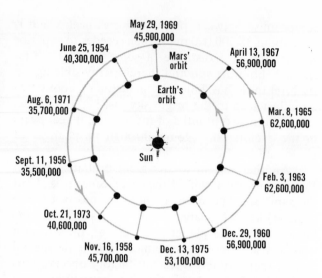

Fig. 14–2  Opposition distances of Mars. The differences are due to the eccentricities of the orbits of Mars and the earth, in particular that of Mars.

earth, since it is presented toward the earth at times of opposition. The cap changes size with the seasons and its nature has been in dispute for years. Observations with the spectroscope show that Mars' atmosphere contains large amounts of carbon dioxide—13 times as much as in the atmosphere of the earth. Theory leads us to believe that there should be a large percentage of nitrogen, which is not observable with the spectrograph from the earth. A small percentage of argon should also be present. Search for oxygen and water vapor has been unsuccessful and the amounts are estimated to be of the order of $\frac{1}{1000}$ the amounts found in the air around the earth.

On July 14–15, 1965, the space ship Mariner 4, after a voyage of 7½ months, passed Mars at a distance of 6118 mi. With equipment on board, 21 and a fraction pictures were taken, stored on tape, played back to earth after the planet was passed, and printed in terrestrial laboratories by a special scanning technique. The eleventh photograph is reproduced in Figure 14–4. This has been called

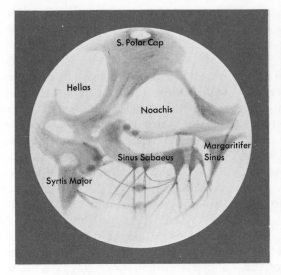 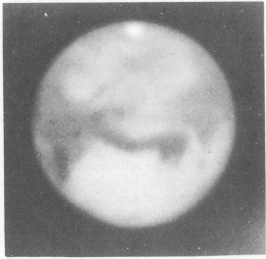

Fig. 14–3    A drawing (left) and a photograph (right) of the same region of Mars. A drawing can take advantage of short intervals of "good seeing," but a photograph is blurred because of the long exposure necessary. South is at the top. (Lowell Observatory photograph)

Fig. 14–4    Photograph No. 11 from Mariner 4 showing a part of the surface of Mars. (NASA)

"one of the most remarkable photographs of this age." It was taken from a distance of 7800 mi and covered an area 170 by 150 mi. The success of the Mariner 4 program depended on superb engineering by the Jet Propulsion Laboratory of the California Institute of Technology. It required the transmission of data by radio techniques from a distance of more than 100 million miles and the proper functioning of 134,000 parts after the long journey of 325 million miles in orbit from the earth to Mars.

The photographs covered a total area of 1 percent of the surface of Mars with a resolution of about 2 mi. Seventy craters from 2½ to 75 mi in diameter were counted. This indicates that there are probably more than 10,000 craters of that size on the planet's surface. Crater walls appear to have slopes up to 10°. They resemble the southern lunar craters. There are no mountain ranges, ocean basins, or continents. Otherwise Mars' surface looks very much like the surface of the moon. The south polar latitudes appear to have peaks with thin deposits of frost, but no other sign of water was found. There is no strong magnetic field, indicating that Mars does not have a liquid core, a result similar to that from the space probe near Venus.

The markings on Mars were discovered in 1877 by Giovanni Schiaparelli, who called them *canali*, an Italian word meaning channels. It was translated into English as *canals,* with the implication that they are artificial. Mariner 4 passed over several canals, but no trace of these features was found. Free water in sufficient quantity to form streams or to fill oceans could not have existed for several billion years. The present surface features must have been present without internal forces (volcanoes) for from 2 to 5 billion years. Craters and other features must have been formed by forces from outside (meteoroids).

Changes in the appearance and color of the surface areas seem to indicate some low form of plant or animal life containing hydrocarbons, like terrestrial organic material and algae. Mariner 4 photographs do not show any evidence of life, but neither do they disprove its existence. It is thought that Martian oceans have never existed and that fossil remains would not be found by a landing party.

Gravitation on the surface of Mars is about 40 percent of that on the earth. Since the velocity of escape is low, 3.2 mi/sec, the amount of atmosphere retained is correspondingly low. This is confirmed by the low albedo, 20 percent. Temperatures measure about 85°F at noon in the tropics when Mars is at perihelion. At night the temperature drops to near $-100°$F. It is impossible to measure the temperature on the dark side, but the night temperature is estimated from measures made just after sunrise. At times the planet shows a slightly gibbous phase.

Mars rotates in $24^h 37^m$; there are 670 Martian days in a Martian year, and its equator is inclined 25° to the plane of the orbit. Except for the greater distance from the sun and the more extreme distances at perihelion and aphelion, the seasons on Mars are not too unlike those on the earth. However, living conditions are much more extreme and

Mars would be a very unpleasant place to live.

Mars has two small moons, which were discovered by Asaph Hall in 1877 at the United States Naval Observatory in Washington. The inner moon is named Phobos, or Fear. Its diameter is about 5 mi and its mean distance from the center of the planet is 5,800 mi. Its sidereal period of revolution is $7^h 39^m$, only one-third of the period of rotation of the planet. Phobos therefore rises in the west and sets in the east.

The outer satellite, named Deimos, or Panic, is only about 3 mi in diameter. Both satellite diameters are very uncertain and are estimates only. Deimos is 14,600 mi from the center, or 12,490 mi from the surface of the planet. It revolves in $30^h 18^m$ and rises in the east and sets in the west, remaining above the planet's horizon for 2⅔ days at a time. The two satellites pass each other in opposite directions every 6.1 hr. Phobos would be about 175 times and Deimos 5.6 times brighter to an observer on the surface of Mars than Venus is to an observer on the earth.

The mass of a planet with a satellite can be calculated easily. Since Mars is a good example, the method is given here and the mass of Mars is worked out using Deimos as the satellite. Data for all satellites in the solar system are given in the Appendix.

Newton's modification of Kepler's third law of planetary motion has been stated in Chapter 6 as: $P^2(M + m) = A^3$. Since this equation was derived by Newton as the result of gravitational attraction, it can be adapted to any two pairs of bodies moving in orbits about their common centers of gravity. The resulting equation is a proportion, as follows (the equation is stated as applying to Mars and its motion around the sun and Deimos in its revolution around Mars):

$$\frac{P^2_{Mars}}{P^2_{Deimos}} = \frac{A^3_{Mars}}{A^3_{Deimos}} \times$$

$$\frac{\text{mass of Mars} + \text{mass of Deimos}}{\text{mass of sun} + \text{mass of Mars}}.$$

Neglecting the mass of Mars as small compared to

the mass of the sun and also that of Deimos compared to Mars, this proportion may be written:

$$\frac{P^2{}_{Mars}}{P^2{}_{Deimos}} = \frac{A^3{}_{Mars}}{A^3{}_{Deimos}} \times \frac{\text{mass of Mars}}{\text{mass of sun}}$$

provided the same units are used for all corresponding terms.

Substituting for the periods and mean distances and solving:

$$\frac{\text{mass of Mars}}{\text{mass of sun}} = \frac{(686^d95)^2}{(1^d262)^2} \times \frac{(14,600 \text{ mi})^3}{(141,640,000 \text{ mi})^3}$$

$$= \frac{1}{3,081,000}.$$

Multiplying by the ratio of the sun's mass to the earth's mass, the mass of Mars is 0.108 times the mass of the earth.

## 14.6  The Asteroids

During the eighteenth century a formula was developed that gives the approximate mean distances of the known planets from the sun. This so-called "law" is known as Bode's law, although he was not the first to state it; and it is not a law in the strict physical sense. If to a series of 4s the numbers 0, 3, 6, 12, . . . are added and the sum divided by 10, a sequence of numbers is obtained, each of which is the approximate distance of a planet. These numbers and the actual distances of the planets are given in Table 14–2.

When Bode's law was first stated in 1766, there was an apparent gap in the series between the distances of Mars and Jupiter. It was thought that there was a "missing planet" in the gap. On the first night of the nineteenth century, January 1, 1801, an uncharted star was found by Giuseppe Piazzi, an Italian astronomer. This star was found to move and was observed for about a month before it became lost due to the illness of its discoverer. By that

**TABLE 14–2**
**Bode's Law**

| Planet | Mean Distance[a] Bode's Law | Actual | Planet | Mean Distance Bode's Law | Actual |
|--------|------|--------|--------|------|--------|
| Mercury | 0.4 | 0.387 | Jupiter | 5.2 | 5.203 |
| Venus | 0.7 | 0.723 | Saturn | 10.0 | 9.539 |
| Earth | 1.0 | 1.000 | Uranus | 19.6 | 19.191 |
| Mars | 1.6 | 1.524 | Neptune | | 30.071 |
| Ceres | 2.8 | 2.767 | Pluto | 38.8 | 39.518 |

[a]The mean distance is given in astronomical units.

time it had been recognized as a small planet from its motion. Also its orbit was computed by a new method developed by Karl Friedrich Gauss, a German mathematician, and fit almost exactly the mean distance computed by Bode's law. It was assumed to be the missing planet and was named Ceres.

Gauss' method depended on accurate positions of the body on three dates, perferably separated by a few weeks. It is still used in modified form. Ceres was found again at the end of 1801 in the location predicted by Gauss. It is the brightest of a system of small bodies now called *asteroids,* or *planetoids,* which are in orbit mostly between the orbits of Mars and Jupiter. It sometimes reaches naked-eye brightness at favorable oppositions. Its diameter is 480 mi—much less than the diameter of the smallest of the major planets. The mass of Ceres has never been determined, but a reasonable guess is that it is about 1 percent of the mass of the moon, if it has the density of rock.

Much to the surprise of astronomers, another small planet was discovered in 1802 and later named Pallas. It was followed by the discovery of Juno in 1804, Vesta in 1807, and Astraea in 1845. At present some 2000 are known. Since they have orbits similar to those of the major planets, they are sometimes called minor planets. Each one is named by its discoverer. At first the asteroids were found by visual telescopic observations. After the invention of photography and its adaptation to astronomy, dis-

Fig. 14–5 A field of stars with trails of two asteroids (marked by arrows). (Yerkes Observatory photograph)

covery was easier. By exposing a photographic plate for an hour or more and by guiding so the stars show sharp, round images, an asteroid shows a trail (Figure 14–5). With the use of Schmidt cameras, asteroids are now being photographed in great numbers. The orbits of some 1700 have been calculated and it is estimated that 25,000 or more are within reach of modern telescopes. Their sizes run all the way down to "mere mountains broken loose," to use the expression of a famous American astronomer, Henry Norris Russell.

The asteroids all revolve around the sun in the same direction, but the inclinations of their orbits vary considerably—up to 52°. The eccentricities of the orbits are mostly moderate, but one is as large as 0.83. A few come inside the orbit of Mars and one even comes closer to the sun than Mercury. Icarus will come within 4 million miles of the earth in 1968 and Geographos to 6 million miles in 1969. One of the most famous of the asteroids is Eros, which was used to determine the solar parallax (see Chapter 12).

In studying the orbits of asteroids, Daniel Kirkwood, an American astronomer, discovered gaps in the system, which were named for him (Kirkwood's Gaps). The asteroids, which may at one time have occupied positions at certain particular distances from the sun, have been pulled out of orbit by the perturbations of the planet Jupiter.

One group of asteroids is of importance. They are the Trojans, all named for heroes of the Trojan war. From the study of the problem of three bodies in celestial mechanics, it has been found that if a small body, such as an asteroid, gets into the vertex of an equilateral triangle with the sun and Jupiter at the other two vertices, it will stay there unless pulled out by some perturbation. Twelve such asteroids are known which are near the triangular points. This discovery is a proof that the problem of three bodies has been solved correctly. A thirteenth asteroid lies at a mean distance which is about the same as Jupiter's, but at perihelion it comes close to Mars and at aphelion nearly to the orbit of Saturn.

The origin of the asteroids is still very uncertain. Some theories say that a planet may have been formed between Mars and Jupiter and later broke up under unknown forces. There may have been explosions at different times, since the asteroids seem to be grouped into families. If a planet broke up, it must have been a small one, since the entire mass of the system of minor planets is estimated at only about 1/1000 the mass of the earth.

It is also possible that a mass of material failed to condense into a planet. Certainly the solar system is full of particles in the form of comets and meteoric material, to say nothing about the solar wind particles and cosmic dust. Collisions between particles have never been observed, but they must be going on all the time. Perhaps the future will produce evidence that will lead to a satisfactory theory about the formation and evolution of these pieces of matter.

## 14.7 Jupiter

The giant planet Jupiter orbits the sun in an ellipse which is five times larger and somewhat flatter than the orbit of the earth. It comes to perihelion at a distance of 460,260,000 mi and recedes to 506,900,000 mi at aphelion. Its sidereal period is nearly 12 years, and since its synodic period is 399 days, it comes to opposition every 13 months. In spite of its opposition distance of approximately 400 million miles, which is variable because of the eccentricity of the orbits of the earth and of the planet, it can be seen fairly well through a moderate-sized telescope. Its rotation of only $9^h 50^m$ has produced a noticeable flattening at the poles.

The equatorial diameter is 88,700 mi and the polar diameter is 83,200 mi. On the disk of the planet a series of markings, called belts, can be seen running parallel to the equator. These bands appear to change shape and position from year to year. Another feature is the great red spot, which was first noticed in 1878 and has been visible intermittently since then. If the spot itself is not visible, the indentation of its position in a belt can usually be seen, except when it is behind the planet during half of the 10-hour period of rotation. The red spot apparently also changes size and position on the surface of the planet. Its real nature is still unknown. The belts and the great red spot are plainly visible in Figure 14–6.

The mass of Jupiter can be determined from the periods and mean distances of its satellites as in the case of Mars. The mass is 317.8 times the mass of the earth. The average density is 1.33 g/cm³. The amount of flattening, combined with the low average density, indicates that the planet must have a core of rather high density. A recent model suggests that the planet is (by mass) at least 78 percent hydrogen, and that the core has a density of 31 g/cm³, under a pressure of 100 million atmospheres. (1 atmosphere = 14.7 lb per square inch.)

The rotation of Jupiter can be studied by watching the motion of the indentations in the cloud belts and confirmed by the Doppler effect in the lines of the spectrum at the two limbs. The speed of rotation is about 10 mi/sec—about five times the speed of rotation of the sun. The Doppler shift is about 0.25 A and can be measured easily. Like the sun, Jupiter rotates most rapidly at the equator.

The temperature at the surface of Jupiter measured by radiation instruments on the earth have indicated a cold −200°F (144°K). However, radio measures in 1959 gave a temperature much higher. These measures seem to indicate that the planet is surrounded by a radiation belt similar to the Van Allen belts around the earth, but with an intensity

Fig. 14–6 Photograph of Jupiter taken through a blue filter to emphasize the great red spot; the cloud belts are also conspicuous. (Photograph from the Mount Wilson and Palomar Observatories)

which may be 1000 times greater. The planet itself emits radio waves which have been attributed to some sort of electrical disturbances, perhaps like giant lightning discharges on the earth. These waves are not radiated continuously, but come in bursts.

Jupiter has a very interesting family of satellites. Four of them were discovered by Galileo. They have been named Io, Europa, Ganymede, and Callisto. The four large Galilean satellites are about as large as our moon. Two are smaller and two are larger. Those in the next group are small and have orbits with mean distances from the planet slightly larger than 7 million miles. The outermost group require about two years to complete their orbits about the planet at distances of 14 million miles. The eight inner satellites have direct motions, the same as the rotation of the planet. The outer four have retrograde motions. It is possible that they were once asteroids which Jupiter captured. There is also a theory which says that Jupiter once had 25 satellites and has lost 13 (the 12 Trojan satellites and one other at about the same distance from the sun).

The atmosphere of Jupiter shows the spectrum of molecules of ammonia ($NH_3$) and methane ($CH_4$). The latter is the more abundant. There is also

a trace of hydrogen in the infrared, but hydrogen does not radiate in the visual part of the spectrum at the low temperature of the atmosphere. An occultation of a star by Jupiter in 1952 showed that the average weight of the molecules in the planet's atmosphere is 3.3. Since hydrogen has a molecular weight of 2.0, there must be a heavier gas present. It is thought that the atmosphere is mostly hydrogen and helium.

## 14.8  Saturn

The most beautiful planet is unquestionably Saturn, the second largest planet and the only one with a ring system. (Figure 14–7.) The rings and a few surface details are visible with telescopes of moderate size. Galileo saw them in 1609, but did not recognize them as rings. He thought the planet was triple, or "eared," and the rings are still sometimes referred to as *ansae*, meaning handles. Christian Huygens in 1655 saw the ansae as a ring. That the rings are flat is proved when the earth moves into their plane twice every 29.5 years, when they are seen in large telescopes as a very thin straight line on each side of the planet. They are not visible at those times in small

Fig. 14–7  A photograph of the ringed planet Saturn. Cassini's division is shown separating the inner and outer rings. The crape ring is shown only as a shadow on the planet. (Photograph from the Mount Wilson and Palomar Observatories)

instruments. This happened in 1936 and again in 1966, but in 1951 the planet was behind the sun at the most favorable time.

Most of the time the ring looks like a flat disk, tipped at an angle. In the seventeenth century Giovanni Cassini, an Italian astronomer who became director of the Paris Observatory, discovered a sharp, black division in the ring, which is called Cassini's division. It separates the ring into two parts, an inner, brighter ring and an outer, fainter ring. There is still a third ring which lies inside the other two, called the crape ring (British spelling, crepe). It is very faint and is usually invisible, but its shadow can be seen on the ball of the planet.

The dimensions of Saturn and its ring system are as follows:

1. Equatorial diameter, 75,100 mi.
2. Polar diameter, 67,800 mi. Oblateness (flattening) $\frac{1}{10}$, compared to $\frac{1}{16}$ for Jupiter, and $\frac{1}{297}$ for the earth.
3. Gap between the planet and crape ring, 7000 mi.
4. Width of crape ring, 5500 mi.
5. Width of inner ring, 16,000 mi.
6. Width of Cassini's division, 3000 mi.
7. Width of outer ring, 10,000 mi.
8. Diameter of ring system, 171,000 mi.

The ring was originally thought to be a solid between 10 and 25 mi thick. Then it was found that there are gaps through which stars can be seen faintly. These gaps are similar to Kirkwood's gaps in the asteroid system and are produced by perturbations by the planet's satellites. Cassini's division, for example, is the most obvious gap. It is caused by the pull of the nearest satellite, which has removed particles from that part of the ring system, forming the gap between the two bright rings.

At the end of the nineteenth century, James Keeler, an American astronomer at the Alleghany Observatory in Pittsburgh, placed the slit of a spectrograph across the rings and the ball of the planet. The result is shown in Figure 14–8. The rotation of the planet causes the lines in the spectrum to shift toward the blue on the approaching side and toward the red on the receding side. The result is that the lines are tipped as shown in the spectrogram in the figure. However, the surprising part of the study was that the inner edge of the ring is moving at a speed of 12 mi/sec, which is faster than the speed of the outer edge, 10 mi/sec. This proved immediately that the ring could not be solid, since in that case the outer edge would rotate faster than the inner edge. Furthermore, the speeds were exactly the speeds predicted, if Kepler's law were restated for the satellite system of Saturn and applied to the particles at the distance of the inner and outer edges of the ring. Therefore, the ring must be composed of small particles; in other words, they are very small satellites. The size cannot be determined, but they are estimated to be like grains of sand with possibly a few larger pieces.

One last proof: A French astronomer, Albert Roche, proved mathematically that if a satellite moved inside a certain limit, called *Roche's limit,* it would break up under the gravitational force of the bulge of the planet's equator. This limit is 2.44 times the radius of the planet and (you guessed it!) is between the outer edge of the ring and the first satellite.

The oblateness of the planet itself is a result of its rapid rotation of $10^h 02^m$ at the equator, and its low average density of 0.68 g/cm³. Like Jupiter and the sun, Saturn's rotation is fastest at the equator and slower toward each pole. The latest model shows a central density of 16 g/cm³ under a pressure of 50 million atmospheres. The mass is 95.2 and the surface gravity 1.06 times those of the earth. The velocity of escape is 22.3 mi/sec, so Saturn is able to retain atmospheric molecules of all types. Methane and ammonia have been detected. It is thought that the planet is composed of 60 percent hydrogen.

Saturn has nine satellites, eight of which revolve in direct motion, the same as that of the planet's rotation and of the ring. But the ninth satellite, one of the two smallest of the nine, has retrograde motion. It may have been captured by the pull of gravitation of the planet. Seven of the satellites are visible in telescopes of modest size, particularly

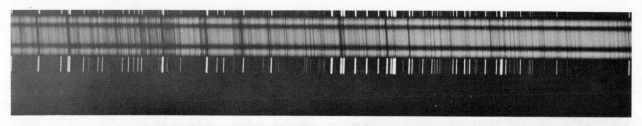

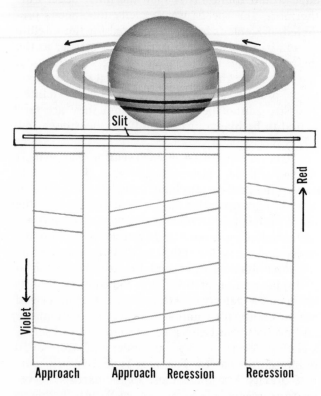

Fig. 14–8   James Keeler's spectrographic proof that the ring system of Saturn is composed of satellite-like particles. The lines in the center are tipped because of the rotation of the planet. The lines in the spectrum of the ring are tipped in the other direction and are curved because the ring particles act as small satellites and obey Kepler's third law. (Lowell Observatory photograph)

"sweeping" the sky with his telescope for an estimate of the number of stars. It shows a small disk, yellow in color, which distinguishes it from the stars. In studying the motion of Uranus and in the computation of its orbit, which was based on accidental observations made for many years before it was recognized as a planet, it was found that the orbit was strongly perturbed by some then unknown object. Two astronomers, John Couch Adams in England and Urbain Joseph Leverrier in France, worked on the mathematical problem of determining the position of the perturbing body. Adams finished his calculations in October 1845 and sent the results to Sir George Airy, who was Astronomer Royal at the time. No search was made for the body.

Leverrier finished his computations in 1846 and published his results in June of that year. In July he suggested to Johann Gottfried Galle in Germany that a search be made. Galle had the proper star charts and in about one hour found and identified the body, which turned out to be a planet in almost exactly the position predicted by Leverrier and also by Adams. The planet was named Neptune. This was the first astronomical discovery made as a result of mathematical computation.

Uranus has a mass 14.5 times and surface gravity 1.08 times that of the earth. Its velocity of escape

when the ring is seen on edge. Titan is the second largest satellite in the solar system. It has an atmosphere and may be covered with snow.

### 14.9   Uranus and Neptune

In size, Uranus and Neptune are a pair of twins. (Figure 14–9.) The latest figures list diameters of 29,000 and 28,000 mi, respectively. Uranus was discovered by Sir William Herschel in 1781, while

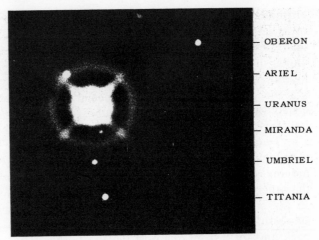

— OBERON

— ARIEL

— URANUS

— MIRANDA

— UMBRIEL

— TITANIA

Fig. 14–9   Neptune and its two satellites (left) and Uranus and its five satellites (right). Miranda (just under the planet) was discovered in 1948. The rays on the four corners of the planets are caused by diffraction of light by the supports of the secondary mirrors in the telescopes used. (Yerkes Observatory photographs)

is 13.9 mi/sec. It has a dense atmosphere containing hydrogen and methane, with an albedo of 66 percent.

One peculiar fact about Uranus is that it rotates about an axis in $10^h 49^m$ in a plane which is nearly at right angles to the plane of its orbit. The exact inclination is 98°, so the planet actually rotates backwards. Its five satellites revolve around the planet in the same plane, the plane of the planet's equator. Two satellites were discovered by Sir William Herschel, who thought he had discovered six, but four were stars. Two more were found by an astronomer named Lassell in 1851 and the fifth by Gerard Kuiper, a Dutch-American astronomer, in 1948 with the 82-inch telescope in Texas. The first four are 500 or 600 mi in diameter, the fifth only 200.

Neptune rotates in normal, direct fashion in about 15 hr. Its large satellite was discovered by Lassell in 1846. It revolves backwards in $5^d 21^h$. The smaller satellite's motion is direct with sidereal period about one year. Neptune has an atmosphere, its albedo is 62 percent, and it has a greenish color as seen in the telescope. There is methane present in its atmosphere, but apparently hydrogen has not yet been definitely detected. Both planets undoubtedly contain large amounts of hydrogen, but not as high a percentage as in Jupiter and Saturn, since their densities are higher, 1.7 and 2.2 g/cm³, respectively. They are so far from the sun, 1.78 and 2.78 billion miles, that their temperatures are probably lower than −300°F (94°K).

## 14.10   Pluto

The most distant planet and the orphan of the solar system is Pluto. It is far from the other terrestrial planets and does not belong to the group of major planets, but little is known about it.

The computations of the perturbations of both Uranus and Neptune did not satisfy all astronomers. Some thought there should be another, more distant planet which was also perturbing the two. A mathematical computation was made, but the disturbing body was not found at the predicted positions. But Percival Lowell did start a search from his observatory on Mars Hill. After his death in 1916, his brother gave a 13-inch photographic telescope to the observatory and the search was continued. With this telescope, photographs of the sky were made along the ecliptic, where most planets are to be found. Any moving object could be found by viewing the plates in pairs with a special instrument called the blink microscope. Figure 14–10 shows how this might be done.

Two plates are placed side by side such that each can be seen separately in a single eyepiece. By moving a prism in the eyepiece, first one and then the other can be seen. If the instrument is adjusted so the stars are superposed when seen rapidly in succession, a moving object will appear to jump back and forth from one position to another. That is, in Figure 14–10, the image of Pluto would be seen to move suddenly from its position shown in the top photograph to a lower position, as in the bottom photograph. In this way the new planet was discovered in 1930 by a young American astronomer, Clyde Tombaugh, at the Lowell Observatory.

Pluto was named for the god of the underworld, since it must be dark and cold at a distance of nearly 4 billion miles from the sun. The planet's size is not definitely known, but is estimated at 3600 mi diameter. If its mass is 0.8 that of the earth, as has been estimated from perturbations, its density is 48, which is too high to be acceptable.

Pluto's sidereal period is nearly 250 years. Its orbital eccentricity is so great, 0.246, that by the end of this century it will be closer to the sun than Neptune. However, because of the high inclination of the orbit, the two planets will never be closer together than several hundred million miles. One guess about the origin of Pluto is that it once was a satellite of Neptune. This is hard to understand because of the difference between the two orbits.

From Pluto the sun would have an angular diameter of less than one minute (1′) of arc. It would appear dazzlingly bright, but still 1600 times fainter than it does to us on the earth. It would be some 250 times brighter than our full moon. The earth would be always less than 1.5° from the sun

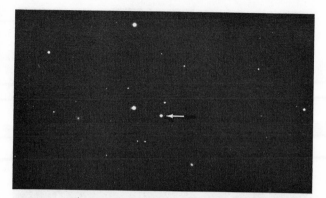

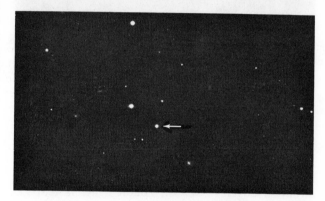

Fig. 14–10 Two photographs of Pluto, identified by the arrows. The motion of the planet among the stars in 24 hr is obvious. (Photographs from the Mount Wilson and Palomar Observatories)

and would therefore be invisible from Pluto, as would Mercury, Venus, and probably Mars. All the major planets would show phases when seen from Pluto, as Mercury and Venus do to us.

## QUESTIONS AND PROBLEMS

1. Give two reasons why Venus at maximum brightness appears brighter than Jupiter at its maximum brightness.
2. When at maximum brightness, is Mars or Venus closer to the earth?

3. Why have few people ever seen Mercury?

4. Why does Mercury have the smallest albedo of all the planets?

5. How does the fact that the orbits of Venus and Mercury are inside the earth's orbit hinder observations of their surfaces?

6. Why did Galileo discover only 4 of Jupiter's 12 moons?

7. Are any of the satellites of the planets as large as a planet?

8. Jupiter is farther from the sun than Mars and farther than Mars from the earth. But the maximum apparent magnitudes are almost the same (Jupiter, −2.5; Mars, −2.8). What two factors compensate for Jupiter's greater distance?

9. If an astronaut were able to travel at the speed of light, how long would it take for him to go from the earth to (a) the most distant planet, and (b) the nearest star?

10. Phobos and Deimos both revolve around Mars in direct motion. But as seen from Mars, Phobos would rise in the west and Deimos in the east. Explain.

11. Dione, a satellite of Saturn, is about the same distance from the planet as the moon is from the earth. Its period, however, is only about ⅒ the moon's period. Why? Using Newton's modification of Kepler's third law, calculate the ratio of Saturn's mass to the earth's mass. Neglect the mass of the moon and of Dione. Check the answer with the data in Table 14–1.

12. Compare the equatorial velocities of Jupiter and the earth due to rotation.

13. By drawing a diagram showing the orbits of Venus and the earth, show why Venus becomes an evening star after superior conjunction.

14. Assuming that Phobos and Deimos have the same albedo, compute their ratio of brightness as observed from Mars. (Hint: Use the distances from Mars' surface and their surface areas.)

# Chapter Fifteen

# Comets and Meteoroids

Before the time of Tycho Brahe, comets were thought to be apparitions of mysterious bodies in the earth's atmosphere, and were considered to be omens of political significance, usually of some disaster. A bright comet was seen in A.D. 78 at the fall of Jerusalem; in 1066 at the time of the invasion of England; and in 1453 at the fall of Constantinople.

## 15.1 Orbits of Comets

Tycho could find no parallax for the great comet of 1577. A parallax should have been detectable, if the comet were viewed from two positions a short distance apart and if it were in the atmosphere. He therefore deduced that comets are celestial bodies at considerable distance from the earth, at least three times the moon's distance. He thought they probably revolved around the sun as he surmised the planets did—the earth excepted.

Newton came to the conclusion that comets are attracted to the sun by gravitation. His work was extended by Edmund Halley, who calculated the orbits of 24 comets. Among them were several at intervals

of about 75 years. Halley concluded that these comets were one and the same, and predicted a return about 1758. He did not live to see his prediction fulfilled, but the expected comet was sighted on Christmas Day of that year by an amateur astronomer. This comet has been called Halley's Comet since that time. Its last appearance was in 1910 and it is expected to return in 1986. However, comets are strongly perturbed by planets, and the computation of the exact date of perihelion of Halley's Comet has not yet been made.

It is well known that comet orbits are very elongated. Methods for computing the orbits accurately date back to 1801 as has been noted in connection with the asteroid Ceres. All the elements, like those of the planets, can be calculated from three observations of the comet's position on 3 nearly equally spaced dates. Formerly, it was customary to assume the orbit to be a parabola, since the eccentricity was therefore equal to one, leaving only five more elements to be found. But with the invention of desk calculators and, later, high-speed electronic computers, all six elements can be calculated together. A desk calculator method requires 30 or more hours,

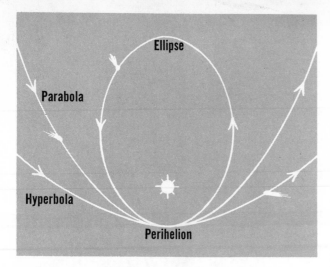

Fig. 15–1  In the neighborhood of perihelion, it is impossible to decide whether the orbit of a comet is an ellipse, a parabola, or a hyperbola. Earlier or later observations can distinguish among the three types. (Lowell Observatory photograph)

but the IBM 1620, or larger computers, can do the entire job in a few seconds. However, the preliminary preparations still take a few hours.

The parabolic orbit is a limiting case between an ellipse and a hyperbola. Usually a comet is observed during a short arc of its entire orbit. Near perihelion, all three types of curves nearly coincide as Figure 15–1 shows. But if observations can be made before the comet comes to perihelion or after it has receded, it is possible to make corrections to the elements and represent the motion of the body more accurately. Such corrections may require observations made over several months. The result of all studies is that it is possible to conclude that all— or at least nearly all—comets go around the sun in elliptical orbits, but most of them have eccentricities very near the parabolic eccentricity of one. The exact answer to this problem depends to a large extent on an acceptable theory of the origin of comets.

## 15.2  Origin of Comets

A recent theory was proposed by Jan Oort of Holland. He suggested that there is a cometary cloud lying about halfway to the nearest stars. These comets are moving at random and are attracted gravitationally by the stars. If a comet is attracted by some star in such a way that it is given a pull in the direction of the sun, it may move into the solar system. Its orbit would be a hyperbola or a parabola, depending on its velocity, with the sun at the focus. If the orbit is either one of these conic sections, the comet would approach the sun only once and would then go back into space.

But if its velocity were slowed, as it might be if it passed a large planet, particularly Jupiter, the perturbations might change the orbit into an ellipse and the comet would become a member of the solar system and stay in orbit around the sun, unless pulled out by some other force. In fact, Jupiter is known to have radically changed the orbits of several comets, either to make them smaller ellipses, or to send them back out into space at increased velocities. Oort has estimated that there are 100 billion comets in the interstellar group, but only about 800 have come close enough to the earth to have had their orbits computed. About 20 percent of these seem to be in elliptical orbits with periods less than 200 years. They are known as short-period comets.

Still more recently, Fred L. Whipple, director of the Smithsonian Astrophysical Observatory, has proposed a theory that there is also a flattened belt of comets in orbit around the sun just beyond the orbit of Pluto. However, most comets come from the outer belt proposed by Oort.

## 15.3  Comet Designations

Each comet is designated by the year of its discovery and a letter which indicates the order of discovery. For example, 1960c was the third comet discovered in 1960. Later, when all orbits have been computed, the comet is given a permanent number and Roman numeral to indicate the order of perihelion passage. For example, Comet 1960c might have been the eighth comet to come to perihelion in 1959. Its designation would then be 1959 VIII. (This is a hypothetical case.)

Comets are also named for their discoverers.

In 1957 Comet Arend-Roland was named for two independent discoverers. Mrkos' Comet of 1957 was named for a Czech amateur astronomer, who first reported it. Halley's Comet and Encke's Comet were named for the men who first recognized them as periodic. The period of Encke's Comet is the shortest known, only 3.3 years. Its period is getting shorter at each return. This was originally assumed to be due to some resisting medium near perihelion. Now it is believed to be caused by jets erupting from the comet's nucleus, which act as retrorockets to slow the motion. The comet seems to have lost most of its tail-making material. The nucleus may be protected by a layer of dust which slows evaporation. Encke's Comet has been seen at nearly every approach since 1786, the 55th in 1964. The orbit of Halley's Comet and a photograph taken in 1910 are shown in Figure 15–2.

Fig. 15–2   The orbit of Halley's Comet and a photograph taken in 1910. The comet is now on its way in to perihelion which is expected about 1986. (Lowell Observatory photograph)

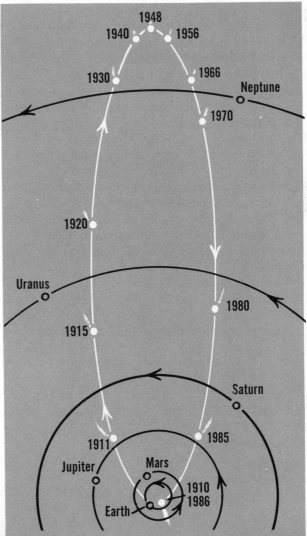

In September, 1965, a comet was discovered by two Japanese astronomers, Ikeya and Seki. The orbit was computed as a parabola with perihelion date October 20 (October 21, Greenwich time). The brightness of the comet was predicted by a formula which included terms for distance from the sun (a heating effect) and distance from the earth (the inverse square law). The best computation of the orbit was that the comet would pass within 300,000 mi of the sun's surface. Some predictions were that the comet would actually collide with the sun, or at least be broken up by the sun's heat. The maximum brightness was to be $-9$, about five magnitudes (100 times) brighter than Venus. It was reported to have been seen in daylight when only 1° from the sun on October 20. As it swung around the sun from the morning sky, it was in the evening sky for only four hours, then went more than half-way around the sun and back into the morning sky.

Positions before perihelion were unfavorable, since the tail was nearly parallel to the horizon from observing stations in the United States. A few photographs were published in the newspapers and the comet attracted a great deal of attention in view of the unusual predictions. The comet did not hit the sun. Neither did it disintegrate, but reappeared in the predicted position in the morning sky. As it pulled away from the sun, it developed a tail more than 10° long and was seen in the brightening dawn sky for several mornings in succession in California. This comet may be one of the fragments of a very large comet which was broken up by the sun. The last comet to come close to the sun was in 1882, the comet breaking into five pieces. It has been reported that Comet Ikeya-Seki has broken into two pieces.

Forty-five comets have periods between three and nine years. They have low inclinations to the ecliptic, direct motion, and in general have aphelion distances near the orbit of Jupiter. This group of comets is called Jupiter's family, since in all probability they were captured when the giant planet pulled them out of their former orbits and into their present orbits.

## 15.4 The Nature of Comets

All comets have approximately the same structure. When far from the sun a comet is merely a small, loosely compacted mass of material, which has been called a flying gravel bank. This may not be a good expression, because a collection of small particles could not hold together under its own gravitation. The most recent theory is that of Whipple, the leading American expert on comets. He has suggested that the particles are embedded in ice composed of radicals of carbon, hydrogen, nitrogen, oxygen, and sodium. The ice holds the solid particles together in the *nucleus,* which contains practically all the mass of the comet. It is being depleted in the periodic comets when they come near the sun. This theory has been called the "dirty iceberg" theory.

When a comet approaches the sun at a distance of three or four astronomical units the heat of the sun melts part of the ice and releases the smallest particles to form a sort of atmosphere around the nucleus. This is called the *coma,* because of its hair-like appearance. The nucleus and the coma form the *head* of the comet. The head of a comet may be hundreds of thousands of miles in diameter. As the particles further divide, and when they reach a size approximately equal to a wavelength of light, they are pushed away from the head to form the *tail* of the comet. In various stages the comet may consist of the nucleus only, or the nucleus may be hidden and the coma alone is visible. This is the case in a good many periodic comets. Finally the tail forms, provided there is sufficient tail-forming material. Comets have been seen to lose their tails and grow new ones. Again, several tails may be visible at the same time!

It is difficult to estimate the size of the nucleus. The diameters apparently range from a few miles for the larger comets to a half-mile for small ones. The coma changes size with distance from the sun. The head of a great comet in 1811 was 1 million miles in diameter. The coma is smaller near perihelion, expands until the comet is about two astronomical units from the sun, and then decreases again. The nucleus reflects sunlight; the coma absorbs sunlight and reradiates it at a different wavelength—a process known as fluorescence. The spectrum of the nucleus is therefore the spectrum of sunlight; the spectrum of the coma is the spectrum of the molecules which compose it. The tail may be hundreds of millions of miles long, is very diffuse and usually curved. It shines by reflected light from the sun.

In 1910 Halley's comet came directly between the earth and the sun. The comet could not be seen then, confirming the belief that the nucleus is small and that the coma is transparent, composed of very small particles and gas. The earth passed through the tail and nothing happened. It was expected to produce a shower of meteors, but the tail particles are much too small. The tail density is of the order of a billionth of a billionth ($10^{-18}$) of the density of the earth's atmosphere. Since the tail was known to have carbon monoxide molecules in it, some people were worried about possible asphyxiation, but the air prevented these molecules from reaching the earth's surface.

Some comets appear to have two kinds of tails. One is composed of gaseous particles and is straight, pointing directly away from the sun. The other is composed of finely divided dust particles and is curved. A notable example was the Arend-Roland Comet of 1957. There was an unusual spike pointing toward the sun. (Figure 15–3) This was the dusty tail seen on edge from the earth. Part of this flat tail was between the head of the comet and the sun. The angle from which it was seen gave it the appearance of a spike.

An example of a comet whose orbit was changed by Jupiter was Oterma's Comet, which was

Fig. 15–3 Comet Arend-Roland of 1957 was unusual in that it seemed to have a short tail pointing toward the sun. (Photograph from the Mount Wilson and Palomar Observatories)

in the neighborhood of Jupiter between 1936 and 1939. Its period was changed from 18 to 8 years. Between 1962 and 1964 it came again near Jupiter, to a distance of about 10 million miles or less. It was strongly perturbed and went out so far from the sun that it may never be seen again.

If a comet is a loose collection of particles held together by ice, when the ice melts it is easy for the particles to become separated from the main mass of the comet. This happens when the comet is close to the sun. The particles, however, still have motion in the orbit and possibly a change of motion due to explosive ejections from the nucleus. They therefore become more or less stretched out along the orbit and are then referred to as a stream—or a swarm, if they are very numerous. The particles are small and not very close together, and are therefore invisible when seen from the earth's distance. Perturbations by a planet, Jupiter in particular, help to pull them away from the comet and to stretch them out in a path either in front of or behind the comet.

### 15.5   Meteoroids

Occasionally a stream of these meteoroids intersects the orbit of the earth. If the earth gets there at the same time, the meteoroids enter the earth's atmosphere at high speeds. The speeds can vary from 7 mi/sec for those that overtake the earth to 44 mi/sec for those that collide head-on with the earth. Therefore each particle, having mass and velocity, has kinetic energy. The friction between the particle and the molecules of air decreases the speed and the kinetic energy is transformed into heat and light, but mostly heat.

It has been estimated that only $1/10,000$ of the kinetic energy is changed into light for the slowest moving meteoroids, but increases by a factor of seven for the fastest ones. If a meteoroid remains intact, it will have a brightness which can be calculated from its velocity. But if it breaks up (this is known as fragmentation), the small pieces burn up more rapidly, because they are ejected into the air

at lower altitudes than normal and the meteor is 100 times brighter than it would be if it remained whole. A 1 g meteoric particle with a velocity of 20 mi/sec seen at 60 mi is about as bright as the first magnitude star Vega. The duration of the trail is about 1.6 sec. In general, the heights vary from 70 mi for the fastest meteors to 40 mi for the slowest. These figures are for moderately bright meteors and are probably lower for the brighter meteors.

According to modern terminology adopted by the International Astronomical Union in 1961, the term *meteor* is used to describe the entire phenomenon associated with the collision of a particle from space and the atmosphere of the earth. The particle is called a *meteoroid,* which is a ball of dust once part of a comet. The average density is low. A *meteorite* is a piece of higher density, which has survived passage through the air and has hit the earth's surface. It has come from the region of the asteroids. Extremely small meteoroids are called *micrometeorites,* if they are small enough to melt completely from the friction produced. Samples have been collected in special boxes flown to great heights in the nose cones of rockets and returned to earth by parachute.

Meteors appear as moving streaks of light called trails, which are comparable in brightness to neighboring stars. They have been called shooting stars. The duration of a trail may be only a fraction of a second. Persistent light from a trail is called a train. The observed maximum duration of a train is 3 hr.

The meteoroid itself is too small to be seen. When it is about 70 mi above the earth, the heating is so great that atoms boil off from the surface of the particle at speeds of about 0.6 mi/sec relative to the particle. These atoms collide with air particles, causing the electrons in the air molecules to be put into violent motion or even pulled away from their nuclei. These processes are called excitation and ionization, respectively. A luminous cloud is formed around the meteoroid and may become visible. The particles lost by the meteoroid and the air molecules are heated to luminescence and form the meteor trail.

## 15.6  Meteor Showers or Swarms

A swarm of meteoroids striking the earth was formerly called a shower. But this term has now given way to the term swarm, meaning a group of meteoroids, which, moving in nearly parallel paths, appear to radiate from a point or small area in the sky called the radiant point. Many of these swarms have been identified as particles from the breakup of known comets. A few are still not identified with any known comet. Only a few swarms produce meteors at a rate sufficiently high to be worth the time of the casual observer. Some of the most productive showers are:

| Name | Date of Maximum | Hourly Rate | Comet |
|------|-----------------|-------------|-------|
| Perseids | August 12 | 50 | 1862 III |
| Geminids | December 14 | 60 | ? |
| Leonids | November 17 | ? | Tempel 1866 I |

Swarms are named for the constellation in which the radiant point is located. If the paths of the meteors of a particular swarm are plotted on a star map, they all appear to have come from the same area in a constellation, although they may appear to be going in any direction and may be seen in various parts of the sky.

The Perseids radiate from Perseus, a constellation which rises shortly after dark in August, but is not on the meridian until about 5:00 A.M. This is the most dependable swarm and lasts for several weeks in July and August, although the rates are low except on August 12. Also more meteors may be seen in years when there is no moon in mid-August to interfere. Their speeds are some 35 mi/sec., so the trails are fast and long, somewhat reddish in color. Forty to sixty per hour may be expected under good observing conditions, and preferably after midnight, at the time of maximum.

The Geminid radiant passes overhead at 2:00 A.M. on December 14 for locations in the southern United States. The hourly rate exceeds that of the Perseids. Velocity is intermediate at 21 mi/sec.

The Leonids are in the orbit of Tempel's comet, which was discovered in 1866. The Leonid shower had been very spectacular in that year and previously in 1799 and 1833, when meteors were "as thick as snowflakes." But the swarm passed Jupiter in 1898, the particles were pulled away from the earth, and the expected shower in 1899 failed to appear. From an hourly rate of 10,000 in 1833, the numbers dropped sharply but rose to 240 in 1932. In 1962, 100 meteors per hour were seen; in 1966, 1000 per minute were reported. As the radiant point does not rise until near midnight in November, these meteors are best observed after midnight. The radiant crosses the meridian after 6:00 A.M.

Two other notable showers were the Andromedids in 1872 and the Draconids of 1933 and 1946. (See Figure 15–4.) Both were associated with short-period comets and both have been perturbed to such an extent that they probably will not be seen from the earth again.

Heights of meteor trails may be measured from ground stations. If a meteor is seen from two stations

Fig. 15–4  Meteor trails photographed during the Draconid shower of October 9, 1946. The radiant point is off the field to the upper right. Other, nearly parallel, streaks are star trails.

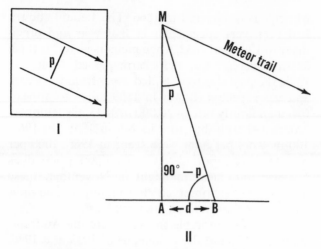

Fig. 15–5   The height of a meteor trail determined by the parallax method. In I, the parallax, $p$, is the distance in angle on a star map between the meteor trail as seen from two stations. In II, $p$ is shown as an angle of the triangle $ABM$, which can be solved for the height $AM$ of a point of the trail.

separated by a known distance, the trails plotted on the same map will be displaced by an angle which can be determined from the locations of stars on the map. This angle of displacement is the parallax of the meteor. As Figure 15–5 shows, the parallax is the angle $p$ of the triangle formed by a point on the trail and the two stations. The triangle can be solved by the ordinary methods of trigonometry and the distances $AM$ and $BM$ determined.

▶*Example:*   The path of a meteor was displaced 12° when viewed from two stations that are 20.0 mi apart. The meteor was directly over one of the stations. Compute its altitude over this station.

*Solution:*   Referring to Figure 15–5, the distance ($d$) between stations $A$ and $B$ is 20.0 mi. The beginning of the visible path of the meteor ($M$) is directly above station $A$. Triangle $ABM$ is, therefore, a right triangle. The parallax ($p$) is 12°, and angle $B$ is 90° − 12°, or 78°.

Using trigonometry, the altitude of the meteor ($AM$) is:

**Formula:**

$$AM = d \times \tan B$$

**Substituting and solving:**

$$AM = 20.0\,\text{mi} \times 4.705 = 94.1\,\text{mi}$$

Using radians (see Appendix), the altitude of the meteor ($AM$) can be found as follows:

**Formula:**

$$AM = \frac{d \times 57.3°}{p}$$

**Substituting and solving:**

$$AM = \frac{20.0\,\text{mi} \times 57.3°}{12°} = 95.5\,\text{mi}$$

The difference of 1.4 mi between the two answers is due to the use of radians for an angle as large as 12°. The first answer is more accurate.

Observations of meteors were formerly made visually, but are now made by taking photographs simultaneously from two stations with wide-angle, fast Schmidt cameras (Figure 15–6). The heights are more accurately determined by this method. Even better determinations are made by radar, and can be made in the daytime as well as at night. A radar pulse is sent out and is reflected by the cloud of electrons in the trail. The time between the sending and receiving of the pulse is used for a determination of the height. The speed of the meteor may also be found by pulses from various parts of the trail. The photographic method interrupts the trail about twenty times per second for accurate timing. These times combined with the heights permit a determination of the speed.

Spectra of the hot, excited vapor of meteor trails have been made. Bright emission lines of calcium, silicon, aluminum, and manganese have been

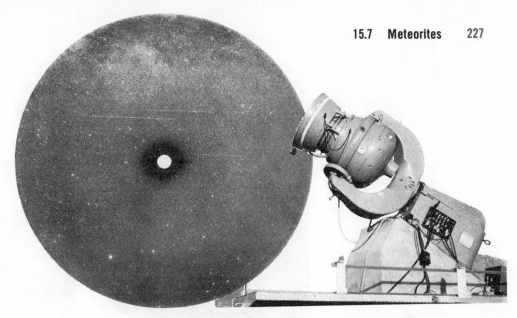

Fig. 15–6 A Baker Super-Schmidt camera (right) used for photography of meteor trails. At the left is a photograph showing three trails. Note the interruptions made 20 times per second for determining the speed of the meteoroid. (Harvard College Observatory photographs)

found. These elements are similar to those in asteroids. While oxygen and nitrogen lines would be expected from the atmospheric molecules, they have not been detected, because these elements do not have lines in the visible part of the spectrum. The meteoroids themselves should also contain oxygen and nitrogen.

## 15.7 Meteorites

Meteorites can be grouped into three general classes. The irons, called *siderites*, contain about 10 percent nickel and the rest is almost all iron. Stony-irons are a combination of about equal parts of iron and stone. They are called *siderolites*. Since the stony material decomposes more rapidly than the irons, they have a tendency to separate into fragments. The stones, called *aerolites*, contain from 10 to 15 percent iron and the remainder is composed of silicates and associated material.

The iron meteorites are easy to identify because they frequently are found in regions where there is little native iron. The stones are more difficult to identify, but an expert can usually prove their meteoric nature by finding small pieces of iron embedded in the stone. When iron meteorites are cut and etched, their identification is made certain by the crystal structures which appear.

Another group of objects, called *tektites,* are suspected of having their origins beyond the earth. It is not certain that this theory is correct, however. Tektites are rounded glassy bodies found in Australia, the Philippines, Indonesia, and other places. Some scientists even believe them to be pieces of the moon which have been broken off by the impact of meteoroids and which were given a high enough velocity to escape from the moon and to be captured by the earth.

Figure 15–7 shows aerolites, siderites, and three samples of tektites. The largest known meteorite in America is the large siderite in the American Museum of Natural History in New York. It rests on a specially built scale and weighs a little over 34 tons (68,085 lb). It was obtained from the Eskimos in Greenland by Admiral Peary in 1897. There is a still larger specimen in southwest Africa, which is estimated to weigh more than 50 tons. It has not been moved to a museum.

One theory of the origin of meteorites and their division into the various classes is that two asteroids about the size of Ceres collided. The collision broke the asteroid into pieces, the irons coming from the central core and the stones from the outer crust.

Fig. 15–7 An aerolite (left), three tektites (upper right), and a siderite (lower right). The siderite is the largest known meteorite in America. It weighs 68,-085 lb. (Nininger Collection and American Museum of Natural History)

These meteoroids are not found during showers, but come in contact with the earth at random. They are usually spoken of as sporadic and their falls are unpredictable. On the average, about 12 meteors per hour may be seen visually. About 80 percent are sporadic.

On the earth's surface are several scars believed to have been produced by the fall of large meteoroids or collections of meteoric particles. The best known crater of meteoric origin in the United States is the Barringer Crater near Winslow, Arizona. (Figure 15–8). This crater is nearly circular, 4200 ft wide and 600 ft deep, with mounded walls 150 ft high. There has been little erosion, but the age cannot be definitely determined. It is estimated at between 5000 and 75,000 years. Drillings have been made in the floor of the crater without finding any definite trace of the meteorite which produced it. The Barringers estimate that a mass of 1 million tons is located under the south rim and once made plans to excavate it for the iron ore it is supposed to contain. However, it is not likely that any deposit will be found. Large pieces weighing hundreds of pounds have been picked up near the crater and many smaller ones have been found at a distance of several miles with a magnetic probe. It is likely that the small particles were from the outer skin of the meteorite, fragments which boiled off as a result of the heat produced by friction with the air. The larger pieces may have been ejected when the entire mass broke up as a result of heat produced by the collision with the earth, and the resulting explosion.

The New Quebec Crater in northern Canada is the largest one known. It is about 2 mi in diameter and is now filled with water. Since no meteoric particles have been found, there is some doubt that it is actually of meteoric origin. In 1908 a fireball, which may have been the head of a small comet, was seen in Siberia; and pieces landed in a swampy, forested region. Trees were blown down for more than 20 mi, but the meteoroid pieces were apparently buried in inaccessible locations. A second Siberian fall took place in 1947. This impact produced about 100 craters up to 90 ft in diameter and 30 ft deep. Iron fragments have been picked up near the craters. Other isolated cases of meteorites falling near people have been reported, but there is no record of anyone being killed by a meteorite.

Fig. 15–8  The Barringer Meteorite Crater near Winslow, Arizona. (American Meteorite Museum photograph)

## 15.8  Interplanetary Particles

In addition to meteoroids and micrometeorites, space in the region of the earth seems to be full of interplanetary dust. The zodiacal light is sunlight reflected by these minute particles. It can be seen as a faint band of light along the ecliptic (zodiac). It is best seen in the evening or morning sky when the light from the Milky Way does not interfere. It is not visible in twilight or moonlight or from a city where the sky is bright from artificial lights. There is some indication that the zodiacal light is partly due to the reflection of sunlight from free electrons in addition to solid particles.

The morning and evening branches of the zodiacal light meet and spread out into what is known as the *gegenschein,* a German word meaning counterglow. This extremely faint light has been photographed and scanned with a photoelectric cell, but is more difficult to see than the zodiacal light. It undoubtedly has the same composition. It appears as a circular patch some 10° in extent. One theory is that these particles are held temporarily in position by the attractions of the earth and the sun in locations predicted by the problem of three bodies. The solution of this problem states that if a small body comes near a point on a straight line with two major bodies, it will be captured and stay there unless pulled out by some outside force. There are three positions on this line with the earth and the sun, but only the gegenschein is observable.

It is also possible that the earth is accompanied by a stream of particles much like the tail of a comet, but there is no direct evidence that this is the case.

No tail has ever been observed on any other planet. It is also possible that the zodiacal light and the gegenschein are particles, ions, and electrons from the solar wind. This mixture is known as *plasma*. The plasma is dense enough to reflect sunlight in sufficient amounts to become visible. The particles would be trapped for a short time by gravitation at a distance of nearly 1 million miles from the earth, forming the gegenschein. This term seems to be preferable to its translation.

## QUESTIONS AND PROBLEMS

1. How many names may a comet have? Give the meaning of each.

2. What type of spectrum is shown by (a) the nucleus, (b) the coma, and (c) the tail of a comet?

3. Can a meteor shower be seen equally well from all parts of the earth? Explain.

4. About ⅔ of the total number of recovered meteorites are siderites. About 90 percent recovered from an observed fall are aerolites. Explain.

5. Show by a diagram how it would be possible for the earth to meet the same meteoroid swarm twice in one year. Why is it unlikely?

6. How would the earth be affected by encountering the (a) tail, (b) coma, or (c) nucleus of a comet?

7. At what part of a comet's orbit is it most easily observed? Why is a comet usually observable only in a short arc of the entire orbit?

8. Define the following: (a) shooting star; (b) meteor; (c) meteoroid; (d) meteorite; (e) micrometeorite.

9. Assume the spherical nucleus of a comet is at perihelion, traveling in direct motion. As the nucleus travels it rotates slowly. Assume that each part facing the sun emits jets when heated by solar radiation, the jets gradually decreasing as that part rotates away from the sun. How will the comet's orbit be affected by the jets if the nucleus rotates direct or retrograde? Illustrate with a diagram.

10. Are meteors that are seen (a) before midnight, and (b) after midnight, overtaking the earth or colliding with it head on?

*11. Two stations 15 mi apart photograph the same meteor simultaneously. On comparing photographs, an apparent displacement of 10° against the sky background due to parallax is measured. If the meteor is directly above one station, what is its altitude?

*12. One mechanism for dispersing the particles of a comet's head into the tail is light pressure from the sun, which is proportional to the surface area of a particle. The opposite, attracting force of solar gravitation is proportional to the volume of a particle (assuming the particles all have the same density). Show that the ratio of the light pressure to gravitation is inversely proportional to the size of the particle.

13. At first the orbit of the Ikeya-Seki comet of 1965 was computed to be a parabola. Later it was found to be an ellipse of long period—about 4500 years, but uncertain to about 1000 years. How could this have happened?

# Chapter Sixteen

# The Evolution of the Solar System

The problem of evolution has interested philosophers, theologians, geologists, astronomers, and others for hundreds of years. The beginning of what might be called a modern, scientific approach to the problem of evolution of the solar system came from the German philosopher, Immanuel Kant, in 1755. Kant suggested that the sun and its family of planets with their satellites were formed from a single cloud of gas, which, in the present terminology, is called a *nebula.* This cloud was in rotation and somehow condensed into discrete units with smaller ones in motion around the larger ones and the larger ones moving around the sun. The sun was also in rotation. Apparently Kant did not work out the details, but he at least had in mind the fundamental data as they were known at the time and which had to be considered in his theory.

## 16.1 The Nebular Hypothesis

In 1796 Pierre Simon, Marquis de Laplace, a famous French mathematician, published a book called *Le Systeme du Monde,* a popular nonmathematical de-scriptive astronomy text. The title translated would be *The System of the World,* where world in this case means *universe.* In the seventh and last appendix, Laplace wrote down his ideas on the possible origin of the solar system. In spite of the fact that he was one of the foremost mathematicians in the world, he did not examine his proposed theory from a mathematical point of view, and he undoubtedly borrowed his basic ideas from Kant. Laplace's theory has been named the *Nebular Hypothesis.*

The structure of the solar system and the motion of all its parts, which must be accounted for in any theory, are as follows:

1. The planets were known out to Uranus, which had been discovered 15 years before by Sir William Herschel.
2. Some planets were known to have satellites: the earth 1, Jupiter 4, Saturn 7, and Uranus 2.
3. The planets revolve around the sun in the same direction and in approximately the same plane.
4. The satellites revolve around the planets in approximately the orbital planes in which the planets move around the sun. The exception is that Uranus' satellites were known to revolve in a plane nearly perpendicular to the plane of the planet's orbit. No small satellites had

yet been discovered and none of the known satellites moved in retrograde direction.

5. The rotation of the sun was known from the motion of sunspots.

Laplace proposed the theory that the original cloud was a nebula, probably like a so-called spiral nebula. It was composed of hot gas and was supposed to be in slow rotation. As it cooled, it began to shrink and therefore to rotate faster. This was in agreement with the theory of the conservation of angular momentum. As this happened, there came a time when the inward forces of gravitation were balanced by the outward forces of rotation. The result was that a ring separated from the central mass. This caused a further increase in the speed of rotation of the nebular material, but not of the ring. Other rings broke off, one for each planet.

There were condensations in each ring (Figure 16–1). These condensations collided with the smaller particles and grew into the planets. The outer planets were thus formed first. In a similar way, the growing planets split off rings which formed into satellites. Thus the planets revolved around the central mass, which became the sun, and the satellites revolved around their planets. The outer bodies moved around their primaries at slower rates than those farther inside. The rotating nebula became flatter

Fig. 16–1   The Nebular Hypothesis. One ring for each planet split off from a central nebular mass and condensed into a planet, which in turn, as it formed, split off rings to form satellites.

and the rings split off in the equatorial plane. Therefore all the planets revolved around the sun in the same plane and in the same direction. The satellites also revolved around the planets in the same plane and in the same direction.

It is not certain that the rotations of the planets were known at the time of Laplace. Certainly the rotation of the sun and probably Jupiter had been observed. It is known today that the rotation period of the sun is shorter than the periods of revolution of the planets. Also the rotations of the planets known to Laplace rotate in the same plane (nearly) and in the same direction as their satellites known in 1796. The rotation of Uranus and its four satellites are in the same plane, but inclined 98° to the orbit of the planet around the sun.

However, there are at least three major errors in this theory. Granting that rings could split off, it is impossible to see that the ring material could form into planets. The speeds of the gas molecules would be so large that they would disperse into space, rather than collect into solid bodies.

Then in 1877 the two little moons of Mars were discovered. The period of revolution of the inner moon, Phobos, was found to be shorter than the rotation period of the planet, which was contrary to the theory.

Finally, about 1895 the American geologist, Thomas C. Chamberlin, began to question the Nebular Hypothesis from a geological point of view. He and Forest R. Moulton, a colleague in the mathematics department at the University of Chicago, showed that the distribution of the angular momentum of the system was wrong. Angular momentum might be defined as the quantity of motion due to rotation or revolution. It is calculated by the formula:

$$\text{angular momentum} = mvr = mr^2\omega \quad (16\text{–}1)$$

where $m$ is the mass, $r$ its distance from the center of motion, $v$ the linear velocity, and $\omega$ is the angular velocity, the number of turns in a unit of time.

For example, the mass of Jupiter is $2.16 \times 10^{30}$ g. Its distance from the center of the sun is

$7.8 \times 10^{13}$ cm and its angular velocity is 30° per year or $16.7 \times 10^{-6}$ radian per second. Hence its angular momentum can be calculated by substituting the values in the formula.

The angular momentum of the sun is more difficult to compute, since each particle must be treated separately. Moulton accomplished this and also found the angular momentum of all the planets and their satellites, using both rotations and revolutions. It is also a law of physics that each part of a rotating nebula should retain its original angular momentum unless changed by a force from outside the nebula. The sun contains 99.8 percent of the total mass of the solar system and should therefore have nearly all of the system's angular momentum. But Moulton's computation showed that the sun's angular momentum is only two percent instead of 99.8 percent of the whole, most of which is due to the motions of the largest planets.

## 16.2   The Planetesimal Hypothesis

When all these objections are considered, it is impossible to accept the Nebular Hypothesis. Chamberlin and Moulton, about 1900, decided to try to put together a theory which would explain how angular momentum might have been added to that of the planets from outside. The resulting theory was named the *Planetesimal Hypothesis*.

They assumed that the sun was already in existence with about the same state of activity (spots, prominences, and accompanying phenomena) as at present. They suggested that another star came close to the sun and raised two tides, one on each side, as the moon raises tides in the oceans on the earth. But since the sun is more explosive, the tides erupted, throwing great masses of solar matter out into the nearby space. This happened five times in rapid succession, an hour or so apart. The tides, now called bolts, were given a motion in the same direction and in approximately the same plane as the orbit of the passing star. Thus motion was put into the material in the bolts by outside gravitational attraction.

If only the motion of the passing star relative to

the sun is considered, its orbit must have been a hyperbola and the star's speed must have been several hundred miles per second. After the close approach, it went off into space and there would be no possibility of identifying it. The star came near the sun only once. (See Figure 16–2.)

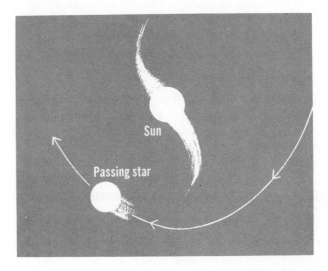

Fig. 16–2   The Planetesimal Hypothesis. A passing star pulled bolts of material from the sun, two at a time. A total of ten bolts in rapid succession developed into the system of planets and satellites.

Some of the material in the bolts was assumed to follow the star or to disperse into space, particularly the lighter materials, hydrogen and helium. The other, heavier particles fell back under the gravitational pull of the sun but were given forward motion by the attraction of the star. They went around the sun in elliptical orbits of high eccentricity (flatness). There would have been many collisions among the particles, which were called *planetesimals*. Moulton showed that, because of the collisions, the orbits became less eccentric and nearly circular. Also the collisions caused condensations to form, which grew by the infall of other planetesimals (accretion) and became the planets. Planetary atmospheres were formed after the planet became massive enough to retain gas molecules. The velocity of escape became larger and the atmosphere was held to the planet by its attraction.

When the planetary condensations, now called *protoplanets,* came to perihelion the first time, they were themselves disrupted by the tidal attraction of the sun and formed their systems of satellites in the same way the planets were formed from the bolts. Thus, the orbits of both planets and satellites and their direct motions were accounted for. The angular momentum came about by the pull of the passing star, which provided the angular velocity, $\omega$, for the planets. The 90° motion of the satellites of Uranus and its rotation was not explained. The few retrograde satellites were supposed to have been captured later by the planets from passing asteroids.

Rotation was accounted for by collisions of planetesimals with the limbs of the protoplanets and with the sun in such a way that they were given a forward spin. The sun's rotation is not exactly in the plane of the orbits of the planets, but is inclined by about 7° to the ecliptic. This angle was thought to be a combination of the sun's original rotation and that given by the infall of planetesimals.

The sun lost only a small percentage of its original mass, according to the Planetesimal Hypothesis, most of which condensed to form the planets and their satellites. The other particles which did not escape from the solar system, became comets and meteoroids which wandered around, occasionally coming near or into contact with the planets. Collisions are still grinding the asteroids and small particles into still smaller particles to form the interplanetary dust.

The Planetesimal Hypothesis was accepted until about 1935 when various criticisms appeared. Henry Norris Russell of Princeton University in one of his monthly articles in the *Scientific American* said that he failed to see how a passing star could pull heavy particles like iron out of the sun. He was not aware of the fact that iron is present in the solar corona. Others had already called attention to the improbability of a close approach of a star to the sun in view of the tremendous distances between stars in the solar neighborhood. But the work which was most damaging to the theory was by Lyman Spitzer, Jr., then at Yale University. He showed that if enough material were pulled out of the sun to form the planets, much of it would have had to come from deep enough inside the sun to have a very high temperature, perhaps 1,000,000° K. In that case, the molecules would have very high velocities and the bolts would leave the sun with almost explosive force and would disperse instead of condensing to form the planets.

Also the distribution of angular momentum still did not satisfy the theorists. Russell showed that the inner planets would be larger than the outer ones. He also showed that the resisting material, which Moulton had shown would produce nearly circular orbits, would not be sufficiently effective. Others showed that the sun's attraction could not have produced the satellites from the forming planets, and that the material falling onto the protoplanets could not have set them into rotation. So the Planetesimal Hypothesis was also discarded.

Jeans and Jeffreys in England had been among the critics of the Chamberlin and Moulton theory. They proposed the theory that a passing star pulled only one bolt out of the sun. This bolt was thicker in the middle and the major planets were formed there. Otherwise their theory is very similar to the Planetesimal Hypothesis and subject to the same criticisms. It was therefore not very widely accepted. Jeans and Jeffreys were apparently willing to modify their theory and proposed that the passing star actually hit the sun, knocking off the material necessary to form the planetary systems. This material would also have been too hot to collect into smaller bodies.

## 16.3  Recent Theories

Other theories were proposed by various astronomers. Among them was a theory that the sun was accompanied by a pair of small suns, which combined, became unstable, and broke up to form the planets. Another was that the sun had only one companion which exploded as a supernova. H. P. Berlage in Holland developed a theory which combined many of the features proposed by Kant and Laplace, especially the nebular disk and rings, and the theories which include the encounter of the sun and a star. However, he left the rest of the devlopment to a spontaneous coming together of particles in just the right way to form the planets and their satellites. These theories of Berlage have many good points, but do not seem to have attracted much attention.

Another theory came from Germany near the end of World War II. C. F. von Weizsäcker assumed that the sun was surrounded by a large disk-shaped envelope of extremely low density ($10^{-10}$ g/cm$^3$) and mass about 1/10 that of the sun. This disk was supposed to be turbulent and to develop vortices—five of them in a ring, one ring for each planet and at the correct distances to satisfy Bode's law. Friction between the vortices caused the particles to condense. This theory was later modified by Kuiper, who assumed a mechanism by which condensations were formed. The planets came from the central parts and their satellites from smaller condensations orbiting the planets. Only the larger, planet-forming particles collected to form the planetary systems, with the smaller, lighter particles being blown away from the sun by radiation pressure and by the solar wind. The terrestrial planets could not hold the lighter gases and hence have greater densities than the major planets, which did have enough mass originally and have much lower densities. This modification of the turbulence theory is still being discussed and changed.

A discovery, made about twenty years ago, has changed the thinking about the problem of evolution. It was found that small, dark areas on photographs of certain nebulae (for example, as in Figure 16–3) are dark clouds of opaque material in front of luminous material. They had been discovered by Edward Emerson Barnard of the Yerkes Observatory many years before, but not recognized as real. He thought they were defects on the photographic plates. Some of the dark areas are very small in appearance and almost perfectly round. They are called *globules*. Their diameters are now calculated to be about 250 times the diameter of the entire solar system out to the orbit of Pluto. Their densities are extremely small, but are enough to keep light from passing through from behind. The total mass of a globule must be at least as great as that of the sun.

The gravitation of a globule is sufficient to hold it together, but in addition the particles are being pushed together by radiation pressure from stars outside. In other words, this mass of dust is slowly condensing to form a star. It is assumed to be in slow rotation, thus accounting for the small amount of angular momentum of the sun in case it had been formed in this way. It is estimated that such a globular cloud would collapse in about 100 million years. The contraction would be slow at first, but increase its rate as the gravitation toward the center became more effective.

A theory of evolution of the solar system based on the discovery and theoretical development of dark globules was written up by Whipple in 1946. He was one of several astronomers who collaborated in formulating this theory, which was called the *Dust Cloud Hypothesis*. It was assumed that the original dust cloud either developed smaller clouds inside or captured a small group of partly condensed clouds. They were not drawn into the central protosun, but spiraled inward, growing by picking up more particles until they reached planetary size. The orbits would be nearly circular because of collisions. The rotations of the sun and the planets were also accounted for by the infall of particles in a cloud whose density increased toward the center. Also the high density of the terrestrial planets was explained by the loss of the lighter gases when the central star (the sun) developed enough internal energy to radiate and push the hydrogen and helium away, as assumed in earlier theories.

Fig. 16–3    A nebula in the constellation Scutum showing dark areas, called globules, which may be condensing into stars. (Photograph from the Mount Wilson and Palomar Observatories)

In view of the difficulties of explaining all the details of the evolution of the solar system and the fact that no single theory is adequate, the following suggestions have been made which combine many of the details of the old and new theories:

1. The solar system was formed from a cloud of dust and gas, several hundred times larger than it is at present.

2. The dust cloud may have been a double condensation with the larger cloud about the mass of the sun and the other about $\frac{1}{10}$ as massive.

3. The smaller dust cloud formed into the planetary system by some mechanism which disposed of 99 percent of the mass in the form of light gases and kept 1 percent to form the planets and their satellites.

4. Comets and meteoroids are debris that was left over.

5. The distribution of angular momentum is accounted for by the slow rotation of the larger cloud and the resulting slowly rotating sun. The planets obtained their angular momentum from the revolution of the small cloud around the larger one.

If this theory actually accounts for the solar system, there should be other similar systems, with perhaps one star out of 1000 having a system like ours. That would mean a total of 100 million solar systems in our galaxy.

The stages in the formation of the sun would then be something like the following:

1. The interstellar cloud forms and is slowly condensed, partly by external radiation pressure and partly by internal gravitation.
2. The cloud becomes unstable and breaks up during the time of compression.
3. When the density reaches a point where the cloud is opaque to radiation, the temperature inside begins to rise and the breaking up stops.
4. The protosun collapses under its own gravitation.
5. When the temperature of the interior reaches about 100,-000°K and the protosun is about 100 times the diameter of the present sun, or about the size of the earth's orbit,

all the hydrogen and helium is ionized and further contraction takes place.
6. Production of energy begins when the internal temperature reaches about 1 million degrees Kelvin and hydrogen nuclei combine to form helium nuclei. In other words the sun begins to shine as a star at this stage.

The future of the sun has been discussed in Chapter 12.

## QUESTIONS AND PROBLEMS

1. What observational evidence is there that stars may be forming today?
2. Compare the angular momentum of the earth with that of (a) Mars and (b) Saturn. Assume their periods are 2 and 30 years and that their distances are 1.5 and 10 a.u., respectively. Neglect their rotations. **Ans:** (a) Earth's angular momentum is 8 times that of Mars.
3. During this century, astronomers have changed their thinking concerning the possible existence of life-bearing planets in the universe. How would this thinking be influenced by replacing the Chamberlin-Moulton planetesimal hypothesis with more modern theories of evolution?

# Chapter Seventeen

# The Stars

In discussing theories of evolution of the solar system, the words sun and star were used interchangeably. The question is: How do we know that the sun is a star? Or, it might be rephrased: Are all stars suns? To answer these questions, the sun must be compared with the stars in a number of ways. How bright would the sun be, if it could be seen from stellar distances? How big are the stars? What is their composition? Do they have the same elements we know on the earth? What are their temperatures? In other words, the comparison of sun and stars depends on a knowledge of their physical nature. This study belongs to a branch of astronomy called astrophysics.

Astronomy began as a science when Hipparchus made his first star chart. His purpose was to describe the locations of the stars; and, incidentally, he observed differences in brightness and set up his system of star magnitudes. Hipparchus also discovered precession. Tycho Brahe constructed a star globe, but he was more interested in the motions of the planets. His work led to the discoveries of Kepler and Newton.

The fact that the stars are not "fixed" but are in motion was first discovered by Edmund Halley. He noticed that the positions of the bright stars Arcturus and Sirius had changed position by a noticeable amount (1° and ½° respectively) since the time of Ptolemy's Almagest (A.D. 150). This change of position was interpreted as a real motion of the stars and is called *proper motion*. The amounts were small, but had accumulated in 1500 years. Proper motion is the rate of change of position in one year and is measured with respect to the faint background stars which are assumed to be too far away to show any measurable proper motion.

## 17.1  Stellar Distances

As has been pointed out, Tycho refused to accept the Copernican theory because he was unable to detect any motion of the stars due to the motion of the earth around the sun. The reason Tycho failed to find this effect was that it is actually very minute and requires the use of a fairly large telescope to detect. Between 1833 and 1838 three astronomers, using the most accurate methods possible, measured this effect, called *parallax,* and used the results to compute the distances of three stars. Thomas Henderson at the Cape of Good Hope measured the parallax of Alpha Centauri in 1833, but did not publish the result until 1838. Also in 1838 Wilhelm Struve in Russia and Friedrich W. Bessel in Prussia found the distances of several stars. These distances were the first to show the vastness of the universe.

In determining distances in the solar system, it is customary to define parallax as an angle with the radius of the earth as the base line. If this definition were to be used for stars, the parallax would be less than $1/10,000$ of a second—an angle much too small to measure by any known method. Fortunately, another longer base line is available—the diameter of the earth's orbit, or 186 million miles. Stellar parallax is therefore defined as the angle at a star subtended by the average radius of the earth's orbit, or one astronomical unit.

To determine stellar parallax, photographs of star fields are taken with long-focus telescopes. Then the shifts of the nearer stars are measured under a microscope with respect to the background stars. The parallax is then computed in seconds of arc. The principle is shown in Figure 17–1. The result is the relative parallax, unless that of the distant stars can also be computed. If so, a correction is made to find the absolute parallax. Since the parallax of the distant stars is so small, it can usually be neglected, because it is less than the errors of measurement of the stars under observation.

Fig. 17–1  Stellar parallax. The parallax, $p$, is determined by measuring the shift of a close star with respect to distant stars, as the earth moves in its orbit around the sun. The base line is 1 astronomical unit.

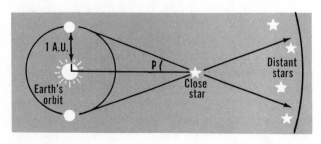

The ideal procedure would be to take photographs of the star field frequently for six months or a year and measure the diameter of the small, apparent circle a near star would describe on the plates. But since this is not practical, observations at six month intervals can be made when the star is at each side of its circle. In order to be sure that the star itself is not in motion (proper motion), observations are continued at intervals of six months for about two years. The effect of proper motion on parallax determinations will be discussed later in this chapter.

Referring again to Figure 17–1, the earth, sun, and star form a slender triangle with $p$, the parallax, as the angle at the star. This triangle can then be solved by the radian method previously discussed, where the side opposite $p$ is one astronomical unit in length, as shown. Here $p'' = 206265''/d$, where $d$ is the star's distance, also in astronomical units, and $d = 206265''/p''$.

Since the distance in astronomical units is not convenient to use, a new unit of distance, the *parsec*, has been introduced. The word parsec is a combination of the first three letters of parallax and second. It is defined as the distance to an object whose parallax is $1''$, or 206,265 astronomical units. Multiplying by the number of miles or kilometers in 1 astronomical unit, 1 parsec equals 19.16 trillion miles or 30.84 trillion kilometers.

The distance to a star is inversely proportional to its parallax; that is, the smaller the angle of parallax, the greater is the distance. The formula for distance is therefore simplified to

$$d = \frac{1}{p''} \text{ parsecs} \qquad (17\text{–}1)$$

where $p''$ is the parallax in seconds and $d$ is the distance in parsecs. However, for popular use, the light year is a more familiar unit of distance. Light travels 186,282 mi in one second. Multiplying this by 31,557,000, the number of seconds in one year, the length of the light year is 5.88 trillion miles. From the preceding value of the parsec, 1 parsec = 3.26 light years. The formula for distance can then be

$$d = \frac{3.26''}{p''} \text{ light years.} \qquad (17\text{--}2)$$

▶ *Example:* The parallax of Sirius, the nearest bright star visible in most of continental United States, is 0.375″. Compute its distance in astronomical units, parsecs, and light years.

**Solution:**
$$d = \frac{206265''}{0.375''} = 550,000 \text{ a.u.}$$

$$d = \frac{1}{0.375''} = 2.67 \text{ parsecs}$$

$$d = \frac{3.26''}{0.375''} = 8.7 \text{ light years}$$

Because of the difficulty of measurement of parallax, most determinations are accurate only to about $\frac{1}{100}$ sec, and are independent of the size of the parallax. This means that distances greater than 100 parsecs or about 300 light years become very inaccurate by this method. Fortunately, other methods of determining distances are available for more distant stars.

Data for the twenty nearest stars are given in Table 17–1. It will be noted that only seven are

TABLE 17–1
**The Twenty Nearest Stars[a]**

| Star[b] | Right Ascension (1967) | | Declination (1967) | | Distance (light years) | Radial Velocity (km/sec) | Proper Motion (sec/year) | Visual Magnitudes and Spectral Types of Components (btr) | (ftr) | Absolute Visual Magnitudes of Components (btr) | (ftr) |
|---|---|---|---|---|---|---|---|---|---|---|---|
| α Centauri* | 14$^h$ | 37.3$^m$ | −60° | 42.0′ | 4.3 | −23 | 3.68″ | 0.1 G0 V | +1.4 K5 V | +4.3 | +5.6 |
| Barnard's Star* | 17 | 56 | +4 | 36 | 6.0 | −108 | 10.30 | 9.5 M5 V | ?   ? | +13.2 | |
| Wolf 359 | 10 | 55 | +7 | 13 | 7.7 | +13 | 4.84 | 13.7 M6e V | | +16.8 | |
| Luyten 726–8* | 1 | 37 | −18 | 07 | 8.0 | +29 | 3.35 | 12.5 M6e V | 12.9 M6e V | +15.6 | +16.0 |
| Lalande 21185 | 11 | 02 | +36 | 10 | 8.2 | −86 | 4.78 | 7.5 M2 V | | +10.5 | |
| Sirius* | 6 | 43.7 | −16 | 40.2 | 8.7 | −8 | 1.32 | −1.6 A0 V | +8.5 wd | +1.3 | +11.4 |
| Ross 154 | 18 | 48 | −23 | 51 | 9.3 | −4 | 0.67 | 10.6 M4e V | | +13.3 | |
| Ross 248 | 23 | 40 | +44 | 01 | 10.3 | −81 | 1.58 | 12.2 M6e V | | +14.7 | |
| ε Eridani | 3 | 31.4 | −9 | 34.1 | 10.8 | +15 | 0.97 | 3.8 K2 V | | +6.2 | |
| Ross 128 | 11 | 46 | +1 | 01 | 10.9 | −13 | 1.40 | 11.1 M5 V | | +13.5 | |
| Luyten 789–6 | 22 | 37 | −15 | 31 | 11.2 | −60 | 3.27 | 5.2 K5 V | +6.0 K7 V | +7.5 | +8.3 |
| 61 Cygni* | 21 | 06 | +38 | 36 | 11.1 | −64 | 5.22 | 12.6 M6e V | | +14.9 | |
| Procyon* | 7 | 37.6 | +5 | 18.6 | 11.3 | −3 | 1.25 | 0.5 F5 IV | +11 wd | +2.8 | +13.0 |
| ε Indi | 22 | 00.8 | −56 | 55.4 | 11.4 | −40 | 4.67 | 4.7 K5 V | | +7.0 | |
| Σ 2398* | 18 | 42 | +59 | 35 | 11.6 | +8 | 2.29 | 8.9 M4 V | +9.7 M5 V | +11.1 | +11.9 |
| Groombridge 34* | 0 | 17 | +43 | 51 | 11.7 | +18 | 2.91 | | | | |
| τ Ceti | 1 | 42.5 | −16 | 06.6 | 11.8 | −16 | 1.92 | 8.0 M2e V | +11.0 ? | +10.4 | +13.4 |
| Lacaille 9352 | 23 | 04 | −36 | 02 | 11.9 | +10 | 6.87 | 3.6 K0p V | | +5.8 | |
| BD+5°1668 | 7 | 26 | +5 | 28 | 12.4 | +26 | 3.73 | 7.4 M2 V | | +9.6 | |
| Lacaille 8760 | 21 | 15 | −39 | 00 | 12.8 | +21 | 3.46 | 9.8 M4 V | | +11.9 | |
| Kapteyn's Star | 5 | 11 | −45 | 00 | 13.0 | +242 | 8.79 | 6.7 M1 V | | +8.7 | |

[a]Adapted from list published by Peter van de Kamp.
[b]An asterisk indicates a double star.

brighter than magnitude 6.0 and are visible to the naked eye. Also seven are double stars. The nearest stars also usually have the largest proper motions.

## 17.2  Stellar Motions

We have shown in Chapter 10 that a star's position on the celestial sphere is continually changing because of precession, nutation, and aberration; and, of course, its measured position is changed by refraction. So when a star is observed with a meridian circle for the purpose of determining its right ascension and declination, corrections must be made for all possible sources of change. We have also called attention to the fact that the celestial equator is not a fixed circle, but moves with respect to the ecliptic.

Therefore, it is customary to select some equator, such as the equator of 1900 or 1950, and refer all star positions to it as a standard. After this has been done, the star may still show a change in right ascension and declination. This is the star's *proper motion*. The corrections are practically the same for all stars in a given small region, bright stars as well as faint ones. In general, the faint stars are farther away than the bright stars and do not show much, if any, proper motion. This is not always true, as can be seen from Table 17–1.

With the modern use of photography, proper motion is easily measured by comparing two photographs taken some years apart. The instrument used for its detection is the same as was used for the discovery of Pluto—the "blink microscope." The proper motion is computed from the amount of shift of the fast moving star with respect to the background stars between the two dates.

Figure 17–2 is an example of two plates taken 22 years apart. The faint star shown by the arrow is Barnard's Star, which has the largest proper motion known, 10.30″ per year (see Table 17–1). It was discovered by Barnard at the Yerkes Observatory in 1916. It is the second nearest star to the sun, in distance only six light years. Usually the stars with the largest proper motions are among the nearest stars

Fig. 17–2   The proper motion of Barnard's star. The interval between the two photographs is 22 years. The arrows show the position of the star at the two dates. (Yerkes Observatory photograph)

and are put on observing programs for parallax determination.

If the earth did not move around the sun, the proper motion of a star would appear as a straight line between two points on a photograph. Actually it would be a short arc of a great circle. In Figure

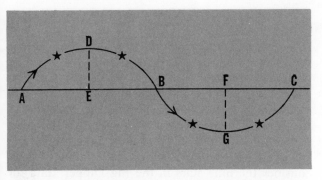

Fig. 17–3   The apparent path of a star in one year against the background of distant stars due to the parallax and proper motion of the star.

17–3 the proper motion is drawn as the straight line, $AC$, in the time interval of one year. If the star were stationary, its parallax would produce a small circle because of the earth's motion. Combining the two, Figure 17–3 shows the apparent motion in one year as a wave, the amplitude of the wave being $DE$ or $FG$, which is the parallax of the star. If the observations could be continued for several years, the amplitude (parallax) would remain the same. The length of the line would be proportional to the time interval, provided the proper motion remained constant. For accuracy, the longer the line, the more accurate would be the determination of the proper motion, which is the length of the line in seconds of arc divided by the interval in years. Hence, parallax and proper motion are both determined by the same series of observations.

In computing stellar motion, the sun is considered to be stationary. This is now known to be a false assumption, but historically all proper motions have been referred to the sun without consideration of whether or not it is also in motion. The *space velocity* of a star is its motion with respect to the sun. It is desirable to find both the speed and direction of this motion. Space velocity can be represented, therefore, as a vector—a straight line having both length and direction.

Let the space velocity of a star be represented by the straight line $S_1S_2$ in Figure 17–4. It can be broken down (resolved) into two straight lines, which are perpendicular to each other, $S_1Y$ and $YS_2$. Let $S_1Y$ be directed away from the sun. (Another case could be found in which it is directed toward the sun.) The vector $S_1Y$ is called the *radial velocity* of the star which is in motion. If a spectrogram of the star is taken, its lines are shifted according to the Doppler law. By measurement of the amount of shift, the velocity in the line of sight, the radial velocity, can be found, usually given in kilometers per second. Thus the component $S_1Y$ can be immediately determined by the Doppler effect.

The other component of the space velocity, $YS_2$, is called the *tangential* or *transverse velocity*. It cannot be measured directly, but may be found by computation. Figure 17–4 cannot be drawn to scale. The radius of the earth's orbit, $SE$, is one astronomical unit. The nearest star's distance, $SS_1$, is 270,000 astronomical units. It is obvious from the figure that the space velocity, $S_1S_2$, will form an angle with the sun which is the star's proper motion, $\mu$. Also the star's parallax is the angle, $p$, at the star between two ends of the radius of the earth's orbit, $SE$. This angle could have been drawn from $S_1$ instead of $S_2$ and the two angles would have been equal, if the scale had been correct. In the figure, this is not the case because of the distances.

Fig. 17–4   Diagram showing the space velocity of a star, $v$, and its components, radial velocity, $V$, and tangential velocity, $T$. It is also necessary to know the parallax, $p$.

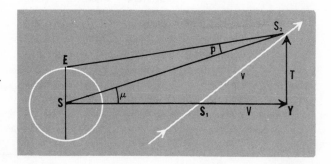

Now consider the two slender triangles, $SS_2E$ and $SS_2Y$. From radian measure, $p = SE/ES_2$ and $\mu = S_2Y/SY$, both in radians. Dividing the second by the first, we find

$$\frac{\mu}{p} = \frac{S_2Y}{SY} \times \frac{ES_2}{SE} = \frac{S_2Y}{SE} \qquad (17\text{-}3)$$

since $ES_2$ and $SY$ are approximately equal and their ratio can be taken as unity without loss of accuracy. The above equation can now be rewritten

$$S_2Y = \frac{\mu \text{ sec/yr}}{p \text{ sec}} \times 1 \text{ a.u.} \qquad (17\text{-}4)$$

Hence the tangential velocity,

$$T = S_2Y = \frac{\mu}{p} \text{ a.u./yr.}$$

But in combining tangential and radial velocity, the units must be the same, kilometers per second. Substituting in the equation 17-4, since 1 a.u. = 149,500,000 km and 1 year = 31,500,000 sec,

$$T = \frac{\mu}{p} \times \frac{149,500,000 \text{ km}}{31,500,000 \text{ sec}} = 4.74 \frac{\mu}{p} \text{ km/sec.} \qquad (17\text{-}5)$$

Finally, since $S_1YS_2$ is a right triangle,

$$v^2 = V^2 + T^2 \qquad (17\text{-}6)$$

where $v$ = space velocity, $V$ = radial velocity, and $T$ = tangential velocity, each expressed in kilometers per second. This equation gives the value of the space velocity. The direction of the angle between $S_1Y$ and $S_1S_2$ can be found by trigonometry.

As an illustration of the proper motions of stars, consider the nine stars in the Big Dipper, data for which are given in Table 17-2. It will be noted that Zeta, also called Mizar, is a double star and is accompanied by a 4th magnitude star 80 (g) named Alcor. These two stars are sometimes called the Horse and Rider. Mizar was the first telescopic double star to be discovered.

Several remarkable things can be seen at once from the table. First, the seven middle stars are all at approximately the same distance. Their parallaxes are about 0.040″ with distance, therefore, about 25 parsecs or 80 light years. Second, these seven stars are all moving in approximately the same direction as indicated by their proper motions. This is not quite so obvious from the table, because of the different positions of the stars in the sky, which partly conceal the fact that they are all moving in

TABLE 17–2
**The Stars of the Big Dipper**

| Star | Apparent Visual Magnitude | Spectral Class | Parallax (sec) | Proper Motion (sec) | Absolute Visual Magnitude | Radial Velocity (km/sec) | Distance (light years) |
|---|---|---|---|---|---|---|---|
| Alpha | 1.95 | K0 | 0.030 | 0.136W | −0.65 | −9 | 109 |
| Beta | 2.44 | A0 | 0.043 | 0.089E | +0.63 | −14 | 76 |
| Gamma | 2.54 | A0 | 0.041 | 0.095E | +0.64 | −11 | 79 |
| Delta | 3.44 | A2 | 0.044 | 0.113E | +1.63 | −16 | 74 |
| Epsilon | 1.68 | A0p | 0.045 | 0.117E | −0.03 | −10 | 72 |
| Zeta 1 | 2.40 | A2p | 0.043 | 0.134E | +0.59 | −10 | 76 |
| Zeta 2 | 3.96 | A2 | 0.043 | 0.134E | +2.15 | −10 | 76 |
| 80 (g) | 4.02 | A5 | 0.040 | 0.125E | +2.13 | −12 | 82 |
| Eta | 1.91 | B3 | 0.013 | 0.115W | −2.52 | −2 | 251 |

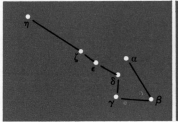 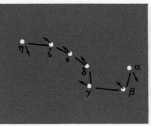 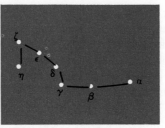

Fig. 17–5 The Big Dipper, a moving cluster, as it looked 100,000 years ago (left); as it looks today (center); and as it will look 100,000 years hence. Proper motions are shown by the lengths and directions of the arrows in the center.

parallel paths. Third, their radial velocities are all about the same and their space velocities average 17 km/sec, all being within 2 km/sec of the average. This group of stars is part of a larger cluster, all of which are moving toward a common vanishing point. They thus form a so-called *moving cluster*. Figure 17–5 is a plot of the calculated positions of the Big Dipper stars at present (center) and about 100,000 years ago (left) and 100,000 years in the future (right).

The end stars, Alpha and Eta, do not belong to the cluster, but are moving in the opposite direction. It will be shown later in this chapter that the middle stars all have the same temperature. The conclusion might be drawn that they are members of the same family, are of the same age, and will continue to shine as stars for about the same length of time.

## 17.3 Stellar Spectra

Spectra of most stars are dark-line spectra; that is, continuous bands of color crossed by dark lines. This type of spectrum indicates that the stars, like the sun, have incandescent interiors surrounded by cooler atmospheres under low pressure. It is assumed that the interiors are composed of gases under high pressure and temperature and that the gas laws hold throughout.

Since each chemical element under low pressure produces a spectrum with lines in definite positions, the element can be located as either in the star's atmosphere or in a gas cloud in space. In the stars, the lines are produced by the absorption of energy by atoms in the atmospheres. All spectral lines in stars are subject to the same effects as in the sun. The Doppler effect, a broadening of lines due to pressure in the atmosphere, and an effect produced by magnetic fields can be used to study atmospheric conditions in the stars.

In 1824 Joseph Fraunhofer, who had discovered the dark lines in the spectrum of the sun, also found dark lines in stellar spectra. In 1863, Pietro Angelo Secchi, a Jesuit astronomer at the Vatican Observatory, found important differences and divided the stellar spectra into four major classes, as follows:

I. Heavy dark lines of hydrogen.
II. Numerous lines of metals, less intense than the hydrogen lines in Class I.
III. Bands, sharp toward the red, later identified as due to titanium oxide.
IV. Bands, sharp toward the violet, now identified as due to carbon and carbon compounds.

Father Secchi observed the spectra visually and was therefore unable to see the fainter lines, which were not observed until the application of photography to this study.

A new system of classification of spectra was devised at the Harvard College Observatory. The work of classifying the spectra was done by Miss Annie J. Cannon, beginning in 1911. The spectra were photographed using an objective prism (see Chapter 5). A catalog of stars giving their positions for 1900, their visual and photographic magnitudes, and their spectral classes, was published in 1918. It contained data for 225,300 stars in a 10-volume set. The catalog was called the Henry Draper catalog in honor of the first astronomer to use photography in astronomy and the first American to study the spectra of stars. The system of classification has been called the Harvard system, but is officially the Henry Draper classification.

The original intention in the Draper system was to have the sequence of spectra arranged in order of the letters in the alphabet. This was changed later when it was found that certain classes really did not exist, but had been assumed from the bad photo-graphs at the beginning of the studies. Later the order was changed when it was found that the sequence was really dependent on temperature. There are no C, D, and other classes due to bad photography, and the order of B and A was interchanged because the B-stars are hotter than the A-stars.

There are eight major classes and four minor ones, each designated by a letter. Each class is further subdivided into subclasses ranging from 0 to 9, in order to take care of small changes in the appearance of lines from one class to the next. Table 17–3 shows the important changes in the Draper sequence, including one subclass between the major classes. (See also Figure 17–6.)

It is obvious from the table that the classes are arranged in order of temperature. It will also be seen that there is a continuous change in color. This is in agreement with the laws of Stefan and Wien dis-

TABLE 17–3
**Draper Classification of Stellar Spectra**

| Class | Example | Elements Present | Approximate Temperature (°K) | Color |
|---|---|---|---|---|
| O5 | No bright star | H,He,O,N, with electrons removed | 50,000 | Blue-white |
| B0 | Orion stars | He maximum intensity at B2 | 25,000 | Blue |
| B5 | Achernar | H, He strong | 15,000 | Blue |
| A0 | Sirius | H maximum, Ca present | 11,000 | Blue-white |
| A5 | Fomalhaut | Metals near maximum | 9,000 | White |
| F0 | Canopus | Ca increases; other metals | 8,000 | White |
| F5 | Procyon | Fe and other metals | 7,000 | White |
| G0 | Capella | Fe and others; solar type | 6,000 | Yellow |
| G5 | | Ca weakening, molecules increasing | 5,000 | Yellow |
| K0 | Arcturus | H weak; atomic lines and molecules strong | 4,500 | Orange |
| K5 | Aldebaran | Not much change | 4,000 | Orange-red |
| M0 | Antares | TiO present | 3,500 | Red |
| M5 | Faint stars | TiO stronger | 3,000 | Red |
| N,R,S | Faint stars | Molecules strong | 3,000 | Very red |
| I | ε Aurigae | Infrared spectrum, not yet observed | 1,000? | Not visible |

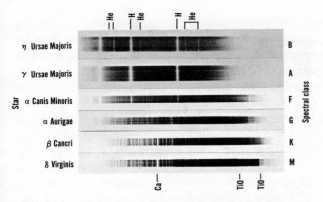

Fig. 17–6 The spectral classification of stars. The upper classes contain strong lines of hydrogen and helium. The lower classes show many lines of metallic elements and their compounds, such as calcium and titanium oxide. The lines are identified above and below. (Yerkes Observatory photographs)

cussed in Chapter 12. The latter predicts a change in maximum wavelength in exactly the order of the Draper classification.

Temperatures are known to be high in the O- and B-stars, because the removal of electrons from the nuclei of atoms requires a great deal of energy. In class O5 one or two electrons have been removed from the oxygen and nitrogen atoms. This is possible only at very high temperatures, estimated as high as 100,000°K by some astronomers. There is no star known to be hotter than an O5-star. Theoretically an O0-star would have an infinite temperature!

At the lower end of the sequence, the temperatures are low as indicated by the red color and also by the fact that compounds (molecules) are present. In the sun, for example, at temperature 6000°K in the photosphere there are no compounds, but compounds are present in sunspots, as shown by the molecular spectra, at lower temperature. The classes M, N, and R differ from each other in the compounds present. All are red stars with temperatures about 3000°K. In class M titanium oxide (TiO) is present, but in classes N and R it is absent and combinations of carbon with nitrogen and hydrogen are present. The R-stars are frequently called carbon stars, and most, if not all, at times have such heavy carbon compounds in their atmospheres that the light they emit is greatly weakened. They vary in light output as the compounds form and then dissolve at unpredictable times. There are no bright stars visible without a telescope in classes O, R, N, and S.

More recently, still another class has been added, but is not recognized by all authorities. There is evidence that a very few stars are so cool that they do not radiate visible light, but give out some energy in the infrared. These stars are called I-stars, meaning infrared. One such star is a component of Epsilon Aurigae, an eclipsing star system. The temperature has been estimated at 1000°K. It is extremely large, about 3,000 times the diameter of the sun, and its density is so low that it is semitransparent. It is known to exist only because it eclipses its companion, a bright star, every 27 years.

## 17.4 Stellar Magnitudes

The work of Hipparchus and Ptolemy has been mentioned in earlier chapters. Both used a scale of magnitudes to indicate the brightness of stars on their charts. In this system, the brightest stars were called first magnitude. Next in order were second, third, and so on to sixth for the faintest stars which could be seen without a telescope.

By 1856 *stellar photometry*, the branch of astronomy which uses a photometer (see Chapter 5) for the determination of star brightness, had developed to such a degree that accurate magnitudes could be determined by visual methods. Photography was adapted to astronomy about the same time. Sir William Herschel and Norman R. Pogson both noticed that a first magnitude star was about 100 times brighter than a star of sixth magnitude. It also appeared that each magnitude had about the same ratio of brightness to the next magnitude through the six classes. The following mathematical equation was then developed and adapted to the magnitude scale:

Let $l_1$ and $l_2$ be the brightness of stars of magnitude $m_1$ and $m_2$. Then

$$\frac{l_1}{l_2} = x^{(m_2 - m_1)}. \qquad (17\text{--}7)$$

If $m_1 = 1.0$ and $m_2 = 6.0$, then $m_2 - m_1 = 5.0$ and $l_1/l_2 = 100$. Substituting in equation 17–7:

$$x^5 = 100, \text{ and } x = \sqrt[5]{100} = 2.512.$$

Putting this value of $x$ in the equation, it becomes

$$\frac{l_1}{l_2} = 2.512^{(m_2 - m_1)}. \qquad (17\text{--}8)$$

For the student who has studied logarithms, $\log x = \frac{1}{5} (\log 100) = \frac{2}{5} = 0.4$ and, from a table of logarithms, $x = 2.512$. The reduction from light ratios to magnitudes, or the reverse, can then be done easily using logarithms. It can also be done with a log-log slide rule. Table 17–4 is a table which gives the ratio of brightness for given differences of magnitude.

TABLE 17–4
**The Magnitude Scale**

| Difference of Magnitude | Ratio of Brightness | Difference of Magnitude | Ratio of Brightness |
|---|---|---|---|
| 0.1 | 1.096 | 1.0 | 2.512 |
| 0.2 | 1.202 | 2.0 | 6.310 |
| 0.3 | 1.318 | 3.0 | 15.85 |
| 0.4 | 1.445 | 4.0 | 39.81 |
| 0.5 | 1.585 | 5.0 | 100.0 |
| 0.6 | 1.738 | 6.0 | 251.2 |
| 0.7 | 1.905 | 7.0 | 631.0 |
| 0.8 | 2.089 | 8.0 | 1585 |
| 0.9 | 2.291 | 9.0 | 3981 |
|  |  | 10.0 | 10,000 |
|  |  | 15.0 | 1,000,000 |

It soon became apparent that not all of the first magnitude stars are the same brightness. For the brighter stars, by the help of the formula, it is possible to use zero magnitude and even negative magnitudes. The scale can thus be extended to bright objects such as Jupiter, whose magnitude is $-2$; Venus, $-4.4$ at maximum brightness; full moon $-12.6$; and the sun $-26.7$. The magnitudes of the twenty brightest stars are given in Table 17–5.

The formula makes it possible to compute the magnitudes to decimals, provided the ratio of brightness can be determined accurately. For telescopic stars, the magnitude is extended beyond $+6$. A 1-inch telescope will show stars down to magnitude $+9$; 16-inch to $+15.0$; and the 200-inch telescope down to magnitude $+20$ and even fainter by photography.

The eye is not a very sensitive photometer. A practiced observer using a telescope to compare stars close together, can possibly distinguish differences to 0.1 magnitude. The photographic plate can be used to measure magnitudes accurately to 0.01 magnitude. The most sensitive instrument of all, the photoelectric photometer, under the best conditions and by averaging several observations, can make measures down to 0.001 magnitude in accuracy or to $\frac{1}{10}$ of 1 percent.

Magnitudes determined by eye estimates are called *visual* magnitudes. *Photographic* magnitudes are measures made on blue-sensitive plates. If a yellow filter is used, the magnitudes are called *photovisual*. *Photoelectric* magnitudes, made with photo cells which are somewhat color blind, are very similar to photographic magnitudes, although there are some slight differences. All these magnitudes are for apparent brightness (brightness as seen by the photometer) but reduced to the magnitude as it would be if the star were located at the zenith.

Because of absorption in the earth's atmosphere, corrections are made by calculating the angular distance of the star from the zenith at the time its brightness is measured and applying a correction factor, which has been computed from a series of

TABLE 17–5
**The Twenty Brightest Stars[a]**

| Star | Right Ascension (1967) | | Declination (1967) | | Visual Magnitudes | | Spectral Types of Components | | Proper Motion (sec/year) | Distance (Light Years) | Absolute Magnitudes of Components | |
|---|---|---|---|---|---|---|---|---|---|---|---|---|
| Sirius | 6$^h$ | 43.7$^m$ | −16° | 40.2′ | −1.6 | +8.5 | A0 V | wd | 1.32 | 8.8 | +1.4 | +11.5 |
| Canopus | 6 | 23.2 | −52 | 40.6 | −0.9 | | F0 II | | 0.02 | 98 | −3.1 | |
| α Centauri | 14 | 37.3 | −60 | 42.0 | 0.1 | +1.4 | G0 V | K5 V | 3.68 | 4.2 | +4.4 | +5.8 |
| Vega | 18 | 35.8 | +38 | 45.1 | 0.1 | | A0 V | | 0.34 | 26 | +0.5 | |
| Arcturus | 14 | 14.2 | +19 | 21.2 | 0.2 | | K0 III | | 2.28 | 36 | −0.3 | |
| Capella | 5 | 14.2 | +45 | 58.0 | 0.2 | +10 | G0 II | M1 V | 0.44 | 46 | −0.7 | +9.5 |
| Rigel | 5 | 13.0 | −8 | 14.3 | 0.3 | +6.6 | B8p Ia | B9 | 0.00 | 815 | −6.8 | −0.4 |
| Betelgeuse | 5 | 53.3 | +7 | 21.0 | 0.4v | | M2 I | | 0.03 | 490 | −5.5v | |
| Procyon | 7 | 37.6 | +5 | 18.6 | 0.5 | +11 | F5 IV | wd | 1.25 | 11.4 | +2.7 | +13.0 |
| Achernar | 1 | 36.5 | −57 | 24.2 | 0.6 | | B5 V | | 0.10 | 65 | −1.0 | |
| Altair | 14 | 49.2 | +8 | 46.8 | 0.5 | | A5 IV | | 0.66 | 16.6 | +2.2 | |
| β Centauri | 14 | 01.5 | −60 | 12.9 | 0.9 | | B1 III | | 0.04 | 293 | −4.1 | −0.8 |
| Aldebaran | 4 | 34.0 | +16 | 26.7 | 1.1 | +13 | K5 III | M2 V | 0.20 | 53 | −0.2 | +12 |
| Spica | 13 | 23.5 | −10 | 59.4 | 1.2 | | B2 V | | 0.05 | 260 | −3.6 | |
| α Crucis | 12 | 24.7 | −62 | 55.0 | 1.4 | +1.9 | B1 IV | B3 | 0.04 | 391 | −4.0 | −3.5 |
| Antares | 16 | 27.4 | −26 | 21.6 | 1.2 | +5.1 | M0 I | A3 V | 0.03 | 391 | −4.5 | −0.3 |
| Pollux | 7 | 43.3 | +28 | 06.4 | 1.2 | | K0 III | | 0.62 | 39 | +0.8 | |
| Fomalhaut | 20 | 55.8 | −29 | 47.8 | 1.3 | +6 | A3 V | K4 V | 0.37 | 23 | +2.0 | +7.3 |
| Deneb | 20 | 40.3 | +45 | 09.7 | 1.3 | | A2p I | | 0.00 | 1400 | −6.9 | |
| β Crucis | 12 | 45.8 | −59 | 30.5 | 1.5 | | B1 IV | | 0.05 | 490 | −4.6 | |

[a] "v" after a magnitude indicates that the star is a variable.
"p" after the spectral type indicates that the spectrum is not exactly that listed, but is peculiar; that is, has some irregularity.
"e" after the spectral type indicates that the spectrum has bright (emission) lines.
"wd" means white dwarf.

changing positions of the star. The corrections to photoelectric observations in particular are made very carefully, even the colors of the stars being taken into consideration.

The magnitudes of the moon and planets change with variations in distance and phase. The magnitude changes of the moon are very conspicuous. Mars changes by several magnitudes between conjunction and opposition. The changes in magnitude of all the other planets are observable by a practiced sky watcher.

It has been pointed out that the stars are not all at the same distance from the sun. In order to compare them properly with each other, it is necessary to be able to calculate their magnitudes as if all were at the same distance. The term *absolute magnitude* means the magnitude of a star calculated for a standard distance, which is taken to be 10 parsecs

(32.6 light years). For example, the sun's apparent magnitude, $m$, is $-26.7$. How bright would it be, if seen from a distance of 10 parsecs?

It is known that light decreases as the square of the distance; that is, light varies inversely as the distance squared. Thus the brightness of the sun decreases as the distance increases from one to 2,062,650 astronomical units (10 parsecs), by a factor of 2,062,650 squared. Substituting this figure into equation 17–8 and computing the magnitude change, the absolute magnitude of the sun is found to be about $+4.87$ (see Sample Problem). This figure may be slightly in error because of the difficulty of comparing the apparent brightness of the sun with the stars.

---

▶ *Sample Problem:*    Compute the absolute magnitude $M$ of the sun.

By logarithms:    $2.512^{(M-m)} = (2,062,650)^2$,

$$(M - m) \log 2.512 = 2 \log 2,062,650$$

or    $(M - m) \times 0.4 = 2 \times 6.31443$

$$(M - m) = \frac{2 \times 6.31443}{0.4} = 31.5722$$

and    $M = -26.7 + 31.57 = 4.87,$

which is the absolute magnitude of the sun.

By the table of magnitudes (Table 17–4):

$$(2,062,650)^2 = (2.062 \times 10^6)^2 = 4.254 \times 10^{12}$$

$$= 4.254 \times (100)^6 = 2.512 \times 1.694 \times (100)^6.$$

This large number has been broken down in order that the table of magnitudes may be used without further computation. Each part can be found in the table, or found by interpolation. Light ratios are multiplied together, magnitudes are merely added or subtracted. From the table, the magnitude corresponding to a ratio of brightness of 2.512 is 1.0; 1.694 is between 0.5 and 0.6. Call it 0.57. One hundred is equivalent to 5.0 magnitudes, which must be taken six times. Therefore the difference of magnitude of the sun, the amount its brightness decreases for a change from its actual distance to the standard distance, is

$$M - m = 1.0 + 0.57 + 6 \times 5.0 = 31.57,$$

which is exactly the result obtained by the use of logarithms, neglecting the digits after the second decimal place.

---

It is possible to calculate all absolute magnitudes by using the inverse square law, but computation is easier if reduced to a formula. Let $l$, $m$, and $d$ be the amount of light, apparent magnitude, and distance of a star, and $L$, $M$, and $D$ be its brightness (luminosity), absolute magnitude, and distance in parsecs at the standard distance (10 parsecs). Hence, using the inverse square law

$$\frac{l}{L} = \frac{D^2}{d^2} = \frac{10^2}{d^2} = 2.512^{(M-m)}. \tag{17-9}$$

Taking logs of both sides of this equation (the last two members)

$$2 \log 10 - 2 \log d = 0.4 (M - m)$$

and    $M - m = \dfrac{2 \log 10 - 2 \log d}{0.4}$

$$= \frac{2 - 2 \log d}{0.4} = 5 - 5 \log d. \tag{17-10}$$

Thus,    $M = m + 5 - 5 \log d$    (17–11)

where $d$ is the distance in parsecs. Since $d$ is inversely proportional to the parallax, $p$, the equation may be written,

$$M = m + 5 + 5 \log p \tag{17-12}$$

where $p$ is expressed in seconds of arc.

This equation requires the use of logarithms. There is no simpler way of computing the absolute magnitudes of stars. In simple language, the formulas say: If a star's brightness and distance are known, it is possible to compute its brightness at a distance of 10 parsecs. To turn the formula around, if the absolute and visual apparent magnitudes can be found, the distance can be determined. This is a very important statement, since it leads to a determination of the distances of galaxies by the use of Cepheid variable stars which will be discussed in later chapters. This method has made it possible to estimate the extent of the universe.

The *luminosity* of a star is its brightness compared to the brightness of the sun. To compute luminosity, it is necessary to know the absolute magnitudes of the sun and the stars. The formula for the relation between brightness and magnitude can be restated as:

$$L = 2.512^{(4.87-M)} \qquad (17\text{--}13)$$

where 4.87 is the absolute magnitude of the sun and $L$ and $M$ are the luminosity and absolute magnitude, respectively, of any star. If $M$ is less than 4.87, the star is brighter than the sun. If $M$ is greater than 4.87, the star is fainter.

Magnitudes, both apparent and absolute, are called visual, photographic, or photoelectric, depending on how they are determined. There is still another kind of magnitude, called bolometric magnitude. This is based on the total amount of energy emitted by a star and can be observed only under special conditions by the use of a bolometer, an instrument sensitive to the infrared regions of the spectrum as well as to visible light.

If the temperature of a star is known, its bolometric magnitude can be computed from its photovisual magnitude by a correction, which has been determined from theory. One definition of luminosity is that it is a measure of the total amount of radiation emitted by a star and therefore must be based on the bolometric magnitude.

The colors of stars can be found by measurement. If a star is observed with a photoelectric photometer or by photography, its photovisual magnitude can be determined by passing its light through a yellow filter before it strikes the photometer. Similarly the photographic magnitude can be determined by using a blue filter. The difference between the photographic and visual magnitudes is called the *color index*.

More recently, measures have been made with photometers equipped with three or more filters. One standard set of filters is called the *UBV* system, meaning ultraviolet, blue, and visual. The color index of a star is determined by comparing the magnitudes when the filters are used in various combinations. There is a definite relation between the spectral type, based on temperature, and color expressed by the color index, as shown in Table 17–6.

TABLE 17–6
**Stellar Spectra and Color Indices**

| Spectral Class | Color Index | Spectral Class | Color Index |
|---|---|---|---|
| B0 | −0.32 | G0 | 0.60 |
| B5 | −0.16 | G5 | 0.68 |
| A0 | 0.00 | K0 | 0.82 |
| A5 | 0.15 | K5 | 1.18 |
| F0 | 0.30 | M0 | 1.45 |
| F5 | 0.44 | M5 | 1.69 |

## 17.5 The Spectrum-Luminosity Diagram

As the data of absolute magnitudes and spectral types were being collected, Ejner Hertzsprung in Holland in 1911 and Russell in the United States in 1913 noticed that, on a diagram correlating the two, the points were divided into distinct groups. They called the stars represented on the diagram giants and dwarfs. This was a fortunate guess as it was shown later that there are indeed groups of stars based on size. This diagram has been continued with the addition of data from thousands of stars. It is called the spectrum-luminosity diagram or the H-R diagram in honor of its two discoverers. (Figure 17–7)

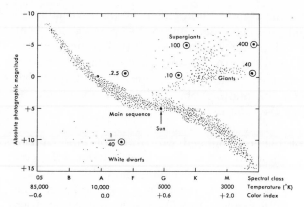

Fig. 17-7 The Hertzsprung-Russell diagram for stars of known distance. The numbers refer to star sizes compared to the diameter of the sun.

As the temperature scale on the diagram shows, the highest temperatures are plotted on the left, the lowest on the right. They vary from 85,000°K for the O5-stars to 3,000°K for the M-stars. Absolute magnitudes at the top are −10 for stars 1 million times brighter than the sun, to +15 at the bottom for stars 10,000 times fainter than the sun. Others still fainter are not shown. The diagonal line is called the main sequence, since most of the stars are represented by points on that part of the diagram.

Another group with absolute magnitude about zero is composed of giant stars. Supergiants have magnitudes $M$ above −2 (an arbitrary division). Giant stars are therefore about 100 times brighter than the sun and supergiants are more than 600 times brighter. White dwarfs, at the lower left, have temperatures about 10,000°K and absolute magnitudes averaging +10. They are actually stars, but they are more like planets in size.

Stellar diameters can also be calculated from the diagram. A star of class G with $M = 0$, a giant star, radiates 100 times as much energy as the sun. But, since its temperature is the same, the amount of radiation per square mile must be the same. Therefore, the surface area of a star of this class must be 100 times larger than the area of the sun or its diameter must be 10 solar diameters. A supergiant

with $M = -5$ would be another ten times larger, or 100 times the diameter of the sun.

The red giant stars radiate at a lower rate than the sun and must therefore be still larger. To calculate the diameter, the rate of radiation can be found from Stefan's law. If the temperature is 3,000°K, one-half the 6,000°K of the sun, the radiation per square mile is only $(\frac{1}{2})^4$ or $\frac{1}{16}$ that of the sun, and the area must be 16 times greater to produce the same amount of energy. That is, the diameter must be $\sqrt{16}$ or four times the solar diameter. Likewise, a star of $M = 0$, and spectral type M, is four times larger than a star of $M = 0$ and spectral type G. So the cool, red giants and supergiants must be very large.

Similarly, the white dwarfs must be very small. A white dwarf whose temperature is 12,000°K and $M = +10$ has a diameter only $\frac{1}{40}$ that of the sun. Another kind of investigation shows that this white dwarf must have nearly the same mass as the sun and therefore its density must be $(40)^3$ or 64,000 times the density of the sun. This density is unlike any known on the earth and can be possible only if the electrons are stripped from the atoms and the nuclei packed closely together. This is the predicted state of the sun 7 or 8 billion years from now.

Fortunately, there is another way of determining the absolute magnitudes of stars. Consider the sun and the bright star Capella. Capella has the same type spectrum as the sun, G0. But it is 170 times brighter and therefore 13 times larger. The mass of Capella is about twice that of the sun and its density is only $\frac{1}{1000}$ that of the sun. With such a low density, the atoms in the star's chromosphere have more room to move around than they do in the sun's chromosphere. The lines in the spectrum of Capella are therefore sharper than the solar lines, because the atoms do not interfere with each other as much. Also the temperature in the chromosphere is lower in the star.

The difference in temperature between main sequence stars and giants was noticed in 1913 by Adams and Kohlschutter at the Mount Wilson Observatory. They also noticed that there are differences in the ionization of atoms, since ionization is easier at lower pressures than at high pressures. So certain lines due to ionized gases are stronger in the spectra of giant stars than in the main sequence stars. Also in the latter the neutral lines are stronger than in the giants, because there is a higher percentage of un-ionized atoms where the pressure is greater. This led to a new method of determining absolute magnitudes.

The method was improved by William W. Morgan and his associates at the Yerkes Observatory. They divided the stars into luminosity classes, as follows:

Ia. Brightest supergiants

Ib. Less luminous supergiants

II. Bright giants

III. Giants

IV. Subgiants (class between giants and main sequence)

V. Main sequence stars

VI. Subdwarfs (Sd)

VII. White dwarfs (Wd)

The sun in this classification is G0V, and Capella is G0III. The authors also worked out a graph showing the absolute magnitudes for each of the first six classes.

Since the absolute magnitudes are known with considerable accuracy, it is possible to substitute $M$ and $m$, the apparent magnitude in the formula (17–11 or 17–12) and determine the distances and parallaxes of stars for which spectra can be obtained and classified. Parallaxes determined in this way are called *spectroscopic parallaxes*. (See Figure 17–8 for the relation between the luminosity classes and the H-R diagram.)

## QUESTIONS AND PROBLEMS

1. Compute the number of seconds in a year.

2. Assuming that observations could be made with the same equipment on Mars as on the earth, what would be the limit of accurate distance measurements by the parallax method?

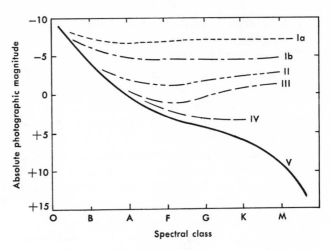

Fig. 17–8   The luminosity classes of stars on the Hertzsprung-Russell diagram.

3  By using Wien's law, determine in which spectral classes the maximum wavelengths of stars are in the visible spectrum. Assume limits of the visual spectrum to be 4000 to 7000 A.

4  The wavelength of maximum radiation of class O5 stars is in the ultraviolet. Do these stars appear to be as bright as stars of equal size whose maximum radiation is in the visible spectrum? Explain.

5. How much is the parallax of a star increased by using the radius of the earth's orbit, instead of the radius of the earth, as a base line?

6. The distance of Barnard's star is 5.9 light years. Compute its distance in parsecs and astronomical units. What is its parallax?

7. Why are the motions of stars measured with respect to the sun?

8. An observer can see stars six magnitudes fainter with a 16-inch telescope than with a 1-inch telescope. Verify this by comparing the brightness ratio with the light-gathering power of the two telescopes. (See Chapter 4 for light-gathering power.)

9. Compute the tangential and space velocities of

the following stars of the Big Dipper: (a) Gamma; (b) Epsilon; (c) Eta. **Ans:** (a) $T = 11$ km/sec; $v = 15.6$ km/sec.

10. Since differences of magnitude correspond to ratios of brightness, magnitudes are added and ratios are multiplied. (a) Verify this by multiplying the brightness ratio for a magnitude difference of 0.6 by that for a magnitude difference of 0.4. Check this product with the ratio corresponding to the sum of the magnitude differences. (b) Repeat for magnitude differences of 3 and 6.

11. Brightness ratios that are not listed in Table 17–4 can be computed if magnitude differences that add up to the desired total can be found; the desired brightness ratio is the product of the corresponding ratios, as shown in Problem 10. By using this method, find the ratio of brightness of (a) the sun and moon; (b) Sirius and Beta Crucis. **Ans:** (a) magnitude difference is $14.1 = 10 + 4 + 0.1$; brightness ratio $= 436,000$.

12. As discussed in Chapter 4, the intensity of light decreases as the square of the distance. Assume an observer is comparing the apparent brightness of identical street lights, $A$ and $B$, located at different distances from him. Fill in the missing numbers in the following table:

| Distance of Light A (blocks) | Distance of Light B (blocks) | Brightness Ratio | Difference of Magnitude |
|---|---|---|---|
| 1 | 10 | 100 | 5 |
| 1 | 100 | 10,000 | |
| 10 | 100 | | |
| 10 | | | 10 |
| | 1000 | | 15 |

13. The absolute magnitude of a star is the apparent magnitude it would have if located at the standard distance of 10 parsecs. The apparent magnitude, due to its actual distance, can be converted to absolute magnitude by calculating

the ratio of brightness at its actual distance to its brightness at 10 parsecs. The brightness ratio and corresponding difference in magnitude are found in the same way as for the street lights in Question 12. Fill in the missing numbers in the following table; the first row is an example.

| Distance of Star (parsecs) | Distance Ratio (to 10 parsecs) | Brightness Ratio | Difference of Magnitude | Apparent Magnitude | Absolute Magnitude |
|---|---|---|---|---|---|
| 100 | 10 | 100 | 5 | +8 | +3 |
| 1000 | 100 | 10,000 | | +11 | |
| | | 1,000,000 | | | +2 |
| | | | | −2 | +3 |

14. Show that a star of absolute magnitude −10 is 1,000,000 times more luminous than the sun, and a star of absolute magnitude +15 is 10,000 times less luminous than the sun. Assume the absolute magnitude of the sun is +5.

15. Two stars have the same surface temperature. One is five magnitudes brighter than the other. (a) Calculate the ratio of their surface areas and diameters. (b) Repeat for the case where one star is 10 magnitudes brighter than the other. **Ans:** (a) area ratio, 100; diameter ratio, 10.

16. Two stars have the same absolute magnitude. The temperature of one is 6000°K; that of the other is 3000°K. (a) Compute the ratios of their energy radiation per square mile, their areas, and their diameters. (b) Repeat for temperatures of 5,000°K and 15,000°K. **Ans:** (a) Ratios: energy, 16; area, 16; diameter, 4.

17. Compute the ratio of the diameters of the following stars to the diameter of the sun: (a) $T = 12,000°$K: abs. mag, $M = 0$. (b) $T = 2000°$K; $M = +15$. Assume Sun's $M = +5$. **Ans:** (a) 2.5.

18. Compute the ratio of the diameters of Sirius $A$ and Sirius $B$ from their temperatures and absolute magnitudes (or visual magnitudes, since their distances are the same). (See Chapter 19 for data.)

# Chapter Eighteen

# Variable Stars

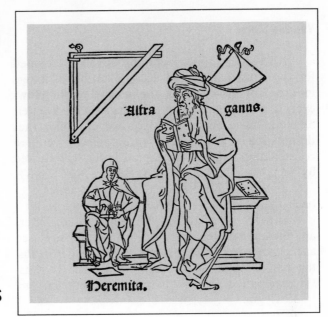

In the year 134 B.C. Hipparchus observed a star in the constellation Scorpius where no star was visible before. This was contrary to the belief at that time that the stars were set in a crystal sphere where nothing could change. Hipparchus' star remained bright for a few months and then faded and disappeared. Another new star was seen in the constellation Cassiopeia from November, 1572, to the spring of 1574. It was discovered in Germany and was observed by Tycho Brahe in Denmark. Tycho described it as a "nova stellis," meaning new star. The name *nova* is still used for similar stars, several of which are discovered every year. Kepler observed a nova in 1604. Between 1890 and 1960 ten novas have been visible to the unaided eye. It is estimated that some 25 appear in our galaxy every year, but most of them go unnoticed or increase in brightness to telescopic visibility only.

Since the time of Hipparchus and the discovery of novas, other stars have been seen to vary in brightness. A *variable star* is variable not only in the amount of light it emits, but may show other changes, such as variations in the spectrum, or even in diameter. A plot of the magnitude of a variable star against time is called a *light curve*. A study of a light curve, combined with observations of the spectrum, gives a great deal of information and is fundamental to the study of the physical nature of this type of star.

## 18.1 Classification of Variable Stars

Variable stars have been grouped into many classes. We shall adopt only a simple classification, since further subclasses would be too confusing. They are:

I. Novas, now called temporary or exploding stars.
II. Cepheid variables, now called pulsating or eruptive stars.
III. Semiregular Variables.
IV. Irregular Variables.
V. Eclipsing Binary Stars.

The first four classes are also designated as intrinsic variables, since their variations are caused by changes inside the stars. The fifth class is variable only because of its orientation, and the variations are caused by eclipses of one star by a companion.

A 1958 Russian catalog lists the following numbers of variables: 959 novas, 9855 cepheids, 1134 semiregular and irregular variables, and 2763 eclipsing binaries.

All variable stars, including novas, are named for the constellation and a combination of letters in order of discovery in the constellation. However, if a variable star already has a Greek letter, or name (Beta Persei = Algol, for example), that designation is retained. The first discovery in a constellation is given the capital letter R, followed by S, T, . . .Z. Then RR, RS, RT, . . .RZ, SS, ST, . . .SZ. When ZZ has been reached, the series goes back to AA, AB, . . .QZ (except that the letter J is omitted). When all 334 combinations of letters are filled, the designations V335, V336, . . . are used as far as needed. Examples are: R Coronae Borealis, the first variable discovered in Corona, RZ Cassiopeiae, an eclipsing binary in Cassiopeia, and V335 Cygni.

## 18.2  Novas or Temporary Stars

A nova is given a designation consisting of the word nova and the constellation in which it is located and the year in which it was discovered; as Nova Puppis 1942.

It is now known that a "new" star is not new but is a star that has been in existence for billions of years. Because it flares up unexpectedly, very little is known about the prenova stage. Usually a nova is discovered when near its maximum brightness. Subsequent changes can be followed for years, but the chance of observing the rise to maximum is extremely small. The figure showing the light curve of Nova Puppis is typical (Figure 18–1). Nova Herculis (Figure 18–2) was discovered when it was near maximum in 1934. When the spectrum of Nova Aquilae 1918 was observed several years before it flared, it was of class A or earlier, but the star was very faint and the spectrum was difficult to classify. Spectra of other stars have been obtained only when they were within about two magnitudes of maxima.

Changes in the spectral class of Nova Puppis 1942 are indicated on the light curve in Figure 18–1. As this star became brighter, its spectrum was about class A or F (continuous spectrum crossed by a few dark lines). The dark lines are produced by that part

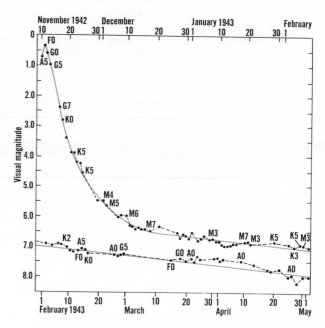

Fig. 18–1  The light curve of Nova Puppis 1942, indicating the changes in spectral type with change of brightness. The star was not observed during its rise to maximum before November 10, 1942. The top dates correspond with the upper curve.

of a star's atmosphere between the star and the earth. This is typical of all novas, also. Their spectra show large shifts of the lines toward the blue, indicating that the atmosphere is moving rapidly toward the earth on the near side with speeds reaching nearly 1000 mi/sec. It is assumed that the stars have exploded uniformly in all directions, the lines being broadened because the component of velocity from the observable part of the atmosphere varies from zero at each limb to a maximum in the center, the far side being hidden from view.

The usual nova slows its brightening process during the last two magnitudes of rise and then, as the brightness decreases, the spectrum shows a sudden change. The absorption spectrum is still visible, but now has also strongly widened bright lines. These lines are from hydrogen, ionized calcium and iron, widened about the zero velocity position. The explanation is that the star's atmosphere is no longer

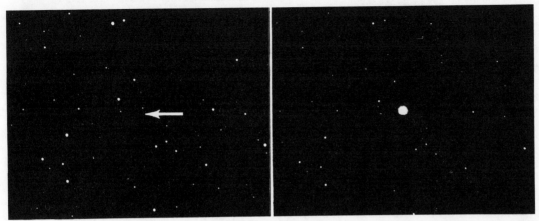

Fig. 18–2 Two photographs of Nova Herculis 1934 (DQ Herculis), which increased in brightness from about 15th magnitude to 2nd magnitude before it was discovered to be a nova. (Yerkes Observatory photograph)

opaque, but is so transparent that the light from the far side, which is receding from the earth, is seen and the lines are strongly shifted toward the red. These changes are shown in Figure 18–3 and the explanation is diagrammed in Figure 18–4.

Meanwhile, the star's color has changed from white through yellow to red. During that time there are other changes in the spectrum until the "forbidden" lines of doubly ionized oxygen and neon appear (somewhat like the ionized lines in the spectrum of the solar corona). The nova then has the appearance of a very small gaseous nebula and may take on a greenish color. The nova finally fades away, the star loses its nebular spectrum and returns to its original white color and shows a continuous spectrum, sometimes without visible lines.

During the nova stage of several stars, luminous clouds of atoms have been observed around them. This material is composed of gas and dust particles in the region which reflect light from the nova. Since most novas appear in the Milky Way, it is not surprising to find these dust clouds, since they are located almost exclusively in the arms of the galaxy. A year or two later, the material ejected by the star at the high speeds measured by the Doppler effect has moved far enough from the star to be seen. After the star resumes its former brightness, it is at the center of a faintly glowing planetary nebula. Figure 18–5 shows photographs of two planetary nebulae, each of which was probably produced by a nova several thousand years ago.

The distance to a nova can be calculated from the rate of expansion of the nebular shell in seconds per year and the known speed of its material from the velocity measures. It is like the relation between tangential velocity of a star and its proper motion and distance. Adapting equation 17–3 to this problem and solving for $p$ or $d$, since $T = 4.74\ \mu/p''$km/sec and $d = I/p''$, we have

$$p'' = 4.74 \times \frac{\text{angular rate of increase}}{\text{velocity from Doppler effect}} \quad (18\text{–}1)$$

and

$$d = \frac{1}{4.74} \frac{\text{velocity (km/sec)}}{\text{seconds per year increase}} \text{ parsecs.} \quad (18\text{–}2)$$

▶*Example:* If the measured velocity is 1000 km/sec and the angular rate of increase is 1″ per year, the distance to the nova is

$$d = \frac{1}{4.74} \times \frac{1000\,\text{km/sec}}{1\,\text{sec/yr}} = 211 \text{ parsecs} = 690 \text{ light years}$$

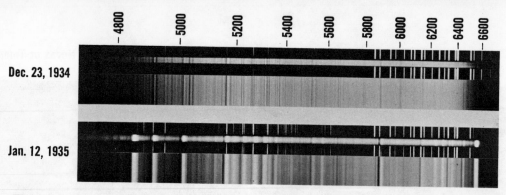

| | | | | | | | | | | | |
|4800|5000|5200|5400|5600|5800|6000|6200|6400|6600|

Dec. 23, 1934

Jan. 12, 1935

Fig. 18–3 Spectra of Nova Herculis 1934 at maximum brightness (top) and after the atmosphere had formed. Note the widened lines in the lower spectrum. In each case, the narrow spectrum between the pairs of comparison spectra has been artificially widened to show more detail. (Lick Observatory photographs)

After the distance has been calculated, it is possible to compute the absolute magnitude of the nova at any stage. At maximum, the absolute magnitudes average about −7, or 12 magnitudes brighter than the sun. That is, the average luminosity of a nova is 60,000. At minimum the stars are thought to have about the same luminosity as the sun. That is, a nova brightens by about 60,000 times. If the star were hotter than the sun (class A or F) its diameter could be computed as was done from the H-R diagram. The average is about one-fourth the solar diameter. Thus the prenova star is off the main sequence in the subdwarf class. At maximum it would be classed as a supergiant, about 60 to 200 times the diameter of the sun.

The novas seen by Tycho and Kepler were much brighter than the usual nova. Other similar novas have been found in distant galaxies, Andromeda and others. Their absolute magnitudes range from −12 to −18 and their luminosities from 6 million to 10 billion! These luminosities are greater than some entire galaxies composed of billions of stars. Such novas are called *supernovas*. Their velocities measure up to 3000 mi/sec and it is probable that almost the entire mass of the nova explodes into space. It is estimated that a supernova should appear in a galaxy about once every 300 or 400 years. Since our galaxy has not produced a supernova since 1604, we are due for another any time now!

A well-known remnant of a supernova is the Crab Nebula, shown in four colors in Figure 18–6.

This nova appeared in 1054 according to records from China. It is still expanding at a rate of about 0.21″ per year at a speed of 1300 km/sec. From the formula (18–2), its distance can be computed as

Fig. 18–4 Expanding atmospheric shells around a nova. $A$ is a small shell around a star at its center. The larger circles represent the principal expanding shell. Material in regions $D$ between the nova and the earth produce absorption lines. All other regions in this shell at $B$ produce emission lines.

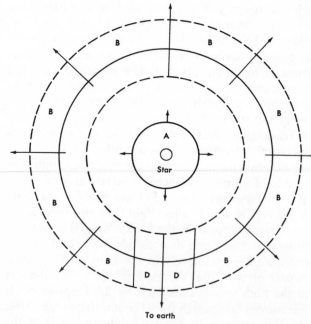

 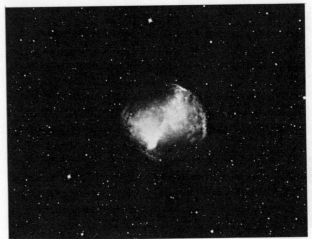

Fig. 18–5   Two planetary nebulae in Vulpecula (left), known as the Dumbbell nebula. The nebula on the right, photographed in red light, is Monoceros. (Photographs from the Mount Wilson and Palomar Observatories)

1300 parsecs, or about 4250 light years. The Crab Nebula is one of the strongest sources of radio waves from space.

## 18.3  Cepheid Variables

The star Delta Cephei was found to be a variable star in 1784 by a British astronomer, John Goodricke. Delta is one of three stars in a small triangle in the constellation Cepheus, a circumpolar constellation, which is visible all year in northern latitudes. It is visible to the unaided eye, but to study its light variation, a good pair of binoculars is recommended. It can be compared easily with the two other stars in the triangle. It varies from magnitude 4.1 to 5.2 in 5.4 days. Other variable stars which have similar light curves have been found (almost 10,000 of them) and have been named *cepheids*.

The light curve of a cepheid variable is not at all like that of a nova. (See Figure 18–7.) The observations used for drawing the curve in the figure were made with a blue-sensitive photocell and are not quite the same as those made with the eye. The variation in blue light is about 1.3 magnitudes com-

pared to 8 magnitudes for Nova Puppis 1942 and 12 magnitudes for the average nova. Moreover, the light curve repeats; that is, it is periodic and the period of variation is 5.37 days. With the eye, Delta Cephei will be bright on some night, will fade to about one-third its maximum brightness in four nights and then regain it all in about 1.5 days.

At the same time, there are variations due to the Doppler effect in the spectrum. This is interpreted as a velocity effect. As shown in Figure 18–8, the velocity curve has the same period as the light curve. The velocity changes by some 20 mi/sec in 5.37 days. The shapes of the two curves are almost mirror images of each other. This is typical of stars of this class. The variations in light are roughly one magnitude, although changes of less than 0.1 magnitude have been found for some cepheids, including Polaris, the Pole Star. In most, but not all, cases the rise in light is faster than the decline, as in the case of Delta Cephei. Some have definite humps in the descending branch of the light curves. The periods range from 3 to 50 days.

The spectral classes to which these stars belong are mostly F, G, and K, and their median (midway

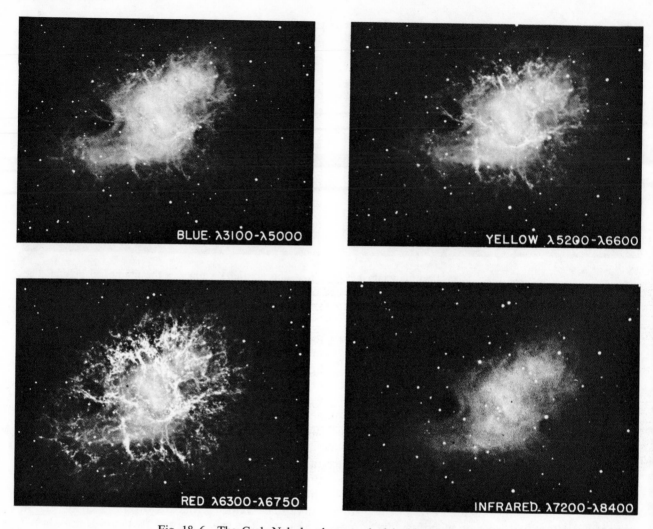

Fig. 18–6   The Crab Nebula photographed in blue, yellow, red, and infrared light. It is a remnant of a supernova and is still expanding. (Photographs from the Mount Wilson and Palomar Observatories)

between maximum and minimum) absolute magnitudes vary from 0 to −5. In fact, they fit pretty well into the H-R diagram, the fainter stars being giants of class F with periods of about three days, ranging to supergiants of class K with periods of 45 days. But during the light variations, the spectral class changes by approximately one class. This indicates a change of temperature, amounting to about

1500° K in the case of Delta Cephei. These variables are hottest when they are at maximum light and coolest when at minimum. In addition, the lines in the spectrum oscillate about their normal positions during the light variations, as shown in the velocity curve. Near maximum, the lines are shifted the greatest amount toward the blue and at minimum toward the red. This indicates that the variable is

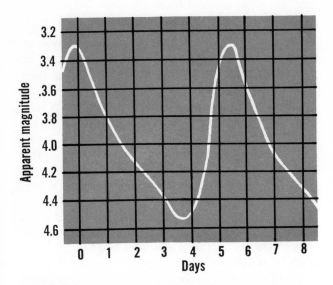

Fig. 18-7 A photoelectric light curve of Delta Cephei.

brightest and hottest when expanding at the maximum rate and not when it is largest. It is coolest when contracting at the maximum rate.

The interpretation of the changes in light, spectral class, and radial velocity is as follows: The lines are produced in the part of the star's photosphere which is toward the earth, and are absorption lines. The Doppler shift toward the blue at maximum light is now believed to be caused by a movement of the stellar material toward the earth, followed by a recession away from the earth as the star fades to minimum light. This indicates, on the assumption that the motion takes place in spherical shells, that the star is alternately expanding and contracting.

When the star contracts, the internal temperature and pressure increase to the point where they are too high. The star then expands to reduce these

conditions. This expansion acts like a mild explosion, sending the material out to a distance where the balance is again upset, and the star contracts under its gravitational attraction. This contraction and expansion is a periodic adjustment of the pressure and temperature about conditions of equilibrium. The amount of pulsation depends on the size of the star. The smallest stars require the shortest times for their pulsations and the periods increase in length as the size of the star and the amount of change of size increase. Since this theory was first accepted these stars have been called *pulsating* stars.

Actually this interpretation is a little too simple and does not fit all the facts. Martin Schwarzschild at Princeton University has suggested that there is an internal pulsation, but that the outer regions of the star do not expand and contract together with the inner regions. So there is a lag in the light curve. Also some lines in the spectrum are shifted toward the blue at the same time that others are shifted toward the red. It appears that there may be two shells moving in opposite directions at the same

Fig. 18-8 Radial velocity and light curves of Delta Cephei, a well-known cepheid variable star, explained as an expansion and contraction of the star. Maximum velocity inward is at $A$, maximum velocity outward is at $C$. The star is smallest at $B$ and largest at $D$.

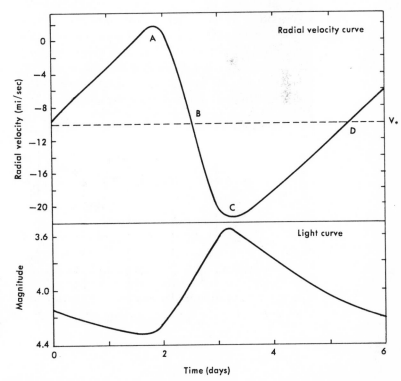

time. In fact, the two shells seem to collide with a relative speed of some 100 km/sec. Also the humps in some light curves have never been satisfactorily explained.

In addition to the stars just described and now called *classical cepheids*, there are other variable stars with similar light curves. One group, formerly called cluster variables but now called *RR Lyrae stars*, is composed of stars with periods of variation less than one day. They have absolute magnitudes near zero, belong to spectral class A or F and are assumed to be pulsating stars. Because of the difficulty of determining the parallax of these stars by the trigonometric method, the scale is still uncertain. That is, their absolute magnitudes are near, but not exactly, zero. The scale will almost certainly be further adjusted in the near future.

## 18.4    The Period-Luminosity Law

The fact that there is a relationship between period and luminosity of these variables is well established and has led to their use in determining distances where other methods fail. The relationship is shown in the curves of Figure 18–9. It was discovered by Henrietta Leavitt at the Harvard Observatory in 1912. She found that the fainter variable stars in the Small Magellanic Cloud have shorter periods than the brighter ones. At that time the distance to the

Cloud was not known, but later the absolute magnitude scale was fixed approximately by observations of stars of this type nearer the sun. All cepheids were plotted on the same scale with absolute magnitudes between 0 and −4.

Still later, Walter Baade of the Mount Wilson-Palomar Observatories looked for cluster variables in the Andromeda Galaxy with the 200-inch telescope, but could not find any. He reasoned that they are too far away to be observed even with the largest telescope. He did, however, find stars of the classical cepheid type. This led to the discovery that there are two distinct types of stars, which Baade called Population I and Population II. He estimated that the former are about 1.3 magnitudes brighter than the latter. This difference is shown in Figure 18–9. Population II or Type II stars are found in globular clusters, which is the reason for calling them cluster variables, and are also found in the nucleus of our galaxy and in a halo around it. Some Type II cepheids with periods between 10 and 30 days are also called W Virginis stars.

Type I or classical cepheids are found in the spiral arms of the galaxy. Almost all the cepheids in the neighborhood of the sun belong to this type. None of them have periods shorter than one day. They are supergiants from 400 to 5000 times brighter than the sun and their diameters are from about 20 to 300 solar diameters.

There is no difficulty in identifying RR Lyrae variables, since their light curves are unmistakable and their periods are less than one day. Hence, if the period-luminosity curve is right, their absolute magnitudes are zero. If the median apparent magnitude of a variable star of this type is known, the formula (equation 17–9) can be used for a determination of the distance.

▶*Example:* Suppose a 15th magnitude star in a globular cluster is found to be a variable star of this type. Then equation 17–9 can be rewritten as:

$$5 \log d = m - M + 5$$

$$= 15 - 0 + 5 \text{ (in this case)}$$

Fig. 18–9    The period-luminosity law for cepheid variables.

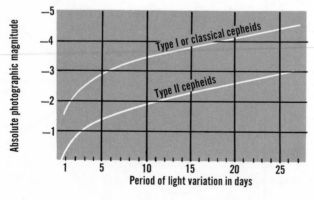

$$\log d = 4$$

and $d = 10,000$ parsecs $= 32,600$ light years.

This is the way the distances to the globular clusters have been determined. $(m - M)$ is called the *distance modulus.*

From the velocity curve it is possible to compute the change in diameter of a cepheid variable. And from the absolute magnitude and temperature the maximum and minimum diameters can be found. In the case of Delta Cephei, for example, the maximum diameter of 39.4 times the diameter of the sun occurs at minimum light. This occurs after the star has expanded and the temperature has dropped to about 5500° K. Minimum diameter occurs at maximum light, where the temperature has risen to about 6700° K. Here the light is at maximum because the radiation is more effective at the higher temperature in accordance with Stefan's law. The diameter is then about 37.2 times the solar diameter. Hence the change in diameter is about 6 percent, which is about the same percentage as in other classical cepheids. Apparently the smaller the star, the faster is the rate of pulsation.

## 18.5  Irregular Variables

The semirregular stars, as the name suggests, have periods that are not quite regular. Their light curves have irregular and unpredictable maxima and minima. Mira (omicron Ceti) was the first to be discovered and is the best known of this class. Mira means the Wonderful. Its spectral class varies from M9 at minimum to M6 at maximum and its temperature varies from 1900° K to 2600° K. The period of Mira averages about 330 days, but the times of maximum or minimum cannot be predicted accurately in advance. The maxima vary from second to fifth magnitude and the minima from eighth to tenth. From Stefan's law, the change in temperature shows a variation of total energy by a factor of 3.5. However, most of this energy is in the infrared. The light in the visible region may vary by as little as 15 times to as much as 1500 times, as is indicated in Figure 18–10. There are changes in the spectrum, but the real cause of the variation is not known. One explanation is that there is some irregular pulsation deep inside the star and a lag in the radiation due to the large stellar atmosphere.

No periods can be found for the variation of the irregular variable stars. A study made at the Washburn Observatory of the University of Wisconsin showed that practically all stars of spectral class cooler than about M1 and brighter than absolute magnitude −1 are variables of this type. The bright reddish star Betelgeuse in Orion belongs to this class, as do Antares, Alpha Herculis, and Mu Cephei. Betelgeuse varies irregularly by nearly a magnitude in the photoelectric (blue) region of the spectrum with a period of five or six years with irregular, small variations in addition. During the six years, the star varies in diameter. The distance of Betelgeuse is very great and its parallax correspondingly small. Its angular diameter has been measured and the linear diameter, which is very difficult to compute, may be nearly 1000 times that of the sun.

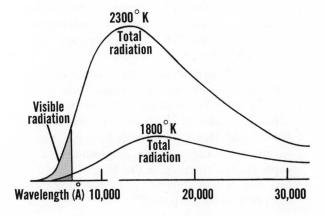

Fig. 18–10  The energy curves of a semiregular variable star at maximum and minimum temperature. The total radiation, the area under the curve, varies by a factor of about 2.5, while at the same time the visible radiation (the shaded area) shows a much greater amount of variation.

2300° K
Total radiation

Visible radiation

1800° K
Total radiation

Wavelength (Å) 10,000     20,000     30,000

Other variables of this class have nearly constant brightness for days or even weeks, then flare suddenly by several magnitudes. These stars are known as nova-like variables. A star of this class well-known to amateur observers is SS Cygni. The T Tauri stars show rapid and irregular variations. They are located in young clusters and may be new stars in the process of forming. R Coronae remains constant for long periods and then unexpectedly becomes fainter. After some irregular variations in brightness, it returns to its normal brightness. The cause may be the formation of absorbing clouds in its atmosphere, since it is a carbon star of spectral class R.

Some dwarf stars have been observed to flare. The flares last from a few minutes to perhaps half an hour. The cause of flaring is unknown, but seems to take place in some part of the star's photosphere much as the sun flares in areas of solar activity.

Stars have been observed to vary in light, in total energy, and in the lines of their spectra. The light variations range from many magnitudes, as in the novas, to such small fractions of one magnitude that they are detectable only by the sensitive photoelectric cell. The sun's total energy (the solar constant) varies by a percent or two. So the conclusion might be drawn that all stars are variable stars.

## QUESTIONS AND PROBLEMS

1. What was the order of discovery of the following variables in their respective constellations? (a) U Ophiuchi; (b) RZ Cassiopeiae; (c) ST Tauri. **Ans:** (b) 18th.

2. It is possible to determine the distance to a nova even though its absolute magnitude is not known, whereas for other stars the parallax or cepheid variable method must be used. Explain.

3. How could Henrietta Leavitt be sure that the variation in the average magnitudes of the cepheids she observed in the Magellanic Cloud was not due to differences in distance rather than related to the period?

4. Referring to the magnitude and velocity curves for Delta Cephei in Figure 18–8: (a) What is the velocity of the star with respect to the sun? (b) What are the maximum velocities of expansion and contraction of its surface with respect to the center of the star? (c) Explain from the diagram why the star has its maximum and minimum diameters at the indicated points. (d) How can it be deduced that the surface temperature is lower at maximum size?

5. The nebular shell of a nova is observed to expand at a rate of 0.25″ per year. The velocity measured by the Doppler effect is 750 km/sec. What is the distance to the nova in light years?

6. (a) Verify the quoted distance to the Crab Nebula by using the angular rate and velocity of expansion in the distance formula. (b) Compute the present diameter of the nebula in kilometers and in astronomical units.

7. Can a better estimate be made of the number of novas or supernovas that will occur in our galaxy in a given year? Explain.

8. Compute the distance to a RR Lyrae star, if its apparent magnitude is +20.

9. The apparent magnitude of a Type I cepheid variable is 1.7; its period is 10 days. (a) Find its absolute magnitude from the period-magnitude curve in Figure 18–9. (b) What is the difference between its absolute and apparent magnitudes? (c) Compute its distance in parsecs. (d) Repeat for a Type I cepheid of apparent magnitude +5.4 and period 30 days. **Ans:** (a) $M = -3.3$; (b) 5; (c) 100 parsecs.

10. What error would be made in the computation of the distance to a Type II Cepheid, if its absolute magnitude were found from the curve under the mistaken assumption that the star is Type I?

11. Show from Stefan's law that the energy radiated per square mile of Mira's surface changes by a factor of 3.5 during its cycle.

12. If a weight is hung on a spring, the position it occupies when the opposing forces of gravity

and the tension in the spring are balanced and it is not moving is called the rest position. If the weight is pulled down and then released, it will oscillate about the rest position. (a) What kind of energy (kinetic or potential) does the weight have at the ends of its motion? (b) What kind of energy does it have when passing through the rest position? (c) Why does it not stop at the rest position? (d) The oscillation of the weight is somewhat analogous to the oscillation of the surface of a variable star. What are the opposing forces in the star that correspond to the opposing forces acting on the weight? (e) What condition would be necessary for the star to stop oscillating? (f) Answer questions (a), (b), and (c) in terms of the star's surface.

# Chapter Nineteen

# Double Stars

We have pointed out that Mizar, one of the stars in the Big Dipper, is not single, but is really a double. The discovery was made in 1650 by John Baptist Riccioli, an Italian astronomer. His discovery was followed by thousands of others as larger and better telescopes were built. One of the most famous of double star observers was Sir William Herschel. Herschel found that most double stars are unequal in brightness and thought that the brighter star was closer to the earth than the fainter one. He proposed to determine its parallax by watching it describe a small circle around its companion in the course of one year. However, he found that this is not the case, but that the two stars move around each other in periods of many years. He probably did not actually observe a complete period in any case, since all the stars he observed require years or even centuries to complete an orbit.

## 19.1 Classification

At present, several types of double stars are recognized. If two stars are accidentally lined up, one being at a much greater distance than the other, they are called *optical double* stars. But if they are actually close together and describe orbits around a common center of gravity, they are called *binary stars*.

If a binary system is composed of two stars too close together to be seen separately, or if the pair is so far away from the earth that they cannot be separated visually in any telescope, they may still be recognized as binary by spectroscopic observations. In that case the system is called a *spectroscopic binary*. Sometimes the spectroscopic binary orbits are in line with the earth so that each star at some time in its orbit passes in front of its companion. They are then said to eclipse each other and the pair is called an *eclipsing binary* star. The following classifications of double stars are thus recognized:

1. Optical doubles
2. Visual binaries
3. Spectroscopic binaries
4. Eclipsing binaries

Each of these classes will now be discussed.

Optical doubles are recognized by their common proper motions or by the fact that they have different proper motions. For example, the two pairs of stars in Epsilon Lyrae might be said to form an optical double star, since they have the same proper motion. It is possible that they are in orbit around each other, but this is improbable unless the orbital period is measured in thousands of years and is too long to produce even a short detectable arc of motion.

In another optical double star, the proper motions may be at right angles to each other and therefore easily recognized. The proper motion of each star would be along a great circle, appearing as a straight line. This motion would take the two stars away from each other in a relatively short time.

### 19.2 Visual Binaries

Visual binary stars are recognized by their curved motions with respect to each other. In Figure 19–1 the changing positions of two stars in 12 years plainly show the binary nature of the pair. The method of measurement with the filar micrometer was described in Chapter 5. Three things must be known: the time of measurement, the angle between the two stars and a north-south line, and the distance between the two components in seconds of arc. A plot is then made, as in Figure 19–2, showing the angle and distance for each date of measurement.

When the observations are plotted, usually as the fainter star around the brighter, the motion is

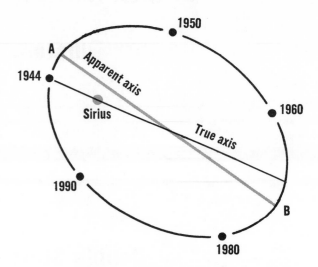

Fig. 19–2   The elliptical orbit of the companion of Sirius around the brighter star, Sirius A. The displacement of Sirius from the focus of the apparent ellipse is due to the inclination and orientation of the true orbit in space.

in an ellipse. If the law of gravitation holds for binary stars, one star should lie at the focus of the ellipse. This does not always appear to be the case. But, assuming that the law does hold and that the bright star does lie at the focus of the true ellipse, the displacement in the apparent ellipse is due to the orientation of the orbit in space.

Fig. 19–1   Changing positions of a binary star in an interval of 12 years. The star is Kruger 60. (Yerkes Observatory photographs)

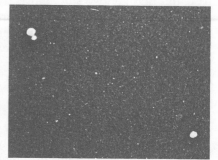

From the apparent ellipse, six elements may be found as in the case of the planets. They are:

1. The period, $P$, in years.
2. The semimajor axis, $a$, in seconds of arc.
3. The eccentricity, $e$, a number less than 1.
4. The inclination of the orbit, $i$.
5. The position of the line of nodes, $\Omega$, the orientation of the orbital plane in space.
6. The position of the periastron, $\omega$, the orientation of the ellipse in the plane.
7. The time of periastron, $T$, is also required, but is not an element. Periastron is the position in the orbit where the two stars are closest together. (Compare this word with perihelion and perigee.)

Of particular interest in the study of double stars is the computation of the total mass of the system from the elements. In Chapter 6, Newton's modification of Kepler's third law was stated and in Chapter 14 it was applied to the determination of the mass of a planet. It can be used in the same form to determine the combined mass of the two components in a binary star.

Let $m_1$ and $m_2$ be the masses of the two stars.

Then
$$m_1 + m_2 = \frac{A^3}{P^2} \qquad (19\text{–}1)$$

where $A$ is the semimajor axis in astronomical units and $P$ is the period in years. Since the semimajor axis is given in the list of elements in seconds of arc, if the parallax of the star is known,

$$A = \frac{a''}{p''} \text{ astronomical units} \qquad (19\text{–}2)$$

or rewriting equation 19–1,

$$m_1 + m_2 = \frac{a^3}{p^3 P^2}. \qquad (19\text{–}3)$$

The total mass is expressed in solar masses.

▶*Example:*  The period of Sirius is 49.9 years; $a = 7.67''$; and $p = 0.374''$. Compute the total mass of the system.

From equation 19–3,

$$m_1 + m_2 = \frac{(7.67)^3}{(0.374)^3(49.9)^2} = \frac{(20.5 \text{ a.u.})^3}{(49.9 \text{ yr})^2}$$

$$= \frac{8615}{2490} = 3.46 \text{ solar masses.}$$

Now if the center of mass of the two stars can be found, the ratio of their masses can be found from the relative size of the orbits of each star and the individual masses can be computed. Fortunately, this can be done in some cases, including Sirius. The binary nature of Sirius was first discovered when the bright star's proper motion was found to be a curve instead of a straight line. This is shown in Figure 19–3, where the curves due to the proper motion of each component are shown. The ratio of the heights of the two curves is inversely proportional to the ratio of the masses, which by measurement is found to be 2.5. Hence,

$$m_1 = 2.5\, m_2$$

and $2.5\, m_2 + m_2 = 3.46$ from the previous example.

Hence    $3.5\, m_2 = 3.46$

and    $m_2 = 0.99$

and    $m_1 = 2.5 \times 0.99 = 2.47$

both in terms of the sun's mass. This is one of the fundamental methods of determining the masses of stars.

To continue the story of Sirius: The existence of the less massive star was predicted from the curved proper motion of the bright star. It was found visually in 1862 by Alvin Clark while testing the objective for the 18-inch refracting telescope now at the Dearborn Observatory of Northwestern University in Evanston, Illinois. The magnitude is $+ 8.5$, 10,000 times fainter than its bright sister. This makes

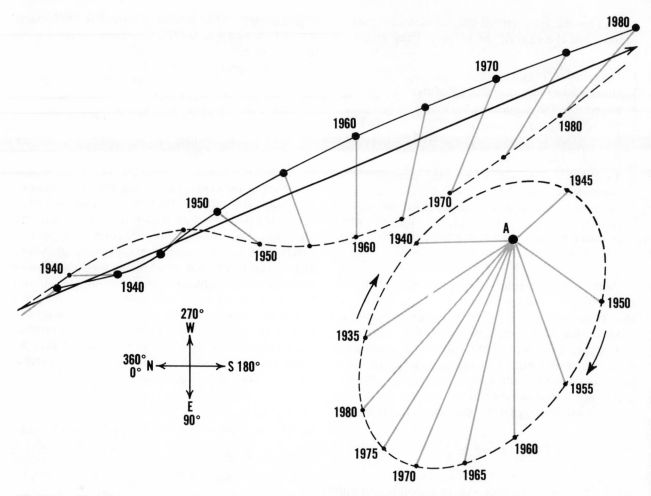

Fig. 19–3   The proper motions of Sirius A and B. The heavy curved line is for Sirius A, the dotted line for Sirius B, and the heavy, straight line represents the motion of the center of gravity of the pair.

it very difficult to observe except when the two stars are near apastron. The spectral type of the faint star was finally measured—an extremely difficult observation.

By methods previously discussed, the diameters of the two stars can be found from their absolute magnitudes and spectral types. The data are listed in Table 19–1. The companion of Sirius, Sirius B,

was the first white dwarf to be discovered.

The most complete catalog of visual double stars was published in 1932 by Robert G. Aitken of the Lick Observatory. It lists 17,180 pairs of which relatively few have yet been observed long enough to show orbital motion. Aitken's card catalog is still kept up to date at the observatory. Some 23,000 stars are now known to be double.

TABLE 19–1
**Summary of Data for Sirius**

| | Brighter Star Sirius A | Fainter Star Sirius B |
|---|---|---|
| Apparent Visual Magnitude | − 1.43 | + 8.5 |
| Absolute Visual Magnitude | + 1.4 | + 11.5 |
| Spectral Type | A1 V | wd (A5) |
| Temperature | 10,500°K | 8,700°K |
| Diameter (sun's diameter = 1) | 1.71 | 0.024 = 1/42 |
| Mass (sun's mass = 1) | 2.47 | 0.99 |
| Density (sun's density = 1) | 0.50 | 73,000 |
| Density, g/cm³ | 0.65 | 96,000 |

## 19.3 Spectroscopic Binaries

The spectra of most stars are made up of single absorption lines shifted toward the red or blue from their normal positions by the Doppler effect. The shift is caused by the component of the star's space motion in the line of sight, as discussed in Chapter 17. An exception to this is the bright component of the visual double star, Mizar (Zeta 2 Ursae Majoris), which is in the handle of the Big Dipper. In 1889 E. C. Pickering at Harvard found that the lines in the spectrum of this star are alternately single and double. (See Figure 19–4.) This was the first spectroscopic binary star to be discovered. The interpretation is as follows.

The bright component of Mizar is composed of two stars which are equally bright. They move around a common center of mass in orbits of approximately equal size and shape ($e = 0.54$). The orbits are in a plane which is directed toward the sun, but inclined at an angle of about 50° to the "plane of the sky," which is a plane at right angles to the line from the sun to the star. The period of revolution is 20.54 days and the orbital velocities measure up to 69 km/sec. However, because of the tilt of the orbits, their actual orbital velocities are about 90 km/sec.

When one of the two bodies is approaching the earth, the other is receding. Thus their lines are shifted in opposite directions by amounts which are large enough to permit them to be seen separately. Five days later, both are moving at right angles to the line of sight and the two sets of lines are superposed. Five days later still, the lines are again separated. Thus they are alternately double and single.

The lines of a spectroscopic binary can be seen double if the velocities are large enough, and if the two stars are not too different in brightness. If the magnitude difference is greater than about one magnitude, the lines of the fainter star are covered up by the continuous spectrum of the brighter star. If there is only one spectrum visible, the binary nature of the system can still be detected, because the one visible set of lines is seen to shift back and forth in

Fig. 19–4 Two spectra of the double-line spectroscopic binary star Mizar. (Yerkes Observatory photographs)

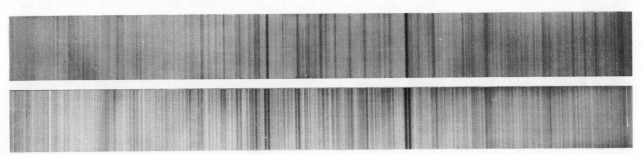

the period of revolution of the brighter star (and also the fainter one) about the center of mass.

The angle of inclination cannot under ordinary circumstances be determined. A fast moving star will show the same amount of shift, if the angle of inclination is small, as a slower moving star with large inclination. The inclination of Mizar was determined by a special study with a stellar interferometer. The student is referred to an advanced text on astrophysics for an explanation of this method. If the binary happens to be also an eclipsing binary, the angle of inclination can be found.

### 19.4  Eclipsing Binaries

If the orbital plane is directed almost exactly toward the earth, the two stars of a spectroscopic pair will obviously line up with the earth twice during each revolution. The light from the more distant star will be cut off by the nearer one. Such a star is called an *eclipsing binary*.

When the two stars in an eclipsing binary are equally bright, one-half the light of the system is lost to us when one star is exactly behind the other. This decrease in brightness, equal to 0.75 magnitude, is easily detected visually. When one star is completely behind the other, the eclipse is said to be total. Partial and annular eclipses are defined in the same way as corresponding eclipses of the sun.

If the two stars are equal in size, a total eclipse can last for only a few seconds. This is not likely to happen, since the orbital inclination must then be exactly 90°. If the stars are unequal in size, however, and the angle is near but not necessarily exactly 90°, the total phase can last longer and the light will be constant for that length of time. Between the time when the eclipse begins (first contact) and the beginning of totality (second contact) the farther star is partially eclipsed. The eclipse ends in the reverse order. Between two total eclipses, usually but not always halfway, the smaller star is projected onto the disk of the larger star and the eclipse is annular.

Usually the plane of the orbit is not directed exactly toward the earth and, if eclipses occur, they are partial only. Total eclipses are more rare than partial eclipses, but they are more important since they give the astronomer more information about the system. During a partial eclipse the light decreases gradually to a minimum and then returns immediately to normal at the same rate as during the decline. The light loss can range from a small amount, detectable only by the most sensitive equipment, to deep eclipses of about four magnitudes. No case is known in which the fainter star is completely dark.

The computation of all the elements in an eclipsing binary star is complicated because of the numerous factors involved. For a complete solution, it is necessary that spectroscopic observations be added, that the lines of each component star be visible in the spectrum, and that the eclipses be total and annular alternately. In the most favorable cases, the inclination of the orbit, the size, mass, density, and distance apart of the two components can be found, along with other minor data. For partial eclipses, only approximate solutions can be made. Some of these will now be discussed.

First of all, the nature of the eclipses can be determined by the appearance of the light curves. (See Figure 19–5.) In the case of AR Cassiopeiae (usually the three-letter abbreviation of the constellation is used) the minima are flat at the bottom, indicating total and annular eclipses. But which is which? Only a closer inspection of each eclipse can give the answer. The deeper eclipse (primary eclipse) of AR Cas is annular and the shallower (secondary eclipse) is total. This cannot be determined from this figure because of the small scale. A detailed light curve shows that the secondary is flat and the primary eclipse is rounded at minimum. This is because the smaller star is completely hidden at secondary, while the larger star is darker at the limb than at the center and the loss of light continues during the annular phase as the smaller star moves across its disk.

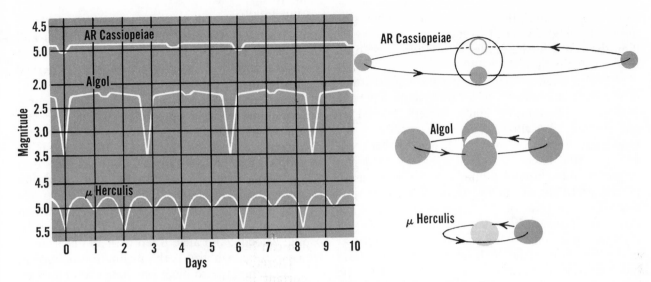

Fig. 19–5   Light curves of three eclipsing binary stars. An explanation of the type of eclipse is shown at the right. The size of the stellar components and their distances apart are drawn to scale.

The two stars are spheres, because the maxima are also flat. Compare the curve of AR Cas with the lower curve for Mu Herculis. In the latter case, the maxima are rounded at the top because the stars are elongated toward each other by tidal attraction and the light varies continuously as the stars move around in their orbits presenting areas of different size toward the earth.

In the case of Algol, the light curve rises between primary and secondary. This is a reflection effect. The darker companion is behind the brighter star and reflects light in the direction of the bright star, which is toward the earth at the middle of the secondary eclipse, as the drawing shows.

In addition, the eclipses of Algol and Mu Herculis occur at equal intervals. This is not true for AR Cas, which has a longer interval from primary to secondary than from secondary to primary. This shows that the orbits are elliptical and of course the velocity increases from apastron to periastron. The orbits of Algol and Mu Her are circular.

The duration of totality or of the annular phase compared to the duration of the entire eclipse permits the relative size of the stars to be determined. In AR Cas the diameter of the smaller star is only 40 or 50 percent of that of the larger. Because of the shallow eclipses, this determination is uncertain. The bright star is about 60 percent as bright at the limb as at the center. There is no evidence of a reflection effect or of tidal distortion. The larger star is about the size of the sun and the smaller star is about half that. The fainter, smaller star is nearly four magnitudes fainter than its companion and so there is no possibility of photographing its spectrum. Therefore, the mass and density of each cannot be calculated accurately.

Algol was the first eclipsing star to be discovered. The name means the demon star, and it is represented on old star maps as the head of the Medusa held in the hand of Perseus. (See the star maps at R.A. 3$^h$; Decl. +40°.) Algol loses nearly two-thirds of its light every 2.87 days. The eclipses, which are partial, last about eight hours. The changes of brightness are observable with the unaided eye, provided the observer knows when primary eclipse occurs. The two stars are slightly larger than the sun with the fainter a little larger than its brighter companion.

The problem of determining the temperatures of the faint components of eclipsing stars has been assisted by observations made through colored filters. Figure 19–6 shows light curves made at the University of Wisconsin through the standard yellow and blue filters. Since the telescope used is a refractor, the ultraviolet filter could not be used. (Ultraviolet light will not go through a glass objective.) The spectrum of the faint component of RZ Cas is too faint to show, but the depths of the two minima (yellow and blue) show that the fainter star is slightly cooler than the brighter. If the two stars had the same temperature, they would be the same color, there would be no change of color during the eclipses and the light curves would have the same depth. As the curves in Figure 19–6 show, the eclipses are partial and there is a slight darkening at the limb.

Another eclipsing star studied at the University of Wisconsin, with a reflecting telescope, shows light losses of four magnitudes in ultraviolet, three magnitudes in blue, and only two magnitudes in yellow

Fig. 19–6   Light curves of the eclipsing binary star RZ Cassiopeiae through a yellow and a blue filter. The light loss is expressed in magnitudes in the vertical scale. The time scale at the bottom is in decimals of the period, which is $1^d$ $5^h$. The eclipse is partial. (Light curves by Charles M. Huffer)

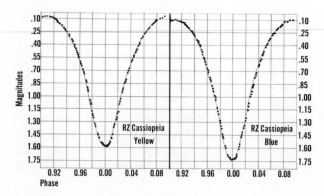

light. In this case, since the fainter star is in front during totality, its spectrum can be obtained and the spectral type determined. It is listed in the catalogs as G5, which is in agreement with the observed change of color. The brighter star is A0.

All eclipsing binary stars are also spectroscopic binaries, but this can be verified only if they are bright enough for their spectra to be observed. Methods are available by which the elements of these stars can be determined by the solution of a complicated mathematical formula. Among the elements is the inclination of the orbit, $i$. This angle cannot be found for spectroscopic binaries which are not also eclipsing binaries. The semimajor axis, orbital velocity, and mass is left with an uncertainty which can be removed if the inclination is known.

Therefore, the study of eclipsing stars has been important in the investigation of star diameters, masses, and densities. Putting together the data found from studies of all favorable cases of binary stars, a curve (Figure 19–7) has been drawn, which shows that there is a relation between the mass and luminosity of the stars. This curve shows that the brightest stars have the most mass. That is, it is the mass of a star that determines the amount of energy which it can generate. This curve is called the *mass-luminosity relation*. It is assumed that all normal stars conform to this relation. However, there are some stars, particularly the white dwarfs, which do not, as the figure clearly shows. Most of the main sequence stars conform, but about 10 percent do not. Fortunately, most of them can be identified by some peculiarity in their spectra.

### 19.5   Summary of Results

From studies of visual binaries and spectroscopic binaries, including eclipsing stars, the following results have been noted:

1. The periods range from $4^h$ $39^m$ for an eclipsing star in Nova Herculis 1934 to thirty years for some spectroscopic binaries and to probably thousands of years for the longest visual binaries. The short-period stars are too close together to be separated visually. The velocities of the short-period stars are great enough for the lines to be separated when

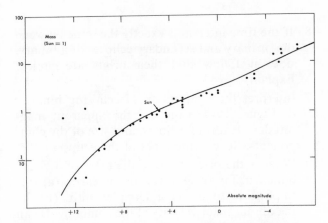

Fig. 19–7 The mass-luminosity relation. The three points to the left of the curve represent white dwarf stars, which have more mass than normal for their luminosities.

two spectra are visible. The components farther apart require longer periods of time to complete their revolutions. Thus there is no essential difference between visual and spectroscopic binaries, except the amount of separation.

2. There is a continuous increase of period from eclipsing to visual binaries. Most eclipsing stars have periods of less than ten days, because the probability of an eclipse decreases as the separation increases. The short-period spectroscopic binaries have the highest velocities, because the components are so close together their orbital speeds must be high to keep them from colliding. The shortest period for a visual binary is about five years. Only three or four eclipsing binaries with periods near thirty years have been discovered.

3. The eccentricities vary from zero for the shortest periods to about 0.9 for the longest period visual binaries, increasing gradually with lengthening periods. Only a few eclipsing binaries with eccentricities different from zero are known.

4. The orientations of the orbits in space seem to be completely at random.

5. Most binaries have both components on the Main Sequence. However, there are visual binaries which have white dwarfs as the fainter components. The two parts of eclipsing binaries are usually about the same size, mass, and luminosity, although in about 3000 cases it would be expected that all combinations are possible. At least one case is known where the larger star is 40 times the diameter of the smaller one. Their magnitudes are also nearly the same, but a difference of at least four magnitudes is not uncommon.

6. Triple stars are usually composed of two close companions and one widely separated component. Algol, for instance, has an eclipsing pair with period less than three days and a third (and maybe a fourth) star orbiting the other two in more than one year. Another more recent discovery has been that two or three visual binary orbits show short-period motion superposed on the elliptical orbit. This is similar, but on a much different scale, to the proper motion of the bright component of Sirius. In one visual binary case, 61 Cygni, the variations have been attributed to the perturbations of a third body which is orbiting one of the two stars in the visible pair. This body must have a mass about 1/60 the mass of the sun. The period is about five years, compared to 720 years for the two bright stars. This mass is too small to generate sufficient energy for the star to be luminous, so it is an invisible companion. It might be called a planet, since its mass is about sixteen times that of Jupiter.

It is now possible to compare the sun with the other stars. The data come from many sources: photometry, spectroscopy, mathematical and physical studies, particularly from pairs of stars. It is evident that the sun is an average star in almost all respects. To simplify the comparison, the data are collected in tabular form (Table 19–2). The entries for the maxima and minima of the stars are approximations only.

TABLE 19–2
**Comparison of the Sun and the Stars**

|  | The Sun | The Stars (Maximum) | (Minimum) |
|---|---|---|---|
| Apparent Magnitude | −26.7 | −1.42 | ? |
| Absolute Visual Magnitude | +4.87 | −10 | +19 |
| Spectral Type | G0 | O5 | I |
| Temperature (effective) | 6,000°K | 85,000°K | 1,000°K |
| Color | Yellow | Blue | Infrared |
| Luminosity | 1 | 1,000,000 | 1/400,000 |
| Diameter | 1 | 3,000 | 1/400 |
| Mass | 1 | 50 | 1/20 |
| Density (g/cm$^3$) | 1.31 | $10^6$ | $10^{-10}$ |

## QUESTIONS AND PROBLEMS

1. Do both stars of a binary necessarily have the same period? Why?

2. Can the mass of a star be determined if it has no companion?

3. Do spectroscopic or visual binaries have shorter periods? Why?

4. Show by a diagram why the probability of an eclipse decreases as the separation of a binary increases.

5. The total mass of a binary system is six solar masses. Star A is twice as far from their center of motion as star B. Compute the mass of each star.

6. Assume the two components of a binary system to be too close together to be detected visually. Under what conditions could they be detected (a) spectroscopically only, or (b) by light intensity measurements only?

7. By means of a diagram show why the minima of a light curve have flat bottoms when caused by total or annular eclipses, but are rounded when caused by partial eclipses.

8. If the time interval is exactly the same between the primary and secondary eclipses of a binary, does it follow that their orbits are circles? Explain.

9. Interpret the light curves of eclipsing binaries in Figure 19–5. Compare the apparent magnitudes, depths of eclipses, and size of the components. Specify the types of the eclipses.

10. What is the orientation of the orbit of a visual binary if, for an observer on the earth, (a) it is impossible to detect a Doppler shift, (b) the maximum space velocity of the components can be measured by the Doppler shift, and (c) the maximum space velocity of each component is equal to its tangential velocity?

11. Star A of an eclipsing binary has a temperature of $12,000°K$ and half the diameter of star B, whose temperature is $6000°K$. What is the percentage decrease in brightness when star A is directly (a) in front and (b) in back of star B? **Ans:** (a) 5 percent.

12. The period of the visual binary 70 Ophiuchi is 88 years. Its parallax is $0.199''$ and its semimajor axis is $4.6''$. Compute the total mass of the system. **Ans:** 1.5 solar masses.

# Chapter Twenty

# Star Clusters and Nebulae

Newton's law of gravitation explains why binary stars stay together. A third or fourth star, also held by gravitation, may be added to a binary. In addition there are entire groups of stars, called *star clusters,* which are close together in space. Their common bond is also gravitation, or they may be moving together like the Ursa Major cluster discussed in Chapter 17, which is a cluster of stars with parallel proper motions.

There are several recognized types of clusters, which range in number of stars from loose aggregates of a few stars to vast collections of stars too numerous to count in even the largest telescopes. The following classes are recognized:

TABLE 20–1
**Types of Star Clusters**

| Class | Example |
|-------|---------|
| 1. Moving clusters | Ursa Major cluster |
| 2. Open clusters | Pleiades |
| 3. Globular clusters | M13 the great cluster in Hercules |
| 4. Star clouds | Milky Way in Sagittarius |
| 5. Star associations | Entire group of O and B stars in the constellation Orion |

## 20.1 Moving Clusters

The first moving cluster to be discovered was a naked-eye group of stars in Taurus, near the first-magnitude star Aldebaran—a V-shaped cluster called the Hyades. Like the Ursa Major cluster, it was discovered by the common proper motions of its members, which will eventually carry them to a point east of Betelgeuse. This cluster contains at least 150 members, is some 30 light years in diameter at its densest part, and is now 130 light years from the sun. It is also classed as an open cluster.

Another moving cluster is in Scorpius, the Southern Cross, and Centaurus. The stars have small proper motions and small parallaxes. In Scorpius the average distance is 360 light years and in the Southern Cross is 217 light years. Beta Centauri, Antares, and Spica (in Virgo) belong to this group, which is about 900 light years in its longest dimension.

Moving clusters stay together for a long time and after they reach the vicinity of their convergent point will be seen as open clusters.

The parallax of a moving cluster can be found, if the position of the convergent point is known, provided the proper motion and radial velocity of any one star are accurately known. The formula in equation 17–5, is, after being rewritten:

$$p = \frac{4.74\ \mu}{T\ (\text{km/sec})} \qquad (20\text{--}1)$$

where $p$ is expressed in seconds.

▶ *Example:*  For a certain star in the Hyades, the following data are given: $\mu = 0.115''$; the angle between the star and the convergent point, $\theta = 29.1°$; the radial velocity, $V = 38.6$ km/sec. The tangential velocity $T$ can be found from the equation

$$T = v \sin \theta \qquad (20\text{--}2)$$

and the space velocity $v$ from the formula,

$$v = V \sec \theta \qquad (20\text{--}3)$$

where,    $$v^2 = V^2 + T^2. \qquad (20\text{--}4)$$

**Substituting** in equation 20–1,

$$p = \frac{4.74 \times 0.115''}{21.4\ \text{km/sec}} = 0.025''.$$

The cluster is therefore 40 parsecs away. Its tangential velocity from equation 20–2 is 21.4 km/sec and its space velocity from equation 20–3 is 44.2 km/sec.

### 20.2  Open Clusters

Open clusters, as the name suggests, are groups of stars which are far enough apart to be easily resolved in the telescope (Figure 20–1). They are now usually called galactic clusters, because they are in or near the Milky Way, now called our galaxy.

The Pleiades, or the Seven Sisters, is the best known example of an open cluster. Six stars (or nine under the most favorable observing conditions) are visible to the unaided eye. With binoculars perhaps 25 are visible and with a telescope it is estimated that there are 250 members ranging from 3rd to

Fig. 20–1   An open cluster in the constellation Libra, photographed with the 200-inch telescope. (Photograph from the Mount Wilson and Palomar Observatories)

14th magnitude. The cluster is embedded in nebulous material, which is not visible to the eye, but can be seen on a long-exposure photograph, such as Figure 20–2, or detected with a photocell. This material is not self-luminous, but either reflects light from nearby stars or radiates by fluorescence. These two processes depend on the distance and temperature of the stars. The stars in the Pleiades are of spectral class B, and the nebulosity is of the reflection type, probably composed of dust. The Pleiades cluster is also classed as a moving cluster.

There is a double cluster in Perseus, designated as $h$ and Chi Persei. Its distance is about 9,000 light years. Another open cluster is the Praesepe, or Beehive, cluster in Cancer. Still another is in the faint constellation Coma Berenices (Bernice's Hair) near the Handle of the Big Dipper. The open clusters vary in size from 20 members to more than 1000. Some of the galactic clusters have common motions which are often opposite to the direction of motions

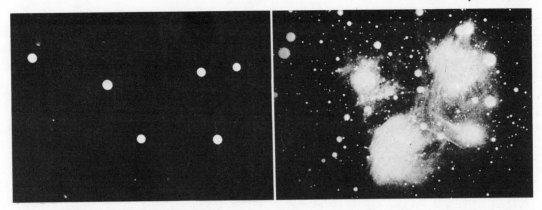

Fig. 20–2   An extra-focal photograph of the Pleiades, an open cluster, showing the brightest stars (left). A long-exposure photograph (right), showing the nebulosity around the Pleiades stars. (Yerkes Observatory photographs)

of nearby fields of stars. It has been suggested that they will not always stay together, but will be broken up by gravitational attraction as the stars move in different directions. About 900 open clusters are known in our galaxy.

The distances of open clusters can be found if they are also moving clusters, as in the case of the Hyades. The diameters can be found when the distances are known. The diameters range from about 10 to 40 light years, but the stars on the borders of a very populous cluster may be as much as 50 light years from the center. The star density in the neighborhood of the sun is about one star per 14 cubic parsecs. Or it may be computed as one star per 11 cubic parsecs, if the components of double stars are included. These figures may be verified from the table of the nearest stars (Table 17–1). The density of stars in open clusters range from about 1 to 80 stars per cubic parsec.

For clusters which do not show measureable proper motions, it is more difficult to determine the distances. Fortunately, there is a way of determining distances even if the clusters are too distant to use the proper motion method. In the H-R diagram the most conspicuous feature is the main sequence. In the main sequence the stars are arranged by absolute magnitude and spectral class, or temperature. The spectral classes cannot be obtained if the stars are too faint. But temperature also determines the color of a star. With sensitive photographic and photoelectric photometry, the color index of a star may be determined. When the color index is plotted against visual magnitude, as in Figure 20–3, a line similar to the main sequence on the H-R diagram is obtained. Assuming that it is a main sequence, that the absolute magnitude of the sun is $+5$, and that its color index is 0.60 (see Chapter 17, page 251), the scale of the color-magnitude may be fixed. From this information the distance can be found, as shown in the following example.

▶*Example:*   In Figure 20–3, the apparent magnitude of a star with color index $+0.6$ is 15. Substituting in the formula, $M = m + 5 - 5 \log d$; $+ 5 = 15 + 5 - 5 \log d$ and $\log d = 3$. Thus $d = 1000$ parsecs or 3260 light years.

The color-magnitude diagrams of open clusters (Figure 20–4) also show stars off the main sequence. The hypothetical curve $A$ is similar to the actual diagram for $h$ and Chi Persei, which bends toward the right at the top of the main sequence, and a branch of supergiant red stars ($A$ upper right). Other curves bend at lower points on the main sequence and have giant branches to the right (curves $B$ and

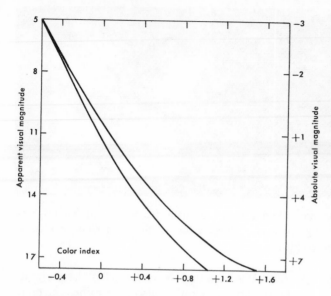

Fig. 20–3  Color-magnitude diagram for a typical hypothetical open star cluster. The main sequence of its component stars should lie inside the band outlined by the curved lines.

*C*). This is interpreted as due to the evolution of the stars. In cluster D, the faint stars are off the main sequence. It may be that these stars are still in the process of contracting from interstellar matter.

Hot giants and supergiants combine their hydrogen atoms into helium at much higher rates than the cooler stars of class F, G, and K. The turn-off points are therefore interpreted as those phases in the evolution where the stars have developed hot helium cores and are expanding into the giant stage. This was briefly discussed at the end of Chapter 12. In modern terminology, the stars are leaving the main sequence. The stage of evolution is more rapid from left to right than in the stage where the stars move up along the main sequence. Hence there are fewer stars in the giant branch and there are corresponding gaps in the H-R diagram. These regions in the diagram were originally called the Hertzsprung gap.

Cluster A has more stars of spectral class B than the other two. These hot stars are burning their hydrogen at a rapid rate. Since cluster A does have type-B stars, it must be younger than clusters B and C, which have lost their hot stars. The turn-off point for stars of one solar mass is about where the C-branch leaves the main sequence. The stars on this diagram are all Population I stars. The broken line shows a similar branch for Population II stars found in globular clusters.

## 20.3  Globular Clusters

The stars in globular clusters are much more numerous and closely packed than in open clusters. (See Figure 20–5.) Thirty thousand stars have been counted in the great cluster in Hercules in the outer regions. The density in the center is so great that it cannot be resolved even in the 200-inch telescope. There must be at least 100,000 stars in a typical cluster of this type.

There are several ways in which the distances of globular clusters can be determined. In the nearer

Fig. 20–4  Composite H-R diagram for four hypothetical open star clusters, *A*, *B*, *C*, *D*. The globular star clusters are composed of stars lying along line *E*.

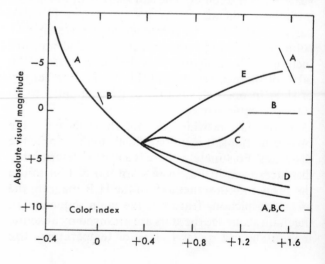

Fig. 20–5   The globular star cluster. Omega Centauri. (Harvard College Observatory photograph)

and larger clusters, individual stars in the outer regions can be photographed. Many of these stars are found to be variables of the RR Lyrae, or cluster variable, type. Their absolute magnitudes are about zero; but there is a possibility that the scale might need further revision, possibly from zero to +0.5. If this is the case, the distances of these clusters may be decreased by a factor of 1.26. Still another correction is necessary. If a cluster is located behind a cloud of dust or gas, and many of them are located near the Milky Way where such clouds are found, the cluster stars are actually brighter than they appear to be.

▶*Example:*   In M13, the cluster in Hercules, the modulus, $m - M = 14.8$. The correction for absorption, $K$, is 0.4 magnitude. The formula for the computation of absolute magnitude must be written:

$$M = m + 5 - K - 5 \log d \qquad (20\text{–}5)$$

or
$$5 \log d = m - M - K + 5. \qquad (20\text{–}6)$$

For M13,
$$5 \log d = 14.8 - 0.4 + 5 = 19.4$$

$$\log d = 3.88$$

and
$$d = 7,600 \text{ parsecs} = 24,800 \text{ light years.}$$

A second way of determining distances is similar to the color-magnitude method for open clusters. (See Figure 20–6.) In this figure, the stars are

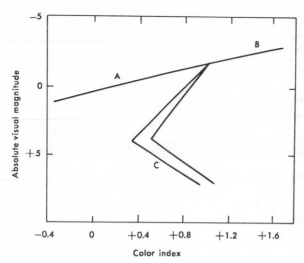

Fig. 20–6 Typical color-magnitude diagram of a hypothetical globular cluster. *AB* is the giant branch of the H-R diagram. *C* is the main sequence. The stars are of Population II. Existing telescopes cannot reach the fainter stars.

all of Population II and there are no young stars. This method requires the matching of the main sequence and also of the giant branches. These methods lead to an average absolute magnitude for this type of cluster. The average can then be assumed and substituted in equation 20–5 and the distance calculated. This will of course be an approximate distance. The apparent magnitude can be measured by photography with short-focus cameras, which make the image of a cluster as small as that of a bright star to which its magnitude is compared. Or even better, the total light of the cluster can be measured with a photocell and compared with that of a nearby bright star. Then the magnitudes, with a correction for space absorption, *K*, can be used for *m* in equation 20–6.

The absolute magnitudes of globular clusters range from about −5 to −9, averaging −7. The modulus is this figure subtracted from the apparent magnitude. The average globular cluster is 12 magnitudes brighter than the sun; that is, the average luminosity is 60,000. The brightest globular cluster is about 400,000 times brighter than the sun.

After the distances have been computed, it is possible to compute the size, if their angular diameters can be measured.

▶ *Example:* M13 has an angular diameter of 18′. Assuming its distance as 24,800 light years from the previous example,

$$\frac{d}{D} \times 3438' = x'$$

from equation 11–3, adapted to this problem. Here $R = D =$ distance; $d =$ linear diameter; and the angular diameter has been substituted for $p$, the parallax.

**Substituting:**

$$d = \frac{18' \times 24,800 \; l-y}{3438'} = 130 \text{ light years} = 40 \text{ parsecs.}$$

The dense center, where the stars cannot be seen separately, is about 20 light years in diameter.

Assuming that all globular clusters are about the same size, their distances can be computed by measuring their angular diameters and reversing the above formula. The distances range from about 15,000 to 200,000 light years, although there are two clusters known to be 400,000 light years distant. They may not be members of our group of globular clusters.

Most of the globular clusters are located alongside the Milky Way. They usually appear as spheres, but some are slightly flattened by rotation. About 120 are known, but there are probably others behind the thick parts of the Milky Way. None is within 4° of the *galactic equator*, the central line (a great circle) of the Milky Way, because the light of any cluster in that direction would be totally absorbed by clouds of gas and dust in space.

A normal globular cluster has a spectrum much like the low-dispersion spectrum of the sun, and the color of a cluster away from the Milky Way is about the same as the color of the sun. Clouds of gas absorb blue light more strongly than they do red light. Therefore a cluster behind a gas cloud is redder and also dimmer than one where there is no material to interfere with the light. Clusters at some distance from the Milky Way, say 30° or 40°, are free from absorption and are yellow. Nearer the Milky Way the clouds of gas and dust increase in thickness and the clusters are redder and fainter, until their light is completely absorbed and none gets through. The difficulty in allowing for the absorption correction is that the clouds are not of uniform density and it is necessary to measure the amount of absorption as near the direction of each cluster as possible.

The globular clusters form a nearly spherical system whose center is in the constellation Sagittarius, which is located at the center of the galaxy (see Chapter 21). Their motions indicate that they are moving independently about the center in highly flattened elliptical orbits with periods of hundreds of millions of years. It is thought that they come in close to the center of the galaxy and pass through regions thick with stars, gas, and dust. There is little probability of colliding with stars, but the gas particles in the clusters collide with the gas and dust in space and are swept up in the encounter. This may account for the fact that the globular clusters contain only Population II stars.

With knowledge of the size of globular clusters, it should be possible to calculate their densities. However, the stars are so close together at the centers that it is impossible to count them. It is known that the number of stars increases greatly toward the center, with the central density something like 100 times the average. That is, there may be as many as 1000 stars per cubic parsec at the center.

The sky would indeed be very spectacular, if we could see it from the center of such a cluster. The stars would be ten times closer together than in our sky; they would therefore be 100 times brighter. There would be nearly 6000 first magnitude and 1 million sixth magnitude stars. There would be no obscuring material, and no Milky Way. There would be plenty of room for the stars to move around. Collisions would be infrequent, if not impossible. But the perturbations during close approaches would be very difficult to compute!

## 20.4   Star Clouds and Associations

Star clouds are so called because the stars are so numerous and close together that they look like luminous clouds. The brightest clouds are located in the constellations Sagittarius and Scutum in the densest regions of the Milky Way. They are probably visible only because the clouds of gas and dust in the Milky Way, which are dense enough to hide the globular clusters, have open regions which permit us to see the stars behind. It is likely that the Milky Way has other star clouds which are hidden as are the globular clusters.

The star clouds apparently have greater densities than the open clusters, but are far less densely populated than the globulars.

It has been known for many years that the stars of classes O and B are not scattered at random, but occur in groups mostly in the Milky Way. The Russian astronomer, V. A. Ambartsumian, proposed that these stars are physically related and gave them the name *associations*. About 80 are known which contain between 10 and 100 stars.

The most striking and first recognized association is in Orion. This association is 1600 light years distant and 400 light years in diameter. In the Orion region are large clouds of material, which are faintly visible in long-exposure photographs. (See Chapter 1, Figure 1–1.) Since the association stars are all at the same temperature, they are also about the same age. It is assumed that they were formed from clouds of dust and gas in the region at about the same time. Since they are hot, they convert their hydrogen to helium at a fast rate and must be fairly young—a mere few million years.

In Orion there are certain variable stars, called T Tauri stars, which are also young and hot. In fact, several stars have been discovered which were not found on previous photographs of the same area of the sky. They are thought to have formed recently.

There are other associations, for example in the Scorpius-Centaurus cluster, in Lacerta, and in Perseus, which are also young and very much like the Orion association.

TABLE 20–2
**Summary of Star Clusters**

| | Globular | Open | Associations |
|---|---|---|---|
| Number known | 119 | 867 | 82 |
| Location in galaxy | Halo and Nucleus | Arms | Arms |
| Diameter | 25–120 parsecs | less than 10 parsecs | 30–200 parsecs |
| Mass (sun = 1) | 10,000–100,000 | 100–1000 | 100–1000? |
| Number of stars | 10,000–1,000,000 | 50–1000 | 10–100? |
| Color of brightest stars | Red | Red or blue | Blue |
| $M$ (absolute visual) | −5 to −9 | 0 to −10 | −6 to −10 |
| Stars per cubic parsec | 0.5 to 1000 | 0.1 to 10 | less than 0.1 |
| Examples | Hercules, M13 | Pleiades | Orion |
| | Omega Centauri | Hyades | Perseus |
| | | Praesepe | Scorpius, Centaurus |

(Adapted from Abell: *Exploration of the Universe.*)

Most associations lie in the Milky Way where there is star streaming. That the stars are moving in streams was first discovered by J. C. Kapteyn, a Dutch astronomer, in 1905, and is now known to be a result of the rotation of the galactic system. The relative motions of the association stars and the general field stars in the Milky Way tear any group of stars apart in less than 100 million years. The effect on an association is to stretch it out along the Milky Way. Two or three stars have been found which are moving away from each other and from Orion. If they were originally part of the association, they have been in motion only 2,500,000 years, a figure which is in agreement with recent theories of evolution of stars and the short lives of the O and B stars.

Table 20–2 is a summary of our knowledge of star clusters.

## 20.5   Nebulae

In the eighteenth century a French astronomer, Charles Messier, was trying to discover new comets. He was bothered by immovable objects which looked like comets and which he was continually "discovering." He therefore decided to make a list of these objects and in 1781 published a catalog which is still referred to. Messier's catalog listed over 100 objects, which were called nebulae. The word nebula comes from a Latin word meaning clouds, mist, or vapor. But Messier included star clusters and other objects, which today are called galaxies, as well as true nebulae. We have previously mentioned M13, the globular cluster in Hercules. This is the 13th object in Messier's catalog. The Great Nebula in Andromeda, now called the Andromeda galaxy, is M31. The Pleiades cluster is M45 and the Great Nebula in Orion is M42.

In 1890, Messier's list was combined with several others in a book called the *New General Catalog* (NGC), which was later continued under the name *Index Catalog* (IC). The NGC or IC number is used today in referring to all but the most familiar objects. M31 is also NGC 224. In recent years, the number of photographic objects of these types has increased so rapidly that new discoveries are no longer numbered, but located on star charts, such as the *Palomar Sky Atlas* and others.

The spectra of the three classes of "nebulae" made it necessary to revise the designations. A star cluster is easily recognized. The spectrum of a cluster is much like the spectrum of the Milky Way, if both are taken with a low-powered spectrograph. That is, they have continuous spectra crossed by dark lines. Objects formerly called spiral nebulae also show this kind of spectrum, are therefore rec-

Fig. 20–7 The Horsehead Nebula in Orion, an example of a dark nebula. (Photograph from the Mount Wilson and Palomar Observatories)

ognized as collections of stars, and are now called galaxies. The true nebulae, such as M42, have either bright-line spectra or reflect the spectra of nearby stars, possibly with some bright lines. They are now recognized as gaseous objects, not collections of stars. The luminous gas around the stars in the Pleiades cluster satisfies this definition of a nebula.

There are three kinds of nebulae: bright, dark, and planetary. There is no essential difference between the first two classes. If a gas is near a bright star, it is luminous—a bright nebula. If there is no star near, the nebula is dark and can be "seen" only because it is silhouetted against the bright stars or gas in the background. The best example of a dark nebula is the Horsehead Nebula in Orion (Figure 20–7). It will be noticed that the upper part of the photograph of this nebula contains bright nebulosity, while the lower part seems to be devoid of stars, those which are visible being foreground stars, in front of the dark gas. This nebula appears to be completely opaque to light. The bright part is illuminated by the bright stars in Orion. Both classes belong to a larger classification called *diffuse nebulae.*

The ability of a star to illuminate a mass of gas depends on its brightness and its distance from the gas. For example, a supergiant of absolute magnitude $-5$ can illuminate gas at a distance of about 30 light years. A star as faint as the sun is effective only to a distance of one-fourth of a light year, much farther than the limits of the solar system, but well short of the distance of the nearest star.

If a star is cooler than class B1 (about 20,000°K), the light of the star is reflected by the gas and the spectrum of the nebula is that of the spectrum of the star. A good example is the nebulosity around the Pleiades. If the star is hotter than 20,000°K, the nebula shows bright lines typical of a gas under low pressure. In this case, we know that the density of the gas is a million million times less dense than the earth's atmosphere at the surface of the earth. Thus the atoms are very far apart and do not interfere much with each other, as is the case in stars. The gas absorbs energy from the nearby hot star, stores it for a very short time (a microsecond), and then reradiates it in the natural frequency of the gas. This is called fluorescence. A good example is the Orion nebula, which has a bright-line spectrum and is associated with hot stars of class O and B. About 30 elements have been identified in the Great Nebula. (A 3-hour exposure with the 100-inch telescope is shown in Figure 20–8.)

At first some unidentified lines in nebular spectra were attributed to an unknown gas called *nebulium*. These lines are now known to be similar to the lines in the solar corona and are due to doubly ionized oxygen and neon and singly ionized oxygen and nitrogen. The strong lines in the green are responsible for the colors of nebulae. There are also strong lines in the blue and in the red, but they do not affect the color very much, since the human eye is more sensitive to green and yellow light than to the other colors. Weak lines due to other elements are also found in the brighter nebulae.

There are some dark nebulae in the Milky Way. In the constellation Cygnus and running toward the south, the Milky Way appears to split into two parts. The western part fades and almost disappears in Ophiuchus, but reappears again in Scorpius. This apparent split is called the Great Rift. In two areas, dark regions are found which are almost completely devoid of stars. The northern one is in the constellation Cygnus (also called the Northern Cross), the southern one is near Crux (the Southern Cross). They are so black in contrast with the bright areas that they are called Coalsacks. It is a coincidence that they are found near the two crosses.

Barnard at the Yerkes Observatory was among the first to photograph the Milky Way. In certain

Fig. 20–8   A 100-inch telescope photograph of the Orion Nebula, an example of a reflection nebula. (Photograph from the Mount Wilson and Palomar Observatories)

Fig. 20–9   A portion of the Milky Way in Cygnus, showing the Great Rift. (Photograph from the Mount Wilson and Palomar Observatories)

THE ANDROMEDA GALAXY is one of the members of the Local Group of Galaxies and is listed as NGC 224 (M31) in Table 22–1. It is slightly larger than our galaxy and has about twice its mass. Both galaxies are spirals of Type Sb. The stars in the arms of M31 are hot and blue and are classified as Population I. That is, they are young stars still embedded in masses of dust and gas. This interstellar material is evident as black streaks where it obstructs the light of the stars behind it. The nucleus (center) is composed of Population II stars. That is, they are yellow and red and are older than the stars in the arms. The large spiral is accompanied by two smaller galaxies, NGC 205 and NGC 221 (M32) of Type E5 and E3, respectively.

The six reproductions on this and the following pages are among the first color photographs made with the 200-inch Hale telescope and the 48-inch Schmidt telescope on Palomar Mountain. They were made in 1959 by Mr. William C. Miller, staff research photographer of the Mount Wilson and Palomar Observatories.

THE ORION NEBULA is a mass of interstellar gas, which is excited to fluoresence by hot stars embedded in the nebula, and which have probably evolved from the gas. The blue color is mostly light emitted by ionized oxygen; the red light is due mostly to hydrogen. The central region of the nebula appears green through the telescope, but has been overexposed in the photograph to show the fainter outer parts. A dark nebula obscures some of the light in the lower part of the photograph.

THE CRAB NEBULA is the remnant of a supernova, first observed in A.D. 1054. Most of the white light is emitted by high-speed electrons spiraling in the nebula's magnetic field (synchrotron radiation). The light from the outer filaments is emitted mostly by hydrogen.

THE NORTH AMERICA NEBULA resembles our continent because of a chance arrangement of bright and dark nebulae. The reddish color is due mostly to hydrogen. Intervening dust filters out most of the blue light. The stars superposed on the nebula in the photograph are foreground stars, which are between the earth and the nebula. The stars and the nebula are members of our galaxy.

THE VEIL NEBULA IN CYGNUS is a gaseous nebula which seems to thread its way through a dense part of the Milky Way. This nebula is only a small part of the diffuse remains of a supernova, which is still moving away from a central point. Its light is probably due to the collisions between atoms in the leading edge and other particles in space.

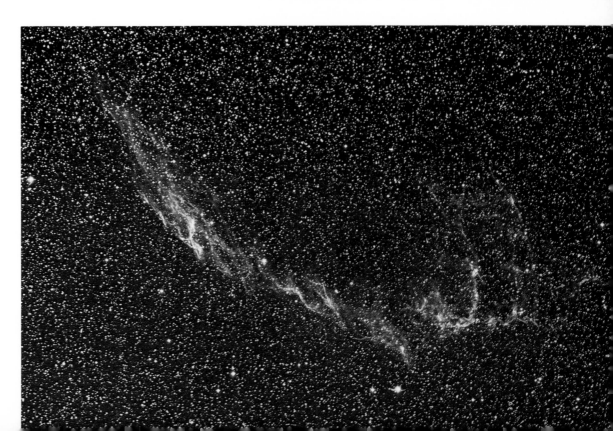

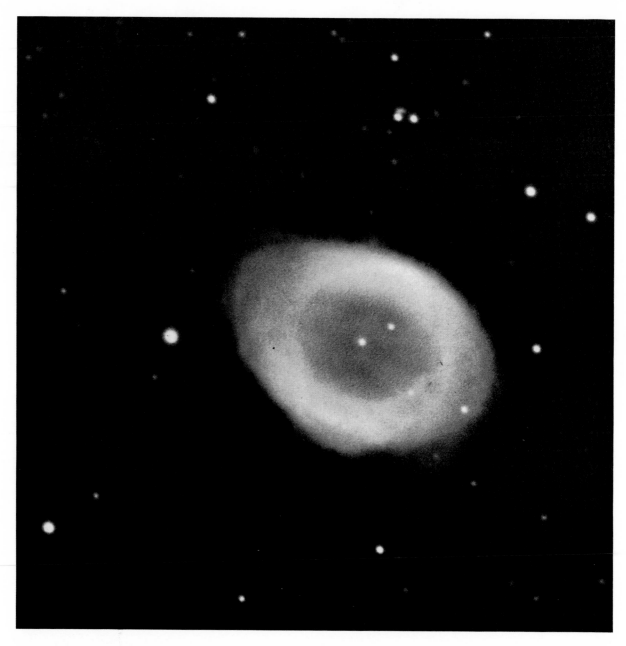

THE RING NEBULA IN LYRA forms a series of colored rings around a blue star in the center.
This planetary nebula is a sphere, rather than a ring. It is so thin that stars can be seen through it.
The gases at different distances from the parent star are excited to glow at different wavelengths, depending on the amount of energy they receive. The eye is unable to perceive the changes of color
shown in the photograph. Mr. Miller worked with a group of experts in color photography before
achieving these historic results.

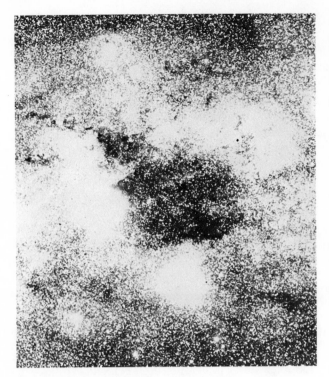

Fig. 20–10 The region of the Coalsack in Cygnus. (Yerkes Observatory photograph)

areas other dark regions were once thought to be holes between the stars where the observer looked into "the blackness of space." Barnard suggested that these "holes" are regions where the light of distant stars is absorbed by invisible clouds in space. His work was continued and extended by Frank Ross, also of the Yerkes Observatory. The dark areas are now called dark nebulae. The Great Rift can be traced across Figure 20–9 and some of Barnard's dark nebulae can be found on Figure 20–10.

## 20.6 Interstellar Dust

Robert Trumpler at the Lick Observatory investigated the open clusters and noticed that while they all seem to be the same size, the stars are not all the same brightness. He also noticed that stars are redder in certain areas than in others. This discovery led him to suspect that there are clouds of obscuring material in addition to Barnard's dark nebulae. This work was followed by two-color photoelectric photometry by Joel Stebbins and his associates at the Washburn Observatory in Wisconsin and at the Mount Wilson Observatory in California, and later by others using three-color photoelectric measures.

The technique in colorimetry (the accurate measurement of color) is to measure the amount of starlight which passes through a colored filter. If two or more filters are used, the color index of a star may be determined. (See Chapter 17.) If stars of class B are observed (the spectrum determines the class) these stars can be seen and identified to distances of perhaps 1000 parsecs. The nearby stars and those well away from the Milky Way are blue, as is normal for class B, and their color indices are a little less than zero, as listed in Chapter 17. However, as the Milky Way is approached, the colors become redder and the color indices are positive until, in some regions of Sagittarius, the B-stars are as red as K-stars. This is because the blue light is absorbed and scattered more strongly than the other colors and the red light gets through. This is similar to the reddened color of the sun at sunrise and sunset, but of course the stellar reddening takes place out in space. The reddening effect of the earth's atmosphere is allowed for in computing color indices. By this method, clouds of absorbing material are located other than those already mentioned.

The difference between the measured color index of a star and the normal color index of an unreddened star of the same class is called its *color excess.* The color excess determines whether or not the star's light is selectively absorbed in its journey through space. It has been found that the total absorption is roughly three times the color excess, if both are expressed in magnitudes. This is the correction term $K$ used in finding the distance to a star cluster. (See equation 20–5.)

The result of studies by photography and by

photoelectric photometry is that clouds of obscuring materials are found concentrated in the plane of the Milky Way. The stars near the sun and at some distance from the galactic equator are assumed to have normal color indices, but there is some evidence that the sun itself is in a region not entirely free from obscuring matter. The stars would be about twice as bright as they are now, if the sun were in dust-free space.

The discovery of black globules, which had also been photographed by Barnard, led to the dust-cloud theory of evolution of the solar system, which has been discussed in Chapter 16.

Near the beginning of the twentieth century, J. Hartmann, a German astronomer, in his studies of spectroscopic binary stars of class B, found that the lines of calcium did not show the changes of velocity as the other lines in the spectrum did. He also found that these lines are sharper than the others. It was decided that the calcium atoms absorbing those particular wavelengths were not in the stellar atmospheres, but in clouds of calcium atoms between the stars and the earth. Other similar clouds in space were detected by Otto Struve and others at the Yerkes Observatory. The lines in the violet region of the spectrum are produced by singly ionized calcium. The density is very low, resulting in very sharp lines. Other atoms identified are sodium, potassium, and even iron. It is also possible that molecules of hydrocarbon (CH) and cyanogen (CN) are present at very low densities and in small quantities. Also some of the stationary lines may be produced by shells of gas around binary stars.

In some stars there are bright lines in addition to the absorption spectra. Many of these lines are narrow, but in some stars they are broad. If one side of the star is coming toward the earth, the other must be receding because of the star's rotation. Hence the lines are broadened by a Doppler effect, the speed of rotation being as high as 200 km/sec in some cases. When the lines are sharp, the pole of rotation is turned in the direction of the earth and the Doppler effect is not present.

## 20.7   Planetary Nebulae

There is a subclass of O-type stars called Wolf-Rayet stars for the two men who discovered them. The class designation is W. About 200 of these stars are known. They are among the most luminous of all stars (novas and supernovas excepted) with absolute magnitudes $-4$ to $-8$. They are also very hot with temperatures estimated between $50,000°$ K and $100,000°$ K. Their spectra consist of greatly broadened, diffuse lines of highly ionized helium, nitrogen, oxygen, silicon, and carbon, with absorption lines on the violet side of each. A few W-stars are components of binary systems.

One explanation of the physical nature of the W-stars is that there is a central star about 1.5 to 2.0 times the diameter of the sun, which is surrounded by a semitransparent atmosphere about three or four times larger. The velocities indicate that this atmospheric shell is expanding away from the star, since the absorption lines, produced by the atmosphere between the star and the earth, have Doppler shifts indicating high velocity. It has been suggested that the envelope has been ejected from the star with velocities as high as 1000 km/sec.

Other stars show evidence of similar shells. At times the star Pleione in the Pleiades has shown bright lines which later disappeared. The shell may have been blown away by the radiation pressure from the intense heat. The bright star Deneb in Cygnus shows similar bright lines.

A few binary stars are known to have envelopes of gas. Probably the best known example is Beta Lyrae, an eclipsing star with a period of 12.9 days. The two components are elongated toward each other by tidal attraction and there are streams of gas being exchanged between them. The entire system is surrounded by a disk of diffuse gas which rotates around the center of mass of the binary system. It is estimated that the more massive and brighter star is losing mass at the rate of about $\frac{1}{6000}$ of the mass of the sun per year. Since its total mass is about 50 solar masses, the total mass

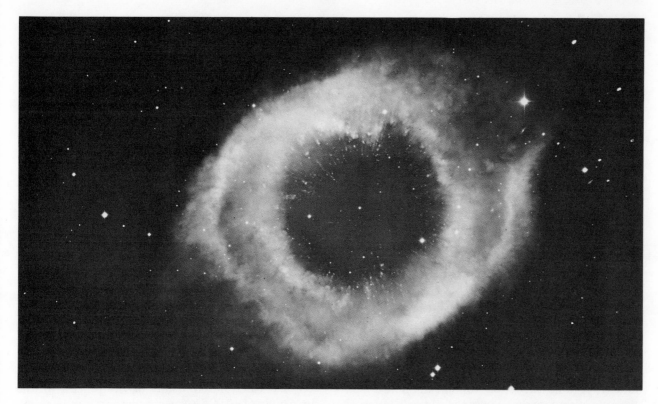

Fig. 20–11   The planetary nebula NGC 7293, photographed in red light with the 200-inch telescope. (Photograph from the Mount Wilson and Palomar Observatories)

would be lost in 300,000 years. However, it is probable that the mass loss will continue only until the two stars have equal masses.

It is quite obvious that many stars, which appear to the eye to be single, uninteresting stellar bodies, are actually double or multiple with complicated atmospheres which are in violent motion.

A group of short-period eclipsing stars consists of pairs which are small and close together. They are known as W Ursae Majoris stars, because W UMa was the first of this type to be discovered. The period of W UMa is only eight hours and the surfaces of the two stars are nearly touching. They are thought to be embedded in nebulosity. The two stars are nearly equal in size and brightness, but not

in mass, so there is an exchange of material between the two.

It is evident from this discussion that the size of stellar envelopes varies from the smallest pairs of the W UMa type to the large ones like the W-stars and on to the envelopes around novas and supernovas. The largest shells of gas are found in the planetary nebulae. The name is intended to suggest that they have visible detail, but not that they are like planets. The best known example is the Ring Nebula in Lyra, Figure 8–4. The largest in angular diameter and the nearest is NGC 7293 in Aquarius, Figure 20–11. This is the only planetary whose parallax has been determined. It is 85 light years distant and appears about half as big as the moon.

It is very diffuse and difficult to see and is not listed in Messier's catalog, so he must have missed it.

About 500 planetary nebulae are known and there must be thousands of others which have not yet been photographed. They vary in size from NGC 7293 to small star-like objects which can be recognized as nebulae by the bright lines in their spectra. The greenish color results from the strong lines of doubly ionized oxygen in the green region of the spectrum. These lines are emitted by gas at extremely low density. The density of planetaries is estimated to be only about 10,000 atoms per cubic centimeter.

The planetary nebulae vary from about 20,000 to 200,000 astronomical units in diameter—several hundred times the diameter of the orbit of Pluto. Since the parallaxes cannot be measured directly, it is necessary to use indirect methods to determine their distances and diameters. The statistical study of their proper motions and radial velocities show them to be very distant and probably associated with stars of Population II. If the number of atoms in a unit volume can be estimated from the spectrum, and the volume calculated from the diameters measured on photographs, combined with distance, the mass of the atmospheric shell can be calculated. The average is about 0.1 or 0.2 the mass of the sun.

Inside the nebular shell is a star, probably in all cases, although the star is sometimes too faint to be seen. The nature of the central star in NGC 7293 is fairly well known. Its absolute magnitude is only +9.8. Its blue color indicates that it is a star of spectral type O. Since it is much fainter (330,000 times) than the usual O-type star, it must be a very hot white dwarf. Its size can therefore be computed by the usual method. Its diameter is only 1/60 that of the sun and its density 300,000 times the density of water! The ionization of oxygen in the nebular shell is caused by the intense ultraviolet radiation from the star. This nebula is probably typical and is a stage in stellar evolution in which a white dwarf is produced by the explosion of a nova.

From the number of known nebulae of this class, it has been estimated that three stars per year in our galaxy become planetaries and three planetaries become white dwarfs. Thus in 5 billion years —the estimated age of the solar system—15 billion white dwarfs have been produced. This is not an unreasonable figure, since the white dwarfs are too faint to be seen at a distance of more than a few parsecs, and must be very numerous.

One final object should be mentioned, since it is receiving a great deal of attention from radio astronomy observers. The Crab Nebula (M1 in Taurus) has been classed as a planetary nebula, but the motions in its gaseous envelope are much greater than in the typical planetary. It is known to be expanding outward at a rate of some 1300 km/sec. From this rate of expansion, it has been identified as the expanding shell around the supernova of 1054, which was brighter than Venus and was visible for two years. Its distance is about 1300 parsecs. Photographs of the Crab Nebula in four colors are reproduced in Figure 18–6.

There is a white dwarf at the center of the Crab Nebula, which may possibly be the remains of the supernova of 1054. Its surface temperature has been given by Rudolph Minkowski, formerly at the Mount Wilson and Palomar Observatories, as 500,000° K; its diameter about twice that of the earth; luminosity 30,000; and density 135,000 times the density of water. The mass of the nebulosity is not accurately known, but it is probable that the star was almost completely blown apart by the explosion, having ejected a mass of material equal to the mass of the sun.

Radio waves from the Crab Nebula have been detected. Their wavelengths are those expected, if the lines are produced by electrons spiraling at nearly the speed of light in a magnetic field. The source of the magnetic field is still a mystery. This nebula is occulted by the moon. It was used to study the refraction of light by a possible lunar atmosphere.

## QUESTIONS AND PROBLEMS

1. How does the spectrum of nebular light reflected from nearby stars differ from that due to fluorescence?

2. List the possible sources of error when determining the distance to a cluster by means of the color-magnitude diagram.

3. How does the modern definition of the term nebula differ from that used by Messier? Why did Messier include such diverse objects in his catalog under the heading of nebula?

4. Why do the Wolf-Rayet stars show bright-line spectra, whereas most stars show dark-line spectra?

5. How would the motions of the stars of a small moving cluster appear to an observer on the earth if the stars were moving in parallel paths, if (a) they were moving directly away from the sun; (b) directly toward the sun; (c) at right angles to the direction of the sun?

6. What is the diameter of a globular cluster that (a) is 20,000 parsecs from the earth and has an angular diameter of 15', and (b) one which is 30,000 parsecs from the sun and has an angular diameter of 5'? **Ans:** (a) 280 light years.

7. If there are 1000 stars per cubic parsec in the center of a globular cluster, what is their average distance apart? (Hint: Assume the stars to be uniformly spaced throughout a cube, one parsec on each side.) (b) How many suns could be placed between two adjacent stars, if the suns were touching each other? **Ans:** (b) 2,200,000.

8. If the average absolute magnitude of the stars in the faintest cluster listed in Table 20–2 (Total $M = -5$) is $+5$, show that the cluster should contain 10,000 stars.

9. The apparent magnitude of an RR Lyrae star in M13 is 14.8. Its absolute magnitude is 0 and the correction for absorption, $K$, is 0.4 magnitude. (a) What is the ratio of brightness corresponding to the absolute and apparent magnitudes after correction for absorption? (b) Compute the distance.

10. In the color-magnitude diagram of a cluster it is found that the apparent magnitude of main sequence stars of color index 0 is $+11$. Find the absolute magnitude of these stars from the H-R (spectrum-luminosity) diagram (to the nearest whole number) and compute the distance to the cluster.

11. Compare the diameter of the central star in NGC 7293 to that of the usual star of its spectral class.

# Chapter Twenty-one

# The Galaxy

## 21.1 The Milky Way System

In Chapter 8 attention was called to the use of the word galaxy, derived from a Latin word meaning milk. The term galaxy, sometimes the Milky Way Galaxy, is now used to designate the great system of stars of which the sun is a part. We on earth are inside this system. The various kinds of stars and nebulae which compose it have been defined and discussed in previous chapters. Now we shall examine in more detail their locations and motions, and consider the galaxy in its entirety. Then we shall continue with similar collections of stars and other material, which are also called galaxies.

In order to describe the location of objects with respect to the Milky Way, and, particularly during the twentieth century, to study the distribution of stars and other objects, a great circle has been drawn on the celestial sphere which follows the center line of the Milky Way as nearly as possible. This great circle is called the *galactic equator*.

The galactic equator is inclined to the celestial equator at an angle of 62°. It reaches declination +62° at right ascension $0^h$ $49^m$ in the constellation Cassiopeia, and declination −62° at right ascension $12^h$ $49^m$ in the Southern Cross. The distance in degrees from the galactic equator to any point on the celestial sphere, measured on a perpendicular great circle, is called the *galactic latitude*.

*Galactic longitude* is a second coordinate on the galactic equator. It was formerly measured along the galactic equator from its intersection with the celestial equator of 1900 at right ascension $18^h$ $44^m$. Now the zero point of galactic longitude has been moved farther south to the former longitude 327.7°, at the center of the galaxy, which will be defined later in this chapter. Galactic longitude is now measured from this point, toward the north, to the perpendicular great circle through the point in question. The poles of the galaxy, which are points 90° from all points of the galactic equator, are $12^h$ $49^m$; +27.4° and $0^h$ $49^m$; −27.4°.

The Milky Way passes through the following constellations, from north to south: Cassiopeia, Cepheus, Cygnus, Sagitta, Aquila, Serpens, and Sagittarius, all of which are visible from the northern hemisphere in the summer. Continuing toward the south and below the horizon are Scorpius, Centaurus, Crux, and Vela. The greatest star density is

Fig. 21–1   A composite photograph of the Milky Way. The galactic center is in Sagittarius with the Great Rift to its left. Auriga is at both ends. (Lund Observatory, Sweden)

in Sagittarius and Scutum, where the great star clouds are located. Figure 21–1 is a composite of the Milky Way with the star clouds near the center. The Great Rift is shown extending from Cygnus to Sagittarius.

It can also be seen from Figure 21–1 that the western branch, the upper side of the figure, disappears to the left of center. This is the region of the constellations Ophiuchus (above) and Scutum (below). The dark areas are produced by absorption by the dark clouds mentioned in Chapter 20. It will also be seen in the figure that the number of stars decreases greatly from the equator to the poles, which are at the top and bottom of the figure. Also, the number decreases towards the constellation Auriga at each side. A point 180° from the galactic center is the *anticenter*. The Milky Way is widest

in Sagittarius and Scorpius (about 40° wide) and narrowest in Auriga. The galactic center was fixed at R.A. 17$^h$ 42$^m$; Decl. −29° by the International Astronomical Union in 1958.

## 21.2   Early Investigations

The first systematic attempt to investigate the structure of the galaxy was made by Sir William Herschel, who made star counts—he called them gauges—for nineteen years and published his results in 1785. He divided the sky into star fields and counted the stars in each. His "universe" is reproduced in Figure 21–2. Herschel did not know any stellar distances. Since he observed in England, he could not see very far below the celestial equator. He located the sun near the center—shown by the

Fig. 21–2    The universe of Sir William Herschel. The sun is represented by the heavy dot to the left of center.

large dot slightly to the left of center on the diagram. The split in the Milky Way is shown to the right. He did not explain what he meant by the large dots around the edges, but perhaps intended them to show the positions of the globular clusters, which lie along the edges of the Milky Way.

Herschel counted stars in 683 selected fields and obtained star densities running from 1 to about 600. These gauges show the galactic concentration, if the galaxy is considered to be a flat disk with the sun near the center. The number of stars is much greater if one looks to the right and left of the sun, rather than up and down. This work was continued in the southern hemisphere by his son, Sir John Herschel, who took his father's 20-foot-long telescope to South Africa. These two men could have counted 200 million stars with their large (48″) 40-foot telescope instead of the smaller instrument. The planet Uranus was discovered with the 20-foot (18″) telescope, which Herschel preferred to the larger one because it was easier to operate.

The star gauges were made by the Herschels visually, before the invention of photography. Star counts have been continued from photographs made in various parts of the sky. One difficulty with counts is the obscuration by dust and gas clouds in space. As was pointed out in Chapter 20, these clouds increase in density toward low galactic latitudes. The fact that there are no globular clusters visible between 4° north and south galactic latitudes shows that the clouds are so dense that they are perfectly opaque. There are undoubtedly other globular clusters on the far side of the Milky Way.

Also, the color excesses of stars increase from north to south along the galactic equator. The clouds of dust and gas are not uniformly distributed, but are most dense in the Great Rift and near the Sagittarius region. As the galactic latitude increases the color excess decreases, though not uniformly. Therefore the K-term used in Chapter 20 must be determined for each area separately. When all corrections have been made as accurately as possible, the result is that the galaxy is considered to be a system of about 100 billion stars and a nearly equal mass of interstellar gas and dust.

One estimate is that one-third of the mass of the galaxy is in the form of gas, which is mixed with dust. Hydrogen is the most abundant element in the clouds, with helium second. For every 20 atoms of hydrogen, there is 1 atom of helium. Because helium is four times heavier than hydrogen, about one-fifth of the clouds is helium by mass. The dust, which might be called an impurity in the gas, makes up about 1 percent of the total mass of the clouds.

The ratio of the number of stars in a unit area on the galactic equator to the number in a unit area at the galactic poles is called the galactic concentration. This ratio varies with the magnitude of the stars counted. The figures, before correction for absorption, are as follows:

| Photographic Magnitude | Galactic Concentration | Visible with |
|---|---|---|
| 5.0 | 3.4 | naked eye |
| 9.0 | 3.9 | 1″ telescope |
| 15.0 | 10.4 | 16″ |
| 19.0 | 27.0 | 100″ |
| 21.0 | 44.2 | 200″ |

It has been estimated that there are 1 billion stars of visual-magnitude 20; and, because most stars have positive color index, about one-half as many of photographic-magnitude 20. Because of absorption and the fact that the far side of the galaxy cannot be seen, P. J. van Rhijn of Holland estimated the total number of stars in the galaxy as 30 billion, and their combined light as equal to the light of 1092 stars of visual magnitude 1.0. This number is almost certainly too small, as indicated by the computed mass of the galaxy.

If the stars are uniformly distributed in space, and if there is no absorption, the number of stars should increase by a ratio of 3.98 for an increase of one magnitude. This can be shown from the inverse square law of light and the increase in volume of a sphere, which is proportional to the cube of the radius. The derivation is given below.

Suppose all stars were equally bright and uniformly distributed in space. A star twice as far away as another would be four times, or 1.5 magnitudes, fainter. For a difference of one magnitude, the ratio of distance is $\sqrt{2.512}$ or 1.585. Now consider two spheres of radii 1.0 and 1.585. Their volumes are proportional to $(1.0)^3$ and $(1.585)^3$, or 1.0 to 3.98. Therefore if the stars were uniformly distributed, there should be 3.98 times as many in the larger volume. That is, considering stars of each absolute magnitude class, for a decrease of one magnitude, there should be four times as many stars. However, it has been found that the increase in number of stars per magnitude is not 3.98, but between 2.5 and 3.0, depending on the galactic latitude. This indicates that either or both of the assumptions—that the stars are equally bright and uniformly distributed—are false.

Considering the galactic concentration and the increasing absorption towards the galactic equator, the idea grew during the first half of the twentieth century that the galaxy is a disk-shaped collection of stars and nebulous material. The sun is not at the center, but is located at some distance from the center by an unknown amount. By counting the number of stars per unit of area, since the greatest concentration is in the direction of Sagittarius, the galactic center must be in that direction. The distance cannot be determined by star counts alone.

## 21.3  Rotation of the Galaxy

Flattening by rotation is well known. The rapidly rotating planets, Jupiter and Saturn, the ring system of Saturn in particular, the solar system itself with the planets all confined to nearly the same plane, all indicate that the galaxy also must be in rotation, since it is known to be flat. When the Great Nebula in Andromeda was found to be a collection of stars, spiral in form, and in rotation, the theory of rotation of our galaxy was strengthened.

Another hint that the galaxy may be rotating was not recognized at first. The sun's motion among the stars was investigated during the first part of the twentieth century. Sir Arthur Eddington in England studied star streaming. W. W. Campbell in the United States calculated the sun's velocity among the nearest stars. His results gave a velocity of 19.0 km/sec toward a point at right ascension $18^h 0^m$ and declination $+28°$, in the constellation Hercules. As more distant stars were used in the problem, such as O-stars and giant and supergiant variables, a greater velocity for the sun's motion was obtained. When the globular clusters were used, the sun's velocity appeared to be nearly 300 km/sec toward right ascension $20^h 24^m$ and declination $+62°$, in Cygnus.

Many globular clusters are located on both sides of the Milky Way in the region of Scorpius and Sagittarius. Harlow Shapley had determined their distances by the use of cluster variables (RR Lyrae stars) and by their apparent diameters. He concluded that they form a nearly globular system concentric with the galaxy. Before Shapley's study of clusters, the galaxy was thought to be a disk-shaped galaxy about 10,000 parsecs (32,600 light years) in diameter with the sun at the center. Shapley's new galaxy was 75,000 parsecs (245,000 light years) in diameter, with the center in the direction of Sagittarius 20,000 parsecs (65,000 light years) from the sun.

Shapley tried to measure absorption in space by studying the times of minima of eclipsing binary stars in red and blue light. He thought that blue light traveled more slowly in an absorbing medium than red light. Since he could find no difference in the times of minima, he concluded that there is no absorption in space.

This work was soon shown to be in error by Stebbins and his associates, who found that stars are reddened by selective absorption and that the globular clusters are reddened for the same reason.

The correction to the distances of the globular clusters was made and Shapley's galaxy was cut to a diameter of about 35,000 parsecs, since the clusters are not as far away as Shapley estimated. Stebbins described the galaxy as a "ham sandwich" with the absorbing material in the central plane and with a central bulge in the direction of Sagittarius. The sun was placed at about 10,000 parsecs from the center.

The next step was to measure the speed of rotation of the galaxy at the sun's distance. The possibility of a solution of this problem by observations from a moving body inside the galaxy was first pointed out by Bertil Lindblad in Sweden and Jan H. Oort in Holland in 1926 and 1927. They remembered that the ring of Saturn, the planets in the solar system, and the satellites in orbits around the planets all move in such a way that those closest to the centers of attraction move faster than those on the outside. This is in accordance with the law of gravitation. It was therefore suggested that stars closer to the center of the galaxy than the sun should be moving faster than those toward the anticenter.

The idea of differential motion was followed up by J. S. Plaskett and J. A. Pearce at the Dominion Astrophysical Observatory in Victoria, British Columbia. They had measured radial velocities of stars of class B, which are visible to great distances and could be used in this problem.

Suppose that in Figure 21–3 the sun is located as shown with respect to the direction of the galactic center, and that its speed is proportional to the length of the arrow on its orbit. A star on an orbit nearer the center has a greater speed, and one farther away has a slower speed. Consider only radial velocity, the motion of a star toward or away from the sun.

Stars on the same orbit as the sun, either preceding or following, have the same speed and therefore no radial velocity. Those in the direction of the center and those away from the center also have no velocity of approach or recession. Their motions

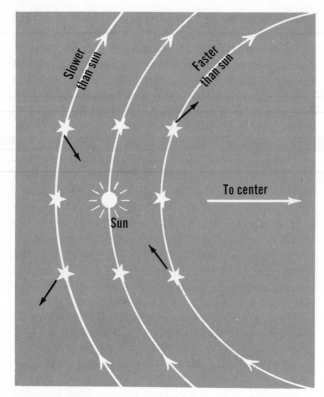

Fig. 21–3   Effects of the rotation of the galaxy on the radial velocities of stars.

are parallel to that of the sun and therefore tangential motions only, not radial. Stars on different orbits and in other directions should be either receding from the sun or approaching, as shown by the black arrows. These radial velocities are small, but measurable. Not only were stellar velocities used, but also lines in the stellar spectra due to clouds of interstellar gas between the stars and the sun.

Since the paper by Plaskett and Pearce was published, there have been other solutions by various people and with different results. The following results are probably as accurate as any available, and we give them here, realizing that at any time there may be a different solution based on more complete and more accurate data.

1. Distance from the sun to the center of the galaxy: 8,300 parsecs = 27,000 light years.
2. Speed of the sun: 220 km/sec = 137 mi/sec.
3. Period of the sun's revolution: 220 million years. This has been called the galactic year.
4. Diameter of the galaxy: 24,500 parsecs = 80,000 light years.
5. Total mass of the galaxy: $2 \times 10^{11}$ = 200 billion suns. It has been estimated that half of this mass is in the form of dust and gas.
6. Thickness of the galaxy: about 2450 parsecs = 8,000 light years.
7. Average density of the galaxy: 1 atom/cm$^3$.

The center of the galaxy lies behind vast clouds of dust and gas and cannot be observed by visual or photographic methods. It is, however, being probed by radio telescopes.

### 21.4   Summary

Before considering the structure of the galaxy in the light of recent observations and theories, it is desirable to summarize the location of the objects which have been described previously, starting from the outside.

The globular clusters form a system which is centered at the center of the galaxy. This system is about 100,000 light years in diameter, but there may be some stragglers at greater distances, or even outside our own system. If it is assumed that the globular clusters are stationary or moving at random, the direction and motion of the sun can be determined. The result is approximately the same as that obtained from observations of stars inside the galaxy and also from nearby galaxies.

The system of globular clusters makes up what has been called the halo or the corona of the galaxy. (See Figure 21–4.) In addition to clusters there are known to be some stars scattered throughout the halo. And radio observations have detected very

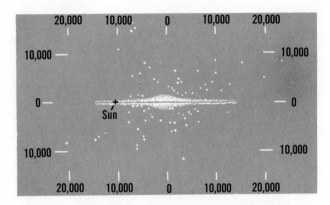

Fig. 21–4   A 1930 diagram of the galaxy, showing the shape of the galactic disk, the central bulge, and the obscuring material in the central plane. The globular clusters, indicated by the dots, are represented as forming the halo.

diffuse gas molecules, but no conspicuous regions of ionized hydrogen.

The Population II stars are associated with the globular clusters and are in regions where the interstellar clouds are lacking or are very diffuse. They are therefore found in the galactic halo and also apparently in the galactic nucleus.

The open clusters lie mostly in the plane of the Milky Way. A few, like the Pleiades and Praesepe, appear to be at some distance from the galactic plane only because they are relatively near the sun. The open (galactic) clusters form a flat system with the sun apparently near the center of those known. Five hundred are known, but there may be many more at greater distances, which are unobservable. Some probably mingle with the dense star clouds and others may be behind the obscuring dust.

The Population I stars are associated with the open clusters and with the interstellar clouds. The idea is growing, and is confirmed by radio observations, that the open clusters, interstellar clouds, and Population I stars lie in spiral arms of the galaxy. This is also in agreement with the structure of other galaxies, particularly the Andromeda galaxy, where the spiral structure is quite obvious. There the dis-

tribution of similar star groups, nebulae, and clusters is along the spiral arms.

Special wide-angle cameras have been developed at the Yerkes Observatory, which can be used to photograph large areas of the sky at one time. When photographs are taken with these instruments on special red-sensitive plates, luminous clouds of ionized hydrogen can be located. These are called HII (ionized hydrogen) regions.

The HII regions are very near hot stars which ionize the gas; that is, each atom is broken down into its proton and electron. This is possible only where there are great amounts of ultraviolet light. The gas shines faintly by fluorescence as a bright, or emission, nebula mentioned in Chapter 20. The density is between 1000 and 10,000 atoms per cubic centimeter, most of which are ionized. The temperature is around 10,000°K. A few of the protons recombine with the free electrons and are then capable of radiating the red H-alpha line during the short interval in which they are neutral and before they are reionized.

HI regions are areas where the hydrogen gas is neutral. It cannot be observed on photographs, but fortunately can be detected by its radio emission. Some of these regions absorb light from hot stars in the background and can be observed by their lines which appear in the stellar spectra, as previously mentioned. There are extensive areas of hydrogen in Orion, Cygnus, and other parts of the Milky Way. They are nearly transparent to light.

The absorption lines of calcium have been mentioned in Chapter 20. Other lines have been found, which have permitted the determination of the abundance of elements in the gas clouds. Many of these interstellar lines are double or even triple, having been shifted in position by the Doppler effect. These lines therefore locate clouds of different velocities and at different distances from the sun.

Dust clouds, on the other hand, are efficient absorbers of light of all wavelengths. Gas absorbs selectively in certain wavelengths and produces the reddening of stars. The Orion nebula is a dust cloud which shines by reflected light. The dark areas in the North America nebula (Figure 21–5) and in others, are opaque clouds of dust. The dust particles are about a wavelength of light ($\frac{1}{30,000}$ to $\frac{1}{50,000}$ in) in diameter and are probably somewhat elongated in shape and aligned by the magnetic field of the galaxy.

The bulge at the center of the galaxy cannot be studied by optical methods, but radio waves penetrate any clouds that lie between them and the sun. The discovery of a wave 21 centimeters long was a tremendous help in radio astronomy. Since it is so much longer than the dimensions of the dust par-

Fig. 21–5  The North America Nebula in Cygnus, photographed in red light with the 48-inch Schmidt telescope on Mount Palomar. (National Geographic Society-Palomar Observatory Sky Survey)

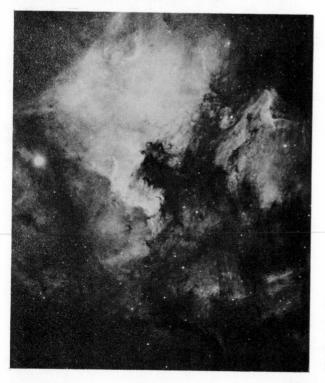

ticles, it goes through a dust cloud without interference and can penetrate the thick parts of the galaxy from the direction of the nucleus.

The 21-cm radiation is a "forbidden" radiation from hydrogen. It comes from regions of space where there are large amounts of material at very low temperature. The atoms are stimulated to radiate at this frequency by collisions with other atoms. This was predicted theoretically by H. C. van de Hulst in Holland in 1944, but was not found until 1951 when radio equipment of sufficient sensitivity had been developed capable of detecting it.

Before the use of radio in this problem, Walter Baade had photographed Population II stars of the cluster variable (RR Lyrae) type and had found them in Sagittarius as far away as 27,000 light years, which placed them at the very center of the galaxy. He therefore concluded that the nucleus is free of dust.

Radio studies at 21-cm wavelength have detected a very turbulent layer of hydrogen, which is 10,000 light years from the center and about 1000 light years thick. It shows velocities between 50 km/sec and 100 km/sec. The density of this turbulent, neutral hydrogen is about 1 atom per 2 cubic centimeters—half the density in the region of the sun. But it must be mixed with ionized hydrogen, which produces the turbulence.

Between this mass of hydrogen and the sun there have been found two separate absorbing clouds moving with different velocities. They have been interpreted as two arms of the galaxy. These arms and others, which have been found by both optical and radio investigations, have been put on a diagram (Figure 21–6) at first by W. W. Morgan and later by others. Our galaxy has been described as a spiral with several arms (possibly five, six, or seven) similar to the Great Spiral Galaxy in Andromeda.

Radial velocities of stars and gas clouds show that the velocities increase toward the center of the galaxy, but that there is a point where the velocity is a maximum of 226 km/sec at a distance of 1800

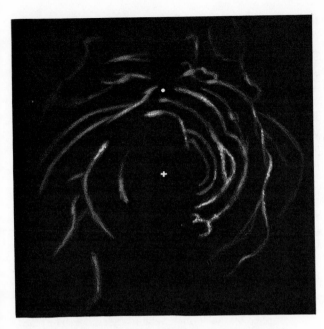

Fig. 21–6 The spiral structure of the galaxy as traced by 21-cm observations in Australia (left side) and in the Netherlands (right side). The galactic center is marked by the cross and the position of the sun by a dot.

parsecs (nearly 6,000 light years) from the center. From there it drops to the solar velocity of 220 km/sec about halfway to the center and decreases still further until a point is reached where the measures are not accurate, about 1500 parsecs from the center. The velocity of escape of a star from the galaxy at the sun's distance is about 310 km/sec. Therefore there are no stars with velocities of 310 − 220 = 90 km/sec with respect to the sun; all stars at that and greater velocities having been removed from the solar neighborhood. The sun is overtaking all stars moving at slower speeds.

In summary, the galaxy is a spiral with several arms. The sun is situated in or near the edge of one of the arms in a region where the interstellar material has already become rarefied. The density in the solar neighborhood is estimated at 1 atom per cubic centimeter. The density of hydrogen between the arms is practically zero.

The spiral arms are estimated to be 1500 light years wide and 3000 light years apart. The density in the nucleus is thought to be seven times the density in the solar neighborhood, where the total mass of gas is equal to the mass of the sun ($2 \times 10^{33}$ grams) per 12 cubic parsecs. The spiral arms lose their identities at the distance of the turbulent hydrogen clouds, 10,000 light years from the center. If this distance is considered to be the outer limit of the nucleus, two-thirds of the total mass of the galaxy is contained in the nucleus. The rotation takes place along the arms toward the nucleus.

## 21.5 Stellar Evolution

There is evidence that the sun has been shining at its present rate for millions, or even billions, of years. But in the few hundred years in which it has been observed scientifically, there is no sign of any significant change. In Chapter 12 a brief history of the past and a prediction of the future of the sun was given, in the view of modern theory. It is thought that the sun is losing mass at a rate of some 4 million tons per second from changes in the nuclei of hydrogen atoms into helium nuclei. This theory is only a few decades old. Now the question arises: Are the stars changing? If so, how fast? How is this accomplished?

Nearly 200 years ago, Sir William Herschel said that studying the evolution of the sun and the stars would be like walking in the forest for an hour. The observer would see trees in all stages of development without seeing a single leaf form, develop, or die. But he would see sprouting seeds, young saplings, small, full-grown, and aged trees, and those which had fallen and were returning to dust. Thus he might be able to form an opinion about the life history of a tree.

In a similar way, if it were possible to observe stars in all stages of formation, development, and aging, and if they could be arranged in a proper sequence, it might be possible to formulate a theory of their evolution. Fortunately, astronomers are now able to do just that, although their theories are still new and in need of testing.

When it was found that a diagram—the H-R diagram—could be drawn which classified the stars in order of temperature, and, later, of size, it was supposed that stars started as large, giant stars of class M, which had formed from nebulae. They were then thought to condense, growing hotter by converting potential energy to kinetic energy by the fall of material toward the center. Finally a stage was reached where they began to cool off, ending their careers first as red dwarfs and at last as dark bodies roaming around in space and unobservable. It was thought that there were a great many dark stars.

Then the mass-luminosity relation (Figure 19–7) was discovered. The most massive stars are the brightest, their masses running to nearly 100 times the solar mass. The less massive stars, with masses down to ½₀ the mass of the sun, were the faint red stars at the lower end of the main sequence. Hence the theory of evolution was modified to state that a red giant remained a giant of increasing temperature, but with decreasing diameter—the mass remaining approximately constant—until it reached the main sequence at a spectral type depending on the amount of mass. That is, a star might evolve into an A-type star or, if it were more massive, into a star of class B or even O. Then it moved more slowly down the main sequence, ending its life as a black dwarf. White dwarfs were stars which exploded because they ran into a small body or a cloud of dust which released internal energy in an explosion.

But it was demonstrated that energy from contraction alone would not account for the amount of radiant energy, and that there must be a source of heat from the interior, probably from the interiors of atoms.

The theory of the production of energy from the conversion of hydrogen to helium was pub-lished by Hans Bethe in 1938. This theory was discussed in Chapter 12 and the calculation of the possible life-time of the sun was computed to be 100 billion years at its present rate of radiation. This method was also applied to other stars and it can be shown that the massive stars of spectral type B (for example with mass equal to 25 solar masses) will use up their atomic hydrogen in a few million years and that the cool M-stars will last much longer than the sun.

With the discovery of black globules in certain bright nebulae (Figure 21–7) and the development of the dust-cloud theory of evolution, the theory now accepted is approximately as follows, with the details omitted here for simplicity:

1. A star begins as a black globule which is being compressed by exterior radiation pressure and finally by

Fig. 21–7    The Rosette Nebula in Monoceros, photographed by the 48-inch Schmidt telescope. The black spots on the bright nebulaosity are dark globules thought to be forming into stars. (Photograph from the Mount Wilson and Palomar Observatories)

internal gravitation. During this stage, it may become a variable of the T Tauri class. This theory is strengthened because of the location of Population I stars in the spiral arms of the galaxy in regions where there are known to be clouds (nebulae and hydrogen clouds with other elements mixed in).

2. When a protostar has attained a central temperature sufficiently high to permit the transformation of hydrogen to helium, it becomes a stable star on the main sequence. Its position depends on the mass of gas it originally had. (See Figure 21-8.)

3. The star will remain on the main sequence, increasing in luminosity and temperature for a long time, again depending on its mass, and in the case of stars with the mass of the sun, probably 10 or 12 billion years. During this stage the star is building up a helium core. The energy radiated by the star is produced by the conversion of hydrogen to helium in the layers above the core.

4. After 10 or 12 percent of the hydrogen is exhausted, the star begins to expand until it reaches the giant stage. In this stage, its luminosity is much greater than that of a star on the main sequence. The core contracts until it reaches a temperature of 140 million degrees Kelvin at which time the helium begins to combine to form still heavier elements. Carbon can be formed and then combines with helium to form other heavy elements. Higher temperatures can be reached in the more massive stars where iron forms when the temperature reaches 3 billion degrees.

5. The star remains in the red giant stage a relatively short time. It then begins to contract and becomes hotter on the exterior. This part of its career has not been worked out very well, but at some stage the star may become a cluster variable (RR Lyrae star) if its mass is right. The star is now a Population II star. Then rather rapidly it crosses the main sequence and blows off its outer layer as a nova.

6. In the final stage, the star becomes a white dwarf, possibly with a planetary nebula surrounding it.

The time scale, as has been noted, depends on the mass. Stage 3, for a star with the mass of the sun, will last some 10 billion years. Stage 4 is shorter, perhaps 1 billion years or a little less. This computation is difficult and quite uncertain. Stage 5 is shorter, from 10 to 100 million years. The white

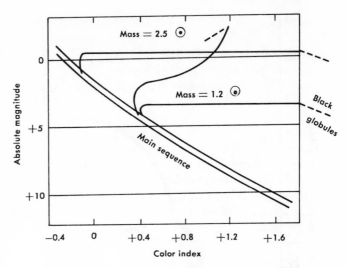

Fig. 21-8   Theoretical tracks in the evolution of stars on the H-R diagram. Numbers above the tracks are masses of the protostars in terms of the sun's mass. Their evolution from black globules is still uncertain.

dwarf stage lasts even longer than all the rest combined—perhaps trillions of years. The galaxy is not old enough yet to produce any black dwarfs.

As a check on the theory, color-magnitude curves have been drawn for several clusters. It is assumed that the cluster stars are all the same age for a given cluster. When the colors, determined by photography and photoelectric photometry, are plotted against absolute magnitude (assuming the distances can be determined), the H-R diagram of the entire cluster or of several clusters at the same time, as in Figure 21-9, can be studied. It is like looking at all the trees in the forest at once. The stars are seen at various stages of their evolution. The point where the curve bends to the right marks the beginning of the stars expansion.

The bright clusters (NGC 2362 and h and Chi Persei) have blue, hot stars. Since the evolution of these stars is much more rapid than any others, these clusters must be very young—only a few million years. M67 is the oldest. The scale gives the

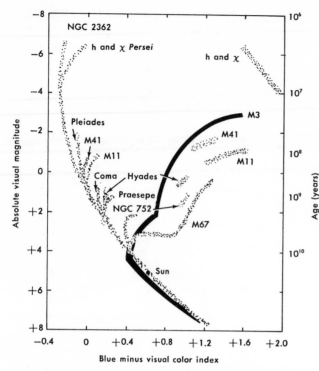

Fig. 21–9  Composite H-R diagram for several star clusters of different ages. (Adapted from studies made by Alan R. Sandage of the Mount Wilson-Palomar Observatories)

approximate age, corresponding to the points where the main sequence of the clusters end. According to this scale, the age of the sun is 5 billion years. Some of the clusters (M11, M41, *h* and Chi Persei) have some stars which are in the giant stage. Probably there are stars in other stages, but they are less numerous and have not been observed. This diagram appears to confirm the theory, since the stars are found in the various stages that had been predicted. Stars at the lower end of the main sequence are too faint to be observed, as are the white dwarfs.

It will be recalled that carbon is one of the elements needed for the carbon cycle of transformation of hydrogen to helium. This element is not produced in the interior of the sun at its present

stage of evolution. So it must have come from outside. Carbon is produced at later stages and is thought to be distributed in space by the explosion of a supernova, which apparently blows a star almost completely apart. The same can be said for iron and other heavy elements known to be present in the sun.

Thus it is now thought that, since the Population I stars are in dusty regions of space, they must have picked up these elements in the formation stages. Therefore the galaxy must be older than the sun. Another source of heavy elements is from binary stars, which are losing mass to each other and to the space around them.

## QUESTIONS AND PROBLEMS

1. Draw a cross section of our galaxy as seen edgewise. Label the center and the approximate location of the sun, as in Figure 21–4. Indicate in light years the approximate radius of the galaxy and the distance of the sun from the center.

2. Why is the Milky Way least dense in Auriga?

3. There are only about half as many stars of photographic magnitude 20 as of visual magnitude 20. Why?

4. If Shapley had been correct in thinking that absorption in space affects the speed of light, what would he have observed about the minima of eclipsing binaries?

5. Is it possible that some of the dark nebulae may eventually become bright? Explain.

6. Why have HI clouds just recently been discovered?

7. Do the most massive, or the least massive, stars have the longer life expectancies? Why?

8. Explain why the stars of a cluster evolve at different rates.

9. (a) During what month is the densest portion

of the Milky Way on the meridian of an observer at 45°N latitude at 9:00 P.M. local time? (b) Is it the same for your latitude? If not, why not?

10. If all stars were equally bright and uniformly distributed in space, how many more 6th magnitude stars should be observable than 4th magnitude stars?

11. Draw a diagram of the celestial sphere showing the galactic equator and poles. Find the inclination of the galactic equator to the celestial equator and to the ecliptic.

# Chapter Twenty-two

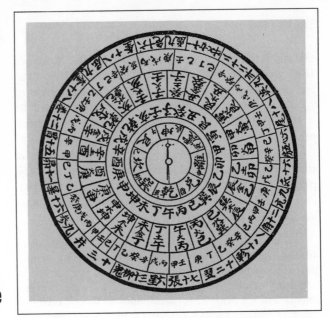

# The Universe

## 22.1 The Andromeda Galaxy

One-third of the objects listed in Messier's catalog of "nebulae" are neither clusters nor nebulae. They have spectra similar to the spectra of globular clusters and the Milky Way, which have been resolved into vast collections of stars. The brightest of these objects, M31, cannot be seen clearly by visual methods. It looks like a diffuse, elongated, faintly luminous area just visible to the unaided eye on a clear, dark sky. But photography soon showed that it is spiral in shape and can be resolved into stars. (See Figure 22–1 and color print.)

The distance to M31 was not determined until 1923 or 1924. The nova that appeared in M31 in 1885 was thought to be similar to the novas in our galaxy, as were others of apparently the same nature. Its visual magnitude was 7.2. Assuming an absolute magnitude of −7, the average for galactic novas, the distance to M31 is only 7,000 parsecs, which is comparable to the supposed distances of stars inside our galaxy as it was known in 1918.

However, Edwin P. Hubble with the Mount Wilson 100-inch telescope photographed cepheid variable stars in M31 and plotted their light curves.

Assuming their photographic magnitudes to be +18, and their absolute magnitudes to be −2 (see Chapter 18), the distance to M31 comes out to be 100,000 parsecs, well outside our galaxy. At this

Fig. 22–1  The Andromeda galaxy M31 and its two companion ellipsoidal galaxies M32 (right of center) and NGC 205 (upper left). 48-inch Schmidt photograph. (Photograph from the Mount Wilson and Palomar Observatories)

distance the absolute magnitude of the nova of 1885 would be −12 and is 100 times brighter than an ordinary nova. Using a modern distance of 800,000 parsecs, the absolute magnitude would be −16.5 and the star would be classified as a supernova.

More accurate studies of cepheid variables in the Andromeda Nebula, as it was called in 1924, placed M31 and M33 at a distance of 270,000 parsecs or 870,000 light years. To quote from a well-known text written in 1927,

> The brightest of them (the cepheids), with periods of 40 days and more, are fainter than the eighteenth magnitude, and the modulus found by comparing their apparent and absolute magnitudes is 22.15, both for the Andromeda nebula and for M33. This corresponds to the gigantic distance of 270,000 parsecs, or 870,000 light-years, and these two are the largest, brightest, and presumably the *nearest* of the multitude of spiral nebulae!
>
> So amazing a conclusion demands confirmation, and there is much additional evidence to support it.†

At a distance of 870,000 light years, the diameter of M31 is about 45,000 light years, since its measured angular diameter is three degrees (3°). M33 is smaller, 16,000 light years. At about the same time, Shapley had proposed a diameter of 250,000 light years for our galaxy, which made it some five times larger than M31.

These estimates were followed by two observations by Stebbins. He showed by the colors of globular clusters that Shapley's galaxy was too large by a factor of two and also that the Andromeda galaxy was about twice as large as measured by Hubble. This was done by scanning M31 with a photoelectric photometer on the 100-inch telescope. M31 and our galaxy were therefore thought to be about the same size. Man was losing his place at the center of the largest collection of stars in the universe!

As has been mentioned in Chapter 18, Baade with the 200-inch telescope looked for cluster vari-

ables in M31 without finding any. If the faintest photographic magnitude in reach of this telescope is +23, cluster variables should have been found, if their absolute magnitudes were the same as those of the cepheids, about $M = -1.5$. Since they were not found, Baade decided that their absolute magnitudes are about zero and that there are two types of cepheids, which differ by about 1.5 magnitudes, or a factor of four in luminosity.

Baade found Population I stars in the spiral arms of M31, where he also found more than 600 emission nebulae. The photographs show dark regions, which he interpreted as absorbing clouds, lying along the arms of which there are at least five and possibly seven. The Population II stars were found between the arms and in the nucleus. The nucleus is transparent and distant galaxies are visible through it and also between the arms. Bright objects along the edges of the galaxy were thought at first to be globular clusters, but many of them turned out to be HI or HII regions. The entire galaxy is rotating with the arms trailing.

The central part of M31 rotates as a single body, but the outer regions rotate in agreement with Kepler's law. Speeds increase to about 1° (45,000 light years) from the center, then decrease as in our galaxy. The inclination of the plane of M31 to the line of sight is difficult to measure, but appears to be about 13°. Therefore, the galaxy is not an oval, but is nearly circular. Several faintly luminous extensions indicate that it is perhaps 130,000 light years in diameter (30 percent larger than our galaxy). There is also evidence of a halo around the central spiral.

## 22.2 Classification of Galaxies

After much discussion, the term *galaxy* has been accepted for these large collections of stars, dust, and gas clouds, which are held together by their mutual gravitation. The terms spiral nebulae, extragalactic nebulae, and island universes were suggested but have now been abandoned.

Hubble classified the galaxies according to shape into the following three major groups.

†Russell, Dugan, and Stewart, *Astronomy,* page 852. Ginn and Company, 1927.

1. *Ellipsoidal galaxies.* They have symmetrical structure ranging from spheres to flattened ellipsoids. Hubble called them E0, E1, . . . E7, where the number divided by 10 indicates the eccentricity of the visible surface. The nearest ellipsoids are resolvable into stars only with large telescopes and with very careful photography. They are made up entirely of Population II stars, the dust clouds having been swept up, possibly by collisions. (Figure 22–2.)

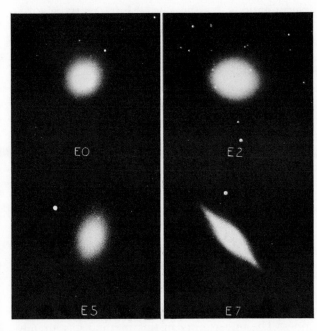

Fig. 22–2  Types of ellipsoidal galaxies, showing variations in the amount of flattening. (Photographs from the Mount Wilson and Palomar Observatories)

Two well-known examples of this type are M32 (E3 type) and NGC 205 (E5 type). They are satellites of M31 and are at the same distance. Their diameters are 8,000 and 16,000 light years, respectively. They can be seen in the photo of M31 in Figure 22–1 and in the color print.

2. *Spiral galaxies.* A spiral galaxy is one which has a distinct nucleus and one or more spiral arms. The arms extend outwards from the nucleus and are composed of stars, dust, and gas. They are made up of Population I stars in the arms and Population II stars in the nucleus, between the arms, and probably in the halo.

There are two distinct classes of spirals, the *normal* and the *barred spirals.* These are further subdivided into Sa, Sb, and Sc for the normal spirals and SBa, SBb, and SBc for the barred spirals. The Sa galaxies have prominent nuclei with small, close-packed arms coming out of the nuclei. The Sb are a little more open with slightly smaller centers. Our galaxy and M31 are Sb spirals. The Sc galaxies have small nuclei and very prominent open arms. The types of normal spirals are illustrated in Figure 22–3.

The barred spirals have elongated centers, called bars, with arms coming from each end. The letters, a, b, and c have the same meaning as for the normal spirals. (See Figure 22–4.) There is no well-known object of this class. The best example is NGC 1300, shown in Figure 22–5.

3. *Irregular galaxies.* As the name suggests, they have no regular shape. They are designated by the letters Irr I, for those with O and B stars and emission nebulae, and Irr II, which cannot be resolved into stars. The best-known irregular galaxies are the two Magellanic Clouds, although the large cloud has been called a barred spiral with one arm.

In Hubble's diagram (Figure 22–6) the E, S, and SB types come together at the point marked S0. This type is flat, like a spiral without arms, which Hubble considered as intermediate between ellipsoids and spirals.

The Magellanic Clouds are the nearest galaxies to ours. The large cloud is in the constellation Dorado at right ascension $5^h$ $26^m$; declination $-69°$. It is $33°$ from the galactic equator and looks like a detached part of the Milky Way, invisible in bright moonlight. (See Figure 22–7.) The distance is somewhat in doubt, but is probably about 160,-000 light years, and the diameter is 30,000 light years. It is composed of both populations of stars, bright-line nebulae (probably planetary), and clouds of gas and dust. The cepheid variables are of the normal, Type I or classical, type. It contains the supergiant star S Doradus, which is the brightest star known ($M = -10$, approximately), except for supernovas. The large radial velocities, about 250 km/sec, discovered about 1915, were surprisingly large. They are of course mostly due to the sun's motion in our galaxy.

Fig. 22–3   Types of normal spiral galaxies, showing the relation between the nuclei and the arms. (Photographs from the Mount Wilson and Palomar Observatories)

The Small Magellanic Cloud is in Tucana at right ascension 0ʰ 50ᵐ; declination −73°. Both clouds are therefore not visible in the United States except Hawaii. The small cloud is 44° from the galactic equator. Its distance is 180,000 light years and its diameter is 25,000 light years. It is composed almost entirely of Population II stars, including the cepheids, which were the first to be used for distance determinations by the period-luminosity relation.

These clouds may be considered as appendages of our galaxy. They apparently are connected by a cloud of hydrogen, which has been discovered by radio astronomy, and may therefore be considered to be a single galaxy. There is also a possibility that they are connected to our galaxy, but so far this has not been proved. They may form a pair of galaxies, which are in rotation about a common center. Even though these two clouds are the closest galaxies to the sun, there is still a great deal to be learned about them.

## 22.3   Distances of Galaxies

Accurate distances to galaxies are difficult, if not impossible, to determine. The most accurate method is by the use of cepheid variable stars, which is possible only if the galaxies are near enough to be resolved into stars with large telescopes. The uncertainty in this method has already been discussed. The ambiguity resulted in an underestimate of the distances of even the nearest galaxies, the Magellanic Clouds and the Andromeda Galaxy. Even now the zero point of the period-luminosity scale is uncertain to perhaps one-half magnitude, leading to an error of 25 percent in distance.

When the brightest stars in a galaxy can be photographed, even though no cepheids can be found, the absolute magnitudes can be assumed to be about the same as those in our galaxy, and the distances can then be computed by the absolute magnitude formula. The absolute magnitudes of the cluster variables are about zero and can be seen to

Fig. 22–4 Types of barred spiral galaxies. (Yerkes Observatory)

Fig. 22–5 NGC 1300, a barred spiral galaxy, photographed with the 200-inch telescope. (Photograph from the Mount Wilson and Palomar Observatories.)

tively close compared to distances of billions of light years obtained by other methods.

After the distances of galaxies up to the photometric limit were determined and their diameters computed, it was assumed that there is not much variation in diameter and brightness between the two classes, spirals and ellipsoids. However, there is considerable range in brightness and probably in diameter in each class, with more variation among ellipsoids than in spirals. The ellipsoids range from $M = -10$ to $-23$, compared to $M = -15$ to $-21$ for spirals.

There is a possibility that the outer arms of a spiral may be too faint to photograph, if the galaxy is too far away. Thus some spirals may be classified

only about 1 million light years. This distance includes the Magellanic Clouds and a half-dozen ellipsoidal galaxies only. The brighter cepheids are found in M31 and M33, as has been noted, and in other galaxies, thus extending the observable limit to some 15 million light years. Some observable blue supergiants can be recognized by their color indices and brightness contrasted with other stars in a galaxy. Assuming absolute magnitudes of $-9$, that of the brightest stars in our galaxy, the computation of distances by photometry can be made to perhaps 60 or 70 million light years. This is rela-

Fig. 22–6 The Hubble classification of galaxies.

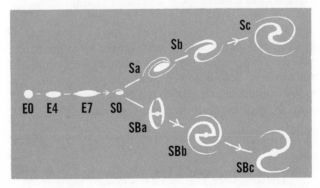

Fig. 22–7 The Large and Small Magellanic Clouds. Both are classed as irregular galaxies, but the large cloud may be a barred spiral with only one arm.

and $\qquad \log d = \dfrac{29.67}{5} = 5.934$

and $\qquad d = 860{,}000$ parsecs.

Of course in this example, the distance was first determined by the cepheid period-luminosity method and the absolute magnitude was computed from the apparent magnitude and the distance.

It is obvious that this method was not accurate. But for statistical investigations, it gave average distances, which were used until other methods became available. A related method is to assume that all galaxies of a given class are the same size. Then the more distant galaxies appear smaller than those closer to the sun and the distance is assumed to be inversely proportional to the angular diameter. This is also an approximate method.

The relation between distance and radial velocity of galaxies was discovered by Hubble in 1929. He used the angular diameter method to compute distances. Then he measured the radial velocities with a fast, low-dispersion spectrograph on the 60- and 100-inch telescopes on Mount Wilson. He found that the velocities increase with distance. That is, the lines in the spectra of galaxies are shifted toward the red by an amount which is proportional to the distance of the galaxy. This effect is called the *red shift;* and, if it is a velocity effect, the Doppler formula can be used to determine the radial velocity of the galaxy. This is shown in Figure 22–8, and the relationship between velocity and distance as a straight line in Figure 22–9. Written as an equation,

$$V = Hr \qquad (22\text{--}1)$$

where $H$ is Hubble's constant and $r$ is the distance.

The distances used by Hubble have been multiplied by 3, based on the revision of the distance scale by Baade. The revised Hubble constant, $H$, is (from Figure 22–9) 91 km/sec per million parsecs change in distance or about 17 mi/sec/million light years. This "constant" is subject to change as the

as ellipsoids. However, if an average absolute magnitude is assumed, and if the total apparent magnitude can be found with a photoelectric photometer or by some other method, the formula can be used and an approximate distance computed.

▶*Example:* For the Andromeda Galaxy, $m = 3.47$ and $M = -21.2$.

Then, $\quad -21.2 = +3.47 + 5 - 5 \log d$

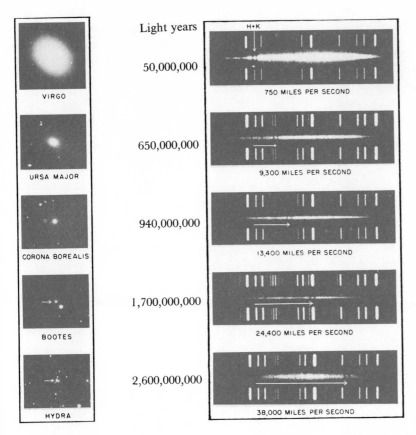

Fig. 22–8   Provisional distances of galaxies estimated from their brightness and their velocities calculated from the red shift. (Photographs from the Mount Wilson and Palomar Observatories)

distance scale is further revised. Velocities of galaxies up to 41 percent of the speed of light (124,-000 km/sec or 76,000 mi/sec) have been measured by this method.

It should be emphasized that the Hubble constant is still only approximate because of the uncertainty in the distance determinations. The relation can be inverted and, if the velocity of a galaxy can be measured, its distance can be computed with an accuracy which depends on the value of $H$. Also, it has been argued for many years that the red shift is not a Doppler effect, but may be caused by some other effect rather than velocity. One pos-

sibility is that light is slowed in a gravitational field, loses some of its energy, and the lines appear to the red of their normal positions. Recent results, however, have shown that this velocity effect extends nearly to the speed of light, which strengthens the belief that it is a Doppler shift.

## 22.4  Distribution of Galaxies

On a large scale view of the universe, the galaxies appear to be scattered at random and to be uniformly spaced throughout the visible universe. Probably a billion are within reach of the 200-inch telescope, which reaches a distance of 2 billion or more light years. However, there is a tendency for the galaxies to cluster. For example, our galaxy is one of 17 galaxies within 3 million light years of each other. Ours is near the outside edge of this group, which is called the *local group* of galaxies. These galaxies are listed in Table 22–1.

TABLE 22–1
**The Local Group of Galaxies**

| Designation | Type[a] | Distance (l.y.) | Diameter (l.y.) | Solar Masses |
|---|---|---|---|---|
| Our galaxy | Sb | | 100,000 | $2 \times 10^{11}$ |
| Lg. Mag. Cloud | Irr I | 160,000 | 30,000 | $2.5 \times 10^{10}$ |
| Sm. Mag. Cloud | Irr I | 180,000 | 25,000 | |
| UMi System | dE4 | 220,000 | 3,000 | |
| Sculptor syst. | dE3 | 270,000 | 7,000 | $3 ? \times 10^{6}$ |
| Draco system | dE2 | 330,000 | 4,500 | |
| Fornax system | dE3 | 600,000 | 22,000 | $2 \times 10^{7}$ |
| Leo II system | dE0 | 750,000 | 5,200 | $1 \times 10^{6}$ |
| Leo I system | dE4 | 900,000 | 5,000 | |
| NGC 6822 | Irr I | 1,500,000 | 9,000 | |
| NGC 147 | E6 | 1,900,000 | 10,000 | |
| NGC 185 | E2 | 1,900,000 | 8,000 | |
| NGC 205 | E5 | 2,200,000 | 5,000 | |
| NGC 221 (M32) | E3 | 2,200,000 | 8,000 | |
| IC 1613 | Irr I | 2,200,000 | 16,000 | |
| NGC 224 (M31) | Sb | 2,200,000 | 130,000 | $4 \times 10^{11}$ |
| NGC 598 (M33) | Sc | 2,300,000 | 60,000 | $8 \times 10^{9}$ |

[a]dE4 = dwarf E4; Irr I = irregular with little or no dust. Other types are discussed in the text.

It will be noticed that the ellipsoids outnumber the rest. If this is true for all of space, there should be about 60 percent ellipsoids and less than 20 percent spirals, with 20 percent irregulars. It seems likely that most of the nearby luminous galaxies have been found and that, in the future, discoveries will be limited to the dwarf galaxies. In the local group, our galaxy and M31 are considerably larger than any of the others, with M31 having a calculated mass twice that of ours. There may be other members hidden behind the obscuring clouds in the Milky Way.

The 48-inch Schmidt telescope on Mount Palomar has made a survey and has found more than 600 large clusters of galaxies. The opinion at the Lick Observatory is that the clusters are uniformly scattered throughout space. The Virgo cluster, listed first in table 22–2, contains more than 3,000 members. It is possible that our local group is an appendage of this cluster. Perhaps the largest is the Coma cluster, which contains some 10,000 members. The names, such as Virgo and Coma, indicate that these clusters of galaxies are in the direction of the stars in those constellations, but of course much farther away. Similarly, the Andromeda Galaxy is not in the constellation Andromeda, but is in that direction at a distance of several million light years.

In Table 22–2, ten clusters of galaxies, their distances, and velocities are listed.

## 22.5    The Expanding Universe

One of the products of Hubble's red shift is the theory of the expanding universe. This theory was first stated in a series of lectures by Abbe Lemaitre in Belgium and published in a book called *The Primeval Atom*. It was assumed that the entire mass of the universe was originally confined to a volume of space about the size of the orbit of the earth. The

TABLE 22–2
**Clusters of Galaxies**
**Their Approximate Distances and Velocities**

| Cluster | Distance (l.y.) | Velocity (mi/sec) |
|---|---|---|
| Virgo | 50,000,000 | 750 |
| Pegasus | 150,000,000 | 2,300 |
| Perseus | 260,000,000 | 3,100 |
| Coma | 390,000,000 | 4,500 |
| Ursa Major 1 | 650,000,000 | 9,300 |
| Leo | 1,000,000,000 | 12,000 |
| Gemini 1 | 1,200,000,000 | 14,000 |
| Bootes | 1,700,000,000 | 24,400 |
| Ursa Major 2 | 1,800,000,000 | 25,000 |
| Hydra | 2,600,000,000 | 38,000 |

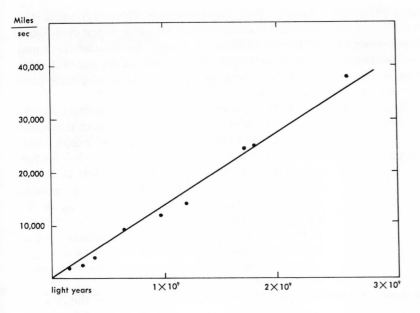

Fig. 22–9 The velocity-distance relation for clusters of galaxies, plotted from the data of Table 22–2. The curve is a straight line. The fact that the points do not exactly follow the line is due to the difficulty in determining the distances.

density at the beginning would have been very great and the temperature correspondingly high—estimated by George Gamow at 10 billion degrees Kelvin. This was the "primeval atom," which was, of course, very unstable and exploded, throwing its material out into space at very high velocities. This material cooled rapidly at a rate calculated to be inversely proportional to the square root of the age of the universe expressed in seconds. Assuming 10 billion years and an average temperature of the universe to be 75°, a figure given in the 1950s, the original temperature was 14 billion degrees. As the material cooled, it had a tendency to collect into separate entities, which became the galaxies and in turn formed into stars.

The fastest moving galaxies, therefore, reached the greatest distances with the distances from each other being proportional to the speed. The center of this system, the point where the explosion took place, is not known. Its location is not important to the theory, since we seem to be completely sur-rounded by uniformly spaced galaxies and there are more beyond the limits of our largest telescopes.

In 1965 a new theory was advanced by Allan Sandage, of the Mount Wilson-Palomar Observatories, that the universe is pulsating with a period of 82 billion years. We are now in the expansion phase.

If the theory of expansion is correct, it should be possible to compute the age—the time since the explosion. Using the data in Table 22–2 for the Hydra cluster, since $s = vt$, we have

$$t = \frac{s}{v} = \frac{2.6 \times 10^9 \text{ yrs} \times 186,000 \text{ mi/sec}}{38,000 \text{ mi/sec}}$$

and $t = 12.7 \times 10^9$ or 12.7 billion years.

This is only one method of arriving at the age of the universe. Other methods compute the age as 16 or 24 billion years. In Sandage's words, "The clues indicate that our universe is a finite, closed system originating in a 'big bang,' that the expanding universe is slowing down, and that it probably pulsates once every 82 billion years."

The *steady state* theory, which was proposed by a group of British astronomers, has now been abandoned. It assumed that energy is being converted into matter continuously. Galaxies are being formed, grow old, and as their stars evolve to the black-dwarf stage, finally die. But the universe as a whole always looks the same. In other words, the universe is thought to be infinitely large and infinitely old, with no beginning and no end.

## 22.6   Evolution of Galaxies

The theory of the development of a galaxy is difficult and not yet worked out in satisfactory detail. Suppose that at first the universe was pure hydrogen. If it were spread uniformly throughout space, it would have a tendency to collect into smaller units, where the density would be a little greater than the average. These units would grow by attracting other particles to themselves by gravitational pull and would form galaxies. The pregalaxy state might be called a protogalaxy. (The prefix proto-, meaning first, is coming more and more into general use in astronomy.)

Smaller collections of gas would similarly form into protostars. They would grow by adding particles, as in the dust cloud theory of the formation of the sun and the solar system. The star at the proper stage of temperature and pressure would begin to convert its hydrogen into helium, would develop through various stages into a giant, and decrease in size until the helium core was too hot and the star would go through the nova stage. The larger masses would evolve at a relatively more rapid rate, as previously noted.

The important part of this development of stars in a galaxy is that helium, and in some cases carbon and heavier atoms, would have been produced in the stellar interiors. Later they would have been ejected into space by the explosion of novas to be captured by other stars in the process of for-

mation. The importance is that carbon is the element that makes the carbon-nitrogen cycle work in the production of energy. By similar nova and supernova stages, the elements in the periodic table could have been produced. This is of course pure speculation.

If this theory is correct, there should be galaxies in various stages of evolution from the young galaxies with blue, hot stars to the older ones where the massive stars would have used up their hydrogen and have left only the older, redder stars. This is indeed the case and has led to a recent revision of the classification of galaxies proposed by W. W. Morgan. Morgan's revision of Hubbles's system is not intended to replace the older system, but to add information regarding the constitution of galaxies in view of the discovery of the two stellar populations.

The Morgan classification retains the condensation of the nucleus (such as Sb or SBc) of the Hubble system, then adds a designation based on the colors of the galaxies as produced by stars of different spectral classes within each galaxy. In the sequence, irregular galaxies and spirals with very small nuclei are placed at one end. They are designated as "a" galaxies consisting of stars of spectral classes B, A, and F, all of which produce strong radiations at the violet end of the spectrum.

At the red end of the sequence are the giant ellipsoids and spirals with high concentration of light in the nuclei. These are called "k" galaxies, because they are composed mostly of giant stars of spectral class K. Other groups are placed between the two extremes. Thus the classification is based on modern developments in the theory of evolution of stars, since it permits the galaxies composed of young stars of the main sequence (the B, A, and F stars) to be distinguished from those composed of the old stars of spectral class K.

An irregular galaxy is an unorganized collection of particles illuminated by light from massive, blue stars. It is possibly a young galaxy that has not yet formed into a spiral. The hydrogen atoms by themselves cannot form into dust grains, which must be the result of a sticking together of heavier atoms. The formation of grains makes it possible for the hot gas to radiate away some of its heat, thus helping in the formation of a galaxy under its own gravitation. This shows the importance of the nova stages in the evolution of stars.

As the galaxies develop, the blue stars evolve more rapidly, leaving the less massive stars, like the sun, to go through their cycles at slower rates. Also the loose particles are used up by falling into the protostars and the older galaxies become nearly free of gas and dust clouds and are eventually composed entirely of dwarf stars.

In his classification of galaxies, Hubble suggested a direction of evolution. He thought that perhaps a galaxy started as a spherical mass of material now thought to have been hydrogen—an E0 galaxy. Because of its rotation it became more flattened. Then it developed arms which extended from the center as in either a normal or a barred spiral. The older galaxies developed more prominent arms. Hence our galaxy is an old galaxy, but is not in the oldest class. Shapley suggested that the evolution was in the opposite direction and that the ellipsoids are the remains after the stars in the arms had been thrown out into space.

Since spiral galaxies seen edgewise (Figure 22–10) are much flatter than the ellipsoidal galaxies, it is difficult to see how Shapley's direction of evolution is possible, since a galaxy would tend to become even more flattened, rather than to become thicker.

The S0 galaxies are known to be dust free and composed of the older Population II stars, which have finished their evolutionary processes because there is no more material on which to grow. The question has come up as to how these galaxies could have become dust free. The suggestion has been made that, since clusters of galaxies contain large numbers of this type, they are produced by collisions. When two galaxies collide (Figure 22–11), there is so much room between the stars that they pass through without colliding. But the gas and dust particles are swept up in the process and are sepa-

rated from the stars. Thus the S0 galaxies could have become dust free from collisions or by the process of star formation from the interstellar clouds.

Fig. 22–10   NGC 4564, an edge-on spiral galaxy, photographed in red light with a 200-inch telescope. (Photograph from the Mount Wilson and Palomar Observatories)

## 22.7   The Role of Radio Astronomy

Radio astronomy developed very slowly after Jansky's discovery of radio waves from space in 1931. Reber began his radio studies in 1936, six years later, and drew a map of the Milky Way (Figure 4–11, Chapter 4), which showed lines of equal intensity similar to the lines of equal elevation on contour maps.

After World War II, developments came much faster when radio telescopes were set up in the United States, England, Holland, and Australia.

Fig. 22–11 The strong radio source Cygnus A, which has been identified as a pair of colliding galaxies. Photographed with a 200-inch telescope. (Photograph from the Mount Wilson and Palomar Observatories)

Radio signals from the sun were first discovered in England in 1942 and by Reber in 1943. These signals were from the quiet sun and the temperature of the emitting material was estimated at 1,000,000°K. We now know that the temperature of the corona is at least that high. When the sun is active, more intense radiation is superposed on that from the quiet sun. Still stronger radiation is received from solar flares.

When radio waves are produced by material at various depths in the solar atmosphere, presumably at different temperatures, the heights at which these waves are produced can be studied by radio observations of different wavelengths. For example, the corona produces radiation 15 meters in length. If our eyes were sensitive to that radiation, we should see a sun 10 percent larger at minimum activity than we do with eyes which see only visible light.

A strong source of radio waves from inside our galaxy is from the Crab nebula (Figure 18–6). This nebula is the remnant of a supernova and its visual and radio radiations are emitted by electrons accelerated in magnetic fields (synchrotron radiation), as already noted. In 1948 the first radio source outside the galaxy was discovered. This source is known as Cygnus A (Figure 22–11) and coincides with a distant cluster of galaxies. Since 1948, catalogs from several radio observatories have been published. The third catalog of radio objects from the Cambridge center in England (3C) lists 471 sources, of which 100 have been made observable by improved resolving power of radio telescopes, which permit right ascensions and declinations to be determined with an accuracy of about 10″.

It has already been pointed out (page 300) that cold hydrogen radiates "forbidden lines" of wavelength 21 cm. Other waves come from ionized hydrogen in various regions of the Milky Way with wavelengths between 3 and 22 cm, but which do not radiate appreciably at 21 cm. These radiations are called thermal. A third class of radio waves, nonthermal waves, are probably produced by high-speed electrons moving in magnetic fields.

The nonthermal radio sources are of three or more kinds:

1. Remnants of supernovas and filamentary nebulae. The most spectacular and best-known example is the loop or filamentary nebula in Cygnus (Figure 22–12). This source is nearly circular with an apparent shell of diameter 50 parsecs in the center. Other sources are the remnants from Tycho's and Kepler's supernovas and the Crab nebula.

2. Normal external galaxies. These include M31, M51, and M81. The radio emission is only about $\frac{1}{1,000,000}$ of the radiation in visible light and is almost a million times the total radiation of the sun. M31 is now thought to consist of a disk component, which is about the same as the optical disk of our galaxy, and a halo of much greater extent.

3. Radio galaxies. These galaxies differ from the normal galaxies in their high output of radio energy, which ranges up to 100,000 times that from a normal galaxy.

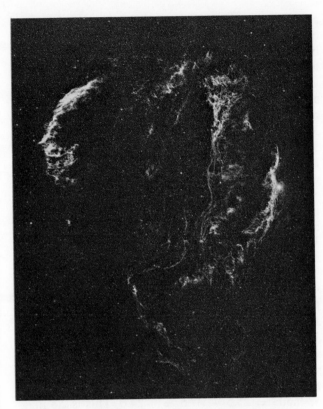

Fig. 22–12   The Filamentary Nebula in Cygnus. 48-inch Schmidt telescope in red light. (Photograph from the Mount Wilson and Palomar Observatories)

The peculiar elliptical galaxy NGC 5128 (Figure 22–13) is an unusual example of a radio galaxy.

## 22.8   Quasi-Stellar Sources

Some radio sources were originally called *radio stars*. Because a few of them look like stars, but almost certainly are not stars, they are now called *quasi-stellar* (seemingly starlike) *radio sources*, or more popularly *quasars*. The first object of this type was discovered in 1960 and was listed as 3C48 in the Cambridge catalog. It looks like a star with broad emission lines. Between 1960 and 1963, three others were discovered and the rate of discovery increased rapidly in the years following. Forty-four were known by May, 1965, of which red shifts for ten had been measured.

That the quasi-stellar objects are different from stars is apparent from their optical properties. While they look like stars, on photographs they show small, fuzzy disks. 3C48 is less than 1″ in diameter. 3C273 is the brightest (magnitude 13). It is double with a jet coming from the center. The two parts are 30″ apart. This source varies irregularly in brightness by 40 percent in a period of about 10 years. It appears on the Harvard sky patrol plates, where it

Cygnus A and others are composed of two centers seen with a faint bridge between them when observed at 21 cm. The bridge is still more prominent at longer wavelengths. Some double galaxies are very large with components ranging from less than 10,000 parsecs to over 100,000 parsecs in diameter with distances between the centers as great as 300,000 parsecs. They may, therefore, be as much as ten times larger than our galaxy.

Fig. 22–13   The peculiar ellipsoidal galaxy NGC 5128 in Centaurus; a strong radio source. 200-inch photograph. (Photograph from the Mount Wilson and Palomar Observatories)

has been photographed since 1887, so the variation can be studied over an interval of nearly 80 years.

These objects also have much more ultraviolet energy than stars, indicating a very high temperature. They show broad emission lines in their spectra. And, perhaps most important of all, they exhibit very large, red shifts. Two lines of hydrogen and one line of ionized oxygen in 3C273 show a red shift of 16 percent. Hence it cannot be a star, since a star with a velocity of more than 600 km/sec would leave the galaxy. Sixteen percent of the speed of light is 48,000 km/sec, which is comparable to the speed of a galaxy at a distance of almost 2 billion light years. Other quasars with still higher speeds were discovered in 1965. 3C9 has such a high speed that the ultraviolet lines in the spectrum are shifted into the visible spectrum. The usual lines measured in the red shift (Figure 22–8) are shifted completely out of the visual region of the spectrum. At these high speeds, the linear Doppler shift cannot be used to compute the velocity, but a formula from the theory of relativity must be used.

---

The usual form of the Doppler equation (equation 3–4) was discussed in Chapter 3. From the theory of relativity, the equation takes the form

$$\frac{\sqrt{1 + \frac{v}{c}}}{\sqrt{1 - \frac{v}{c}}} = \frac{\lambda}{\lambda_0} = 1 + z \qquad (22\text{-}2)$$

where v, $c$, and $\lambda$ have the same meanings as in equation 3–4, and

$$z = \frac{\lambda}{\lambda_0} - 1. \qquad (22\text{-}3)$$

For 3C9, Maarten Schmidt of the Mount Wilson-Palomar Observatories found $z = 2.012$. Substituting in the above formula and solving, v $= 0.8\ c$. That is, the velocity of 3C9 is 80 percent of the velocity of light, or 240,000 km/sec.

---

Schmidt, with the 200-inch telescope, measured the red shifts of nine quasi-stellar objects with $z$ varying from 0.158 to 2.012. One beautiful feature of Schmidt's work was that, starting with 16 percent of the speed of light for 3C273, he could identify lines in successive objects, making them fit ultraviolet lines two or three at a time. As one set disappeared into the invisible part of the spectrum others came into view from the ultraviolet. In 3C254, where $z = 0.736$, he identified five lines; in 3C287, three; and in 3C9 only two lines were measurable. But this succession of lines fit perfectly when the proper value of $z$ was found.

When the results were tabulated and studied, it was found that all quasi-stellar radio sources have diameters less than 1″ (one second of arc). They all have the same intrinsic properties for all red shifts.

It is of course impossible to measure the distances of these very distant objects. Using the Hubble constant of 75 km/sec per million parsecs, as given by Sandage in 1965, the distance of 3C9 is 3.2 billion parsecs or 10.5 billion light years, and is the most distant object yet measured. Its visual magnitude is 18.5, from which its absolute magnitude, $M = 18.5 + 5 - 5 \log 3.2 \times 10^9 = 23.5 - 5 \times 9.503 = 23.5 - 47.5 = -24.0$. This is 2.8 magnitudes, or 13 times brighter than the Andromeda galaxy. If its angular diameter is 1″, then the linear diameter is 16,000 parsecs or about 40 percent of the diameter of M31.

Schmidt estimates that 3C273 at 13th magnitude is 40 times the luminosity of the usual galaxy and 1/10 or less of its diameter. Thus the emission of light per unit volume is much higher than usual. Its light variation in ten years seems to show that it is even smaller. Schmidt's conclusion was that there is no known source of energy which can account for this enormous radiation and that the true nature of these sources is still a mystery.

An important paper by Sandage in 1965 announced the discovery of still a different type of object, which Sandage has called *quasi-stellar galaxies* or QSG for short. It had been recognized as far back as 1947 that there exist abnormally blue stars. They were thought to form a halo around the spiral core of our galaxy. Sandage found that in addition to the halo stars, which are brighter than about 15th magnitude, there are others between 15th and 19th magnitude which cannot be halo stars. He thought that these "stars" might be enormously distant, superluminous galaxies. They were first discovered by radio astronomy, since they emit waves of radio frequency. These new objects are not found near any previously known radio source.

Sandage made a study of plates taken with the Palomar 48-inch Schmidt camera and found that the "blue stars" average three per square degree down to magnitude 18.5. He then made some color measures and found that the fainter objects are much bluer than the brighter ones and that their colors agree more closely with the colors of the quasi-stellar objects which he had been studying. He thus divided these blue objects into two classes. Those brighter than magnitude 14.5 are mostly stellar objects in the halo of the galaxy. The fainter objects are apparently more distant and outside the galaxy. These he called *quasi-stellar galaxies.* Further studies showed that the halo stars outnumber the quasi-stellar galaxies by 25 to 1 at magnitude 12, but the quasi-stellar galaxies are more numerous by the same ratio at magnitude 19.

In April and May, 1965, spectra of six suspected objects were obtained with the 200-inch telescope. One turned out to be a star, two had only continuous spectra without any lines and were therefore unusable. But three showed very large red shifts. The velocities of two were 25,000 and 37,000 km/sec and that of the third was 200,000 km/sec or two-thirds the speed of light. These three objects are like the quasi-stellar radio sources in every way, except that they do not radiate in the radio frequencies.

Sandage estimated the number of quasi-stellar galaxies to be 83 inside a sphere of radius 230 million parsecs. Inside this same sphere there are probably 1.7 million normal galaxies and 40 quasi-stellar radio sources. In other words, there are 20,000 times more normal galaxies than quasi-stellar nonradio galaxies in a given volume of space. And the nonradio sources outnumber the radio sources of this nature by a factor of 500. Sandage also made the suggestion that the quasi-stellar radio sources are quasi-stellar galaxies going through a temporary stage of intense radio emission.

It has been estimated that the life of a quasi-stellar radio source is only 1 million years. Since there are 500 times more quasi-stellar nonradio sources, it seems likely that these galaxies should have a life expectancy of 500 million years.

As has been noted previously, the distance scale is still uncertain and hence the Hubble constant is probably only approximate. Using the 1965 figure of 75 km/sec per million parsecs, the radius of the universe is 4 billion parsecs or 13 billion light years. That is, any galaxy at that distance should be moving away from the center (or from us) at the speed of light. If there are galaxies out to that distance, the age of the universe, since the expansion started, should be 13 billion years, which may be only one phase of a pulsating universe. There is obviously much left to do in the study of this exciting and rapidly developing field of astronomy. Unfortunately, a 200-inch telescope is required to photograph the spectra of these very distant and very faint objects. In this field optical and radio astronomy must work very closely together.

## QUESTIONS AND PROBLEMS

1. In what ways do quasi-stellar objects differ from stars and galaxies?

2. Distinguish between Population I and II stars as to temperature, distribution in galaxies, age, and association with gas and dust.

3. What assumptions are made in measuring distances to galaxies in which individual stars cannot be distinguished?

4. Radio astronomy is well developed in England and Holland. What characteristic of these

countries probably contributed to their early interest in radio astronomy?

5. Compare the apparent diameter of the only galaxy visible to the unaided eye in the northern hemisphere, M31, with that of the moon. The angular diameter of the brighter portion of M31 is 3°.

6. The red-shift relation discovered by Hubble indicates that clusters of galaxies are receding from ours in all directions. Does this imply that our galaxy is at the center of the universe? Explain.

7. If the distances are actually five times larger than those in Figure 22–8, recompute the Hubble constant.

8. Use the velocity-distance relation to find the distances to galaxies that are receding from ours at (a) 20 percent and (b) 30 percent of the velocity of light. **Ans:** (a) 600 million parsecs, if $H = 100$ km/sec/million parsecs.

9. Compare the resolving power of radio telescopes used in determining locations for the third Cambridge catalog with that of the 200-inch telescope.

10. Compute the angular size of the (a) Large Magellanic Cloud, and (b) the Small Magellanic Cloud. **Ans:** (a) About 11°.

11. List the various methods of measuring distances to galaxies and give the approximate maximum distance measured by each method.

12. Show that measuring distances to galaxies depends fundamentally on measuring the diameter of the earth.

13. The apparent visual magnitude of the 1885 nova in M31 was 7.2. If it is assumed to be an average nova of absolute magnitude $-7$, calculate the brightness ratio and verify the distance quoted in the text for these figures.

14. Compare the modern concept of the universe with that held before 1920.

# Chapter Twenty-three

# Man's Conquest of Space

The launching of the first man-made satellite on October 4, 1957, was the culmination not only of years of preparation but of centuries of speculation. There were experiments by people who thought it should be possible to fly through the air or even to leave the earth. The first successful manned flights into the atmosphere were in lighter-than-air balloons. These were followed, much later, by modern airships and airplanes.

## 23.1  The Beginning of Space Research

It has been known for a long time that escape from the earth requires a speed of 7 mi per second (about 25,000 mi per hour), which is far above the speed of a few hundred miles per hour of even the fastest airplanes. It was only after experiments with rockets before and during World War II that speeds of 1 or 2 mi per second were reached.

After the war, information from the German rocket experiments fell into the American and Russian hands. Since these countries had the facilities and manpower for rocket research, it was decided that they should make the major efforts in rocket

and artificial satellite studies of the upper atmosphere. The launching of Sputnik I was the outcome of this effort. Unfortunately, the purposes of the program were soon overshadowed by what many people considered a race for space between Russia and the United States. The first American satellite, Explorer I, was launched on January 31, 1958—less than four months after the first Russian Sputnik.

When it became apparent that successful rocket flights into space were near, an organized, cooperative program of study of the atmosphere and the neighborhood of the earth developed into the International Geophysical Year (IGY). It will be many years before the data collected during the IGY can be completely interpreted. In the meantime, many of the cooperating countries decided to continue. Since the IGY dates were chosen to fall during a period of great solar activity, it was decided to select another period when the sun was at minimum activity. This was known as the International Years of the Quiet Sun (IQSY). These two periods of research were discussed in Chapter 1.

The space effort of the United States and Russia soon extended far beyond the goals originally set for the IGY. Both military and scientific possibilities became evident. An artificial satellite could keep a constant watch on an enemy country as well as on the world's weather. For that reason, both countries allocated liberal amounts of their national budgets to the conquest of space.

The American space program is coordinated by the National Aeronautics and Space Administration (NASA), which was established by Congress in 1958. The purpose of NASA is to join all government agencies, the aerospace industry, and the academic and scientific community into a coherent program of space exploration. This is a very complex undertaking and requires the annual expenditure of billions of dollars. NASA has major installations around the country, including the well-known Launch Operations Center at Cape Kennedy and the mammoth Manned Spacecraft Center in Houston, Texas.

American space plans call for much more than the exploration of the earth's immediate environment. Probes have already been sent to Venus and Mars, and plans call for the landing of a space crew on the moon. We shall now investigate the technology required for such an ambitious plan.

## 23.2  Rocket Power

The forerunner of today's chemical rocket propellants was gunpowder. Developed by the Chinese almost 1000 years ago, it consisted of a mixture of sodium nitrate, sulfur, and charcoal, and was soon used for military purposes. Rockets were used on the battlefield as early as 1400, but space flight was not forgotten. About the year 1500, a Chinese experimenter by the name of Wan-Hoo fastened 47 gunpowder rockets to the bottom of a chair and climbed aboard. Servants ignited the space vehicle, but no traces of Wan-Hoo or his ship were ever found.

It was the "rockets' red glare" over Fort McHenry during the War of 1812 that is immortalized in our National Anthem. A few years earlier,

in 1807, 25,000 military rockets had been used in the destruction of the city of Copenhagen. Oddly enough, the full potential of this weapon was not exploited until World War II, more than a century later. Nevertheless, theorists were busy devising plans for the use of rockets in the exploration of space. One of the foremost of these, Konstantin Ziolkovsky, built Russia's first wind tunnel and also proposed the use of liquid propellants in rockets. Incidentally, Ziolkovsky also coined the term *sputnik*, meaning fellow traveler.

First to launch a liquid-propellant rocket was the American physicist, Robert H. Goddard. Goddard devoted his life to the publishing of treatises on rocket propulsion and conducted many successful launchings. He developed techniques that are essential in today's space program, including the centrifugal pump for rocket propellants and the gyroscopic guidance method. Unfortunately, he did not receive encouragement and support for his work; and he did not live to see the fruition of his work in space research.

In Germany, the Society for Space Travel was organized in 1927. The following year the Society helped to produce a motion picture, *The Woman in the Moon*, in which the concept of the countdown was first used. Some of the American space experts of today received their basic training as members of this Society. During World War II, the Society was asked to develop a long-range military rocket. Known as the V-2, it was powered by alcohol and liquid oxygen and weighed close to 15 tons. It had a range of about 200 mi and attained altitudes of 60 mi. Traveling at speeds of almost 2000 mi per hour, the V-2 was virtually impossible to intercept. A 1946 V-2 is shown in Figure 23-1.

After the war, 300 carloads of V-2 parts were shipped to the White Sands Proving Grounds in New Mexico for further experimentation. Additional test facilities were built later at Cape Kennedy (formerly called Cape Canaveral) and at other sites. The Russians, who captured the German rocket sites, also pursued the development of large

Fig. 23–1   A V-2 rocket being readied for launching at the White Sands Proving Ground in 1946. (U.S. Army Photo).

rockets after the war. From these beginnings, the two countries were able to acquire the capability of launching the first artificial satellites during the IGY.

Rocket power is dependent upon the Reaction Principle, which is another name for Newton's Third Law of Motion (Chapter 6). Contrary to the notion of some people, a jet or rocket is not propelled by the push of escaping gases against the surrounding atmosphere. If this were true, it would be impossible to use a rocket in the vacuum of space. Instead, the craft is propelled by the unbalanced forces inside the engine directly opposite the nozzle, as shown in Figure 23–2. The magnitude of these forces depends upon the weight of the expelled

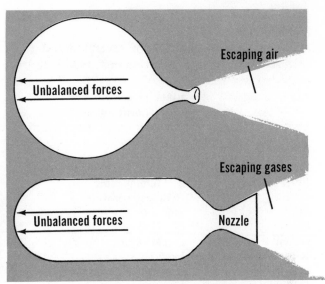

Fig. 23–2   Unbalanced forces inside a balloon and a rocket. The propelling forces are entirely internal and do not depend on any external environment.

gases and the rate at which they leave the rocket. This is called the *exhaust velocity*.

The source of power for a rocket engine consists of a *fuel* and an *oxidizer*. A jet engine uses the surrounding atmosphere as an oxidizer, but a rocket must carry its own in order to operate beyond the earth's atmosphere. Fuels and oxidizers are chosen for maximum thrust and specific impulse. Thrust is the measure of the unbalanced forces inside the rocket and is usually given in pounds. Specific impulse combines thrust, burning time, and the weight of the propellant by the following formula:

$$\text{Specific Impulse, } I_{sp} = \frac{\text{Thrust x Burning Time}}{\text{Weight of Propellant}} \quad (23\text{-}1)$$

Specific impulse is therefore given in pounds-seconds per pound, or merely in seconds, since pound units cancel each other in the formula. Today's rockets usually have thrusts in the neighborhood of 400,000 lb, but engines with millions of pounds of thrust are being developed for flights to the moon and beyond.

The specific impulses of several liquid fuel-oxidizer combinations are given in Table 23–1.

TABLE 23–1
**Liquid Fuel-Oxidizer Combinations**

| Fuel | Oxidizer | $I_{sp}$ |
|------|----------|------|
| Octane | Nitric Acid | 220 |
| Ethyl alcohol | Red fuming nitric acid | 220 |
| Octane | Hydrogen peroxide | 230 |
| Ethyl alcohol | Liquid oxygen (LOX) | 240 |
| Gasoline | Liquid oxygen | 242 |
| Octane | Liquid oxygen | 248 |
| Boron | Liquid oxygen | 330 |
| Liquid hydrogen | Liquid fluorine | 370 |
| Liquid hydrogen | Liquid oxygen | 375 |

In a solid-propellant rocket engine, both fuel and oxidizer consist of dry chemicals. The first gunpowder rockets were of this type. The propellant mixture in a modern rocket is still called *grain*, a term that has been borrowed from gunpowder terminology. The advantage of solid propellants is that they can be mixed and placed in the rocket ahead of time and are instantly ready for launching. Liquid propellants, on the other hand, must be loaded just before launching, since the fuel and oxidizer are usually kept at a very low temperature.

The specific impulses of some solid propellants are given in Table 23–2.

One disadvantage of solid propellants is that cracks may form in the mixture and this may lead to uneven burning and engine failure. Solid propellants also deteriorate with age and are extremely sensitive to temperature changes, so it is important to determine carefully the useful life of a propellant in a rocket that will not be launched immediately after it is loaded.

Two other measures of rocket performance are the thrust-to-weight ratio and the mass ratio. The ratio of an engine's thrust to the total weight of the fueled rocket before lift-off is called the thrust-to-weight ratio. Thus, the thrust of a rocket weighing 200,000 lb must be 400,000 lb if it is to have a thrust-to-weight ratio of 2. Obviously, a rocket with a thrust-to-weight ratio of less than one will not leave the ground; and the higher the ratio the greater will be the acceleration.

A more inclusive term is the mass ratio of a rocket. A rocket may have a high thrust-to-weight ratio and still not go very far, if the propellant is soon exhausted. The mass ratio, on the other hand, is the relationship between the rocket's total mass and its mass after the propellant is used up. The higher the mass ratio, the faster the rocket will travel, even though the specific impulse of the propellant is the same as in that of a slower vehicle. It is for this reason that rockets are staged and that the stages are jettisoned as the propellant in them is used up. In that way, the mass of the final stage will be small in comparison with the total mass of the rocket before launch.

In an effort to overcome the limitations of both solid and liquid propellants, space scientists are looking for other methods of propulsion. One of the most promising is nuclear power. When liquid hydrogen is heated by a nuclear reactor, a specific impulse of over 1000 sec is possible. And the resulting temperatures are no higher than in some of the high-impulse chemical reactions. Theoretically, impulses of 1 million and more are possible by nuclear methods, but the resulting heat problems have not yet been solved. The American program to develop nuclear power for rockets is called Project Rover.

If nuclear engines are used in manned vehicles adequate shielding must be provided for the crew. This, plus the weight of the nuclear engine, offsets much of the high specific impulse the engine provides. In other words, the mass ratio is not as high as might be desired.

Plasma and ion engines are also being developed for use in space vehicles. A hot, ionized stream of gas is called *plasma*. The plasma can be heated by electrical means, by nuclear power, or even by solar energy. Once ionized, the gases are expelled from the engine to provide thrust. If liquid hydrogen is used as the propellant, exhaust velocities of 20,000 ft per second can be attained, compared with 8,000 to 10,000 ft per second for chemical systems.

Even the slight radiation pressure of the sun can be used for rocket propulsion. But the resulting thrust is small indeed. The push of a 100-kilowatt searchlight for example, is less than 0.0001 lb. But once a vehicle is in space, an extremely small thrust will produce constant acceleration. The speed of light is the theoretical limit of how fast a craft will ultimately travel, although it would take many years of constant acceleration to attain such speeds. Rockets powered in this way have been called *photon rockets*. They may look remarkably like sailboats, since large solar sails would be used to make maximum use of the sun's pressure. These sails will be maneuvered very much like their seagoing counterparts, without having to worry about squalls or calms.

TABLE 23–2
**Specific Impulses of Solid Propellants**

| Propellant | $I_{sp}$ |
|---|---|
| Black gunpowder (potassium nitrate, charcoal, sulfur) | 80 |
| Galcit (potassium perchlorate, asphalt, oil) | 180 |
| NROC (ammonium picrate, sodium nitrate, resin) | 180 |
| Cordite (nitrocellulose, diethylphenyl urea) | 200 |
| Yellow gunpowder (tetranitro carbazale, potassium nitrate, carbon, wood flour, polyvinyl acetate) | 200 |
| JPN (nitrocellulose, nitroglycerine, diethylphthalate, diethylphenyl urea, potassium sulfate, carbon black, candelilla wax) | 205 |

Why this urgent search for new and greater power? Simply because the power sources of today's rockets are not adequate for the space missions of the future. By way of illustration, an initial specific impulse of 750 sec is necessary in order to complete a manned round trip to Mars in a year's time. To reduce the time to three months, the impulse must

be raised to 1400 sec. And in order to explore the entire solar system, a specific impulse of approximately 5000 sec is necessary. These requirements are considerably above those listed in Tables 23–1 and 23–2 for present solid and liquid propellants.

### 23.3    Rocket Guidance

Once a rocket has been launched, an elaborate system of tracking and guidance is used to keep it on course and to assure the successful completion of the mission. Electronic devices are used to measure the vehicle's environment and to transmit the data to a ground station. This is called *telemetry*. Telemetry is also used to monitor the performance of the vehicle and its crew. Telemetered data is broken down into sequential segments known as *bits*. These bits are then decoded in the *readout*. In photographs, like the ones from the moon or Mars, the bits are converted into light impulses and pieced together very much like the transmission of photographs by radio methods on the earth.

The process of following the movements of a rocket in flight is called *tracking*. Radar, radio, and cameras are used for this purpose. (See Figure 23–3.) At the present time, optical tracking is the most precise. But it is severely limited both by weather conditions and by distance. NASA operates a network of tracking stations, telemetry ships, and data processing centers for satellite tracking. The stations of the Manned Flight Network are located in a belt around the earth.

During flight, space vehicles require light, dependable electric power for the operation of transmitters and other instruments. Nuclear energy, fuel cells, and solar cells have been used for this purpose. The American program for on-board nuclear power is called SNAP (Systems for Nuclear Auxiliary Power). Regular reactors are being tested for this purpose, as well as heat production through the decay of radioisotopes. SNAP units have already worked for several years without breakdown in American satellites.

Fig. 23–3 A satellite tracking camera capable of photographing a 6-meter sphere at the distance of the moon. The satellite trail (below) shows variation in magnitude corresponding to the 20-second period of rotation of the satellite. (Photographs from the Smithsonian Astrophysical Observatory)

A fuel cell differs from a dry cell or storage battery in that the ingredients can be fed into it while it is operating. Also, in the fuel cell the electrodes are not changed. Only the fuel and oxidizer are consumed. It is also more efficient than the electrolytic cell. The American spacecraft, Gemini 5, was the first to use fuel cells for on-board power. Liquid hydrogen and liquid oxygen were used.

The program for the direct utilization of sunlight in a spacecraft is called Project Sunflower. Reflectors more than 30 ft in diameter focus the sun's rays on a supply of mercury. The mercury vapor is used to run electric generators. The sun's energy can also be converted into electric power by means of solar cells, which utilize the same photoelectric effect found in the familiar electric eye. The

electric current produced by a single solar cell is very small, so it takes literally thousands of them to produce the few watts of power needed to operate the transmitters on today's spacecraft. Mariner 4, for example, contained 28,224 solar cells for the production of 10 watts of power. The solar cells must be aimed at the sun, whereas nuclear power and fuel cells do not. The surface of a solar cell can be damaged by micrometeorites and cosmic radiation.

Because of the large antennas used in tracking facilities, very weak radio signals from spacecraft can be detected over great distances. The 3-watt signal of Mariner 2, for example, was received over a distance of almost 54 million miles. The 85-foot antennas used for this purpose are about 20,000 times more sensitive than the ordinary rooftop television antennas. Because the signals are so weak, they can become garbled with radio emissions from the sun, the stars, and other celestial sources.

Conventional aerodynamic controls can be used to control a rocket only when it is in the atmosphere of the earth or some other planet. Because of the great speed of rockets, their guide fins are smaller

Fig. 23–4 Definition of the three attitude axes of a spaceship.

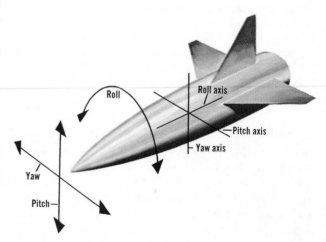

than those on commercial aircraft. Beyond the atmosphere, ballistic controls must be used. With the rocket engines firing, the path of the rocket can be changed by means of exhaust vanes that deflect the gases from the engine. Small jets along the fuselage, called deflection charge controls, are also used. Or, the entire engine can be mounted on swivels so the thrust can be aimed in different directions.

The orientation, called attitude, of a spacecraft may be described by three motions similar to those of a ship or airplane. *Roll* is a rotating motion; *pitch* is an up and down nodding motion; and *yaw* is a side-to-side motion. The three axes about which these motions take place are illustrated in Figure 23–4.

An instrument called the accelerometer is used to measure the effects of the forces acting on a space vehicle. The inertial resistance of a mass in the accelerometer makes it possible to compute both the velocity and distance traveled. Three are required, one for each of the attitude axes. To keep them properly aligned, rapidly spinning gyroscopes are used. The entire array of gyroscopes and accelerometers, with their associated instruments, is known as the inertial guidance system of the rocket.

Reference stars are used to check the position of a space vehicle, as well as to keep the guidance system oriented. Mariner 4 used the bright star Canopus, and a sensor on the craft was set to respond to light of the intensity of that star. If the sensor lost Canopus, due to the reflection of sunlight from dust particles or for some other reason, the sensor could be commanded from the earth to search for the star again.

The type of orbit of a space vehicle depends on the launch velocity. At escape velocity of 7 mi per second the orbit is a parabola with the earth at the focus. If the launch velocity is less than 7 mi per second, the orbit is an ellipse; if greater, the orbit is a hyperbola. The three types of orbit, all with respect to the earth, are illustrated in Figure 23–5. The three orbits coincide at the launching point, but the velocity is different for each at that point and

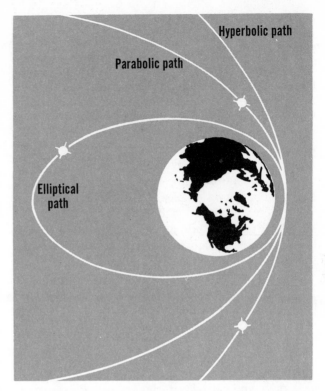

Fig. 23–5   Three possible types of orbit of a spaceship. The orbital speeds increase from the ellipse to the hyperbola. The parabolic path is required if the launch speed is equal to the velocity of escape from the earth.

the body goes into the orbit around the earth which is required by its speed.

Since the earth's velocity around the sun is 18.5 mi per second, the space ship will have this speed plus its velocity with respect to the earth, provided the launch is toward the east, the direction in which the earth is rotating on its axis and revolving around the sun. Space ships have never been launched toward the west, since an eastward launch takes advantage of the earth's speed of rotation. A north-south launch is strictly intended for low-altitude vehicles which are used to study conditions on the earth. If the total velocity of the ship is $\sqrt{2}$

(or 1.414) times 18.5 mi/sec, or 26 mi/sec, the orbit with respect to the sun will be a parabola and the ship will leave the solar system. If less than 26 mi/sec, the orbit will be an ellipse with the sun at one focus. Thus the orbital motion of an artificial satellite is governed by the same physical laws that control the motions of other celestial bodies.

The re-entry of an orbiting space vehicle into the earth's atmosphere is brought about by firing retrorockets to reduce the vehicle's velocity. As the vehicle loses altitude, however, its velocity increases again according to Kepler's laws of orbital motion. This increased speed will send the vehicle to a slightly higher altitude again. But it also increases the atmospheric friction on the rocket's surface, so the original altitude is not reached. This cycle is repeated until the vehicle reaches the ground.

During reentry, the kinetic energy of the moving satellite is converted into heat energy. This heat must be dissipated in order to prevent the destruction of the vehicle. A number of methods are used to deal with the heat. In the ablation method, a heat shield is constructed of a material that will absorb heat, melt, and fall away during reentry. In transpiration cooling, a liquid coolant is forced out through holes in the hull and dissipates heat by evaporation. Electromagnetic fields can also be used to prevent the heated atmosphere from reaching the craft. This method is still in an experimental stage.

### 23.4  Man in Space

Some critics of the space program argue that manned vehicles are an unnecessary and expensive aspect of the space exploration. They claim that the exploration of the moon and planets can be satisfactorily accomplished by instruments in unmanned vehicles without providing the elaborate equipment required by a crew. But it is impossible to foresee all the conditions that a lunar or planetary space vehicle may encounter. Hence a crew is needed to make adjustments and decisions for a successful mission, just as crews are considered necessary in conventional aircraft.

The most obvious need of a space crew is a satisfactory air environment. If sufficiently powerful boosters are available, a normal mixture of oxygen and nitrogen can be carried along. But if weight is at a premium, helium can be substituted for the nitrogen. This has the further advantage of reducing the danger of the "bends," if a sudden decompression should occur. But the light weight of helium also produces changes in the voices of the astronauts, and they have to get used to sounding a little like Donald Duck during the mission. The first American manned flights reduced the weight still further by furnishing the astronauts with pure oxygen at reduced pressure.

When an astronaut leaves his ship, he must take a breathing environment with him. This is accomplished by providing him with a spacesuit. The suit must also protect the wearer against any radiation or micrometeorite bombardment. Because a pressurized flexible suit is difficult to work in, rigid suits with hinged joints are being designed for extended stays in space. In effect, the astronauts will be wearing miniature space capsules.

A second consideration for a space crew is to keep the acceleration and deceleration forces within tolerable limits. These are known as *g-forces*, and are designated as multiples of a person's weight on the earth's surface. Thus a g-load of 3 during a launch means that the crew will experience three times its normal weight. Valuable pioneering work with g-forces was done by Col. John Stapp, a medical specialist with the United States Air Force. By means of a rocket sled, Stapp endured deceleration forces up to 45 g's without being permanently injured. In order to perform adequately for a sustained launch or reentry, the g-forces would have to be kept far below this value. In the first American manned vehicles, maximum loads of 5 g's were usual. (See Figure 23–6.)

Shortly after enduring the crushing forces of acceleration, the astronaut experiences the completely opposite sensation of weightlessness. Actually the term is misleading, because as long as a

Fig. 23–6   A rocket sled in which human reactions to high g-forces can be determined. Here, a fully equipped dummy is shown being ejected during a test run. (North American Aviation, Inc.)

spacecraft and its occupants are under the influence of gravitation, they are not weightless. It is more nearly correct to say that the vehicle is in a state of free fall, and that under these conditions there is no restraining force on the vehicle or its crew. Weightlessness is, therefore, very much like falling, except that in space the surrounding scenery does not rush by like it does when one falls off a building.

While the effects of long periods of weightlessness have not yet been determined, it is certain that some type of regular exercise is necessary to prevent the atrophy of muscles and organs. It has also been proposed that a kind of artificial weight be provided in future space stations by slowly rotating them. In such an arrangement, down would be toward the outside of the vehicle.

In order to conserve as much weight and space as possible in a capsule, the food supply of the crew is in concentrated form. Not only that, but liquids must be dispensed in ways that will prevent them from escaping and floating about the capsules as globules. Some of the food resembles baby food for this reason, and is served in collapsible tubes resembling tooth past tubes.

For longer journeys, all or part of the necessary food and water will be recycled. A number of closed ecological systems are presently under study. The most promising involves the use of a certain species of algae, which contain a large percentage of protein. It has been found that a 2-liter container filled with an algal solution can, if illuminated with a sufficiently powerful light source, supply the food and oxygen needs of an astronaut indefinitely. As the algae are harvested and prepared for food, more are synthesized from the carbon dioxide exhaled by the astronaut and the water is reclaimed within the capsule. Other recycling schemes involve the use of mushrooms and molds for the conversion of waste products into edibles. Still another plan calls for the chemical conversion of waste materials into rocket propellants. With this plan, the vehicle could be launched with a large food supply instead of a large stock of propellants.

A space crew must also contend with the external hazards of micrometeorites and cosmic radiation. It is believed that the density of micro-meteorites in the vicinity of the earth is between 100 and 1000 per cubic mile. Fortunately, they are so small that a spacecraft is not seriously damaged by them. In time, however, they can render solar cells inoperative through a sand blasting effect on the transparent shields covering the cells. For larger objects, meteoroid bumpers might be used, or space ships might be equipped with double hulls. Chances of being struck by a large meteoroid are very small, however; and it should even be possible to detect them by radar and to steer around them.

Likewise, cosmic radiation can be predicted and avoided to some extent. The Van Allen belts, for example, have escape corridors over the poles. In addition the intensity of the Van Allen radiation seems to depend on solar activity. It may become necessary to program launchings for times when solar prominences or flares are expected to be at a minimum.

### 23.5  Programs of Space Exploration

A great many direct and indirect benefits have already accrued from space flights. While it is impossible to list all of them, or to enumerate the hundreds of vehicles that have been launched since 1957, it is desirable to become familiar with some of the major programs that are being conducted and to know the names of the more important series of vehicles.

A space vehicle designed to obtain information about the environment of some celestial body, including the earth, is called a *probe*. The first artificial satellites were probes. Among other things, they discovered the Van Allen radiation belts, verified the pressure of sunlight, mapped the earth's magnetic field, analyzed the effects of sunlight and solar particles on the upper atmosphere, and studied the impact of micrometeorites on space vehicles. The American series of Explorer satellites is designed to serve as a continuing program of probes.

Artificial satellites can also be used as navigation aids that are virtually independent of the weather or the time of day. Successive radio observations of such satellites are used to determine the locations of ships and planes by comparison with special tables. Also, if a satellite emits a signal of its own, the Doppler shift of the signal becomes a valuable navigation aid. A nontransmitting satellite is said to be passive, while a transmitting one is termed active. An active-repeating satellite receives a signal from the earth, amplifies it, and transmits it back to earth. The Transit satellites are active navigation vehicles.

The first American communications satellites were large, passive balloons, called Echo. Some of them are more than 130 feet in diameter and are easily visible to the naked eye during favorable viewing conditions. Active-repeater satellites have the following names: Relay, Syncom, Telstar, Courier, Score, and Early Bird. Telstar I, launched July 10, 1962, was the first to relay live telecasts between the United States and Europe. Syncom orbits at an altitude (22,400 mi) which makes it appear stationary over the rotating earth. Three such synchronous satellites spaced evenly over the equator can provide continuous world-wide communications. The same thing can be accomplished by orbiting a series of satellites at a lower altitude.

An artificial satellite can also serve as an observing station for the study of the earth's surface, the weather, or some celestial object. Obviously, such satellites have important military applications. American military observation satellites are called Midas (missile defense alarm system) and Samos (satellite and missile observation system).

An early American satellite, Vanguard I, discovered irregularities in the shape of the earth that had not been suspected before. Later vehicles provided continous checks on the world's cloud cover and weather patterns. These meteorological satellites have designations Tiros (television and infrared observation satellites) and Nimbus, the scientific name for a rain cloud.

The names of orbiting observatories are determined by their missions. OSO is an orbiting solar observatory, OAO has astronomical goals, and the OGO is geophysical. Unhampered by the earth's atmosphere, these instruments can obtain data far beyond the capabilities of earthbound installations.

Unmanned exploration of the moon was conducted by the Ranger series of space probes. The lunar photos in Chapter 1 were obtained during this program. In all, Rangers 7, 8, and 9 provided 17,255 pictures of the moon before crashing. In the Surveyor series, cameras and other instruments have been soft-landed on the lunar surface.

The Mariner series of space probes is designed to perform fly-by explorations of the neighboring planets. Mariner 2 provided data on the planet Venus, while Mariner 4 relayed photographs of the Martian surface (see Chapter 14). A comparison of the two vehicles shows the relative distances of the two planets from the sun. Mariner 2 had two panels of solar cells for its flight toward Venus and toward the sun. Mariner 4 required four such panels since it probed a planet that is much farther away from the sun.

The American manned space program began with the Mercury series. The first American to orbit the earth was Col. John Glenn, Jr., who made the flight on February 20, 1962, in a Mercury capsule he had dubbed "Friendship 7," in honor of the seven original American astronauts. After a number of successful Mercury flights, the 2-man Gemini series was launched. Extended flights of two-weeks duration were included in this program, as well as the intricate maneuver of a rendezvous of two space vehicles.

The 3-man Apollo program followed the successful completion of the Gemini flights. Project Apollo has the goal of landing an astronaut on the moon. To accomplish this, the Apollo vehicle is made up of three sections. The Command Module

Fig. 23–7   The first National Aeronautics and Space Administration's Saturn IB vehicle. (NASA)

can accommodate three astronauts in a "shirt-sleeve" environment. It weighs 5 tons and is 12 ft high. It is the only part of the craft that will return to the earth. The Service Module is equipped with rockets so it can maneuver into and out of orbit. It weighs 25 tons and is 23 ft long. It will be jettisoned before the return to earth.

The Lunar Excursion Module (LEM) is the part of the craft that will land on the moon. Two of the astronauts will ride it down to the lunar surface, where it will rest on spider-like legs. The legs and LEM's landing rockets will remain on the moon when the astronauts leave to rejoin the Command and Service modules. The original size of the LEM is about 15 ft and its weight is 12 tons. Obviously, a very powerful booster will be required to launch all this equipment at one time. The rockets being readied for this purpose belong to the Saturn class. Figure 23–7 shows Saturn IB being checked out at its Cape Kennedy launching pad. Saturn V is designed to have a first stage with 7½ million pounds of thrust. The second stage will have a thrust of 1 million pounds. This is enough power to place a 120-ton satellite in orbit around the earth, send a 45-ton craft to the moon, or launch a 30-ton vehicle to Venus or Mars. An even more powerful engine, the Nova, is also under development. It will have two to three times the thrust of the most powerful Saturn rocket.

Russian spacecraft bear the names Sputnik, Lunik, Vostok, Cosmos, Polyot, Elektron, and Voskhod. Lunik 3, which was launched exactly two years after Sputnik I, was the first to transmit photos of the far side of the moon. Successive Sputniks carried dogs; and on April 12, 1961, Vostok I carried the first man into an earth orbit. The Polyot vehicles are believed to be maneuvering experiments. The Elektron launches have been multiple vehicles. The first craft to carry a three-man crew was the Voskhod, launched on October 12, 1964. Russian planetary probes go by the name Zond.

In addition to the immediate goals of the space program, there are a great many "spin-off" benefits. For example, the miniaturized monitoring devices used in space vehicles are already being used in hospitals as continuous checks on patients. The heat resistant substances used in nose cones have been adapted for use in kitchenware. And as part of another space project, deuterium in sea water has been converted into electricity. As a result, it is estimated that a gallon of sea water may some day provide the electric needs for a family of five for an entire year.

Another very important result of the space program has been its impact on the nation's schools. According to many of the nations leading scientists and educators, the space-induced effort to improve science instruction in our schools may alone be worth the cost of all our space science.

## QUESTIONS AND PROBLEMS

1. Give another example of propulsion that, like rocket propulsion, depends on Newton's third law of motion.

2. Compare the relative advantages and disadvantages of solid and liquid fuels.

3. One proposed method of providing artificial weight in a space station is to slowly rotate the station. (a) Which direction would be "down"? (b) Could this provide the same sensation of weight experienced on the earth's surface? (c) Could an equivalent sensation be provided by wearing magnetic shoes in a nonrotating station?

4. Can a space vehicle go beyond the pull of the earth's gravity? Explain.

5. In which direction should a satellite be launched if it is to be placed in orbit with the least expenditure of energy?

6. The first manned trip to a planet is planned for Mars even though Venus is closer. Why might more fuel be required for a round trip to the surface of Venus than to the surface of Mars?

7. After launch, the three mutually perpendicular gyros of the inertial guidance system of an earth satellite are oriented with respect to the earth's surface below, so that gyro A is the roll axis, gyro B is the pitch axis, and gyro C is the yaw axis. (a) Which axes are parallel to the earth's surface and which is perpendicular? (b) Since the gyros maintain their same directions in space, they will have changed their attitudes with respect to the earth's surface after the satellite has completed a quarter revolution. Which gyros now define the roll, pitch, and yaw axes?

8. The initial acceleration of a 10-ton rocket is 1 g. The fuel burns at a constant rate until burnout,

after which the rocket weighs only 1000 lb. (a) What is the mass ratio? (b) What was the acceleration just before burnout?

9. Which of the following would be different for a rocket launched from Mars than for the same rocket launched from the earth: (a) thrust-to-weight ratio; (b) mass ratio; and (c) specific impulse?

10. Suppose two space vehicles, A and B, are launched vertically from the same point on the earth's surface at twice the velocity of escape. Vehicle A is launched at 6 A.M., B at 6 P.M. Both go into elliptical orbits around the sun. (a) Which has the greater velocity with respect to the sun when launched? (b) Which has the greater velocity after traveling half way around the sun? (c) Which comes closer to the sun?

11. If a space vehicle orbiting the earth is in a continual state of free fall, why does it never get any closer to the earth?

12. Find the weight of the following propellants required to supply a thrust of 1000 lb for two minutes: (a) octane and nitric acid, and (b) liquid hydrogen and liquid oxygen. **Ans:** (a) 545 lb.

13. A single-stage rocket has a total weight of 1000 lb, including 800 lb of propellant. It has a thrust-to-weight ratio of 2. How many seconds will the propellant burn if it is (a) cordite, or (b) black gunpowder? **Ans:** (a) 80 sec.

14. If the acceleration of a photon rocket due to the radiation pressure on the sail is 0.001 g, how much will its velocity increase in one year?

15. How many watts would be generated if all the solar energy incident on a mirror mounted on an earth satellite could be converted to electrical energy? Assume the diameter of the mirror is (a) 30 ft, and (b) 50 ft. (The solar constant of 2 cal/min/cm$^2$ is equivalent to 130 watts/ft$^2$.) **Ans:** (a) 92,000.

16. Assuming the average density of micrometeoroids in the vicinity of the earth to be 100 per cubic mile, find the number a satellite could be expected to encounter in one orbit. The satellite is 10 ft in diameter and is in a circular orbit 1000 mi above the earth's surface. **Ans:** About 9.

# Chapter Twenty-four

## The Development of Astronomical Thought

### 24.1 Astronomy Before Copernicus (3000 B.C.-A.D. 1500)

Living as we do in an age of unsurpassed technological achievements, it is perhaps difficult for us to appreciate the difficulties under which the ancient astronomers worked and the things they accomplished. We know that thousands of years ago the Egyptians built the pyramids and oriented them accurately toward the pole star. They therefore knew directions and we can assume that, very early, they recognized the meridian. Their time service was based on the gnomon and on the Grand Gallery in the pyramid of Cheops. The changing directions of shadows, which they used to divide the day into watches or hours, indicate that they recognized the correlation of direction with the positions of the sun and the stars. Observations were also made at sunrise and sunset, although the atmosphere dims the light at those times and interferes with accuracy. Refraction was known at the time of Ptolemy. Credit must be given the Egyptians for a calendar probably as long ago as 4000 B.C.

At the same time there were other civilizations which were also contributing to science. In the region of the Euphrates River, the Babylonian civilization overlapped that in Egypt, beginning approximately 3000 B.C. Others flourished in India as far back as 1500 B.C. and in China to about 1400 B.C. Each civilization had fairly accurate calendars. They all observed the stars, named some of the constellations and observed the motions of the planets.

In America, three civilizations—the Incas, the Aztecs, and the Mayans—were interested in astronomy. The Mayan calendar was especially accurate (surprisingly so, since it was based on very primitive observing methods) and arrived at a solar year of 365.2420 days, which was slightly more accurate than our Gregorian calendar. One historian remarks that "the Mayans were well on the road to rational science" until overrun by the Spaniards.

Many civilizations observed eclipses of both sun and moon. Alexander was given a list of eclipses observed by the Babylonians during the previous 1900 years (that is, to 2200 B.C.). Chinese lists date back to 1361 B.C. The Chinese also listed a nova. Because of wars and invasions, the cultures of most peoples were changed and even terminated. Throughout the ancient world there is evidence of communication between widely scattered regions.

Greek science is considered to have begun at

the time of Thales about 600 B.C. Thales was physician, mathematician, astronomer, and geographer. He was followed by a series of Greek astronomers, who were interested in formulating laws of astronomy. They developed hypotheses about the structure of the universe which led to the work of such noted philosophers as Plato and Aristotle. In the fourth century B.C. there were two schools of thought. One group, headed by Aristarchus, believed that the sun was at the center of the universe, but this theory was discarded until revived by Copernicus almost 1700 years later. The geocentric concept led to the theory of Hipparchus and Ptolemy.

The great museum and library in Alexandria was founded by Ptolemy I (not the astronomer, but the founder of a dynasty of kings of Egypt) about 300 B.C. This center of culture attracted such men as Euclid, the geometrician, and his students, as well as many astronomers and others in different fields of science. The most famous of the astronomers were Hipparchus, who went to Alexandria in the second century B.C. to make observations, and Ptolemy, who continued the work of Hipparchus 300 years later. He wrote the *Almagest,* which contained their theory of the universe. Julius Caesar reformed the calendar with the help of Sosigenes at Alexandria in 45 B.C.

After the breakup of the Greek and Roman civilizations, the study of astronomy passed into the hands of the Arabians, who translated the *Almagest* and made observations for improving Ptolemy's tables. Alhazen, a famous physicist who was known for his work with lenses, lived during this period. Later scientists in Spain, particularly those under the sponsorship of Alfonso X, published lists of stars and their celestial coordinates.

During thousands of years, astronomy made use of other branches of learning. In addition to geometry and trigonometry, the Babylonians used a table of logarithms to help in astronomical computations. Hipparchus was supposed to have used spherical trigonometry, perhaps even invented it, for the solution of triangles on the celestial sphere.

Aristotle's celestial mechanics was based on faulty physics. The world (universe) was divided into two parts, the celestial world and the sublunary world. The celestial world was beyond the moon where he taught that all motion had to be in circles, because motion in a straight line would carry a body out of the universe. Rectilinear motion was possible in the sublunary world, this side of the moon, where vertical motion was permitted. The belief in circular motion carried over into the theories of Hipparchus and Ptolemy and even to the time of Kepler in the early seventeenth century.

## 24.2   The Centuries Following Copernicus ( A.D. 1500– A.D. 1900)

The astronomical revolution started by Copernicus removed the earth from the center of the solar system, formerly considered to be the universe, and placed the sun at the center. This idea had been discussed in Europe for some time and had its beginning in Greece even before Aristarchus, who lived in the second century B.C. Copernicus had been interested in astronomy from the time of his studies in Italy, and, about 1510 published a treatise outlining his beliefs, but without observational or mathematical proof. He assumed a rotating earth in motion around the sun, which he located at the center of the universe. Copernicus retained the belief in circular motion and assumed a system of 34 epicycles to explain the irregular motions of the planets. This theory was enlarged into a larger book, *De Revolutionibus Orbium Coelestium,* (On the Revolutions of the Heavenly Spheres), which was not published until the time of his death in 1543. The theory was slow in being accepted, but the "Copernican system" was thereafter accepted by practically all the world. Copernicus did not make many astronomical observations; and it is said that he recorded only 60 or 70 in his life.

Observational astronomy became much more scientific in the work of Tycho Brahe. The accuracy of his measured positions of stars and planets far surpassed any others made before the invention of the telescope.

In 1576, Thomas Digges in England published a translation of the works of Copernicus in which he made a slight change. He suggested that, instead of being located on the outermost sphere, the stars are scattered throughout space. This was the first time the universe was thought of as being unlimited in extent, although at that time no stellar distances were known. (See Figure 24–1.)

With the invention of the telescope, Galileo became the most important observer. His discovery of the satellites of Jupiter confirmed the heliocentric theory, since the system of Jupiter and its four satellites proved that it is possible for such systems to exist. Galileo's discovery of the phases of Venus provided the death blow to the Ptolemaic theory, since a full phase of Venus would be impossible on the assumption that Venus is always between the earth and the sun.

Kepler's first two laws made it possible to abandon the clumsy systems of epicycles used in the Ptolemaic and Copernican theories. The circle is no more important as a geometrical figure than the ellipse. In fact, the circle is a special form of ellipse. The changing speed of a planet in its elliptical orbit agreed with observation, as did the computation of positions in the orbit. Kepler also discovered the relationship between the distances of the planets from the sun and their periodic times of revolution. He also derived the distance of Mars from the sun in terms of the earth's distance, which was not accurately known.

Newton was born a year after Galileo died. He entered college at age sixteen, was professor of mathematics at twenty-six, and did all of his important scientific work before he was thirty years old. His three laws of motion are the foundation of modern celestial mechanics. They contradict the Greek belief that circular motion is a requirement for planetary motion. Instead, Newton showed that the straight line is the basic path because of inertia, unless the rectilinear motion is changed by a force, which is gravitation. This concept was not original with Newton, but he put this belief into scientific, mathematical language.

Newton and Leibnitz were the two inventors of calculus, without which it would have been almost impossible to prove the theorems of celestial mechanics. The law of gravitation can be derived from Kepler's laws, or Kepler's laws can be derived from the law of gravitation. Newton needed Kepler, and Kepler needed the observations of Tycho. It was a link in the chain of astronomical thought, which has extended through the centuries of the great mathematicians to Einstein and beyond.

### 24.3  Celestial Mechanics and Relativity

The theory of relativity was a modification of celestial mechanics based on Newton's laws. The principal problem of celestial mechanics was the computation of orbits. Improvements in telescopes and the invention of photography and its adaptation to astronomy permitted much more accuracy than the former visual observations provided. With the aid of the Newtonian theory of gravitation, the computation of orbits was systematized in the nineteenth century. The theory of gravitation predicts that the planets are pulled out of their orbits by the attractions of all the others. The changes in the positions of planets in their orbits are called perturbations. It was the perturbation by an unknown force on Uranus that led to the discovery of Neptune in the middle of the nineteenth century and started the Lowell Observatory search for still another planet, and Pluto was found in 1930.

In addition, there was a change in the orbit of Mercury which was not accounted for by the Newtonian theory. Because of perturbations, all elliptical planetary orbits should be in slow rotation. By using all the known perturbations, the orbit of Mercury was calculated to rotate (Figure 24–2) at the rate of 531″ in 100 years. The measured rate is 574″ (a difference of 43″ per century). This was explained by

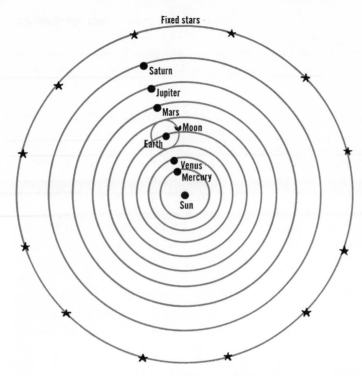

Fixed stars

Saturn

Jupiter

Mars

Moon

Earth

Venus

Mercury

Sun

Fig. 24–1  Copernicus' model of the universe (top).
This system simplified cosmology and was a major
advance in the development of astronomy. In his
conception of the heavens, Thomas Digges improved
the Copernican system by scattering the stars at random in space (bottom). ("Scientific American" diagrams).

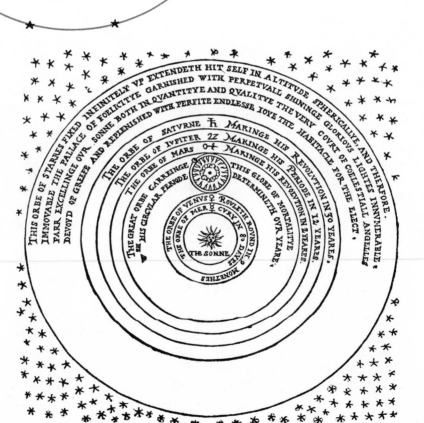

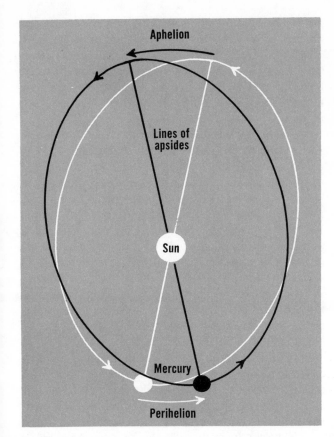

Fig. 24–2 The rotation of the orbit of Mercury, called the advance of the perihelion, due to perturbations by other planets.

Einstein. In his theory of relativity, the mass and length of a moving body change with its velocity, according to the following equations:

$$l = l_0 \sqrt{1 - \frac{v^2}{c^2}} \text{ and } m = \frac{m_0}{\sqrt{1 - \frac{v^2}{c^2}}} \quad (24\text{–}1)$$

In equations 24–1, $l$ and $m$ are the length and mass of the moving body; $l_0$ and $m_0$ are its length and mass when at rest; $v$ is its velocity and $c$ is the velocity of light.

From Kepler's second law, the velocity of Mercury in its orbit increases from apogee to perigee by about 50 percent. Therefore, the mass of Mercury changes by a small amount. But this change of mass is enough to provide the extra perturbation, which accounts for the 43″ discrepancy in the advance of Mercury's perihelion. This was the first confirmation of the theory of relativity.

A second confirmation came in 1919 from observations made before and during a total eclipse of the sun. Relativity predicted that the path of a light beam near a massive body is deflected by its gravitational field of influence. Photographs of the star field, where the sun was predicted to be during the eclipse, were made before the eclipse. During totality, photographs showed that the light was indeed deflected and the amount was almost exactly that predicted. (Figure 24–3) Later eclipse data agreed with the results of 1919.

According to the theory of relativity, when light leaves the gravitational field of influence of the sun or a star, it is slowed and the lines in its spectrum are shifted toward the red. This is a relativity correction to the Doppler effect. The effect on the sun cannot be measured exactly, because of other motions, such as the flow of material in a sunspot. But in the companion of Sirius, a white dwarf, the effect is measurable. The measured velocity of Sirius B is not the same as its velocity in the orbit, which is known from the study of Sirius as a visual binary system. This apparent change in velocity is the same as predicted by the relativity Doppler effect and therefore is a third confirmation of the theory.

Thus there are at least three predictions which have been checked by observation and the theory of relativity is almost universally accepted by astronomers. In computing the distance-velocity relation of the quasi-stellar sources in Chapter 22, a relativity Doppler formula was used.

## 24.4 Conclusion

During the millenia before Copernicus, the universe was thought to consist of the stationary earth at the

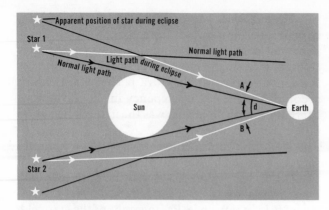

Fig. 24–3 The bending of light in a gravitational field. The straight lines are direct, normal paths of light from two stars. During an eclipse of the sun, the light rays are bent by the sun's gravitational field of influence.

center of a small system, which consisted of seven planets and the sphere of the stars. An exception to this theory was made by a few Greek philosophers, who thought the sun to be the center. This latter idea was revived by Copernicus and thereafter the sun was thought to be at the center of a system of planets called the solar system.

Using Digges' suggestion that the stars are scattered throughout the universe, Herschel placed the sun among the stars, although no distances were known. (See Figure 21–2.) With the measurement of the first stellar parallaxes and therefore distances, it was realized that the universe is very large. At the beginning of the twentieth century, the Milky Way became important as the system to which the sun belongs and the sun was placed approximately at the center. This universe was thought of as a nearly flat entity of stars. In addition to the stars, other smaller systems like the globular clusters and the so-called spiral nebulae were considered part of the Milky Way system.

Then came the discovery that the Andromeda Nebula was nearly 1,000,000 light years away and that there were other similar nebulae. And when, in

particular, some systems were found to be composed of stars, as was shown by their spectra to be the case, and were resolved into stars by photography, they were called *island universes* and were thought to be like our Milky Way system except for size. The name *galaxy* was finally substituted for the word nebula.

Thereafter, *cosmology,* the study of the design and extent of the universe, developed rapidly. The galaxies were found to be nearly uniformly scattered through a universe, which Einstein once thought to be infinite in size. They were found to be moving away from us and from each other. During the 1920s, the theory of the expanding universe was a popular astronomical topic. Our galaxy was placed in a small group of galaxies—the Local Group—and it was estimated that there were 100 million galaxies in reach of the 100-inch telescope. The location of the center of the expanding universe was, and still is unknown. Observation with the 200-inch telescope has helped greatly in these studies.

At the present time, our attention is turning toward the theories of evolution of the galaxies and of the universe and the possibility of life outside our own solar system. Space explorations have almost ruled out any notion of life on Venus and Mars, which were once thought to be the most likely planets capable of supporting life. We are waiting for the time to come when we can leave our earth, land on the moon and on Mars, and even send expeditions to stars beyond our solar system. But even at the speed of light—and according to the theory of relativity, we are limited to this speed—it would take a space ship more than four years to reach the nearest star. At our present attainable speeds, the time of flight would be prohibitively long.

We are also interested in the state of matter in other regions of the universe. One guess is that the universe is half antimatter, but there is little evidence of it in our part of the universe. We have no hope at present of discovering life like our own, unless we can reach some star like our sun with planets at just the right distance to support life.

Progress has been made in recent years with theories of evolution of stars and galaxies, but many points still need to be confirmed and others to be developed. Radio astronomy has been invaluable. Theoretical astronomy is expected to advance rapidly with the help of observations made with huge radio telescopes which are being built in many parts of the world. More large optical instruments, such as other 200-inch telescopes, are needed and can be expected to be put into operation in the near future.

High-speed electronic computers are essential in all kinds of problems which would take an impossibly long time to solve with desk calculators. Computers are presently being used to solve problems concerning the orbits of satellites as well as problems dealing with the flight paths of lunar and planetary space ships. Computers are also important in theoretically investigating the internal structure of stars, a vital part of any theory of stellar evolution.

The number of astronomers and scientists needed in basic astronomy and related fields is growing rapidly, but many more are needed. Observational discoveries and new theories in all branches of astronomy are progressing side by side. Some scientists are thinking in terms of communications from outside the earth, but so far no contact has been made. But perhaps many questions about the state of matter and the possibility of life outside the solar system will be answered in our lifetime. Who knows?

## QUESTIONS AND PROBLEMS

1. List the most important changes in astronomical theories from the time of the most ancient civilization to the present time.
2. List the most important astronomical discoveries since the invention of the telescope.

# Appendixes

## A. METRIC-ENGLISH EQUIVALENTS

| | | | |
|---|---|---|---|
| 1 in = | 2.540 cm | 1 cm = | 0.3937 in |
| 1 in² = | 6.452 cm² | 1 cm² = | 0.1550 in² |
| 1 ft = | 30.48 cm | 1 cm³ = | 0.0610 in³ |
| 1 mi = | 1.6093 km | 1 m = | 39.37 in |
| 1 qt = | 0.946 liter | 1 l = | 1.06 qt |
| 1 oz = | 28.35 g | 1 g = | 0.03527 oz |
| 1 lb = | 453.6 g | 1 kg = | 2.205 lb |
| 1 ton = | 0.9065 metric ton | 1 metric ton = | 1.102 tons = $10^6$ g |

## B. SCIENTIFIC NOTATION

In scientific work, very large and very small numbers are usually written as the product of a number from 1 to 9 and a power of 10. This is called **scientific,** or *standard,* **notation.** For example, 316,000,000 is written as $3.16 \times 10^8$. The power of 10 indicates the position of the decimal point. If it is positive, the decimal point must be moved to the right. In the example just given, the decimal point must be moved eight places to the right. If the power of 10 is negative, then the decimal point must be moved to the left. For example, $4.73 \times 10^{-6}$ stands for the number 0.00000473. (See the additional examples below.)

*If the number is:*
$$6,030,000,000$$
$$7850$$
$$0.0346$$
$$0.00000000902$$

*The scientific notation is:*
$$6.03 \times 10^9$$
$$7.85 \times 10^3$$
$$3.46 \times 10^{-2}$$
$$9.02 \times 10^{-9}$$

Scientific notation has several significant advantages over the ordinary way of writing numbers. For one thing, it makes long numbers easy to read and to compare with each other. Hence, in lengthy problems, it is possible to estimate (and thus check) the answer quite readily. Another important aspect of this method is the fact that the first part of the number can be used to indicate the precision of a measurement. Thus, $3.724 \times 10^4$ centimeters is a more precise measurement than is $3.72 \times 10^4$ centimeters.

## C. TEMPERATURE CONVERSIONS

To change from Fahrenheit (F) to Celsius (C), use the formula:

$$°C = \frac{5}{9}(F - 32°)$$

For example, $40° F = \frac{5}{9}(40° - 32°) = 4.4° C$.

To change from Celsius to Fahrenheit, use the formula:

$$°F = \frac{9}{5}C + 32°$$

For example, 20° C = ⅗ (20°) + 32° = 68° F.

The Kelvin (K) reading is always 273° more than the Celsius reading for the same temperature. For example, 250° C = 250° + 273° = 523° K.

### D. RADIAN MEASURE

Calculations involving small angles can be simplified by using a unit of measurement called the **radian** (abbreviated *rad*) instead of degrees. As shown in the diagram below, the radian is related to the radius r of a circle. When two radii cut off a segment of a circle which is equal in length to a radius, the angle formed by the two radii equals one radian.

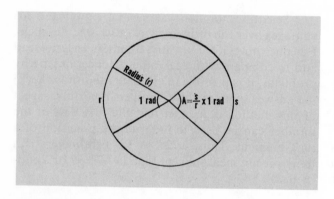

The angle between any two radii is proportional to the segment s of the circle which they cut off. That is, the larger the angle, the larger the segment. Hence, any angle can be expressed in terms of radians. For example, angle A in the above diagram is:

$$A = \frac{s}{r} \times 1 \text{ rad}$$

Since the circumference of a circle equals $2\pi r$, and $2\pi$ equals 6.28 (approximately), it follows that there are 6.28 radians in a 360° angle. In order to find the number of degrees in one radian, therefore, we can use the following formula:

$$1 \text{ rad} = \frac{360°}{2\pi} = 57.3° \text{ or } 3438' \text{ or } 206,265''$$

If an angle is very small, as in the case of the slender triangles used in finding the distances to the moon and the sun, the straight line between two points on a circle is almost equal to the corresponding curved segment, as shown in the diagram below. In distance problems, this straight line is called the *base line*.

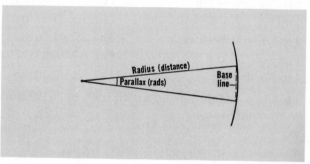

Thus, the formula for the size of the angle becomes:

$$\text{angle (in rads)} = \frac{\text{length of base line}}{\text{length of radius}}$$

In distance problems, the radius is the distance to be measured and the angle is the *parallax*. So the previous formula is solved for the radius as follows:

$$\text{length of radius (distance)} = \frac{\text{length of base line}}{\text{parallax (in rads)}}$$

If the parallax is in degrees, the right side of the formula must be multiplied by 57.3°. It is important to remember, however, that the formula is accurate only when the angle involved is very small.

## E.  TABLE OF PLANETARY ORBITAL ELEMENTS FOR FEB. 9, 1965 †

| Planet | a (a.u.) | e | i (degrees) | Ω (degrees) | ω (degrees) | Time of Perihelion |
|---|---|---|---|---|---|---|
| Mercury | 0.387099 | 0.205628 | 7.00408 | 47.91768 | 76.91256 | 1965 Mar. 15 |
| Venus | 0.723332 | 0.006789 | 3.39429 | 76.36569 | 131.08016 | 1965 Jun. 18 |
| Earth | 1.000000 | 0.01673 | | | 281.396 | 1966 Jan. 2 |
| Mars | 1.523691 | 0.093373 | 1.84990 | 49.28841 | 335.41673 | 1966 Jan. 19 |
| Ceres | 2.7673 | 0.0765 | 10.615 | | | |
| Jupiter | 5.202274 | 0.048226 | 1.30605 | 100.0990 | 13.4206 | |
| Saturn | 9.561192 | 0.054753 | 2.48832 | 113.3923 | 89.6567 | |
| Uranus | 19.17362 | 0.046364 | 0.77249 | 73.8345 | 168.5705 | |
| Neptune | 29.95278 | 0.012348 | 1.77296 | 131.4362 | 45.9009 | |
| Pluto | 39.36621 | 0.246228 | 17.13438 | 109.7854 | 223.6408 | |

† See Section 14.2 for definitions of the elements.

## F. TABLE OF NATURAL SATELLITES

| Name | Discoverer | Date | Mean Distance (miles) | Sidereal Period (days) | Apparent Magnitude | Diameter (miles) |
|---|---|---|---|---|---|---|
| **EARTH** | | | | | | |
| Moon | | | 238,857 | 27.32 | −12.6 | 2160 |
| **MARS** | | | | | | |
| Phobos | A. Hall | 1877 | 5,800 | 0.319 | 12 | 5? |
| Deimos | A. Hall | 1877 | 14,600 | 1.262 | 13 | 3? |
| **JUPITER** | | | | | | |
| V | Barnard | 1892 | 112,000 | 0.497 | 13 | 100? |
| Io (I) | Galileo | 1610 | 262,000 | 1.769 | 6 | 2000 |
| Europa (II) | Galileo | 1610 | 417,000 | 3.552 | 6 | 1800 |
| Ganymede (III) | Galileo | 1610 | 665,000 | 7.155 | 5 | 3100 |
| Callisto (IV) | Galileo | 1610 | 1,170,000 | 16.689 | 6 | 2800 |
| VI | Perrine | 1904 | 7,100,000 | 251 | 14 | 70? |
| X | Nicholson | 1938 | 7,200,000 | 254 | 19 | 10? |
| VII | Perrine | 1905 | 7,300,000 | 260 | 18 | 20? |
| XII | Nicholson | 1951 | 13,000,000 | 625 (ret) | 19 | 10? |
| XI | Nicholson | 1938 | 14,300,000 | 714 (ret) | 19 | 15? |
| VIII | Melotte | 1908 | 14,600,000 | 735 (ret) | 18 | 20? |
| IX | Nicholson | 1914 | 14,700,000 | 758 (ret) | 19 | 15? |
| **SATURN** | | | | | | |
| Mimas | Herschel | 1789 | 115,000 | 0.944 | 12 | 300? |
| Janus | Dollfus | 1966 | 99,500 | | 14 | 75? |
| Enceladus | Herschel | 1789 | 147,000 | 1.370 | 12 | 350? |

| Name | Discoverer | Date | Mean Distance (miles) | Sidereal Period (days) | Apparent Magnitude | Diameter (miles) |
|------|-----------|------|----------------------|----------------------|-------------------|------------------|
| Tethys | Cassini | 1684 | 183,000 | 1.888 | 10 | 630 |
| Dione | Cassini | 1684 | 234,000 | 2.737 | 11 | 550 |
| Rhea | Cassini | 1672 | 327,000 | 4.517 | 10 | 800 |
| Titan | Huygens | 1655 | 758,000 | 15.944 | 8 | 3000 |
| Hyperion | Bond | 1848 | 919,000 | 21.276 | 13 | 200? |
| Iapetus | Cassini | 1671 | 2,207,000 | 79.3 | 10 | 700? |
| Phoebe | Pickering | 1898 | 8,034,000 | 550 (ret) | 15 | 100? |
| **URANUS** | | | | | | |
| Miranda | Kuiper | 1948 | 81,000 | 1.414 | 17 | 200? |
| Ariel | Lassell | 1851 | 119,000 | 2.520 | 15 | 450? |
| Umbriel | Lassell | 1851 | 166,000 | 4.144 | 15 | 350? |
| Titania | Herschel | 1787 | 272,000 | 8.705 | 14 | 700? |
| Oberon | Herschel | 1787 | 364,000 | 13.463 | 14 | 600? |
| **NEPTUNE** | | | | | | |
| Triton | Lassell | 1846 | 220,000 | 5.877 (ret) | 14 | 2000? |
| Nereid | Kuiper | 1949 | 3,500,000 | 359 | 19 | 200? |

## G. GREEK ALPHABET

| | | | | | | | | |
|---|---|---|---|---|---|---|---|---|
| A, | $\alpha$ | alpha | I, | $\iota$ | iota | P, | $\rho$ | rho |
| B, | $\beta$ | beta | K, | $\kappa$ | kappa | $\Sigma$, | $\sigma$ | sigma |
| $\Gamma$, | $\gamma$ | gamma | $\Lambda$, | $\lambda$ | lambda | T, | $\tau$ | tau |
| $\Delta$ | $\delta$ | delta | M, | $\mu$ | mu | $\Upsilon$, | $\upsilon$ | upsilon |
| E, | $\varepsilon$ | epsilon | N, | $\nu$ | nu | $\Phi$, | $\phi$ | phi |
| Z, | $\zeta$ | zeta | $\Xi$, | $\xi$ | xi | X, | $\chi$ | chi |
| H, | $\eta$ | eta | O, | $o$ | omicron | $\Psi$, | $\psi$ | psi |
| $\Theta$, | $\theta$ | theta | $\Pi$, | $\pi$ | pi | $\Omega$, | $\omega$ | omega |

### Table I

**First 2 Digits of Old Style Years**

| First 2 Digits | | col c | col d | col e | col f | col g | col a | col b |
|---|---|---|---|---|---|---|---|---|
| 0 . . . | 14 . . . | c | d | e | f | g | a | b |
| 1 . . . | 15 . . . | b | c | d | e | f | g | a |
| 2 . . . | 16 . . . | a | b | c | d | e | f | g |
| 3 . . . | 17 . . . | g | a | b | c | d | e | f |
| 4 . . . | 18 . . . | f | g | a | b | c | d | e |
| 5 . . . | 19 . . . | e | f | g | a | b | c | d |
| 6 . . . | 20 . . . | d | e | f | g | a | b | c |

**Last 2 Digits of Years**

| col c | col d | col e | col f | col g | col a | col b |
|---|---|---|---|---|---|---|
| **00** 06 | 01 07 | 02 | 03 **08** 14 | 09 15 **20** 26 | **04** 10 | 05 11 **16** 22 |
| 17 23 | **12** 18 | 13 19 | 25 31 **36** 42 | 37 43 **48** 54 | 21 27 **32** 38 | 33 39 **44** 50 |
| **28** 34 | 29 35 | **24** 30 | 53 59 **64** 70 | 65 71 **76** 82 | 49 55 **60** 66 | 61 67 **72** 78 |
| 45 51 | **40** 46 | 41 47 | 81 87 **92** 98 | 93 99 | 77 83 **88** 94 | 89 95 |
| **56** 62 | 57 63 | **52** 58 | | | | |
| 73 79 | **68** 74 | 69 75 | | | | |
| **84** 90 | 85 91 | **80** 86 | | | | |
| | **96** | 97 | | | | |

**Remarks**

1. The numbers in heavy type [56, 64] indicate leap years in the New Style.
2. Years divisible by 400 are leap years in the New Style.
3. The first day of the New Style accepted by the Catholic Church—October 15, 1582.
4. The first day of the New Style accepted in Protestant Germany, March 1, 1700.

**First 2 Digits of New Style Years**

|  | |  |  |  |  |  |  |  |
|---|---|---|---|---|---|---|---|---|
| 26 . . . | 18 . . . | a | b | c | d | e | f | g |
| 25 . . . | 17 . . . | c | d | e | f | g | a | b |
| 24 . . . | 16 . . . | e | f | g | a | b | c | d |
| 23 . . . | 15 . . . | f | g | a | b | c | d | e |

### Table II

|  | | | | | | | |
|---|---|---|---|---|---|---|---|
| LEAP YEAR JANUARY | g | a | b | c | d | e | f |
| LEAP YEAR FEBRUARY | d | e | f | g | a | b | c |
| January | f | g | a | b | c | d | e |
| February | c | d | e | f | g | a | b |
| March | c | d | e | f | g | a | b |
| April | g | a | b | c | d | e | f |
| May | e | f | g | a | b | c | d |
| June | b | c | d | e | f | g | a |
| July | g | a | b | c | d | e | f |
| August | d | e | f | g | a | b | c |
| September | a | b | c | d | e | f | g |
| October | f | g | a | b | c | d | e |
| November | c | d | e | f | g | a | b |
| December | a | b | c | d | e | f | g |
| 1. 8. 15. 22. 29. | M | Tu | W | Th | F | Sa | S |
| 2. 9. 16. 23. 30. | Tu | W | Th | F | Sa | S | M |
| 3. 10. 17. 24. 31. | W | Th | F | Sa | S | M | Tu |
| 4. 11. 18. 25. | Th | F | Sa | S | M | Tu | W |
| 5. 12. 19. 26. | F | Sa | S | M | Tu | W | Th |
| 6. 13. 20. 27. | Sa | S | M | Tu | W | Th | F |
| 7. 14. 21. 28. | S | M | Tu | W | Th | F | Sa |

**Abbreviations**

M = Monday, Tu = Tuesday, W = Wednesday
Th = Thursday, F = Friday, Sa = Saturday
S = Sunday.

**Instructions**

1. Locate in Table I the letter which corresponds to the intersection of the row of First 2 Digits of Years and the column of Last 2 Digits of Years. (Use New or Old Style years as necessary.)
2. Locate this letter in the row of the month of Table II.
3. Follow the column of this letter to the intersection of the row with the given date of the month. The intersection will give the day of the week.

# I. WORLD CALENDAR

| FIRST QUARTER | | |
|---|---|---|

| JANUARY | FEBRUARY | MARCH |
|---|---|---|
| S M T W T F S | S M T W T F S | S M T W T F S |
| 1 2 3 4 5 6 7 |       1 2 3 4 |           1 2 |
| 8 9 10 11 12 13 14 | 5 6 7 8 9 10 11 | 3 4 5 6 7 8 9 |
| 15 16 17 18 19 20 21 | 12 13 14 15 16 17 18 | 10 11 12 13 14 15 16 |
| 22 23 24 25 26 27 28 | 19 20 21 22 23 24 25 | 17 18 19 20 21 22 23 |
| 29 30 31 | 26 27 28 29 30 | 24 25 26 27 28 29 30 |

| SECOND QUARTER | | |
|---|---|---|

| APRIL | MAY | JUNE |
|---|---|---|
| S M T W T F S | S M T W T F S | S M T W T F S |
| 1 2 3 4 5 6 7 |       1 2 3 4 |           1 2 |
| 8 9 10 11 12 13 14 | 5 6 7 8 9 10 11 | 3 4 5 6 7 8 9 |
| 15 16 17 18 19 20 21 | 12 13 14 15 16 17 18 | 10 11 12 13 14 15 16 |
| 22 23 24 25 26 27 28 | 19 20 21 22 23 24 25 | 17 18 19 20 21 22 23 |
| 29 30 31 | 26 27 28 29 30 | 24 25 26 27 28 29 30 |
| | | ** W |

| THIRD QUARTER | | |
|---|---|---|

| JULY | AUGUST | SEPTEMBER |
|---|---|---|
| S M T W T F S | S M T W T F S | S M T W T F S |
| 1 2 3 4 5 6 7 |       1 2 3 4 |           1 2 |
| 8 9 10 11 12 13 14 | 5 6 7 8 9 10 11 | 3 4 5 6 7 8 9 |
| 15 16 17 18 19 20 21 | 12 13 14 15 16 17 18 | 10 11 12 13 14 15 16 |
| 22 23 24 25 26 27 28 | 19 20 21 22 23 24 25 | 17 18 19 20 21 22 23 |
| 29 30 31 | 26 27 28 29 30 | 24 25 26 27 28 29 30 |

| FOURTH QUARTER | | |
|---|---|---|

| OCTOBER | NOVEMBER | DECEMBER |
|---|---|---|
| S M T W T F S | S M T W T F S | S M T W T F S |
| 1 2 3 4 5 6 7 |       1 2 3 4 |           1 2 |
| 8 9 10 11 12 13 14 | 5 6 7 8 9 10 11 | 3 4 5 6 7 8 9 |
| 15 16 17 18 19 20 21 | 12 13 14 15 16 17 18 | 10 11 12 13 14 15 16 |
| 22 23 24 25 26 27 28 | 19 20 21 22 23 24 25 | 17 18 19 20 21 22 23 |
| 29 30 31 | 26 27 28 29 30 | 24 25 26 27 28 29 30 |
| | | * W |

* The Year-End World Holiday, W or 31 December (365th day), follows 30 December every year.

** The Leap-Year World Holiday, W or 31 June (an extra day), follows 30 June in leap years.

## J. BIBLIOGRAPHY

*(The more technical references are marked with an asterisk)*

### General Texts

Baker, R. H. *Astronomy,* 8th ed. Princeton, N.J.: D. Van Nostrand Company, Inc., 1964.

Krogdahl, W., *The Astronomical Universe.* New York: The Macmillan Company, 1962.

McLaughlin, D. B., *Introduction to Astronomy.* Boston, Mass.: Houghton Mifflin Company, 1961.

Motz, L. and Duveen, A., *Essentials of Astronomy.* Belmont, Calif.: Wadsworth Publishing Company, 1966.

Russell, H. N., Dugan, R. S., and Stewart, J. Q., *Astronomy* (2 vols.), Boston, Mass.: Ginn and Company, 1945; 1938.

Struve, O., Lynds, B., and Pillans, H., *Elementary Astronomy.* New York: Oxford University Press, 1959.

### More Elementary Texts

Alter, D., Clemenshaw, C. H., and Phillips, J., *Pictorial Astronomy.* New York: Thomas Y. Crowell Company, 1963.

Inglis, S. J., *Planets, Stars and Galaxies,* 2nd ed. John Wiley and Sons, Inc., 1967.

Trinklein, F. E. and Huffer, C. M., *Modern Space Science.* New York: Holt, Rinehart and Winston, Inc., 1961.

### History of Astronomy; History of Science

Berry, A., *A Short History of Astronomy.* New York: Dover Publications, 1960.

Hoyle, F., *Astronomy.* New York: Doubleday and Company, Inc., 1962.

Pannekoek, A., *A History of Astronomy.* New York: Interscience Publishers, 1961.

Sarton, G., *Introduction to the History of Science* (3 vols.), Baltimore, Md.: Williams and Wilkins, 1947.

Shapley, H., and Howarth, H. E., *Source Book in Astronomy.* New York: McGraw-Hill Book Company, Inc., 1929.

Struve, O., *Astronomy of the Twentieth Century.* New York: The Macmillan Company, 1962.

Taton, R., *Ancient and Medieval Science.* New York: Basic Books, 1963.

Vaucouleurs, G. de, *Discovery of the Universe.* New York: The Macmillan Company, 1957.

### Celestial Mechanics

*Baker, R., and Makemson, M., *Introduction to Astrodynamics.* New York: Academic Press, Inc., 1960.

*Danby, J. M. A., *Fundamentals of Celestial Mechanics.* New York: The Macmillan Company, 1962.

*Moulton, F. R., *An Introduction to Celestial Mechanics.* New York: The Macmillan Company, 1923.

Ryabov, Y., *An Elementary Survey of Celestial Mechanics.* New York: Dover Publications, 1961.

*Sterne, T., *An Introduction to Celestial Mechanics.* New York: Interscience Publishers, Inc., 1960.

### Space Science

*Blanco, V., and McCuskey, S., *Basic Physics of the Solar System.* Reading, Mass.: Addison-Wesley Publishing Company, 1961.

Newell, H. E., *Express to the Stars.* New York: McGraw-Hill Book Company, Inc., 1961.

## Optics and Telescopes

*Jenkins, F. A., and White, H. E., *Fundamentals of Optics*. New York: McGraw-Hill Book Company, Inc., 1950.

*Kuiper, G., and Middlehurst, B. (editors), *Telescopes*. (Volume I of *Compendium of Stars and Stellar Systems*). Chicago, Ill.: University of Chicago Press, 1960.

Miczaika, G., and Sinton, W., *Tools of the Astronomer*. Cambridge, Mass.: Harvard University Press, 1961.

*Sears, F. W., *Optics*. Reading, Mass.: Addison-Wesley Publishing Company, 1949.

Steinberg, J. L., and Lequeux, J., *Radio Astronomy*. New York: McGraw-Hill Book Company, Inc., 1963.

## Earth and Solar System

Hawkins, G. S., *Meteors, Comets, and Meteorites*. New York: McGraw-Hill Book Company, Inc., 1964.

Jastrow, R., *The Exploration of Space*. New York: The Macmillan Company, 1960.

*Kuiper, G. (editor), *The Atmospheres of the Earth and Planets*. Chicago, Ill.: University of Chicago Press, 1957.

*Kuiper, G. (editor), *The Earth as a Planet*. Chicago, Ill.: University of Chicago Press, 1954.

Menzel, D., *Our Sun*. Cambridge, Mass.: Harvard University Press, 1959.

Watson, F., *Between the Planets*. Cambridge, Mass.: Harvard University Press, 1956.

Whipple, F., *Earth, Moon, and Planets*. New York: McGraw-Hill Book Company, Inc., Blakiston Division, 1941.

## Stellar Astrophysics

*Aller, L. H., *Astrophysics* (2 vols.). New York: The Ronald Press Company, 1953; 1954.

Bok, B. J., and Bok, P. F., *The Milky Way*. Cambridge, Mass.: Harvard University Press, 1957.

Campbell, L., and Jacchia, L., *The Story of Variable Stars*. New York: McGraw-Hill Book Company, Inc., Blakiston Division, 1941.

Goldberg, L., and Aller, L. H., *Atoms, Stars, and Nebulae*. New York: McGraw-Hill Book Company, Inc., Blakiston Division, 1943.

*Hynek, J. A. (editor), *Astrophysics, a Topical Symposium*. New York: McGraw-Hill Book Company, Inc., 1951.

*Schwarzschild, M., *Structure and Evolution of the Stars*. Princeton, N.J.: Princeton University Press, 1958.

## Galaxies and Cosmology

Baade, W., *Evolution of Stars and Galaxies*. Cambridge, Mass.: Harvard University Press, 1963.

*Bondi, H., *Cosmology*. New York: Cambridge University Press, 1960.

Bondi, H., *The Universe at Large*. New York: Doubleday and Company, 1960.

*Couderc, P., *The Expansion of the Universe*. London: Faber and Faber, Ltd., 1952.

Couderc, P., *The Wider Universe*. New York: Harper & Row, 1960.

Duquesne, M., *Matter and Antimatter*. New York: Harper & Row, 1960.

Hubble, E., *The Realm of the Nebulae*. New Haven, Conn.: Yale University Press, 1936.

Maran, S. P. and Cameron, A. G. W., *Physics of Nonthermal Radio Sources*. NASA, 1964.

*McVittie, G C., *Fact and Theory in Cosmology*. New York: The Macmillan Company, 1961.

Page, T. (editor), *Stars and Galaxies*. Englewood Cliffs, N.J.: Prentice-Hall, 1962.

Piddington, J. H., *Radio Astronomy*. New York: Harper & Row, 1961.

Rossi, B., *Cosmic Rays*. New York: McGraw-Hill Book Company, 1964.

Sandage, A. R., *The Hubble Atlas of Galaxies.* Washington, D.C.: Carnegie Institution, 1961.

Sciama, D. W., *The Unity of the Universe.* New York: Doubleday and Company, Inc., 1959.

Shapley, H., *The Inner Metagalaxy.* New Haven, Conn.: Yale University Press, 1957.

### Journals and Periodicals

*Astronomical Journal,* published by the Yale University Observatory, New Haven, Conn., 06520.

*Astrophysical Journal,* published eight times per year by the University of Chicago Press, Chicago, Ill., 60637.

*The Griffith Observer,* published monthly by the Griffith Observatory, Los Angeles, California, 90027.

*The Review of Popular Astronomy,* published bimonthly by Sky Map Publications, Inc., St. Louis, Mo., 63105.

*Leaflets and* *Publications of the Astronomical Society of the Pacific,* published monthly and bimonthly, respectively, by the Society, care of the California Academy of Sciences, Golden Gate Park, San Francisco, California, 94118.

*Sky and Telescope,* published monthly by the Sky Publishing Corporation, Harvard College Observatory, Cambridge, Mass., 02138.

# Glossary

**aberration of starlight.** Apparent displacement of a star on the celestial sphere due to the speed of light and the rotation or revolution of the earth.

**absolute magnitude.** Apparent brightness of stars when observed from a distance of 10 parsecs (32.6 light years), expressed in magnitudes.

**absolute zero.** The lowest temperature ($-273°$C), called $0°$K, where almost all molecular motion stops.

**absorption spectrum.** Dark lines superposed on a continuous spectrum, due to the absorption by a cool gas in front of a hot source.

**acceleration.** Rate of change of velocity; may be either positive (an increase) or negative (a decrease).

**achromatic objective.** A telescope lens of two or more components to correct for chromatic aberration.

**active sun.** The sun when producing an unusual number of spots and accompanying phenomena, as during the IGY.

**advance of the perigee.** The eastward rotation of the orbit of the moon or artificial satellite around the earth.

**advance of the perihelion.** The eastward rotation of the orbit of a planet, particularly Mercury.

**albedo.** The ratio of the light reflected by an object, especially the moon or a planet, to the total amount of light shining on it; reflective power.

**alpha particle.** A positively charged particle, consisting of two protons and two neutrons, emitted from the nucleus of a radioactive atom; the nucleus of a helium atom.

**altitude.** The angle between the celestial horizon and a celestial object, measured along its vertical circle.

**angle of incidence.** The angle between an incoming ray and the perpendicular to a reflecting or refracting surface.

**angstrom.** A unit of length used to measure wavelengths of light; $10^{-8}$ cm.

**angular diameter.** The angle between two opposite sides of an object.

**angular distance.** The angle between two objects on the celestial sphere.

**angular momentum.** The quantity of motion of a body due to its rotation; angular momentum $= mr^2\omega$.

**annular eclipse.** An eclipse of the sun where only a ring of the sun is visible around the moon when the moon is too distant to cover the sun completely.

**antimatter.** Matter made up of antiparticles.

**antiparticles.** A particle with the same mass as its counterpart, such as antiproton instead of proton, with opposite electrical charge and other basic physical differences.

**aphelion.** The point in the orbit of a planet or other body where it is farthest from the sun.

**apogee.** The point in the orbit of the moon or artificial satellite where it is farthest from the earth.

**apparent magnitude.** The brightness of a star or other celestial object as seen from the earth.

**apparent noon.** The time when the center of the sun is on the meridian.

355

**apparent solar day.**   The interval between two successive transits of the sun's center across the meridian.

**apparent sun.**   The real sun that moves along the ecliptic.

**appulse.**   A penumbral eclipse of the moon.

**ascending node.**   The point where the orbit of a celestial body crosses the ecliptic from south to north; the point where the orbit of an artificial satellite crosses the earth's equator from south to north.

**association.**   A group of stars with nearly the same physical characteristics, indicating that they probably had the same origin.

**asteroid.**   A small body in orbit around the sun, usually between the orbits of Mars and Jupiter; a minor planet; a planetoid.

**astrometrics.**   The branch of astronomy that deals with the accurate measurement of positions and motions of astronomical objects.

**astronomical unit.**   The mean distance between the earth and the sun as fixed by international agreement in 1900; 92,870,000 mi.

**astronomy.**   The branch of science that deals with the location, motion, and nature of objects in space.

**astrophysics.**   The branch of astronomy that applies the instruments and theories of physics to the study of the nature of celestial bodies.

**atom.**   The smallest particle of an element that has all the properties of the element.

**atomic number.**   The number of protons in the nucleus of an atom; the number of electrons surrounding the nucleus of a neutral atom.

**atomic theory.**   The modern theory of the structure of atoms.

**atomic weight.**   The relative mass of an atom compared to carbon 12.

**aurora.**   A colorful radiation above the earth's polar regions; northern or southern lights.

**autumnal equinox.**   The point on the celestial equator where the sun crosses it on the first day of autumn; R.A. $12^h$; Decl. $0°$.

**Avogadro's number.**   The number of molecules ($6.0238 \times 10^{23}$) in 1 g of hydrogen.

**azimuth.**   The angle measured eastward along the celestial horizon between the north point and the vertical circle through a given object.

**Balmer lines.**   A series of emission or absorption lines of hydrogen in the visible part of the spectrum.

**barred spiral.**   A spiral galaxy having an elongated nucleus with an arm extending from each end.

**beta particle.**   A negatively charged particle emitted from the nucleus of a radioactive atom; an electron.

**"big bang" theory.**   A theory of the evolution of the universe holding that the universe resulted from an initial explosion.

**binary star.**   A double star with components close enough together to be affected by their mutual attraction; a visual, spectroscopic, or eclipsing double.

**black body.**   A hypothetically perfect radiator that absorbs and re-emits all radiation falling on it.

**black dwarf.**   The supposed final stage in the evolution of a star when it has no more energy to radiate.

**Bode's law.**   A sequence of numbers that represent approximately the mean distances of the planets from the sun.

**Bohr theory.**   A proposed model of an atom with electrons in orbits around the nucleus.

**boiling point.**   The temperature of a substance at which the molecules have enough energy to break the attractive forces between them.

**bolometer.**   A physical instrument for measuring the total amount of energy emitted by a radiating body, or reflected from a body; especially well adapted to infrared studies.

**bolometric magnitude.**   A kind of stellar magnitude based on the total radiation from a body.

**bright-line spectrum.**   A pattern of bright spectral lines emitted by an incandescent gas under low pressure.

**bright nebula.**   A visible gas illuminated by a nearby hot star.

**brightness.**   A measure of the luminosity of a body.

**calorie.**   The amount of heat energy needed to raise 1 g of water by $1°$ Celsius, $4.186 + 10^7$ ergs.

**canali.**   Narrow markings on Mars; Italian for channels or canals.

**candle.** The unit of light intensity.

**carbon cycle.** A series of nuclear reactions involving carbon by which four atoms of hydrogen combine to form one atom of helium.

**cardinal points.** The four principal directions: N, S, E, W.

**Cassegrain reflector.** A reflecting telescope that uses a concave primary mirror with a convex secondary; light is brought to a focus through a hole in the primary at the lower end.

**Cassini's division.** A 3000-mile wide gap in the ring system of Saturn.

**celestial equator.** The great circle on the celestial sphere 90° from each of the two celestial poles.

**celestial horizon.** The great circle 90° from zenith and nadir.

**celestial mechanics.** A mathematical branch of astronomy that deals with gravitation and the motions of bodies in space.

**celestial meridian.** The great circle through the celestial poles and the zenith.

**celestial poles.** Two points on the celestial sphere on the axis of the earth's rotation about which the sky seems to rotate.

**celestial sphere.** A sphere of infinite radius with center at the eye of the observer.

**centrifugal reaction force.** The inertial reaction to a centripetal force.

**centripetal force.** A force, directed toward a center of curvature, required to change a body from a straight path into a curved path.

**cepheid variable.** A star whose light output changes because of periodic expansions and contractions; a pulsating star.

**Ceres.** The first minor planet to be discovered; also the largest.

**change of state.** A change of substance from solid to liquid or from liquid to gas, or the reverse.

**chromatic aberration.** The failure of a lens to bring to one focus all the wavelengths of light that pass through it.

**chromosphere.** The layer of the sun's atmosphere directly above the photosphere.

**circumpolar stars.** Those stars near a celestial pole that are always above the horizon.

**clock drive.** The mechanism on a telescope that turns it at the proper rate to counteract the rotation of the earth.

**cluster variable.** A type of variable star with a period less than one day and absolute magnitude about zero; an RR Lyrae variable.

**Coalsack.** One of two conspicuous dark areas in the Milky Way.

**collimator.** A lens in a spectroscope that changes a diverging beam of light into a parallel beam.

**color excess.** The difference between the color index of a star and that of an unreddened star of the same spectral class; measured in magnitudes.

**color index.** The difference between the visual and photographic magnitudes of a star; expressed in magnitudes.

**coma.** The hazy shell-like structure around the nucleus of a comet; an aberration in a telescope whereby images formed off the axis of the telescope are not in focus.

**comet.** A diffuse astronomical body in orbit around the sun; usually in an elongated orbit.

**comparison spectrum.** A spectrum placed alongside the spectrum of a star for the purpose of comparing wavelengths.

**compound.** A substance composed of two or more elements.

**concave lens.** A lens with one or both surfaces curved like the inside of a sphere; it is thicker at the edges than at the center.

**concave mirror.** A reflecting surface curved like the inside of a sphere.

**conic section.** The curve formed by the intersection of a circular cone and a plane; a circle, ellipse, parabola, or hyperbola.

**conjunction.** A lining up of celestial bodies so that they have the same right ascension or celestial longitude.

**constellation.** An apparent grouping of stars named for a mythical figure, animal, or inanimate object; there are 88 constellations.

**continuous spectrum.** An uninterrupted band of color emitted by an incandescent solid, liquid, or gas under pressure, as observed by a spectroscope.

**convex lens.** A lens with one or both surfaces curved like the outside of a sphere and thicker at the center than at the edges.

**Copernican system.** The solar system as described by Copernicus; the sun at the center and its family of planets, their satellites, and other bodies, associated by gravitation.

**core.** The central portion of the earth, the sun, or a star.

**corona.** The outermost layer of the sun's atmosphere.

**coronagraph.** An instrument for photographing the sun's prominences and corona at times other than during eclipses.

**cosmic rays.** High-energy radiations and particles from space.

**cosmogony.** The branch of cosmology that deals with the origin and future evolution of all matter in the universe.

**cosmology.** The study of the structure and extent of the universe and its evolution.

**crape ring.** The faint, innermost ring of Saturn.

**crater.** A depression on the earth or the moon.

**crescent.** The phase of the moon or a planet between new and quarter; bow shaped.

**crown glass.** A high-quality window glass used in telescope objectives.

**crust.** The topmost layer of the solid earth; 3 to 30 mi thick.

**dark nebula.** A nonluminous gas in space, detected because it obscures the light of stars behind it.

**daylight saving time.** Time obtained by advancing the clocks, usually during the summer; standard time plus one hour.

**deceleration.** The rate of decrease of velocity; negative acceleration.

**declination.** The angular distance north or south of the celestial equator, measured in degrees of arc along an hour circle.

**declination axis.** The axis of a telescope about which the telescope can be turned north or south.

**deferent.** A circle in the Ptolemaic system centered in the earth, about which a planet or its epicycle was supposed to move in direct motion.

**deflection of starlight.** The bending of light as it passes near a massive celestial body; predicted by the theory of relativity.

**density.** Mass per unit volume, usually grams per cubic centimeter ($g/cm^3$); also called *mass density*.

**descending node.** A point where the orbit of a celestial body crosses the ecliptic from north to south; a point where the orbit of an artificial satellite crosses the earth's equator from north to south.

**deuterium.** "Heavy hydrogen" with a nucleus composed of one proton and one neutron.

**diffraction.** The bending of light rays after passing through a narrow opening or openings between ruled lines on a grating; also produced by a reflection grating.

**diffraction grating.** A system of finely ruled lines used to produce a spectrum.

**diffraction pattern.** A system of alternate bright and dark lines produced by interference or diffraction.

**diffuse nebula.** A bright or dark nebula, but not a planetary nebula.

**disk of galaxy.** The central, flat part of a galaxy superposed on the spiral structure.

**diffusion.** The tendency of gas molecules to fill a space uniformly.

**diffusion of light.** Scattering of light from an irregular surface.

**dispersion.** The separation of colors of light in a spectroscope.

**direct-focus telescope.** A reflecting telescope where observations are made at the focus without the use of a second mirror.

**direct motion.** The usual west to east motion of a planet or other body.

**distance.** The measure of separation between the centers of two objects.

**distance modulus.** The difference between the apparent and absolute magnitudes of an object; used to compute distances.

**diurnal circle.** A circle described by a celestial object on the sky due to the earth's rotation; a small circle parallel to the celestial equator.

**diurnal libration.** An apparent motion of the moon produced by the rotation of the earth, which permits us to see a little of the moon's limb that is alternately visible and invisible.

**diurnal motion.** The apparent motion of objects in the sky due to the earth's rotation.

**Doppler effect.** The apparent change in wavelength or frequency of sound, light, or other radiation produced by the relative motion of source and observer.

**double star.** A star that appears single to the unaided eye but seen as two stars in the telescope or detected by the spectroscope.

**Draper classification.** A sequence of classes of stellar spectra.

**dust cloud hypothesis.** A theory that parts of the solar system came from a mass of gas and dust which condensed in space.

**dwarf star.** A star of moderate luminosity and mass; generally a main-sequence star.

**dyne.** A unit of force in the metric system; the force required to give a mass of 1 g an acceleration of 1 cm/sec/sec.

**E = mc².** A fundamental equation from the theory of relativity; relates mass and energy.

**earthlight.** Sunlight reflected from the dark part of the crescent moon, having previously been reflected from the earth's atmosphere.

**earthquake.** A movement of the earth's crust.

**east point.** The point on the celestial horizon whose azimuth is 90°.

**eccentricity.** The ratio of the distance between the two foci of an ellipse to the length of the major axis.

**eclipse.** The phenomenon of one body shutting off all or part of the light of another, or by an opaque body passing into the shadow of another opaque body.

**eclipse limit.** The distance in degrees from a node within which an eclipse of the sun or moon is possible.

**eclipse path.** The track on the earth followed by the shadow of the moon during a solar eclipse.

**eclipse season.** A time of year when the sun or the earth's shadow is inside an eclipse limit.

**eclipse year.** The time between successive passages of the sun or the earth's shadow through the same node; 346.6 days.

**eclipsing binary.** A binary star whose orbital plane is so placed that the two components pass in front of each other as seen from the earth, thus producing eclipses.

**ecliptic.** The apparent path of the sun among the stars.

**Einstein effect.** The change in the wavelength of light in the region of a celestial body of large mass; a revision of the Doppler effect.

**electromagnetic spectrum.** The family of radiations that includes light, radio waves, infrared and ultraviolet light, X rays, and gamma rays.

**electron.** A fundamental subatomic particle with negative charge and small mass; revolves in orbit around the nucleus of the atom, unless free to move in space.

**electron volt.** The energy required to accelerate an electron through a potential of one volt.

**element.** A substance which cannot be divided into simpler substances by ordinary chemical means.

**element of an orbit.** One of several quantities which are used to compute the size, shape, and orientation of an orbit; used to determine the position of a body in the orbit.

**ellipse.** A closed plane curve in which the sum of the distances from any point on the curve to two internal points (foci) is always the same; a conic section.

**ellipsoidal galaxy.** A galaxy without arms, ellipsoidal in shape.

**elongation.** The angle between the centers of two objects, measured along a great circle; usually the angle between the sun and the moon or a planet, or a planet and its satellite.

**emission line.** A bright line in the spectrum.

**emission nebula.** A bright nebula.

**emission spectrum.** A spectrum consisting of bright (emission) lines, produced by an incandescent gas at low pressure.

**energy.** The capacity to do work; that part of the universe which is not matter.

**ephemeris.** A table or book that gives the positions of celestial bodies at various times, usually at regular intervals.

**epicycle.** A circle that moves along the deferent of a planet according to the Ptolemaic system; a circle on a circle.

**equation of time.** Apparent minus mean solar time.

**equator.** A great circle on the earth or on the celestial sphere 90° from the poles.

**equatorial mounting.** A telescope set on two axes, one of which is directed toward the celestial poles, the other at right angles; compensates easily for the rotation of the earth.

**equatorial system.** A system of coordinates with the celestial equator as the fundamental plane.

**equinox.** An intersection of ecliptic and celestial equator.

**erg.** A unit of energy in the metric system; amount of work done by a force of one dyne acting through a distance of 1 cm.

**escape velocity.** The speed at which a body overcomes the gravitational pull of another and moves off into space.

**ether.** A hypothetical medium through which light is transmitted; once thought to permeate all space.

**evolutionary theory.** A theoretical explanation of the changes in the universe from its beginning.

**exosphere.** The outermost layer of the earth's atmosphere, where molecules escape the earth's gravitational pull.

**expanding universe.** The theory that the universe started with an explosion; all parts are moving away from a central point.

**eyepiece.** A lens combination in a telescope by which the eye examines the image formed by the objective; magnifies the image.

**facula.** A bright region on the sun near the limb.

**filar micrometer.** A device for measuring angles; used at the eye end of a telescope.

**fission.** The separation of an atomic nucleus into smaller parts.

**flare.** The sudden, temporary brightening of a region on the sun.

**flare star.** A star that increases suddenly, unexpectedly, and temporarily in brightness.

**flash spectrum.** The spectrum of the "reversing layer" of the sun, seen very briefly as a bright-line spectrum just before and after the total phase of an eclipse.

**flint glass.** A hard glass used in one component of an achromatic lens.

**flocculus.** A bright region near a sunspot seen in a spectroheliogram.

**fluorescence.** The absorption of light of one wavelength and its re-emission in another; usually ultraviolet to visible light.

**focal length.** The distance from the center of a lens or mirror to the focus.

**focal ratio.** The ratio of focal length to aperture of a camera or telescope.

**focus.** The point where converging rays of light meet.

**focus of a conic section.** A point which, associated with the directrix, defines a conic section.

**forbidden lines.** Any lines in the spectrum of a gas formed by highly improbable changes in the orbits of electrons.

**force.** That which can overcome the inertia of a body.

**frame of reference.** A set of axes to which positions and motions in a system can be referred.

**Fraunhofer lines.** Absorption lines in the spectrum of the sun or stars.

**frequency.** Number of waves passing a given point in a unit of time.

**fringes.** Successive bright and dark areas produced by the interference of light.

**full moon.** The phase of the moon when the visible disk is fully illuminated; moon is at opposition.

**fusion.** The building up of atoms from lighter ones.

**galactic center.** A region in Sagittarius about which the sun and stars of the galaxy rotate.

**galactic cluster.** A moving or open cluster of stars in the spiral arms or disk of the galaxy.

**galactic concentration.** The ratio of the number of stars on the galactic equator to the number in an equal area at the poles.

**galactic equator.** An imaginary great circle that divides the Milky Way into two approximately equal parts.

**galactic latitude.** The angular distance from the galactic equator to any point on the celestial sphere, measured along a perpendicular circle.

**galactic longitude.** The angular distance from the galactic center northward along the galactic equator to a perpendicular from a given point.

**galactic poles.** Two points 90° from the galactic equator.

**galaxy.** A large collection of stars, dust, and gas in space; a system of millions or billions of stars held together by gravitation.

**gamma ray.** A quantity of high-energy radiation emitted from the nucleus of a radioactive atom; a photon.

**gegenschein (counterglow).** The area of faint, reflected sunlight from a large collection of small particles opposite the sun.

**giant star.** A large star of about zero absolute magnitude.

**gibbous.** The phase of the moon or a planet between quarter and full.

**globular clusters.** Large systems of stars packed into nearly spherical shape, located mostly in the halo of the galaxy.

**globule.** A small, dense, dark nebula; possibly a protostar.

**granules.** Small areas on the sun, formerly called rice grains, which give the sun a mottled appearance through a telescope.

**gravitation.** The attractive force which masses exert on each other.

**gravitational constant.** $G$, the constant of proportionality in Newton's law of gravitation; $6.668 \times 10^{-8}$ dyne-$cm^2/g^2$.

**gravity.** The gravitation of the earth.

**great circle.** The largest circle that can be drawn on a sphere; its center is the center of the sphere.

**greatest elongation.** The largest angular separation between Mercury or Venus and the sun.

**Great Rift.** An apparent split in the Milky Way between Cygnus and Crux, due to heavy absorption of light in space.

**Greenwich meridian.** The prime meridian through Greenwich, England.

**Gregorian calendar.** The present calendar introduced by Pope Gregory XIII.

**H I region.** A region of neutral hydrogen in space.

**H II region.** A region of ionized hydrogen in space.

**half life.** The time required for one-half of the atoms in a radioactive element to disintegrate.

**halo of galaxy.** The system of globular clusters, some stars, and diffuse hydrogen gas surrounding the galaxy.

**harmonic law.** Kepler's third law of planetary motion; $A^3 = P^2$.

**harvest moon.** The full moon nearest the autumnal equinox.

**head of a comet.** The nucleus and coma of a comet.

**heliocentric universe.** A theoretical universe with the sun at the center.

**Hertzsprung gap.** A former gap in the H-R diagram now filled in with Population II stars.

**horizon (celestial).** A great circle 90° from zenith and nadir.

**horizon system.** A system of coordinates with the celestial horizon as the fundamental circle.

**horizontal parallax.** The angle at the center of a celestial object in the solar system, such as the moon or a planet, between the two ends of a radius of the earth.

**hour angle.** The angle between the celestial meridian and an hour circle.

**hour circle.** A great circle on the celestial sphere through the poles and a celestial object; perpendicular to the celestial equator.

**H-R diagram.** A diagram relating spectral types and absolute magnitudes; spectrum-luminosity or Hertzsprung-Russell diagram.

**Hubble constant.** A number relating distance and velocity of galaxies; about 91 km/sec/$10^6$ parsecs; 17 mi/sec/$10^6$ light years.

**hunter's moon.** The full moon following the harvest moon.

**hyperbola.** A conic section; eccentricity greater than 1.0.

**image.** The optical representation of an object, usually seen as a luminous point or area at the focus of a telescope.

**image tube.** A device that combines a photoelectric sensitive surface and a photographic plate for measuring stellar brightness.

**inclination.** The angle between the orbital plane of a moving body and a fundamental plane; one of the elements of an orbit.

**index of refraction.** The ratio of the velocity of light in a vacuum to its velocity in a given transparent substance.

**inertia.** The property of matter that resists a change in its motion.

**inferior conjunction.** Conjunction of Mercury or Venus when between the earth and the sun.

**inferior planet.** A planet with orbit between that of the earth and the sun; Mercury and Venus.

**infrared radiation.** Radiation of wavelength longer than visible red light and shorter than radio waves.

**inner planet.** One of the first four planets: Mercury, Venus, earth, Mars.

**intensity.** The brightness of a light source.

**interference.** The reinforcing or cancelling of light waves.

**International Date Line.** An arbitrary, irregular line near longitude 180°, where the date changes by one day.

**International Geophysical Year (IGY).** An 18-month period in 1957 and 1958 set aside for international cooperation in research of the sun and also the earth and its environment.

**interstellar dust.** Microscopic dust grains in space.

**interstellar gas.** Diffuse gas in space.

**interstellar lines.** Absorption lines in the spectrum produced by interstellar gas.

**interstellar matter.** Dust and gas in space; literally "between the stars."

**ion.** An electrically charged atom formed by the loss or gain of one or more electrons without a change in the nucleus.

**ionization.** The process by which an ion is formed.

**ionosphere.** The layer of the earth's atmosphere between 20 and 500 mi above the earth; contains electrically charged particles.

**irregular galaxy.** A galaxy without regular shape.

**irregular variable.** A star whose brightness changes without a regular period; its amplitude may also vary.

**island universe.** A former name for a galaxy.

**isostasy.** The theory that the crust of the earth is kept in equilibrium by each part being subject to equal pressure from all sides.

**isotope.** One of two or more forms of atoms that have the same atomic number but different atomic weights.

**jet streams.** Fast-moving streams of air in the upper troposphere.

**Jolly balance.** An arrangement of a balance for measuring the mass of the earth.

**Joule's law.** A given amount of mechanical energy is always equivalent to a definite quantity of heat energy.

**Julian calendar.** A solar calendar introduced by Julius Caesar.

**Julian day calendar.** A consecutive numbering of days beginning on January 1, 4713 B.C.

**Jupiter.** The fifth planet from the sun.

**Kepler's laws.** Three laws of planetary motion stated by Kepler.

**kinetic energy.** The energy of motion: K.E. = $\frac{1}{2} mv^2$.

**kinetic theory.** The assumption that matter is composed of molecules in constant motion.

**Kirchhoff's laws.** Three laws of the production of spectra.

**Kirkwood's gaps.** Gaps in the spacing of asteroids, or in the rings of Saturn.

**latitude.** The angle from the terrestrial equator to a point on the earth, measured along its meridian; also similar angles from the ecliptic and the galactic equator.

**latitudinal librations.** Librations due to the tilt of the equator of the moon or Mercury to its orbital plane.

**law of areas.** Kepler's second law: The radius vector sweeps out equal areas in equal intervals of time.

**law of conservation of energy.** Under ordinary conditions, energy can be neither created nor destroyed.

**law of conservation of mass-energy.** Mass and energy are

related; $E = mc^2$; the total mass and energy in the universe remains constant.

**law of conservation of matter.** Matter cannot be created or destroyed by ordinary chemical processes; it can only be changed from one form to another.

**law of illumination.** The amount of light reaching a point varies inversely as the square of the distance from the source.

**law of recession of galaxies.** The radial velocity of a galaxy is proportional to its distance; $v = Hr$.

**law of reflection.** The angle of reflection is equal to the angle of incidence.

**law of refraction.** A beam of light is bent towards the perpendicular to the surface when passing from one medium to another of higher index of refraction.

**law of universal gravitation.** Every particle in the universe attracts every other particle with a force that is proportional to the product of their masses and inversely proportional to the square of the distance between them; Newton's law:

$$F = G \, \frac{m_1 m_2}{d^2}.$$

**lead sulfide cell.** A photoelectric device for measuring infrared radiation.

**leap year.** A calendar year with 366 days.

**librations.** Apparent oscillation of a body which permits more than half of its surface to be seen from another body.

**light.** Electromagnetic radiation visible to the eye.

**light curve.** A graph showing the relation between time and the brightness of an object; usually the curve of changing brightness of a variable star.

**light-gathering power.** The amount of light a telescope can collect; proportional to the area of the objective.

**light year.** The distance light travels in one year; about 6 trillion miles.

**limb.** The edge of the moon, a planet, the sun, or a star.

**limb darkening.** The ratio of brightness at the edge of the sun or a star to its brightness at the center.

**limiting magnitude.** The faintest magnitude observable in a telescope under given conditions.

**line of apsides.** The major axis of an ellipse; the line joining the points farthest from and nearest to a focus.

**line of nodes.** The line connecting the two nodes of an orbit; a line common to two planes; located by one of the elements of an orbit.

**local apparent noon.** The time at which the center of the apparent (true) sun is on the local meridian.

**local apparent time.** The hour angle of the apparent sun.

**Local Group.** The cluster of galaxies that includes our galaxy.

**local mean noon.** The time at which the mean sun is on the local meridian.

**local mean time.** The hour angle of the mean sun.

**longitude.** The angle between the prime meridian and the meridian through a point on the earth.

**longitude of the ascending node.** The angle measured eastward along the ecliptic from the vernal equinox to the ascending node of the moon or a planet; an orbital element.

**longitudinal libration.** A libration due to the variable speed of the moon or Mercury in its orbit.

**long-period variable.** A variable star whose changes of brightness are usually not strictly periodic, but repeat in about 100 days.

**luminosity.** The brightness of a star compared to that of the sun.

**lunar eclipse.** An eclipse of the moon.

**Lyman series.** An array of lines in the ultraviolet spectrum of hydrogen.

**magnetic field.** The region of space near a planet or other body where magnetic forces have been detected.

**magnetic pole.** One of two points on the earth toward which the ends of a compass needle point.

**magnifying power.** The apparent size of an object seen through a telescope compared to its size as seen with the unaided eye.

**magnitude.** An arbitrary number to indicate the brightness of an object.

**main sequence.** A line on the H-R diagram.

**major axis.** The longest diameter of an ellipse; line of apsides.

**major planet.** One of the four largest planets: Jupiter, Saturn, Uranus, and Neptune.

**mantle.** The layer of the earth between the crust and the core.

**maria.** Latin name for lunar seas: singular, mare.

**Mars.** Fourth planet from the sun.

**mass.** The total amount of matter in an object.

**mass-luminosity relation.** The principle which says that the brightness of a star depends on the amount of its mass.

**matter.** Anything that occupies space; that part of the universe which is not energy.

**mean distance.** The length of the semimajor axis of an ellipse; average of perihelion and aphelion distances.

**mean solar day.** Average length of the solar day during the year; interval between successive passages of the sun across a meridian.

**mean solar time.** Time kept by the mean sun; the interval of time since the mean sun crossed a meridian.

**mean sun.** An imaginary sun that moves uniformly along the celestial equator, making a complete circuit in one year.

**melting point.** The temperature at which the particles in a solid overcome the forces that hold them together.

**meridian.** A great circle through the zenith and a celestial pole; a great circle on the earth through the terrestrial poles.

**meson.** A subatomic particle with the charge of an electron, but of greater mass.

**mesosphere.** The layer of the ionosphere immediately above the stratosphere; the "middle sphere."

**Messier catalog.** A catalog of "nebulae" compiled by Charles Messier.

**meteor.** The term used to describe the phenomenon associated with the collision of a particle from space and the earth's atmosphere.

**meteorite.** A meteoroid of density higher than average, which has struck the earth's surface.

**meteorite theory.** The theory that lunar craters were formed by meteoric impact.

**meteoroid.** The particle involved in the meteor phenomenon.

**meteor shower.** Many meteors which seem to radiate from a small area on the celestial sphere.

**micrometeorite.** A microscopic particle in space; an exceptionally small meteoroid.

**Milky Way.** A faint band of light around the sky; composed of a vast number of stars and interstellar matter.

**minor axis.** The smallest diameter of an ellipse.

**minor planet.** An asteroid or planetoid.

**Mohorovicic discontinuity (Moho).** The boundary between the earth's crust and mantle.

**molecule.** A combination of atoms; the smallest particle of a substance that has all the properties of the substance.

**monochromatic.** A word meaning of one color or wavelength.

**Morgan classification.** A modern classification of stellar spectra; a suggested classification of galaxies; both by W. W. Morgan.

**moving cluster.** A group of stars moving in nearly parallel paths and with the same velocity.

**nadir.** The point opposite the zenith; altitude −90°.

**n-body problem.** The problem of determining the positions and motions of more than two bodies from their mutual gravitation; not solvable by ordinary mathematics.

**neap tide.** A tide at quarter moon when the solar and lunar tides partially cancel each other.

**nebula.** A gas or dust cloud in space.

**nebular hypothesis.** The theory of Laplace that the solar system was formed from a nebula.

**Neptune.** The eighth planet from the sun.

**neutrino.** A subatomic particle of very small mass and zero charge.

**neutron.** A subatomic particle of zero charge and mass similar to that of the proton.

**New General Catalog (NGC).** A catalog of "nebulae," successor to the Messier catalog.

**new moon.** The phase of the moon when it is in conjunc with the sun.

**Newtonian reflector.** A reflecting telescope that uses a plane mirror to deflect the beam of light to one side of the telescope tube; devised by Newton.

**Newton's law of gravitation.** The law of universal gravitation.

**Newton's laws of motion.** Three laws of mechanics formulated by Newton.

**node.** One of two points where the orbit of a celestial body crosses a reference plane; e.g., a point where a planet or the moon crosses the ecliptic.

**normal spiral.** A spiral galaxy with a nucleus from which arms extend; not a barred spiral.

**north celestial pole.** The point on the celestial sphere 90° from the celestial equator at one end of the earth's axis of rotation; now located in Ursa Minor.

**north galactic pole.** A point in the northern hemisphere of the celestial sphere 90° from the galactic equator; in constellation Coma Berenices.

**north point.** The point of intersection of the celestial meridian with the celestial horizon under the north celestial pole.

**nova.** A "new" star; a temporary star that shows an unexpected outburst of light.

**nuclear fission.** The splitting of the nucleus of an atom.

**nuclear fusion.** The combination of the nuclei of two atoms to form an atom of larger mass.

**nucleus.** The central part of an atom, a comet, or a galaxy.

**nutation.** A "nodding" of the earth's pole; a variation of precession.

**objective.** The large lens or mirror of a telescope; forms an image of a luminous source.

**objective prism.** A small-angle prism placed in front of a telescope objective to photograph the spectra of a field of stars.

**oblateness.** A measure of the amount of flattening of a body, such as the earth, due to its rotation.

**obliquity of the ecliptic.** The angle between the ecliptic and the celestial equator.

**obscuration.** Absorption of starlight by interstellar material.

**occultation.** The passage of a celestial body behind a larger one.

**open cluster.** A loosely formed group of stars; a galactic cluster.

**opposition.** The aspect of the moon or a planet when opposite the sun as seen from the earth; elongation approximately 180°.

**optical double star.** Two stars that appear close together, but are actually too far apart to be gravitationally held together.

**orbit.** The path of a body in revolution around another body or bodies.

**orbital plane.** The plane in which a planet, satellite, or star revolves around a central attracting body.

**outer planet.** A planet beyond Mars; Jupiter, Saturn, Uranus, Neptune, or Pluto.

**ozone layer.** A layer of the earth's atmosphere; the chemosphere.

**parabola.** A conic section, every point of which is equidistant from a given point (a focus) and a straight line (the directrix).

**paraboloid.** A curved surface formed by rotating a parabola about its axis.

**parallax.** The apparent displacement of an object when viewed from two different points.

**parsec.** A unit of distance; 3.26 light years; 206,265 a.u.

**partial eclipse.** An eclipse that is not total.

**penumbra.** That part of the shadow of an opaque body which only partly cuts off the light from a luminous source.

**penumbral eclipse.** The passage of the moon, during a lunar eclipse, through the penumbra of the earth's shadow without going through the umbra.

**perigee.** The point in the orbit of a satellite where it is nearest the earth.

**perihelion.** The point in the orbit of a planet or comet where it is nearest the sun.

**perihelion advance.** See advance of the perihelion.

**period.** The time required for a single revolution of one body around another; also used for rotation.

**period-luminosity law.** The relation between the period and absolute magnitude of a variable star.

**perturbation.** The gravitational disturbance of a celestial body which pulls it from its regular orbit.

**phases of the moon.** Changes in the apparent shape of the illuminated portion of the moon or a planet.

**photoelectric effect.**   The emission of electrons from a substance when light strikes it.

**photoelectric photometer.**   A device for measuring light intensity by the use of a photoelectric cell.

**photoelectric magnitude.**   The brightness (magnitude) of a star as measured with a photoelectric photometer.

**photographic magnitude.**   The brightness (magnitude) of an object as measured on a photographic plate.

**photometer.**   An instrument for measuring the amount or color of light from a luminous source.

**photon.**   A unit of electromagnetic energy; a quantum of radiant energy.

**photosphere.**   The visible layer of the sun; the "surface" or "light-giving sphere."

**photovisual magnitude.**   The magnitude of an object as measured through a filter, such that it approximates the visual magnitude.

**plage.**   A bright region of the sun observed in monochromatic light; a flocculus.

**plane mirror.**   A mirror with a flat (plane) reflecting surface.

**planet.**   A "wanderer"; one of nine bodies in orbit around the sun.

**planetarium.**   A projector that throws a reproduction of the sky onto the inside of a spherical dome to show the positions and motions of stars, planets, and other bright objects.

**planetary nebula.**   A shell of gas surrounding a hot star.

**planetesimal hypothesis.**   The theory of Chamberlin and Moulton that the planetary system was formed from "bolts" of hot material pulled from the sun.

**planetoid.**   A minor planet; an asteroid.

**Pluto.**   The ninth planet from the sun.

**polar axis.**   The axis of a telescope parallel to the earth's axis and about which the telescope turns to compensate for the earth's rotation.

**polarization.**   A state in which light waves are confined to a single plane.

**Population I and II.**   Two classes of stars based on location in the galaxy and state of evolutionary growth.

**positron.**   A particle with positive electrical charge, but mass equal to that of an electron; a positive electron.

**potential energy.**   Stored energy; can be converted to kinetic energy.

**pound.**   The standard unit of force in the English system.

**precession.**   The conical motion of the axis of a rotating, oblate body.

**precession of the equinoxes.**   The slow westward motion of the equinoxes along the ecliptic due to precession.

**primary minimum.**   The deeper minimum in the light curve of an eclipsing binary star.

**prime focus.**   The point in a telescope where the image is formed by the objective, when no second mirror is used.

**prime meridian.**   The terrestrial meridian through Greenwich.

**primeval atom.**   The single mass into which all matter in the universe was originally collected, according to the Lemaitre theory of the expanding universe.

**Principia.**   Newton's great book on motion and gravitation; *Philosophiae Naturalis Principia Mathematica.*

**principle of the pendulum.**   The law that the time of one complete swing of the pendulum depends on its length.

**prism.**   A piece of glass or other transparent material with plane sides and triangular ends; used in spectroscopes for refraction.

**prominence.**   A flame-like projection seen on the limb of the sun; associated with sunspot activity.

**proper motion.**   The apparent rate of change of direction of a star, measured in seconds of arc per year.

**proton.**   A fundamental subatomic particle of positive electrical charge; the nucleus of a hydrogen atom.

**protoplanet, protostar.**   The original material which condensed to form a planet or star.

**proton-proton reaction.**   One cycle by which four hydrogen nuclei (protons) combine to form a helium nucleus.

**pulsating star.**   See cepheid variable.

**pyrheliometer.**   An instrument for measuring radiant solar energy.

**quadrature.**   The relative position of two bodies as seen from the earth when they are 90° apart; especially the moon or a planet when at 90° elongation from the sun.

**quarter moon.**  The moon in quadrature; also called half moon.

**quiet sun.**  The sun when there is little activity; see active sun.

**radar telescope.**  A radio telescope equipped also with a transmitter.

**radial velocity.**  The component of velocity of an object toward or away from the sun; measured by the Doppler effect in km/sec.

**radiant point.**  The area of the sky from which meteors radiate.

**radiation.**  Energy that can be transmitted through space.

**radiation pressure.**  The slight pressure exerted by light or other radiation.

**radioactivity.**  The natural disintegration of the nucleus of an atom in which subatomic particles and gamma rays are emitted.

**radio astronomy.**  The study of astronomy by means of radio waves, which are beyond the infrared part of the spectrum.

**radio sextant.**  A sextant in which the lenses and mirrors are replaced by a radio receiver.

**radio telescope.**  A large receiver for collecting and measuring radio radiation from space.

**radius vector.**  A line joining any point on an orbit with a focus.

**rays.**  Systems of bright, elongated streaks on the moon.

**reaction.**  The equal and opposite force that accompanies every force; see Newton's third law of motion.

**real image.**  An actual image at the focus of a lens or mirror.

**red giant.**  A large, cool star of absolute magnitude brighter than about 0; plotted on the upper right of the H-R diagram.

**red shift.**  A Doppler shift toward the red end of the spectrum of most galaxies; basis for the theory of the expanding universe.

**reddening.**  The interstellar reddening of starlight by absorption.

**reflecting telescope.**  A telescope with mirrors instead of lenses.

**reflectivity.**  See albedo.

**refracting telescope.**  A telescope with lenses instead of mirrors.

**refraction.**  The bending of light as it passes from one transparent medium (or a vacuum) to another medium of different density.

**regression of the nodes.**  The westward motion along the ecliptic (or equator) of the nodes of a planet (or satellite).

**relativity.**  The theory formulated by Einstein; a modification of the Newtonian theory of gravitation.

**resolving power.**  The ability of a telescope to separate objects apparently close together; expressed in seconds of arc.

**retrograde motion.**  The apparent east to west motion of a planet or comet; opposite to direct motion.

**reversing layer of the sun.**  The layers of the sun where the photosphere and chromosphere meet; reverses the solar spectrum from bright-line to dark-line.

**revolution.**  The motion of one body around another.

**right ascension.**  The angle on the celestial equator eastward from the vernal equinox to the hour circle through a body; the angle at the celestial poles between the hour circles of the vernal equinox and any other point.

**rill.**  A crack in the floor of the moon.

**Roche's limit.**  The distance from a body inside which a satellite would break up under the body's gravitation.

**rotation.**  The turning of a body about an axis.

**saros.**  A cycle of similar eclipses that recur at intervals of about 18 years.

**satellite.**  A body that revolves around a larger body; a moon.

**Saturn.**  The sixth planet from the sun.

**Schmidt camera.**  A type of reflecting telescope that uses a spherical primary mirror and a correcting plate; has a small focal ratio.

**science.**  A branch of learning concerned with observation and classification of data concerning natural phenomena.

**secondary minimum.**  The shallower minimum in the light curve of an eclipsing binary star.

**secondary mirror.**  A small mirror used in addition to the primary mirror in reflecting telescopes.

**seismic waves.**  Earthquake waves.

**seismograph.**  An instrument for recording seismic waves.

**seismologist.**  A scientist who studies earthquakes.

**seismology.**  The science of origin and transmission of seismic waves.

**semimajor axis.**  One-half the major axis of a conic section.

**separation.**  The angular distance between the two components of a visual binary star.

**shell star.**  A star surrounded by a shell or ring of gas.

**shower of meteors.**  See meteor shower.

**sidereal day.**  The time interval between two successive passages of the vernal equinox or a star across the meridian.

**sidereal month.**  The period of revolution of the moon around the earth with respect to the stars; about 27⅓ days.

**sidereal period.**  The period of revolution of one body around another.

**sidereal time.**  The hour angle of the vernal equinox; the right ascension of the meridian; star time.

**sidereal year.**  The period of the earth's revolution around the sun.

**siderite.**  A meteorite composed largely of iron and nickel.

**small circle.**  A circle on the surface of a sphere that is not a great circle.

**solar activity.**  Sunspots, prominences, etc. on the sun.

**solar apex.**  The point toward which the sun is moving with respect to the nearest stars.

**solar constant.**  The amount of solar radiation received at a distance of one astronomical unit; about 2.0 cal/min/cm².

**solar day.**  The time interval between two successive transits of the sun across a given meridian.

**solar eclipse.**  An eclipse of the sun.

**solar flare.**  A short-lived, sudden outburst of energy from the sun, usually from a sunspot area.

**solar interior.**  The mass of hot gas below the solar photosphere.

**solar motion.**  The motion of the sun in space with respect to the nearest stars.

**solar parallax.**  The angle at the sun between two ends of a radius of the earth; about 8.8″.

**solar system.**  The assemblage of planets, satellites, and other bodies under the gravitational influence of the sun.

**solar wind.**  A radial flow of particles and radiation from the sun.

**solstices.**  Two points on the ecliptic where the sun's declination is greatest; +23½° and −23½° declination.

**south celestial pole.**  The point 180° from the north celestial pole; declination, −90°.

**south galactic pole.**  The point 180° from the north galactic pole; galactic latitude −90°.

**south point.**  The point on the celestial horizon 180° from the north point; an intersection of the meridian and the celestial horizon.

**space motion.**  The velocity of a star with respect to the sun.

**spectral class.**  The classification of a star from the appearance of the lines in its spectrum; the Draper or Morgan classification.

**spectograph.**  An instrument for photographing the spectrum.

**spectroheliogram.**  A photograph of the sun's atmosphere in the light of a single element.

**spectroscope.**  Arrangement of prisms or grating to produce a spectrum for examination.

**spectroscopic binary.**  A binary star with components too close together to be separated visually, but detected and measured with a spectrograph.

**spectroscopic parallax.**  A means of determining the parallax of a star (and therefore its distance) by observing its spectral characteristics, such as the width of the lines.

**spectrum.**  The band of colors produced when light is separated into its component parts.

**spectrum-luminosity diagram.**  See H-R diagram.

**speed.**  The rate of change of distance without regard to direction.

**spherical aberration.**  The failure of spherical lenses and mirrors to bring all the rays from a point source to a single focus.

**spicule.**  A narrow jet of hot material rising in the solar atmosphere.

**spiral arm.**  A curved formation that extends outward from the nucleus of some galaxies; composed of stars, dust, and gas.

**spiral galaxy.**  A galaxy with a nucleus and spiral arms.

**spring tide.**  An exceptionally high tide produced by the reinforcement of solar and lunar tides.

**standard time.**  Time used by a region on earth, based on mean solar time with respect to a standard meridian.

**star.**  A self-luminous nearly spherical mass of gas.

**star cloud.**  A portion of the Milky Way where the stars are so close together they appear as a luminous cloud.

**star cluster.**  A group of stars held together by mutual gravitation or by their common motion.

**star map.**  A chart showing positions and magnitudes of stars.

**steady-state theory.**  The belief that the density and shape of the universe are always the same, and that stars are being formed at the same rate at which their mass is being converted to energy and radiated into space.

**Stefan's law.**  The amount of energy radiated by a body varies as the fourth power of its absolute temperature; $E = aT^4$.

**stellar evolution.**  The continual change in size, mass, luminosity, structure, etc. of a star with time.

**stellar parallax.**  The angle in seconds of arc subtended by one astronomical unit at the distance of a star; annual parallax.

**stratosphere.**  The layer of the earth's atmosphere between the troposphere and the ionosphere.

**subdwarf.**  A star of lower luminosity than that of a main-sequence star of the same spectral class.

**subgiant.**  A star of luminosity between those of main-sequence stars and normal giants of the same spectral class.

**summer solstice.**  The point on the ecliptic where the sun reaches its greatest northern declination, $+23\frac{1}{2}°$.

**sun.**  The star that is the gravitational center of the solar system.

**sunspot.**  A dark spot seen on the disk of the sun; dark by contrast with the hotter photosphere.

**sunspot cycle.**  The interval of time from one sunspot maximum to the next; roughly, an 11-year period.

**supergiant.**  A star of absolute magnitude brighter than about $-1$.

**superior conjunction.**  Conjunction of a body on the far side of the sun as seen from the earth; syzygy, with the sun between the object and the earth.

**superior planet.**  A planet beyond the earth.

**supernova.**  An exploding star much more luminous than the normal nova.

**synchrotron radiation.**  Radiation emitted by charged particles that are accelerated in a magnetic field and move with velocity near that of light.

**synodic month.**  The interval between consecutive new or full moons; about $29\frac{1}{2}$ days.

**synodic period.**  The time interval between successive planetary oppositions or conjunctions of the same kind.

**syzygy.**  The lining up of three celestial bodies; conjunction or opposition.

**tail.**  The finest particles of a comet, which extend in a band away from the head.

**tangential velocity.**  The component of a star's space motion perpendicular to the radial velocity.

$$T = 4.74 \ \frac{\mu}{p} \ \text{km/sec.}$$

**telescope.**  An instrument for observing objects at a distance either visually or by other means.

**temporary star.**  A star that suddenly brightens by several magnitudes and eventually returns to near normal brightness; a nova; an exploding star.

**terminator.**  The line of sunrise or sunset on the moon or a planet.

**terrestrial planet.**  A planet about the size and mass of the earth.

**theory.**  A set of hypotheses and well-demonstrated laws to explain a phenomenon.

**theory of relativity.**  The theory advanced by Einstein as a modification of Newton's theory of gravitation.

**theory of the expanding universe.** The proposal, based on the red shift in the spectra of galaxies, that the galaxies in the universe are moving outward from an unknown center.

**thermosphere.** A hot layer of the earth's atmosphere.

**tidal hypothesis.** A theory, proposed by Jeans and Jeffreys, that the planetary system was formed by a single bolt of hot material pulled from the sun by a passing star.

**tide.** The deformation of a body by external forces.

**time zone.** A zone 7.5° each side of a standard time meridian.

**ton.** A measure of weight; 2000 pounds in the English system; 2200 pounds or 1000 kilograms or 1 million grams in the metric system.

**total eclipse.** An eclipse of the sun, moon, or star where the light is completely cut off.

**train or trail.** A temporary, luminous streak left by a meteoroid.

**transit.** The passage of a body across the meridian or the face of a larger body; an instrument for observing the passage of a body across the meridian; an engineering instrument for measuring vertical and horizontal angles.

**transmutation.** The process of changing from one form to another; a reaction by which one element is changed into another.

**transverse wave.** A wave perpendicular to the direction of propagation.

**tropical year.** The year of the seasons; the interval of time between successive passages of the sun through the vernal equinox; 365.2422 days.

**tropopause.** The boundary between the troposphere and stratosphere.

**troposphere.** The layer of the earth's atmosphere immediately above the crust; extends to between 5 and 10 mi.

**twinkle.** The changing brightness and color of stars due to the earth's atmosphere.

**Tychonic system.** A model of the universe proposed by Tycho Brahe.

**ultraviolet.** The part of the spectrum with wavelengths shorter than the visible spectrum.

**umbra.** That part of a geometrical shadow in which the direct light from a luminous body is completely shut off.

**unit mass.** A mass which, when acted on by a unit force, is given a unit acceleration.

**universal gravitation.** See law of universal gravitation.

**universal time.** The local mean time of the prime meridian; Greenwich mean time.

**Uranus.** The seventh planet from the sun.

**Van Allen radiation belts.** Regions of electrically charged particles surrounding the earth.

**variable star.** A star that changes in light or energy with possible changes in its spectrum.

**vector.** A directed quantity; may be represented by a straight line with an arrow at one end.

**velocity.** Rate of change of position along a line; speed and direction.

**velocity of escape.** The speed which a body must have to leave the gravitational field of another body.

**Venus.** The second planet from the sun.

**vernal equinox.** The point on the celestial equator where the sun crosses it from south to north at the beginning of spring.

**vertical circle.** A great circle on the celestial sphere through a body and the zenith; perpendicular to the horizon.

**visual binary.** A binary star of sufficient separation to permit both components to be seen through a telescope.

**volcanic theory.** The theory that the craters on the moon (or a planet) were formed by the action of volcanoes.

**watt.** A unit of power; $10^7$ ergs/sec.

**wavelength.** The distance from one point on a wave to the corresponding point on the next wave.

**wave theory of light.** The theory that light travels as a wave.

**weight.** A measure of the attraction between the earth (or any other massive body) and a given mass.

**weightlessness.** The absence of weight.

**west point.** A point on the celestial horizon of azimuth 270°.

**white dwarf.** A star that has about the same mass, but much smaller diameter, as an ordinary star; a white star several magnitudes below the main sequence.

**Wien's law.** The wavelength of maximum energy radiated by a body is inversely proportional to its absolute temperature;

$$\lambda_{max} = \frac{0.289}{T}.$$

**winter solstice.** The point on the ecliptic where the sun is farthest south; declination, $-23\frac{1}{2}°$.

**World Calendar.** A proposed 12-month calendar of equal quarters so designed that any day of the month will fall on the same day of the week each year.

**X rays.** Electromagnetic radiations of wavelength about 1 angstrom.

**year.** Period of revolution of the earth around the sun.

**zenith.** The point overhead; altitude 90°.

**zenith distance.** The angle between the zenith and any point on the celestial sphere measured on a vertical circle; $z = 90° - h$.

**zodiac.** A band on the celestial sphere extending about 8° on each side of the ecliptic; twelve constellations are in this band.

**zone of avoidance.** An irregular band on the celestial sphere near the galactic equator where practically no galaxies have been found.

# Index